Calculations and Programs For Power System Networks

Y. Wallach

Wayne State University

Prentice-Hall, Inc., Englewood Cliffs, New Jersey 07632

Library of Congress Cataloging-in-Publication Data

Wallach, Y. (Yehuda) (date)
Calculations and programs for power system networks.

Bibliography: p.
Includes index.
1. Electric power systems—Data processing.
I. Title.
TK1005.W27 1986 621.319 85-30174
ISBN 0-13-110321-0

Editorial/production supervision and
interior design: **Diana Drew**
Cover design: **Ben Santora**
Manufacturing buyer: **Gordon Osbourne**

Printed in the United States of America

10 9 8 7 6 5 4 3 2 1

ISBN 0-13-110321-0 025

Prentice-Hall International (UK) Limited, *London*
Prentice-Hall of Australia Pty. Limited, *Sydney*
Prentice-Hall Canada Inc., *Toronto*
Prentice-Hall Hispanoamericana, S.A., *Mexico*
Prentice-Hall of India Private Limited, *New Delhi*
Prentice-Hall of Japan, Inc., *Tokyo*
Prentice-Hall of Southeast Asia Pte. Ltd., *Singapore*
Editora Prentice-Hall do Brasil, Ltda., *Rio de Janeiro*
Whitehall Books Limited, *Wellington, New Zealand*

To those who read
the preface

Contents

Preface

There are a number of good textbooks on power systems, but apparently [IEEE81] none of them deals specifically with the problem of digital computations in an up-to-date manner. This book deals exclusively with this topic.

This book is intended for electrical engineering students (seniors with a background in numerical analysis and computer programming), graduate students in the power engineering area and practicing engineers working in the areas of power system computations or real-time operations (dispatching).

The chapters are:

1. Introduction
2. Solution of Linear Systems
3. Short-Circuit Calculations
4. Load Flow
5. State Estimation
6. Optimal Power Dispatch
7. The Stability Problem
8. Contingency Analysis Problem

This book is different from other texts both in its basic approach and in particular chapters. The differences in the basic approach are:

1. Problems of Chapters 4 to 8 are usually solved by Optimally Ordered Factorization (OOF). A very good new program in FORTRAN has been published [GL81] and is used as a basic program with which others are compared. Also reviewed are: Orthogonalization, Diakoptics, the Fast Gauss-Seidel iterative method and Singular Value Decomposition.
2. Up to now, no error analysis has been performed on power system programs. Such an analysis of the suggested methods will be given, based mostly on [FM67].
3. The examples normally given in textbooks [Br75, El71, SE68] are hand calculated and thus restricted by their very nature. In the 1980s, there is hardly a junior who has not programmed a computer in a high-level language. We therefore present programs for some of the algorithms mentioned and, for reasons given in Chapter 1, use Pascal as the language. A debugged program in a high-level language may be considered as the general solution to a particular problem. More importantly, *a program is the best way to explain and understand a solution method* — an algorithm. A collection of programs is therefore given and may be used by engineers as models for production programs. (The same was done in books such as [GL81] and [LH73].)
4. In this book there are no problems or exercises. Instead, in some chapters, the last section mentions certain projects. In most cases, *the projects involve writing programs.*

MATERIAL IN PARTICULAR CHAPTERS

Chapter 1. It is assumed that the student has previous knowledge of machines, lines, etc., so that only a mathematical model is discussed. It is shown in Chapter 1 that problems of Chapters 4 to 8 all lead to sets of nonlinear equations. When linearized as $\mathbf{A} * \mathbf{x} = \mathbf{b}$, a very large, extremely sparse but irregular matrix **A** results. Solution of such systems is discussed in Chapter 2.

Chapter 2. The book is written for students with some knowledge of numerical analysis. Therefore, the treatment of Gaussian elimination (factorization or Kron's algorithm) is shortened. The algorithms of orthogonalization, singular-value decomposition, and the fast Gauss–Seidel method are also discussed. Since error analysis is quite new to power system engineers, this topic is mention in Chapter 2.

Chapter 3. Short-circuit current calculations nowadays use the **Z**-bus matrix. Unfortunately, **Z** is a dense matrix and requires too much storage. Also, in some cases, extremely unreliable results occur. Here a method based on factorization and updating is used.

Chapter 4. Load flow is basic to steady-state operation and design. An efficient program transcribed from [GL81], which combines decoupled load flow and optimally ordered factorization is developed and discussed.

Chapter 5. State estimation is relatively new and therefore is given little attention in other textbooks. Moreover, whereas most references use the normal equations, it is suggested that optimally ordered orthogonalization or singular values decomposition supply better results. Since state estimation is basic to real-time operations, parallel systems are introduced and an algorithm for implementing state estimation on them is discussed.

Chapter 6. The most widely used optimization method is a combination of the gradient with the Lagrange-multiplier method. In addition, we suggest using the oldest algorithm (**B**-coefficients) in the form of a method based on the least-squares theory. Finally, a gradient method for possible on-line applications is discussed.

Chapter 7. The overwhelming part of the computational effort in solving stability problems is not in the solution of the differential equations but rather in the non-linear algebraic equations. The fast Gauss-Seidel method is shown to have some advantages if applied to stability problems. Equivalencing is also discussed.

Chapter 8. Contingency analysis programs and the selection process are discussed.

NOTATION, ETC.

1. There is confusion concerning the symbols = and *. If we write $a = b$, does this mean we should check if a equals b (and results in a Boolean true or false) or replace a by the value b? Since we are using Pascal, we use := for the replacement operator and reserve = for testing equality.

   Multiplication of two vectors or matrices is an operation not to be confused with multiplication of single numbers (scalars). Therefore asterisks (*) are used for vectors and matrices with the dot · reserved for scalars (sometimes · will be dropped altogether).

A large number of summations are given in the book and notation

$$\sum_{i=a}^{\infty}$$

would take too much space. Instead we write this as: Σ...; $i\Sigma = a..., b$. This should be read as: The index of summation is to be from a to b. Sometimes $i\Sigma\epsilon k$, meaning "The Σ is to be from set k," is used.

Matrices are denoted by uppercase boldface letters, column-vectors by lowercase boldface letters, and scalars by either Greek or italicized uppercase or lowercase letters. Thus for instance, **A** is a matrix, **a** is a vector, and a or α are scalars.

2. References are set out as follows: [GL81] refers to a book by George and Liu, which appeared in 1981, [Wa82] to a book by Wallach, published in 1982.
3. I am sorry for the large number of acronyms. To make life easier, they appear below in alphabetical order.
4. I dislike sentences that start "It can easily be shown that ..." and carry out the arithmetic arguments in detail. The reader can skip these. These passages are identified by equations without numbers.

ACKNOWLEDGMENTS

This manuscript was used in a course and read both by some of my students and by my colleagues. Thanks go to all of them, in particular to Dr. Alfred Frohner, Dr. George Gross, Professor Edmund Handschin, Carmen Milancovici, Norbert Podwoisky, Robert Rudzewicz, Dr. Bruce Wollenberg, my son and student Naor Wallach, and to Dr. Victor Konrad, from whose Ph.D. thesis I quote.

Some programs were written by Dr. Michel Gilles, Dave Janes and Neil Ormos. I would like to thank them very much.

OFTEN USED SYMBOLS

Scalars	Vectors	Matrices
f = function	$\mathbf{b}$ = right hand side	$\mathbf{A}$ = general, normal or incidence
i = current	$\mathbf{e}$ = measurement error	$\mathbf{D}$ = diagonal
p = # of slaves (in ASP)	$\mathbf{i}$ = current	$\mathbf{F}$ = fundamental
$p + j \cdot q$ = power	$\mathbf{r}$ = residuals	$\mathbf{I}$ = identity
s = singular value	$\mathbf{v}$ = voltage	$\mathbf{L}$ = lower (triangular)
t = time	$\mathbf{x}$ = general	$\mathbf{M}$ = as in $\mathbf{A} = \mathbf{M}^T * \mathbf{M}$
$u' = v + j \cdot w$ = voltage	$\mathbf{y}$ = admittances	$\mathbf{Q}$ = orthonormal
$y' = g + j \cdot b$ = admittance	$\mathbf{z}$ = measurements	$\mathbf{R}$ = right (triangular)
$z' = r + j \cdot x$ = impedance		$\mathbf{T} * \mathbf{S} * \mathbf{V}^T$ = in SIVD
α = access time		$\mathbf{U}$ = upper (triangular)
β = branch time		$\mathbf{Y}$ = admittance
ϵ = accuracy (factor)		$\mathbf{Z}$ = bus
ϕ = fill-in or empty set		$\mathbf{S}$ = rotation
λ = eigenvalue		
μ = multiplication time		
Ω = number of operations		
π = bit-handshaking time		
ρ = time ratio		
σ = subtraction time		
ψ = storage space		
τ = transfer time		
θ = angle		

OFTEN USED ACRONYMS

ASP = Alternating Sequential-Parallel
ED = Economic Dispatch
GS = Gauss – Seidel (method)
LF = Load-Flow (problem)
OOF = Optimally Ordered Factorization
SC = Short-Circuit (problem/program)
SIVD = Singular-Values Decomposition
ST = Stability (problem)
SE = State-Estimation (program)

1 Introduction

The *objectives* of this chapter are

1. To review the phasor notation.
2. To describe how to simulate a three-phase network of lines, generators, and transformers.
3. To review briefly the load-flow, economic-dispatch, state-estimation, short-circuit, contingency, and stability problems.
4. To demonstrate that the way to understand an algorithm is to follow its program and to show how to evaluate the efficiency of programs. To stress the need for better programs.
5. To provide examples for computer simulations.

1.1 POWER SYSTEM NETWORKS

The first electric network in the United States was the direct-current (DC) line installed in 1882 at the Pearl Street Station in New York. It supplied 30 kW of power to customers using Edison's newly invented incandescent lamps. The lamp was a huge success, so that more such "illuminating" companies were founded.

Technology progresses in a step-by-step fashion. Solution of one problem leads to another. The incandescent lamp improved lighting, but the lengthening of supply lines led to the problem of how to provide the supply without losing too much energy in the transmission of electric power. Power is

$$p = u \cdot i \tag{1.1}$$

where u is the voltage (volts) and i the current (amperes). The heat loss in a transmission line with a resistance of r (ohms) is

$$p_L = i^2 \cdot r \tag{1.2}$$

The solution to the loss problem is to generate the power at a relatively low voltage, transform it into a much higher voltage for the transmission, and lower it again for the consumers. Because the power $p = u \cdot i$ is constant (except for losses), higher voltage leads to lower current in the transmission lines and consequently to lower losses, $i^2 \cdot r$. The voltage of the generators and lamps must be low enough so as not to endanger people. The problem thus was how to transform the voltage up and down. This could not be done with DC, but the discovery of the alternating-current (AC) transformer solved it and made the AC system prevalent. An AC system to supply 150 lamps was installed by William Stanley in 1885 in Great Barrington, Massachusetts.

Energy can be delivered not only by electric lines. Gas is transported by pipes, coal by railways. However, delivery by electric lines is more easily controlled and is virtually pollution free; moreover, the energy is transferred much faster and is more efficiently changed into other forms, e.g., heat, light, motor or other forms of power.

Next came the problem of loading the generators, namely, what to do with the generated power during those hours when no illumination was needed. A paper on AC two-phase motors presented in 1888 by Nikola Tesla led to the solution of this problem through mixing of two types of loads: motors and illumination. "Illuminating" companies added "power" to their name.

At the 1893 world exposition in Chicago, a two-phase "power system" was presented. Soon a three-phase system appeared, and by 1894 there existed four such systems. The electric utility industry was off and running.

Running, but local. Each geographic area, frequently a town, was supplied by its own utility company. This localization soon changed.

Competition is great, but in the case of utilities compelling reasons for consolidation were found. If a number of utilities were to combine, this might lead to a better load distribution, to standardization of voltage and frequency, to better utilization of water power (available only partially in winter), and to usage of older, less efficient generators only during periods of peak load.

The interconnection of power systems is also advantageous because fewer generators are required as a reserve for peak loads (lower individual reserve capacity) and as a "spinning reserve", i.e., running at essentially no load. Additionally, the reliability of supply is increased. It may also be sometimes cheaper for a company to buy bulk power from others rather than produce it in one of its older plants.

Having a highly interconnected network is not an unmitigated blessing as indicated by reduced competition and as shown by some recent blackouts. We have to learn how to minimize the probability of blackouts, localize them, and quickly restore the supply.

The large, interconnected AC power system (network) consists of power stations, transmission, and distribution networks through which load centers are supplied. *The networks will have to grow* because of the following.

The annual energy production in the United States from 1920 to 1960 was approximately 39, 91, 142, 330, and 753 gigawatt-hours (GWh), i.e., energy production more than doubled every ten years. It was said, in fact, that civilization progresses with the production of electric energy. The oil embargo of 1973 and the resulting depression have slowed down the progress (of energy production and civilization). There is hope, though, that this will not last for long.

Until recently, electric generators were rotated mostly by water and steam turbines (burning oil or coal). Water resources are limited and are used already to such a degree that no substantial increase is to be expected. Coal seems abundant but presents an enormous environmental problem (the "greenhouse effect"). Other sources such as solar, biomass, or wind power may be able to supply a minuscule percentage of power in the twenty-first century. This leaves only nuclear power as a viable short-term alternative for progress. Will it be used?

Probably, it will have to be used because there are few other alternatives. But since the nuclear stations will have to be remote from population centers, transmission networks will grow even more.

It seems that they will also have higher voltages and be highly interconnected. As mentioned, the higher the voltage the lower the current and, for a given resistance and length of the line, the lower the losses. On the other hand, the towers must be taller and the insulation better. Both cost money, and therefore we will have to settle for a lower voltage than might otherwise be possible (it would be too expensive).

All this leads to the conclusion that the high-voltage, highly interconnected AC system is here to stay. In this chapter we define some computational problems of planning and operating such networks.

1.2 FUNDAMENTAL RELATIONS

This section reviews some fundamental relations and introduces notation. It may be read quickly or skipped by the more advanced reader.

Alternating current quantities vary sinusoidally as a function of time. Thus an AC voltage $u(t)$ is the following function of time:

$$u(t) = u_m \cdot \cos(\omega t) \tag{1.3}$$

If applied to a resistance of r ohms, this voltage will produce an AC current of $i(t) = i_m \cdot \cos(\omega t)$ with the maximum (*amplitude*) value i_m related to u_m by $i_m = u_m / r$. The instantaneous power is

$$p(t) = u(t) \cdot i(t) = u_m \cdot i_m \cdot \cos^2(\omega t) = 0.5 \cdot u_m \cdot i_m \cdot [1 + \cos(2\omega t)]$$

The average of $\cos(2\omega t)$ is zero so that if we define the *root mean square* values i and u by $i_m = i \cdot \sqrt{2}$ and $u_m = u \cdot \sqrt{2}$, then the average power will appear similar to DC as

$$p = u \cdot i \quad \left(= \frac{u_m \cdot i_m}{2} \right)$$

De Moivre's (sometimes called Euler's) equation for any α is

$$\epsilon^{j\alpha} = \cos(\alpha) + j \cdot \sin(\alpha) \tag{1.4}$$

The voltage $u(t)$ of Eq. (1.3) can therefore be written as $u(t) = \sqrt{2} \cdot u \cdot \text{Re}(\epsilon^{j\omega t})$ and is pictured in Fig. 1.1(a) as a *phasor* u' rotating counterclockwise with the speed ω.

Phasors can be added as (geometric) vectors. Given two phasors $a' = a \cdot \epsilon^{j(\omega t + \alpha)}$ and $b' = b \cdot \epsilon^{j(\omega t + \beta)}$, their sum [Fig. 1.1(b)] at any time t can be calculated in terms of real and imaginary components as

$$a \cdot \text{Re}(\epsilon^{j\alpha}) + b \cdot \text{Re}(\epsilon^{j\beta}) = a \cdot \cos(\alpha) + b \cdot \cos(\beta) = c \cdot \cos(\gamma)$$

$$a \cdot \text{Im}(\epsilon^{j\alpha}) + b \cdot \text{Im}(\epsilon^{j\beta}) = a \cdot \sin(\alpha) + b \cdot \sin(\beta) = c \cdot \sin(\gamma)$$

A current of the form $i(t) = \sqrt{2} \cdot i \cdot \cos(\omega t) = \sqrt{2} \cdot i \cdot \text{Re}(\epsilon^{j\omega t})$ flowing through a pure inductance L produces a voltage drop of $u(t) = L \cdot di(t)/dt = \sqrt{2} \cdot L \cdot i \cdot j\omega \cdot \text{Re}(\epsilon^{j\omega t})$. The relationship between the two phasors is therefore $u' = (j\omega L) \cdot i'$.

By using Eq. (1.4), j, which equals $\sqrt{-1}$, can also be expressed as $\epsilon^{j90°} = \cos(90°) + j \cdot \sin(90°) = j$. As seen, the voltage is $u' = (\omega L i') \cdot \epsilon^{j90}$. In this case, current lags voltage by 90°.

In the same way, a purely capacitive load leads to $i(t) = (j\omega C) \cdot u(t)$ with a reactance X_c (compare X_c with $X_L = j\omega L$) of $X_c = 1/(j\omega C) = -j/(\omega C)$. Here the current $i(t)$ leads the voltage by 90° (or the voltage lags the current by 90°).

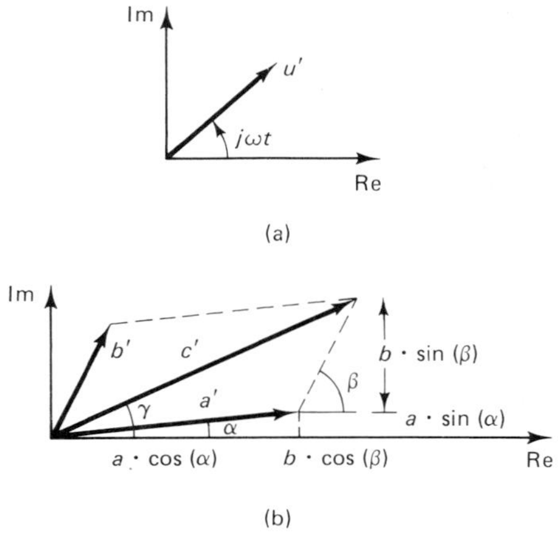

Figure 1.1 (a) A phasor. (b) Addition of two phasors.

A mixture of resistance r and reactance $j\omega L$ [or $-j/(\omega C)$] is called an *impedance*. Being a complex number, it and its complex conjugate will be denoted by

$$z' = r + j\cdot(\omega\cdot L); \quad z'' = r - j\cdot(\omega\cdot L)$$

with a single prime for complex, and a double prime for complex-conjugate items.

If the applied voltage is $u(t) = \sqrt{2}\cdot u\cdot\cos(\omega t + \alpha)$ or $u' = u\cdot\epsilon^{j\alpha}$ and the impedance $z' = r + j\cdot x = z\cdot\epsilon^{j\psi}$, then the current will lag the voltage by the phase angle ψ as in

$$i' = \frac{u'}{z'} = \frac{u\cdot\epsilon^{j\alpha}}{z\cdot\epsilon^{j\psi}} = \frac{u}{z}\cdot\epsilon^{j(\alpha-\psi)} = i\cdot\epsilon^{j(\alpha-\psi)} \tag{1.5}$$

The average power in this case is

$$p = \left(\int_0^T u\cdot i\cdot dt\right)/T = u\cdot i\cdot\cos(\alpha - \alpha + \psi) = u\cdot i\cdot\cos(\psi)$$

with the cycle time T and average power being, respectively,

$$T = 2\cdot\frac{\pi}{\omega}; \quad p = u\cdot i\cdot\cos(\psi) \tag{1.6}$$

It is customary to define the *complex* or *apparent* power by $s' = u'\cdot i'' = u\cdot\epsilon^{j\alpha}\cdot i\cdot\epsilon^{j(\psi-\alpha)} = (u\cdot i)\cdot\epsilon^{j\psi} = (u\cdot i)\cdot\cos(\psi) + j\cdot(u\cdot i)\cdot\sin(\psi)$.

The real part of s' is the *active* power (p), the imaginary part the *reactive* power (q), so that, respectively, for $s' = p + j \cdot q$,

$$p = \mathrm{Re}(s') = u \cdot i \cdot \cos(\psi); \qquad q = \mathrm{Im}(s') = u \cdot i \cdot \sin(\psi) \tag{1.7}$$

From de Moivre's law, Eq. (1.4), we have that $r = z' \cdot \cos(\psi)$, $x = z' \cdot \sin(\psi)$, and therefore $\tan(\psi) = x/r$. The phase angle ψ is therefore $\psi = \tan^{-1}(x/r)$.

Note that the reactive power q is positive if $\sin(\psi) > 0$ or $\psi = \tan^{-1}(x/r) > 0$, and this will be the case for inductive loads. The active power p is measured in watts (W), the reactive power in *reactive volt-amperes* (VAR), and the complex power in volt-amperes (VA).

Suppose we connect three consumers to three generators as in Fig. 1.2(a). If the three line impedances z_L' are equal and so are consumer impedances z_c', and if the three generated voltages u_a', u_b', u_c' are equal in magnitude but successively displaced by 120° as in Fig. 1.2(b), then the sum of currents flowing from points n to points 0 is

$$i \cdot \epsilon^{j\alpha} + i \cdot \epsilon^{j(\alpha - 120)} + i \cdot \epsilon^{j(\alpha - 240)} = 0 \tag{1.8}$$

The three lines $n - 0$ can therefore be combined into a single line and—if we are sure that Eq. (1.8) always holds—can even be completely removed. The same is true if the load is connected as in Fig. 1.2(c). The two connections are called *star* and *delta*, respectively. In both cases we have to distinguish between "phase" and "line" quantities. Figure 1.2(b) shows that for the star connection, $u_{ab}' = u_a' - u_b' = \sqrt{3} \cdot u_a' \cdot \epsilon^{j30°}$ or $u_L = \sqrt{3} \cdot u_{ph}$ and that u_{ab}' leads u_a' by 30° but that $i_L = i_a$. On the other hand, for the delta connection only u_L' exists and $i_{ab}' = i_a' - i_b' = \sqrt{3} \cdot i_a' \cdot \epsilon^{j30°}$ or $i_L = \sqrt{3} \cdot i_{ph}$ and a 30° shift.

The power of a three-phase load is three times that of a single phase (provided the three loads are identical). Thus, the active power for star and delta connections are, respectively,

$$\begin{aligned} p &= 3 \cdot u_{ph} \cdot i_{ph} \cdot \cos(\psi) = 3 \cdot \frac{u_L}{\sqrt{3}} \cdot i_L \cdot \cos(\psi) = \sqrt{3} \cdot u_L \cdot i_L \cdot \cos(\psi) \\ p &= 3 \cdot u_{ph} \cdot i_{ph} \cdot \cos(\psi) = 3 \cdot u_L \cdot \frac{i_L}{\sqrt{3}} \cdot \cos(\psi) = \sqrt{3} \cdot u_L \cdot i_L \cdot \cos(\psi) \end{aligned} \tag{1.9}$$

It is easier to measure line quantities, and therefore active (and reactive or complex) power will be computed using them. It should be remembered, though, that the phase angle ψ is measured between phase quantities.

We shall next review how the various elements of the network are represented.

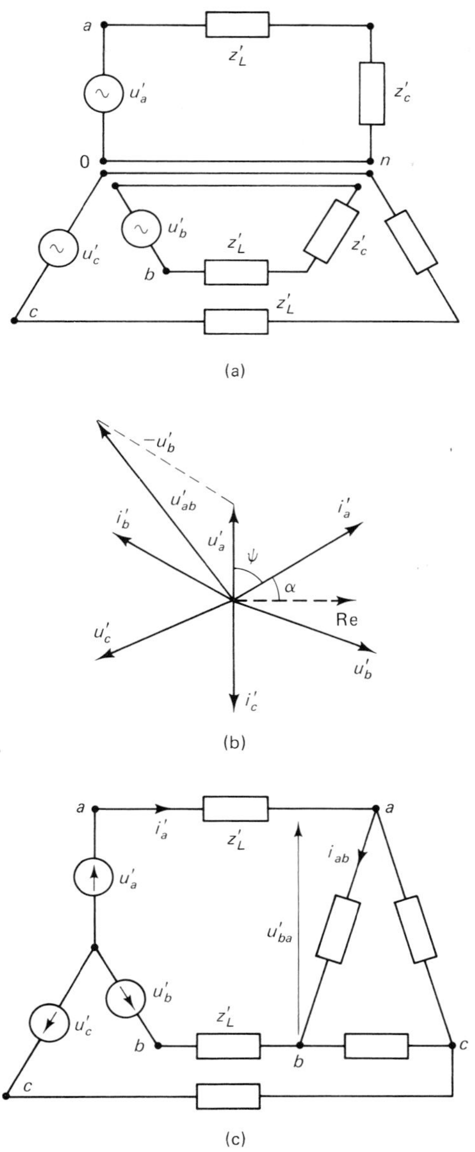

Figure 1.2 (a) Star connection. (b) Voltages and currents. (c) Delta connection.

1.3 SIMULATING POWER SYSTEM NETWORKS

Let us start with the simplest element, the transmission line. Even in this case a complication arises when the lines are *long*, i.e., above 200 miles for 60-cycle networks. We will neglect this case entirely here, since it leads to computations involving partial differential equations. These are treated in reference [BMR76] and are mathematically outside the area of computations discussed in this text.

The medium-length line can be represented as in Fig. 1.3. Actually, the resistance r, inductance L, and capacitance C are uniformly distributed along the line, but for a medium-length line they may be lumped together.

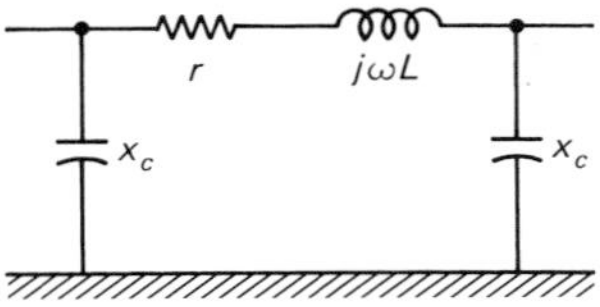

Figure 1.3 Representing a medium-length line.

Thus, the serial impedance $z_s' = r + j\cdot(\omega L)$ and the two capacitive shunt reactances $x_c = -j/(2\cdot\omega\cdot C)$ represent the line. If the line is *short*, we neglect the x_cs. In some cases (fault calculations) we may even neglect r, leaving only $z' = j\omega L$ for less accurate but much simpler calculations.

The most complicated part of the network is the synchronous generator. There is an extensive literature on these generators, and we suggest that readers refer, for example, to [Ad64], [El71], [FKK71], [Ki56], or [SE68].

For our calculations it will be sufficient to simulate synchronous generators as machines which generate power $p^g + j\cdot q^g$, three symmetrical voltages e_a', e_b', e_c' that are star connected, with each phase having a reactance jx_d and providing a terminal voltage u' [Fig. 1.4(a)]. The voltage diagrams depend on the angle ψ between the voltage u' and current i' (load phase angle). For an "overexcited" generator [Fig. 1.4(b)] we have that $0° < \psi < 90°$, that the internal voltage or emf (electro motive force) e' leads the current and terminal voltage, and that $p^g > 0$, $q^g > 0$. In an underexcited generator [Fig. 1.4(c)] the current leads the voltage so that $-90° < \psi < 0°$ and $p^g > 0$ but $q^g < 0$. (In synchronous motors the direction of the current i is reversed.)

The emf of the generator depends on its speed and flux, but since the latter is a nonlinear function of the excitation current, this relationship is best described graphically. The rating depends on heat developed and thus on i^2 and is again best described graphically.

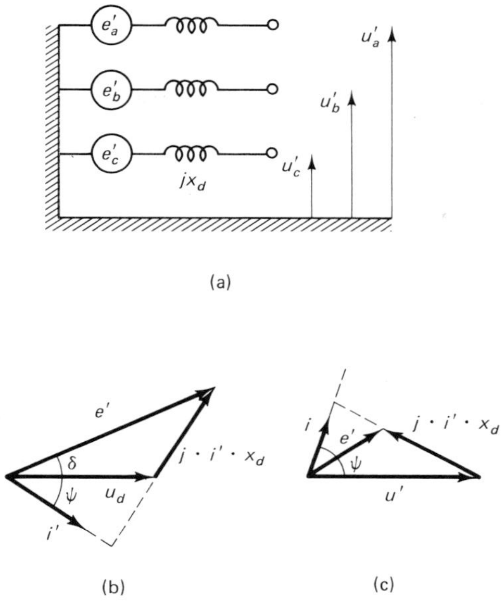

Figure 1.4 (a) Connection of the generator. (b),(c) Phasors.

As mentioned earlier, in order to reduce losses while transmitting power, the voltage has to be high. To transmit power through long lines, we now try to have voltages of between 500 and 1000 kV. Neither the generators nor the loads are built for such high voltages because of the lack of suitable insulating materials among other things. We therefore build a "machine" which changes or "transforms" the voltage of the generator into a high voltage for transmission and lowers it back for the load. At present transformers of up to 1500 MVA, high voltage of 700 kV, and current of up to 25 kA are produced. Since there are many types of transformers, we next develop the simplest models for some of them.

A transformer [Fig. 1.5(a)] consists of an iron core with two coils on it, one having n_1 turns and the other having n_2 turns. If the "primary" coil is connected to voltage u_1 and the current i_1 flows through it, a magnetic flux ϕ is produced such that $u_1 \cong n_1 \cdot d\phi/dt$.

The same flux produces a voltage in the secondary coil of $u_2 \cong n_2 \cdot d\phi/dt$.

Thus, by solving u_1 for $d\phi/dt$ and substituting this value into the equation for u_2 we get

$$u_2 = \frac{n_2}{n_1} \cdot u_1 = k \cdot u_1; \quad k = \frac{n_2}{n_1}$$

which shows this device to be a transformer indeed. Thus, if

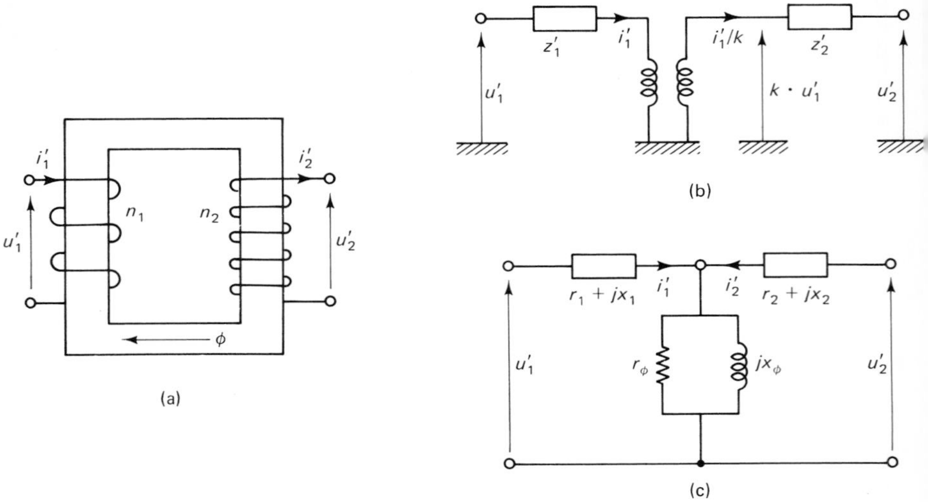

Figure 1.5 (a) A transformer. (b),(c) Equivalent circuits.

$n_2 = 1000 \cdot n_1$, we have a voltage u_2 of $1000 \cdot u_1$, i.e., higher by the factor k of 1000.

Neglecting all losses in the transformer makes the sum of powers zero (energy conservation): $u_1' \cdot i_1'' + u_2' \cdot i_2'' = 0$ or, if we use the turns ratio k and deal with absolute values only, $i_2 = (u_1/u_2) \cdot i_1 = i_1/k$.

Summarizing, we have

$$k = \frac{n_2}{n_1}; \quad u_2 = k \cdot u_1; \qquad i_2 = \frac{i_1}{k} \tag{1.10}$$

The equivalent circuit corresponding to this equation is shown in Fig. 1.5(b). It includes an *ideal transformer* and represents the two coils by the impedances z_1', z_2'. If we represent the core losses resulting from the need to produce the flux by jx_ϕ and the heat losses in the two copper coils by r_ϕ, we get the better model in Fig. 1.5(c).

Suppose we connect a load impedance z_L' to the secondary coil of a transformer. Disregarding the phase angle, the current will be $i_2' \cong u_2'/z_L'$. The same impedance is "seen" from the primary side as $\tilde{z}_L \cong u_1'/i_1' = (u_2'/k)/(k \cdot i_2') = z_L'/k^2$. This is the basis for matching an impedance by a transformer.

We can connect three transformers (or $3 \cdot 2 = 6$ coils) on a common core into a three-phase transformer. If the connections of the primary and secondary coils are the same, i.e., Y—Y or Δ—Δ, then the single-phase equivalent also applies to the three-phase case; but if we have a Y—Δ or Δ—Y transformer, then clearly there is a shift of 30° also in the voltage. We take this into account by using $k' = k\epsilon^{\pm j30^\circ}$.

If we measure the impedances in the equivalent of Fig. 1.5(c), we find that the shunt impedances are so large compared to the series impedances that they may be neglected — at least for some calculations, e.g., those of short-circuit currents. The equivalent circuit (impedance) is then the sum of the primary and secondary impedances. Note, though, that since the secondary should appear as it is seen from the primary, we must divide it first by k^2. Thus

$$z'_{eq} = (r_1 + r_2/k^2) + j\cdot(x_1 + x_2/k^2) \tag{1.11}$$

Typically, the reactive component is an order of magnitude larger than the resistive component. Therefore, in less accurate calculations, the real part may also be neglected and the transformer represented by the inductive reactance $x_1 + x_2/k^2$.

Sometimes we use *autotransformers*. Their theory may be looked up in [FKK71, Gr79]. For our purposes it will suffice to represent them as in Fig. 1.6 with the equivalent impedance $z_e = z_s + (k - 1)^2 \cdot z_c$, where z_s is the series and z_c is the common impedance of the autotransformer.

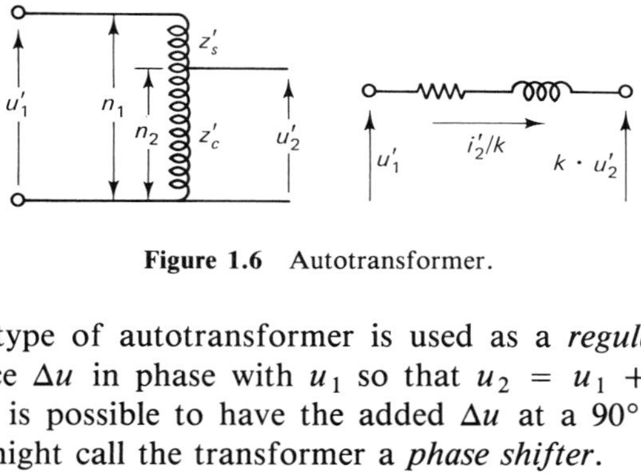

Figure 1.6 Autotransformer.

A special type of autotransformer is used as a *regulator*. It adds a voltage difference Δu in phase with u_1 so that $u_2 = u_1 + \Delta u$. In three-phase circuits it is possible to have the added Δu at a 90° angle to u_1, in which case we might call the transformer a *phase shifter*.

Having introduced equivalent circuits for elements of a power system network, let us combine them. A one-line diagram of a 100-mile line connecting two generators and supplying their own loads z_1', z_2' as well as load z_3' is shown in Fig. 1.7. This network includes three transformers. Those at buses 1 and 2 step up the voltage of the generators; transformer 3 steps it down.

Using the equivalent circuits described above, we can replace the line diagram by an impedance diagram as in Fig. 1.8 where z_{t1}, z_{t2}, z_{t3} represent the transformers, z_1, z_2, z_3 the three loads, and the indices $l1$ and $l2$ refer to the two lines.

As already mentioned, an impedance is "seen" changed by a transformer and therefore we have to redraw the impedance diagram so that all impedances are seen on the same voltage level.

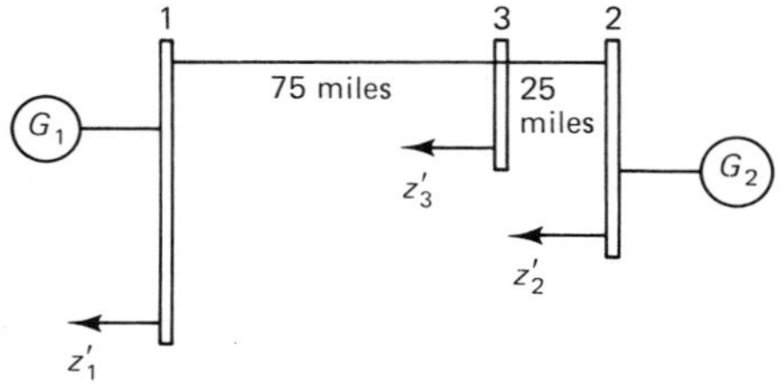

Figure 1.7 A simple network.

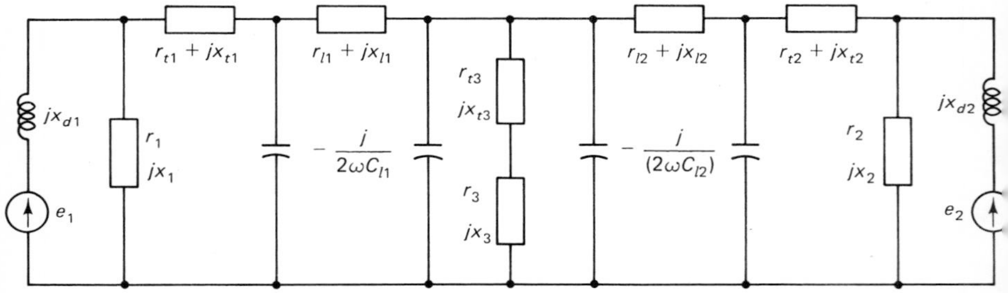

Figure 1.8 Impedance diagram of the network in Fig. 1.7.

Almost always, a per-unit system is also used. For it we must first choose some *base* quantities. Normally, complex power (VA) and voltage (V) are chosen as base quantities. Since $s = u \cdot i$, we have $s_b = u_b \cdot i_b$. It follows that, for base quantities,

$$i_b = \frac{s_b}{u_b}; \quad z_b = \frac{u_b}{i_b}; \quad y_b = \frac{i_b}{u_b} \text{ (}y\text{ is admittance)}$$

The base impedance is usually formulated in a different manner, namely, $z_b = u_b/i_b = u_b/(s_b/u_b) = u_b^2/s_b$. Voltage u_b is expressed in kV, whereas s_b is in MVA, but z_b is not changed, since kV^2 has the same 10^6 factor as has MVA.

Note that if we now consider an equation, say, $s' = u' \cdot i''$ or $s' = s \cdot \epsilon^{j\psi}$, and try to form s_{pu} (complex, per-unit power), we get

$$s_{pu} = \frac{s'}{s_b} = \frac{u \cdot i \cdot \epsilon^{j\psi}}{u_b \cdot i_b} = \frac{u}{u_b} \cdot \frac{i}{i_b} \cdot \epsilon^{j\psi} = u'_{pu} \cdot i''_{pu}$$

which is the same equation that was used earlier.

The same equations could be used for three-phase networks if all items were defined on a per-phase basis. As it is, voltages and currents are usually given as line quantities while complex power is a total quantity (sum of three phases). Therefore we base the calculation on $s_b = \sqrt{3} \cdot u_b \cdot i_b$, so that if s_b and u_b are selected, we get the following equations: $i_b = s_b/(\sqrt{3} \cdot u_b)$; $z_b = u_b/(\sqrt{3} \cdot i_b) = u_b^2/s_b$.

The per-unit values are therefore, with $s_b = u_b \cdot i_b$,

$$s_{pu} = \frac{s}{s_b}; \quad u_{pu} = \frac{u}{u_b}; \quad i_{pu} = i \cdot \sqrt{3} \cdot \frac{u_b}{s_b}; \quad z_{pu} = z \cdot \frac{s_b}{u_b^2} \tag{1.12}$$

where z is in ohms, s_b in MVA, and u_b in kV. Similar equations can be written for y_b.

We should try to select base values such that the rated voltages and currents of most devices are close to unity. If the rated values are not known, reference [We64] can be consulted for approximate values.

Incidentally, for motors, the power (in horsepower), voltage, cos(ψ), and efficiency (η) are normally specified. In that case, since one horsepower equals 746 W, we can use Eq. (1.9) to obtain $s_{rated} = u_r \cdot i_r$; $i_r = (746 \cdot p)/\sqrt{3} \cdot \eta \cdot u_r \cdot \cos(\psi)$.

Let us next list the advantages and disadvantages of using the per-unit (pu) system.

- If a transformer has a 0.05 pu impedance mentioned on its plate, then for a rated voltage of 6600 V, the voltage drop brought about by a 1-pu current is 0.05 · 6600 = 330 V. Conversely, a statement that this transformer has an impedance of, say, 20 ohms does not convey much.
- The parameters tend to fall into a narrow range, so that a value outside this range is possibly wrong. In particular, the voltage magnitude throughout the network should be relatively close to unity.
- The system is defined so that no ideal transformers are needed. Bearing in mind that the network includes hundreds or thousands of such transformers, this simplification of the impedance diagram is readily appreciated.
- If the three-phase transformers are connected Y—Δ or Δ—Y, factor k should take into account the shift in the angle. In contradistinction, the pu impedance does not require any correction factor.

There are disadvantages to the pu system:

- Phase shifts clearly present in the original system disappear in the per-unit system.
- In the same way, significant factors such as 3 or $\sqrt{3}$ disappear.

The percent system is close to the pu system but has a serious disadvantage, namely, the inherent factor of 100. Thus if the impedance is 5%, current is 95%, multiplication would yield the voltage $5 \cdot 95 = 475\%$, whereas the real voltage drop is $475/100 = 4.75\%$. In the pu system $0.05 \cdot 0.95 = 0.0475$, as it should be.

1.4 SHORT DISCUSSION OF COMPUTATIONAL PROBLEMS

1.4.1 Steady-State Equations

Let us redraw Fig. 1.8 with the generator loads removed, the impedances of generators and transformers added as z_1', z_2', and the three shunt branches at bus 3 replaced by z_3'. The resulting figure is Fig. 1.9.

The *loop equations* for the currents i_1' and i_2' are

$$u_1' - i_1' \cdot z_{L1}' - (i_1' - i_2') \cdot z_3' = 0 \qquad +(z_{L1}' + z_3') \cdot i_1' - z_3' \cdot i_2' = u_1'$$

$$u_2' + i_2' \cdot z_{L2}' + (i_2' - i_1') \cdot z_3' = 0 \qquad -z_3' \cdot i_1' + (z_{L2}' + z_3') \cdot i_2' = -u_2'$$

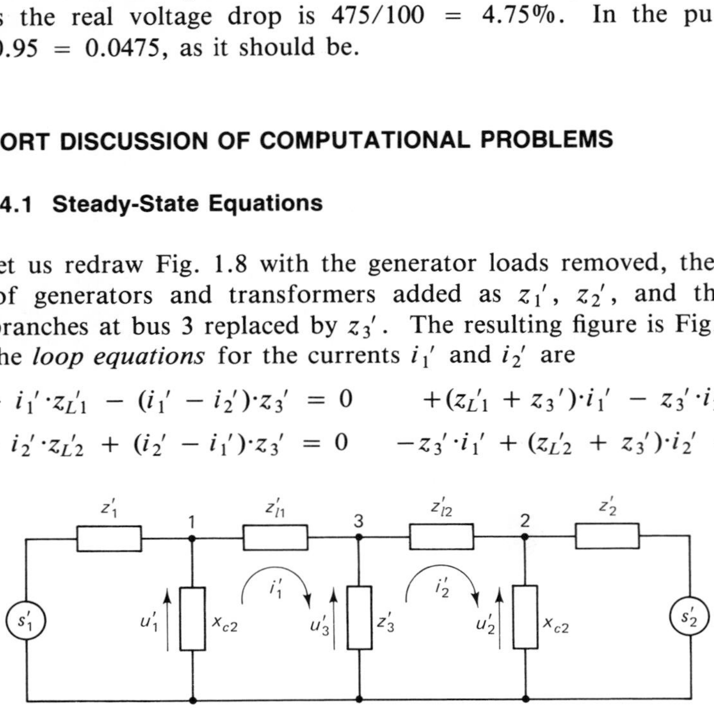

Figure 1.9 A simplified equivalent circuit for the network.

We can rename the impedances as $z_{1,1}' = z_{L1}' + z_3'$; $z_{1,2}' = z_{2,1}' = -z_3'$; $z_{2,2}' = z_{L2}' + z_3'$; we get a set of two equations with two unknowns (currents) i_1', i_2':

$$\begin{aligned} z_{1,1}' \cdot i_1' + z_{1,2}' \cdot i_2' &= +u_1' \\ z_{2,1}' \cdot i_1' + z_{2,2}' \cdot i_2' &= -u_2' \end{aligned} \quad ; \quad \begin{bmatrix} z_{1,1}' & z_{1,2}' \\ z_{2,1}' & z_{2,2}' \end{bmatrix} * \begin{bmatrix} i_1' \\ i_2' \end{bmatrix} = \begin{bmatrix} u_1' \\ -u_2' \end{bmatrix}$$

This is a set of two linear equations with two unknowns i_1', i_2' and can therefore be written in matrix form as

$$\mathbf{Z}' * \mathbf{i}' = \mathbf{u}' \tag{1.13}$$

We use lower-case boldface letters to denote column *vectors* and upper-case boldface letters to denote *matrices*. Multiplication of scalars is denoted by a dot (·), while multiplication of vectors or matrices is denoted by an asterisk (*). The scalar product of two column vectors **a** and **b** is written as $\mathbf{a}^T * \mathbf{b}$, and the vector product is written as $\mathbf{a} * \mathbf{b}^T$. The vector and scalar products produce a matrix and a scalar, respectively:

$$\begin{bmatrix} a_1 \\ a_2 \\ a_3 \end{bmatrix} * \begin{bmatrix} b_1 & b_2 & b_3 \end{bmatrix} = \begin{bmatrix} a_1 \cdot b_1 & a_1 \cdot b_2 & a_1 \cdot b_3 \\ a_2 \cdot b_1 & a_2 \cdot b_2 & a_2 \cdot b_3 \\ a_3 \cdot b_1 & a_3 \cdot b_2 & a_3 \cdot b_3 \end{bmatrix}$$

$$\begin{bmatrix} a_1 & a_2 & a_3 \end{bmatrix} * \begin{bmatrix} b_1 \\ b_2 \\ b_3 \end{bmatrix} = a_1 \cdot b_1 + a_2 \cdot b_2 + a_3 \cdot b_3$$

The trouble with Eq. (1.13) is that vector $\mathbf{u}'$ is unknown and, unless we compute it independently, the equation will not yield vector $\mathbf{i}'$. Let us therefore try *node equations*.

Generators can be viewed as *current generators*. Because of $s' = u' \cdot i''$ and $s'' = u'' \cdot i'$, they supply the current $i' = s''/u''$.

In nodes 1 and 2 part of this current flows through reactance x_c and a part flows through z_L'. Using Kirchhoff's current laws for nodes 1, 2, and 3, respectively, results in

$$\begin{aligned} i_1' &= \frac{s_1''}{u_1''} = -j \cdot \frac{u_1'}{x_{c1}} + \frac{u_1' - u_3'}{z_{L1}'} \\ i_2'' &= \frac{s_2''}{u_2''} = -j \cdot \frac{u_2'}{x_{c2}} + \frac{u_2' - u_3'}{z_{L2}'} \\ &\frac{u_1' - u_3'}{z_{L1}'} + \frac{u_2' - u_3'}{z_{L2}'} = \frac{u_3'}{z_3'} \end{aligned} \qquad (1.14)$$

We next manipulate these three equations. From the last we get $u_1'/z_{L1}' + u_2'/z_{L2}' = u_3' \cdot (1/z_{L1}' + 1/z_{L2}' + 1/z_3')$. Letting $1/z'$ denote the sum in parentheses and remembering that admittance is the inverse of impedance, $y' = 1/z'$, we have $y_3' \cdot u_3' = y_{L1}' \cdot u_1' + y_{L2}' \cdot u_2'$.

Next, insert u_3' into the first two equations and collect terms.

$$\frac{s_1''}{u_1''} = -j \cdot \frac{u_1'}{x_{c1}} + y_{L1}' \cdot u_1' - \frac{y_{L1}'}{y_3'} \cdot (y_{L1}' \cdot u_1' + y_{L2}' \cdot u_2')$$

$$\frac{s_2''}{u_2''} = -j \cdot \frac{u_2'}{x_{c2}} + y_{L2}' \cdot u_2' - \frac{y_{L2}'}{y_3'} \cdot (y_{L1}' \cdot u_1' + y_{L2}' \cdot u_2')$$

$$\frac{s_1''}{u_1''} = \left[\frac{-j}{x_{c1}} + y_{L1}' - \frac{(y_{L1}')^2}{y_3'} \right] \cdot u_1' - \left(\frac{y_{L1}' \cdot y_{L2}'}{y_3'} \right) \cdot u_2'$$

$$\frac{s_2''}{u_2''} = -\left(\frac{y_{L1}' \cdot y_{L2}'}{y_3'}\right) \cdot u_1' + \left[\frac{-j}{x_{c2}} + y_{L2}' - \frac{(y_{L2}')^2}{y_3'}\right] \cdot u_2'$$

Define $y_{11}' = y_{L1}' + y_{c1}' - (y_{L1}')^2/y_3'$; $y_{22}' = y_{L2}' + y_{c2}' - (y_{L2}')^2/y_3'$; and $y_{12}' = y_{21}' = -y_{L1}' \cdot y_{L2}'/y_3'$. Equation (1.14) can be rewritten as

$$\frac{s_1''}{u_1''} = y_{11}' \cdot u_1' + y_{12}' \cdot u_2' \qquad \frac{s_2''}{u_2''} = y_{21}' \cdot u_1' + y_{22}' \cdot u_2' \quad ; \quad \begin{bmatrix} y_{11}' & y_{12}' \\ y_{21}' & y_{22}' \end{bmatrix} * \begin{bmatrix} u_1' \\ u_2' \end{bmatrix} = \begin{bmatrix} \dfrac{s_1''}{u_1''} \\ \dfrac{s_2''}{u_2''} \end{bmatrix}$$

In order to eliminate the unknown values u_1' and u_2', we multiply the two equations by u_1'' and u_2'', respectively. This yields

$$s_1'' = y_{11}' \cdot u_1' \cdot u_1'' + y_{12}' \cdot u_1'' \cdot u_2'$$
$$s_2'' = y_{21}' \cdot u_1' \cdot u_2'' + y_{22}' \cdot u_2'' \cdot u_2'$$

Next we assume that the two voltages are written as

$$u_1' = u_1 \cdot \epsilon^{j\psi_1}; \quad u_2' = u_2 \cdot \epsilon^{j\psi_2} \tag{1.15}$$

and that $y' = g + j \cdot b$. By insertion and Eq. (1.7), we get

$$\begin{aligned} s_1'' &= p_1 - jq_1 = (g_{11} + jb_{11}) \cdot u_1^2 + (g_{12} + jb_{12}) \cdot u_1 \cdot u_2 \cdot \epsilon^{j(\psi_2 - \psi_1)} \\ s_2'' &= p_2 - jq_2 = (g_{21} + jb_{21}) \cdot u_1 \cdot u_2 \cdot \epsilon^{j(\psi_1 - \psi_2)} + (g_{22} + jb_{22}) \cdot u_2^2 \end{aligned} \tag{1.16}$$

These are the basic equations of the steady state of the network. Since they will be used for a number of programs, let us discuss them in more detail:

- These steady-state or *load-flow* (LF) equations are *complex*. This is not a complication, since we can separate the real and imaginary parts:.

$$p_1 = g_{11} \cdot u_1^2 + g_{12} \cdot u_1 \cdot u_2 \cdot \cos(\psi_2 - \psi_1) + b_{12} \cdot u_1 \cdot u_2 \cdot \sin(\psi_2 - \psi_1) \tag{1.17}$$

$$p_2 = g_{22} \cdot u_2^2 + g_{21} \cdot u_1 \cdot u_2 \cdot \cos(\psi_1 - \psi_2) + b_{21} \cdot u_1 \cdot u_2 \cdot \sin(\psi_1 - \psi_2) \tag{1.18}$$

These are the real parts. The imaginary parts are

$$-q_1 = b_{11} \cdot u_1^2 + b_{12} \cdot u_1 \cdot u_2 \cdot \cos(\psi_1 - \psi_2) + g_{12} \cdot u_1 \cdot u_2 \cdot \sin(\psi_2 - \psi_1) \tag{1.19}$$

$$-q_2 = b_{22} \cdot u_2^2 + b_{21} \cdot u_1 \cdot u_2 \cdot \cos(\psi_1 - \psi_2) + g_{21} \cdot u_1 \cdot u_2 \cdot \sin(\psi_1 - \psi_2) \tag{1.20}$$

Since modern computer languages include complex variables, the problem is whether it is better to solve complex Eqs. (1.16) or Eqs.

(1.17) to (1.20) as real equations, and in the last case, if it would be better to order them by their indices, that is, as Eqs. (1.17), (1.19), (1.18) and then (1.20).

- Time does not appear in these equations at all, since we essentially took a "snapshot" of the network at some given time instant. Since time does not appear, LF equations are not differential but algebraic.
- Load-flow equations include trigonometric functions and squares of voltages and are therefore *nonlinear* algebraic equations. As such, they cannot be solved explicitly and in an analytical way; they have to be solved *numerically* (on a computer).
- The angles always appear as *angle differences*. We can thus assume one of them, say, ψ_1, as zero, since this will not change anything. Incidentally, it is difficult to measure angle differences.
- Some variables are known a priori, e.g., the g and b values. We denote these by an a priori vector **a**. If we know the voltages [Eq. (1.15)], then insertion into Eqs. (1.17) to (1.20) would yield p_1, p_2, q_1, q_2. Therefore the voltages here are called the *state vector*, **x**. The powers and voltages, which can be controlled, will be combined into a *control vector*, **c**. Thus the LF equations are

$$\mathbf{f}\,(\mathbf{c}, \mathbf{a}, \mathbf{x}) = \mathbf{0} \tag{1.21}$$

where **f** (the LF) is a set of functions — a *vector function*.

- Let us add Eqs. (1.17) to (1.18), Eqs. (1.19) to (1.20), and remember that $g_{1,2} = g_{2,1}$, $b_{1,2} = b_{2,1}$, $\cos(\psi_1 - \psi_2) = \cos(\psi_2 - \psi_1)$, and $\sin(\psi_1 - \psi_2) = -\sin(\psi_2 - \psi_1)$.

$$\begin{aligned} p_1 + p_2 &= g_{11}\cdot u_1^2 + g_{22}\cdot u_2^2 + 2\cdot g_{12}\cdot u_1\cdot u_2\cdot\cos(\psi_1 - \psi_2) \\ -q_1 - q_2 &= b_{11}\cdot u_1^2 + b_{22}\cdot u_2^2 + 2\cdot b_{12}\cdot u_1\cdot u_2\cdot\cos(\psi_1 - \psi_2) \end{aligned} \tag{1.22}$$

These equations show on their right sides all the *losses* in the network and therefore represent the principle of *energy conservation*. We see now that we need an equation to express the fact that the generated power must equal the consumed power plus the losses.

- There are three unknowns, u_1, u_2, and ψ_2 (or $\psi_1 - \psi_2$), so that in Eqs. (1.17) to (1.20) we seem to have one equation too many. It is seen in Eq. (1.22) that this is not so, since one equation expresses energy conservation.

We next review the computational problems and the organization of the book.

The solution of all problems mentioned below require basically that **A** * **x** = **b**, a set of linear equations, be solved, and all of Chapter 2 is devoted to this topic. We will review the *elimination* method by Gauss known probably from high-school algebra as well as the *factorization* $\mathbf{A} = \mathbf{L} * \mathbf{U}$, which is the basis of all *LF programs*. *Kron's method* is needed for short-circuit calculations, *orthogonalization* for state estimation and economic dispatch, and in all programs sparsity will have to be treated (Chapter 2 discusses these methods in a simplified but rigorous way).

Since for stability studies most of the time is devoted to solving $\mathbf{A} * \mathbf{x} = \mathbf{b}$ by *iterative* methods, these are also discussed in Chapter 2.

The solutions include *errors*, and Chapter 2 introduces this subject and the *singular-value decomposition* applied normally to detect errors.

1.4.2 Fault currents

Up to now we have discussed only the so-called balanced, or *symmetrical* three phase operation of the power system network. A number of undesirable but often unavoidable accidents may disrupt this operation. Such accidents may be caused by lightning, birds (shorting lines), wires falling because of wind, trees falling on them or cars bumping into poles, etc. All of these lead to a faulty performance—most of them to short circuits.

The most frequent of them (at least on high-voltage transmission lines) is caused by lightning, which in turn leads to flashover of insulators. As a result a (short-circuit) current is flowing through this line to ground, and through it back to the grounded neutral of the nearest transformer or generator. This (single-phase) current is so much larger than the prefault current that the latter can be neglected and the entire calculation done as if the applied voltages were supplying only the short-circuit path.

This obviously leads to the problem of solving the linear set

$$\mathbf{Z} * \mathbf{i} = \mathbf{u} \tag{1.23}$$

with two complications: The data are usually in the form of admittances $\mathbf{Y}$ and not $\mathbf{Z} = \mathbf{Y}^{-1}$ as required and the single-line-to-ground fault has made the system *asymmetric*. We will deal with both problems later.

Short-circuit calculations (SC) use at present the Z-bus matrix [Br75]. Since $\mathbf{Z}$ is the inverse of the admittance matrix, it is normally computed by Kron's method, but since $\mathbf{Z}$ is a dense matrix, it requires too much storage. (A 1000-bus network would need 1,000,000 locations.) Thus another method was proposed recently [TFC73], which is really based on using LU factorization and will be applied in Chapter 3. It will be shown that in some cases extremely unreliable results may occur, and an updating method will be suggested as a remedy.

The chapter describes first how to calculate the admittance and impedance matrices needed in every phase of the computations. Since calculation of asymmetrical faults is done by the method of symmetrical components, this method is also reviewed.

The system includes relays which will detect the fault and trip circuit breakers which therefore interrupt the fault current in order to allow deionization of the flashover path to take place. After, say, 20 cycles the circuit breaker recloses the line, and two things can happen: Either the short-circuit path has been cleared so that symmetric, balanced operation can be resumed, or the fault is of the "permanent" type and has to be repaired.

The most frequent of these permanent faults is the single-line-to-ground fault resulting from a wire actually lying on the ground. About 25% of permanent faults occur when either two or three wires touch; the latter is the only case of a symmetrical fault, but it occurs only in about 5% of the cases.

The current (and/or voltage) which activates the relays is that current which flows immediately after the occurrence of the fault and is high. The current which is interrupted by the circuit breaker a short time later is still very high. Both fault voltages and currents have to be calculated.

The voltages and currents during faults are used to set the relays so that they can detect as fast as possible the accident that has occurred. The initial surge of current is used to determine the required momentary duty of the circuit breaker. The current and voltage a short time later are used to calculate the required interrupt capacity of the breaker, which serves in the choice of the breaker in the first place. The voltages and currents are also used to calculate the *short-circuit capacity*, defined as $\sqrt{3} \cdot u_b \cdot i_a$ where u_b is the voltage before and i_a—the current after the fault occurred. The current i_a, as already mentioned, will be much higher than that flowing under normal conditions, and u_b will be higher than that during the fault (since during faults it measures only the voltage drop and is thus lower).

Some programs will compute the short-circuit currents (SC) only in the immediate vicinity of the fault. Sometimes we would like the relays, even if they are far from the fault location, to detect the accident and possibly trip the circuit breaker in order to avoid any possibility of a "snowballing" effect. Since relays will first trip breakers close to the fault location, we have here the additional problem of computing currents using an impedance matrix $\mathbf{Z}$ changed by the removal of lines. Since in this case the impedance matrix changes during the calculation, we will have to deal with three problems connected with the $\mathbf{Z}$ matrix:

- How to calculate it with given admittance data.
- How to calculate it for asymmetric cases.
- How to calculate it for changes of its basic data.

1.4.3 Load Flow

Load Flow (LF) was defined as $\mathbf{f}(\mathbf{c}, \mathbf{a}, \mathbf{x}) = \mathbf{0}$.
The following are some of the cases where its solution is needed:

- When the site of a new power station is chosen, a number of LFs are run to determine not only that the chosen location is suitable, but also how best to connect it with the rest of the system.
- If a new load-center is established or when the network remains unchanged but the load grows, we have to run LFs to make sure that the lines can safely withstand the currents. This shows that after each LF is run, the currents should be computed, since we need their values. On the other hand, note that currents did not appear explicitly in LF.
- When planning new transmission lines, run a number of LF studies with different line values (z, y, etc.) and make the choice of the line to be used according to the results.
- Results from a number of LF studies lead to "distribution factors" (see Chapter 8). Thus, if the load level changes identically across the network, no new LF study is needed.

As seen, LF studies are conducted for *planning* purposes in order to predict the loading of lines and equipment (as well as the voltages and currents) of the entire network. Since we run LF programs for planning, we do not need their results immediately (in real time) and therefore can run them *off-line*.

In Chapter 4 it is suggested that the method of Optimally Ordered Factorization (OOF) as recently published in [GL81] should be used for LF. A Fortran program, as given in that book, is rewritten in Pascal so that it can be compared with other methods.

1.4.4 The State-Estimation Problem

The dispatcher of an on-line control system has to know at all times the values of voltages, currents, and powers throughout the network. Some of these values may be measured directly; the others will have to be estimated. Together they constitute the *data base* of the system at any given time.

The data will be used as input to other programs which assess the *security* of the system. It is therefore of paramount importance that the results of State-Estimation (SE) be *reliable*, since errors may lead to wrong decisions by dispatch personnel. The data will also be used for monitoring and control, so that the importance of it being *accurate* and *reliable* cannot be overemphasized.

The setting up of the correct data base leads to three problems: that the model may be inadequate, that errors exist in the measurements, and that the algorithm applied for calculation may amplify the error. Let us discuss these three problems in turn:

1. The three-phase network is modeled as a single-phase system. The model is true only as long as the network is absolutely symmetrical — which it seldom, if ever, is. The measurements are supposed to be taken simultaneously and instantaneously; it is obvious that not all measurements may be obtained and transmitted to the control center at the same time and that the meters have different and finite time constants. All these errors are inherent to the system model, and nothing can be done to reduce them, except perhaps to change the model.
2. The sources of the data are the power transducers and instrument transformers whose errors are 0.05%-0.25% of full-scale and 2% of measured MVA, respectively. The analog-to-digital converters show an error of approximately 0.1% of full-scale. A high error (1.5%-2%) is likely to be expected if analog transmission is used. With an identical full-scale of say 2000 MVA, analog transmission may lead to error bounds of more than 40 MVA (or MVAR) and is therefore hardly used anymore. Digital transmission reduces the noise considerably although not completely.
3. It could be argued that it is possible to measure all power injections and use the load-flow program on-line to compute the node voltages from which all other system values may then be easily calculated. The following supplies the reasons for not using this approach.

   In any load-flow calculation, the structure of the network and in particular the admittance matrix $\mathbf{Y}'$ is supposed to be known. Sometimes this matrix changes (say, a line is outaged, or dropped), and since a single line contributes values to two complex equations, these two may be wrong.

   Since load-flow algorithms use as many equations as unknowns, we arrive at the conclusion that we are trying to solve a deterministic system of equations on the basis of nondeterministic data; if the connection of a single line is incorrect, the entire calculation may be useless. If predicted values were used, the error would be even greater. Stated differently, in load-flow analysis no redundancy exists to offset the effects of measurement errors — a fact that leads to large deviations between the deterministically calculated and the true values of the voltages. In especially large deviations, the so-called *bad data*, load-flow calculations cannot be carried out and the entire energy control could become inoperative.

To check whether the load-flow algorithm reduces or amplifies errors, an "experiment" as described in [VD73] and adapted in Fig. 1.10 was performed as follows:

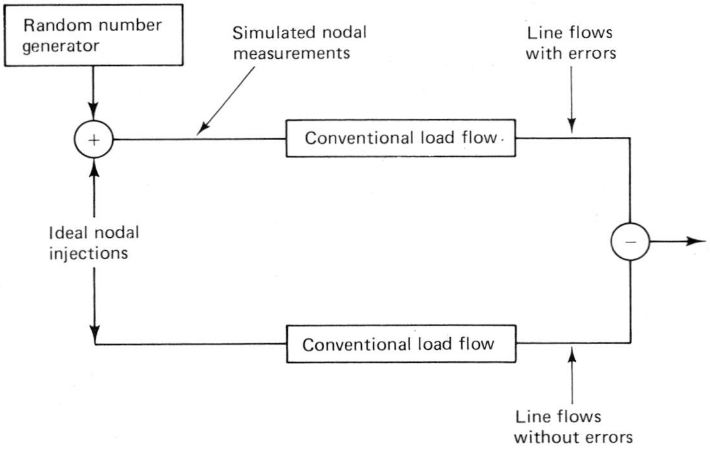

Figure 1.10 An "experiment."

A conventional load flow is performed twice: once on data assumed to be correct and then on data known to include errors. The first calculates line flows without, the second with errors. Comparing the two outputs for many cases showed that load flow algorithms amplify errors to such a degree that "a conventional load flow is almost useless for assessing the MVAR injection at a regulated bus in the presence of even nominal data measurement errors" [VD73]. Stated differently, the solution of load-flow problems is extremely sensitive to changes in the injected powers.

The conclusion is that the gathered data include errors and that load-flow calculations amplify them. Hence it it better to use the so-called *state-estimation* (a better term would be "state-approximation") approach, which [Ha79] "simplistically stated uses a redundant set of measurements to find the correct state of the network.

"Data acquisition can be done in one of the following ways:

1. Data acquisition with no processing
2. Data acquisition with a digital computer used for data-logging, limit-checking and simple logic comparisons between redundant measurements of essentially the same variables; and

3. Data acquisition with a digital computer used in a systematic way, based on a mathematical model, to clean-up the data (by treating small random errors, bad-data, modeling errors and parameter errors), and to estimate (compute) quantities and variables not directly measured. The third approach is static state estimation" [Ha79].

Next we discuss why static state estimation is the best of these approaches.

"A negative feature of conventional data acquisition without a process-control computer (case 1) is the high capital investment required for multiple measurements, transmission and display. This is particularly true for large power-systems, to a point that it is neither technically nor economically feasible to measure and telemeter all network quantities (some companies do). In addition, it is impossible to carry out a systematic fault analysis after the occurrence of a contingency because the data were not stored. Finally, since the measurement system uses dedicated hardware, there exists little flexibility for extending and improving the information system.

"Data acquisition with the aid of a process control computer brings a certain improvement. However, it is not sensible to make a large investment in hardware equipment and in software for data logging only. At the same time, a systematic data processing scheme, based on statistical estimation could and should be set up.

"In all three cases mentioned, some time must be spent on data acquisition itself. In the first two cases another time is needed for recording, display and what is worst, some telephone inquiries. This time is considerably shortened if the data are processed by a computer (case 3), so that much more time remains for carrying out operations on instruments and issuing of commands. This time is crucial and herein lies the greatest advantage of state estimation" [Ha79].

For the state-estimation program (SE) it is suggested in Chapter 5 that orthogonalization [Wa83] should be used. This leads to a more efficient program than if we had used OOF again. Singular-value decomposition, discussed in Chapter 2, provides means of showing that orthogonalization is more accurate than OOF. The material on orthogonalization and SE is based heavily on [LH73], which among other items includes efficient Fortran programs.

State estimation is basic to on-line, real-time dispatch of electrical energy. As long as the only available system was a single computer, speeding up the solution was effected by various simplifications. With the advent of parallel and distributed processing systems, the problems can be solved fast and accurately. A particular system, called alternating-sequential-parallel (ASP), and some examples of using it are also described in Chapter 5. Finally, an algorithm for SE on an ASP or in a distributed system is given and its results are discussed.

1.4.5 Economic Dispatch

An important problem is that of *economic dispatch* (ED).

The system in Fig. 1.7 had two generators: G_1 was located 75 miles from the load to be supplied, while G_2 was only 25 miles from the load. If G_2 by itself could supply the load, we should probably shut down G_1, since it is further from the load and leads to higher power loss (i^2r) in the line. When both generators are needed, if G_1 is a newer and more efficient generator or if it is run by a water turbine and it is springtime, we might supply a larger percentage of power from G_1 despite its remoteness from the load. In any case, in general we have to supply

$$\Sigma\, p_i^g = \Sigma\, p_k^c + \Delta p; \quad i\Sigma = 1, \dots, n; \; k\Sigma = 1, \dots, m \tag{1.24}$$

where p_i^g is the power of generator i, p_k^c is the power of consumer k, and $i\Sigma$ (or $k\Sigma$) is to be read: "i (or k) of the summation runs from...to...." Altogether there are n generators and m consumers, and Δp are the total losses in the network.

As Eq. (1.24) shows, if Σp_k^c is fixed, we may be able to change some of the p_i^gs so that Eq. (1.24) is true but *with smaller losses* Δp. Thus, one definition of ED is that the problem is to determine generation so as to *minimize losses.*

We have already mentioned that some generators are more efficient than others; therefore the *cost* of generating a given amount of power is different for different generators. Since only the sum of powers to be generated is fixed, we might want to *minimize the cost of generation*; this is the other definition of the ED problem.

The ED problem can be solved by running a number of LF programs and changing data until the optimum sought is achieved. The changes may be controlled by the costs, losses, or both using the well-known technique of Lagrange multipliers. For running LFs we also need reasonable short-time load prediction, since loads (powers) are needed to solve LF equations. Unfortunately, such predictions depend on the weather (temperature, wind, humidity, etc.), the time of day (which determines industrial and residential demand for power), the season (water available in spring) and other factors. We will assume here that such load forecasts are available and refer the reader to [Kn72]. The same is true for unit commitment, i.e., ensuring that the best combination of generators is on-line to provide the demand and some reserve — some as *spinning reserve*, i.e., running without load. The reader should look up this part of the problem in the literature.

With fuel prices as high as at present, there is no question that solving ED is extremely important. Reducing the costs or losses is especially important because of the amount of electrical energy used; saving 1% of the 753 GWh that were used in 1960 means saving 7.53 GWh!

The most widely used economic dispatch program will be called a Newtonian method, since it is based on the solution of LF using the Newton–Raphson method. Additionally, the oldest method [Ki58] may be used in conjunction with the method of least squares as used in orthogonalization. This was suggested recently [SGH79] and seems to be good enough for reviving interest in the older method.

The problem as posed above is an *off-line* problem. We predict loads and use a number of LFs and an ED program to calculate how to supply them in the most economical way. Wouldn't it be better to do it *on-line*? And how much more would we save if we could do it in *real time*? What is meant here is that the dispatcher (a person) knows at every moment the *state* of the network, including present demand, and — assuming no great changes of loading during the immediate future— decides with the use of an ED program how to generate power with minimum cost and/or losses. This assumes the existence of a program which provides the state of the network at any given time. Such *on-line* state-estimation programs have already been discussed.

1.4.6 Stability Calculations

The voltages of the two generators in Fig. 1.7 were

$$u_1' = u_1 \cdot \epsilon^{j\psi_1}; \qquad u_2' = u_2 \cdot \epsilon^{j\psi_2} \tag{1.25}$$

The question is: How are the angles measured? For any measurement of an angle a reference axis is needed — what is it? In the two-generator system the angle of one relative to the other generator could be measured, but if the number of generators is k, we would have $k(k - 1)/2 \cong 0.5k^2$ frames of reference. Since this may be a large number, either one generator is chosen as reference and all voltages are measured in relation to its voltage or the choice is the flux rotating according to the frequency f of the network and we measure all voltages relative to this synchronously rotating frame of reference.

As long as the generators rotate synchronously, the voltage angle difference between them is small or zero. But suppose there is a fault on a line such that it produces an angle difference which may tend to increase. If there are no restoring forces, the system may "run away," i.e., be unstable; but in most cases a stable situation will be restored. In all this it was important to note that whatever happened was the result of an angle difference between the two generators and that such a difference may produce voltage differences and consequently very large currents, even if the absolute values of voltages have not changed and $u_1 = u_2$.

Faults produce the most violent changes, but the opening of lines or the sudden dropping of large loads can also produce large changes. Since we have to calculate, say, voltages and currents for the *time* until circuit breakers remove the disturbance, we will have to solve ordinary but nonlinear differential equations. (The imbalance of power as a function of time is the driving force, and its derivative points to the changes to be expected.) The study of transient stability as discussed earlier therefore involves the solution of *differential equations* (time is involved).

If one of the generators in a network does not run synchronously with the remaining generators and motors, large circulating currents result and it is the aim of relays and circuit breakers to remove such a machine from the system (and resychronize it later). Thus the problem of stability is the problem of maintaining the synchronous operation of the generators and motors of the system.

In a recent report [IEEE80] the definitions were:

> *Steady-State Stability of a Power System.* A power system is steady-state stable for a particular steady-state operating condition if, following any small disturbance, it reaches a steady-state operating condition which is identical or close to the prefault operating condition.
>
> *Transient Stability of a Power System.* A power system is transiently stable for a particular steady-state operating condition and for a particular disturbance if, following that disturbance, it reaches an acceptable steady-state operating condition.
>
> *Steady-State Stability Limit.* The steady-state stability limit is a steady-state operating condition for which the power system is steady-state stable but for which an arbitrarily small change in any of the operating quantities in an unfavorable direction causes the power system to lose stability.
>
> *Transient Stability Limit.* The transient stability limit for a particular disturbance is the steady-state operating condition for which the power system is transiently stable but for which an arbitrarily small change in any of the operating quantities in an unfavorable direction causes the power system to lose stability for that disturbance.

Three stability problems are usually defined: Surge phenomena lead to ultrafast transients (and partial differential equations); short-circuit faults, etc., lead to transient problems (and ordinary differential equations); and mechanical oscillations lead to steady-state problems. We will deal only with the last two in a simplified way.

The overwhelming part of the computational effort in solving stability problems (SP) is not in the solution of the differential but of the algebraic, nonlinear equations. These are usually solved using the Newton – Raphson iterative technique and again OOF. Initially the Gauss – Seidel (GS) method was used [SE68] to solve them. The reason that it was abandoned lies in its high time demand. Recently, an algorithm for fast Gauss – Seidel (FGS) was developed ([WK77/79]), and since it reduces the time by half (so that Karl Friedrich Gauss may have been the best mathematician but not the most efficient programmer), the question of which method to use, OOF or FGS, is reconsidered in Chapter 7.

1.4.7 Contingency Analysis Problem (CAP)

A "decoupled" algorithm for solving the load-flow problem is described in Chapter 4 and used for contingency calculations in Chapter 8. An older method, that of *distribution factors*, is also discussed.

Instead of testing for each and every contingency, it is suggested in Section 8.4 that only certain subsets should be tested. Finally, a parallel, optimally ordered factorization algorithm is described; it may be used for on-line contingency analysis.

It should be emphasized again that for all problems we will develop programs. They are not production-type programs but serve as the explanations of algorithms.

1.5 ON PROGRAM SOLUTIONS

The three most widely used textbooks [El71, St62, SE68] exemplify the solution methods by using a hypothetical system with a few buses. This approach has several drawbacks:

- The network is too small to be considered representative.
- The data are deliberately changed to make the calculations easier.
- Because in an iterative solution only the first few iterations are actually followed through, the accuracy of the solution leaves much to be desired.
- It is not the actual numerical values which are of interest, but the algorithm, that is, the step-by-step process of obtaining the results. Thus, the effort should be directed at explaining the algorithm.

The approach mentioned was justified as long as digital computers were either unavailable or, being of the mainframe type, expensive and hard to get. With the introduction and wide distribution of personal and desk-top computers, the approach may be changed.

It is suggested that since most senior and graduate students (and, even more so, practicing engineers) have access to personal and desk-top computers, they can run programs with somewhat more comprehensive data. Such programs will be discussed in this book with the claim of the following advantages:

- Data for larger and more practical networks are available, e.g., networks with 14, 30, 57, and 118 buses as described in [FS67]. A program developed and run on a small test case can be used for such larger or even much larger, actual networks.
- The data do not have to be rounded, since today's microcomputers often have words of 16 or 32 bits and are frequently equipped with floating-point hardware so that scientific calculations are easily made. As a matter of fact, the only differences between them and the mainframe computers may be in limited storage and a reduction of speed. They seem ideal for preparing programs.
- They are available and fast enough to obviate worry about how many iterations are required; as many as are necessary can be run.
- Results of runs can be summarized in tables and graphs, and these will not only provide more easily grasped information about the method used but do it in less space.
- A program is the encoding in some high-level language of the algorithm and is therefore easier to follow than numerical values, especially if the program includes a sufficient number of comments.
- A program in a high-level language may be considered a *general solution* of the problem it solves. In order to be used by a utility, it has to be transferred to its mainframe computer and some features added, e.g., file movements or input/output. These usually require more instructions than the programs we will discuss, but have to deal only with matters extraneous to the basic solution of the problems. To sum up: In this book *algorithms will be explained by programs.*

We next proceed to the problem of the high-level language to be used and suggest that we should use *Pascal.* The advantages of Pascal seem to be:

1. Pascal is a powerful language. It includes the **if** ... **then** ... **else** and the **case** statement for checking conditions. A loop is arranged in Pascal by **while** ... **do**, **for** ... **to** ... **do** and also **repeat** ... **until** statements. The assignments are defined nicely. Thus, even for

simple, numerical formula translation, *Pascal offers a very diversified set of instructions.*

2. Parts of programs deal with *sets*, *records*, and *files*, and for these no mental gymnastics are needed in Pascal.
3. The data types of Pascal are either integers or real values and arrays made up of them as well as Booleans, characters, strings of characters, scalar lists, subranges, pointers, records, and files. Moreover, it is a built-in feature of Pascal that the programmer may declare his or her own types of data. *The range of data types in Pascal is thus very large.*
4. Some of the problems are best defined recursively, and Pascal offers both *iteration and recursion.*
5. Pascal is a *strongly typed* language, i.e., all variables of a program have to be declared. In older Fortran there was no need to declare any variables (except the bounds of arrays) and an integer variable had to start by one of the letters I, J, K, L, M, or N, a real variable by any of the remaining. This made for some strange names such as IDUMY, which is probably a dummy variable with the "I" added because it should be an integer. A misspelled variable, say, IDUMMY, appears to the compiler as an additional variable which will be happily used ever after — mostly with disastrous results. The compiler of Pascal will simply identify IDUMMY as not having been declared.
6. *Parameters* are transferred in Pascal both by values and as "variable" parameters.
7. Pascal is a *block-structured* language. The use of **begin ... end** as a compound statement allows Pascal programs to be designed top-down — a method which is claimed to have saved a lot of programmer time. **goto**s exist in Pascal, but their use is discouraged. Anyway it was proven that the number of instructions in Pascal is such that **goto**s are not necessary. Anybody who has tried to wade through a program with a large number of **goto**s will appreciate the advantage. Together, this can be summarized under the heading of *structured programming*, which is better than the unstructured one.
8. Pascal is not bound to any columns, is free-format, uses white space and indentation, and has a large character set in addition to using upper- and lower-case letters. All this makes *Pascal programs much more legible.* This might seem an insignificant improvement, but it really is quite important. The time of programmers is spent mostly not on writing, but on reading, keeping up, and possibly improving programs written by other programmers.
9. For *real-time applications* a language is needed to deal with on-line programming. For this ADA [DoD83] could be used. Additionally,

ADA allows the programmer to define his or her accuracy and thus aids in portability: transfer of a program to the inevitable new computer is easy. ADA is based on Pascal, which is therefore a preparation for ADA.

10. Despite the advantages of having a varied instruction set, of processing sets, records, and files, of having many more data types, of using recursion, of being block structured, free-format, etc., Pascal was defined so that its *compiler* is so *small* that it fits even the smaller desk-top microcomputers. Since the programs are to be developed for such computers, this is of real value.

There are two disadvantages of using Pascal:

1. In most Pascal compilers no mixing of single- and double-precision real numbers is allowed. This is absolutely necessary in a production program, which will therefore have to be rewritten.
2. Most programs used at present by utilities are in Fortran, and rewriting them will cost too much money and time. In our case, though, we will have rewrite the programs anyway, since the *basic algorithms* have to be reprogrammed.

The problem is the following. The core of programs for solving load-flow, state-estimation, economic dispatch, short-circuit, and stability problems is at present optimally ordered factorization, as described in [TW67]. It can be shown that other methods might be more efficient (for instance, orthogonalization for state-estimation and iterative methods for stability) and will also lead to a higher accuracy than OOF. As a matter of fact, even OOF has to be rewritten since a new and very good program (in Fortran) appeared in literature recently [GL81]. To sum up: We have no choice but to change the existing programs and for reasons mentioned earlier will do it in Pascal (and modify it later in ADA for the mainframe).

It may be asked why ADA is not used instead of Pascal. The reason is simply that ADA compilers are not yet readily available. We therefore have chosen Pascal for its similarity to ADA.

The reader is assumed to know Pascal. For readers who do not, there are several good books on the language, such as [Gr81] and [SWP82]

It was recommended earlier to diversify the algorithms. If there are a number of different programs for solving the same problem, then the next topic is how to compare and choose among them.

For a long time computer programs were compared in two respects: how fast they are and how much storage space they require. The faster they are and the less storage they require, the better.

The two requirements are to some degree interrelated, since some of the data can be stored on secondary devices, such as tapes, and transferred to main storage when needed. This will "save" storage, but "cost" time for the transfer. Since mainframe computers on which the programs will eventually run have large, very fast disk packs, the time involved is relatively small; and since the prices of main storage are still dropping, we can neglect the storage requirement, except for extreme cases.

Basing the speed comparison on actual run times is misleading, since different computers need varying amounts of time for identical operations. It is better to *count* the actual number of operations in the programs.

Such count is in fact the basis of an area of research active in the last 15 years, called *computational complexity*. Unfortunately, only the number of multiplications and divisions is counted, since the assumption was made once that they require so much more time than additions and subtractions that the latter can be neglected. Newer computers, even some microcomputers, are now equipped with floating-point hardware, and the times of arithmetic operations are essentially equal. What should also be counted is the number of times that the memory is accessed, since the time of performing the operations in the central processing unit is actually shorter than the *access time*.

Suppose we have written in Pascal $c := a - b$, which means "subtract b from a and store the result in c." In an assembly language similar to that used in the PDP11 series of DEC computers, this statement would be translated as follows. (The semicolons in the following assembly programs separate the instructions on their left from the comments on the right. The comments describe what is being done.)

```
MOV A,R1  ; Move the value stored in location A to register R1.
SUB B,R1  ; Subtract the value of B from R1. Leave the result in R1.
MOV R1,C  ; Move the value in R1 to memory location C.
```

As seen, we have here three accesses to memory: for A, B, and C. If we had $c := a * d - b$, then the preceding program would have the added instruction MPY D,R1 after moving A to register R1, and the number of memory accesses would be increased by one.

The conclusion seems to be that the number of memory accesses in an arithmetic assignment instruction equals the number of appearances of variables or constants.

Suppose we have to compute $a := b * b$. Its "program" is

```
MOV B, R1;
MPY R1,R1;
MOV R1, A;
```

and only two memory accesses are needed. Thus we count only the number of appearances of different variables or constants.

If we assume that the time of a single access is ω microseconds and the same time is needed to execute any arithmetic operation, then the time it takes to calculate an arithmetic assignment statement with v different variables and p operators is $(v + p) \cdot \omega$. This will be indicated by writing $\Omega = v + p$.

Next an **if** $a > b$ **then** $c := d$ **else** $c := e$ will be translated as follows (note that the "**if**" is reversed):

```
MOV B, R1      ; First move B into register R1 and then
SUB A, R1      ; subtract A from it, so that R1 = B - A.
BRP R1,L1      ; If R1 is positive (i.e., B > A), the program
               ; branches to label L1.
MOV D, R2      ; Otherwise, D is transferred to register R2 and
MOV R2, C      ; stored in location C. Thus, in these two instructions
               ; c := d and the computer moves to L2, which is
BR L2          ; outside this if statement. For a ≤ b, we first
L1:MOV E,R2    ;   move E to register R2 and then
MOV R2, C      ;     move it from R2 into location C.
```

There were $v = 6$ accesses and two branches, or, if we assume that a branch also requires the time of ω, then $\Omega = (v + 2)$.

A number of instructions exist in Pascal for loops. The difference between a **for** ... **to** and a **for** ... **downto** is only in counting up or down. Let us therefore see how **for** i := a **to** b **do** ...; might be translated:

```
MOV A, R1      ; Store in R1 the present value of i (initially A).
MOV B, R2      ; Store in R2 the value of B.
MOV R2,R3      ; R3 will store b - i. It is initialized to B.
L1:SUB R1,R3   ; R3 := R3 - R1 = b - i.
BRN R3,L2      ; If b - i is negative, branch out of the loop.
               ;
               ; Here is the block of instructions to be executed.
               ;
ADD  1,R1      ; Add 1 to i and branch back to L1.
BR L1          ; There exists an assembly instruction which includes
               ; the last two instructions.
```

The three instructions ahead of label L1 are done only once, and if we assume that $b - a >> 1$ (i.e., that the loop is done many times), we can disregard them. The loop itself adds $\Omega = 4$ per iteration.

An often misunderstood problem is that of multidimensional arrays. The memory of the computer is a vector, say, **m**[0] to **m**[max] so that if **a**[IN1, IN2] is used in an expression, the compiler has to decide in which memory location the element A of indices IN1 and IN2 is stored. Suppose that matrices are stored by *rows*, so that if the matrix has n rows of m columns, the first row is stored from **m**[ini] to **m**[ini + m], the second from **m**[ini + m + 1] to **m**[ini + 2·m], etc. Element **a**[IN1, IN2] is stored in **m**[ini + (IN1 − 1) · m + IN2]. Since IN1 − 1 can be prepared, the expression in the bracket requires $\Omega = 3$.

For a vector **a**[IN] we would require only $\Omega = 1$, since it is stored in **m**[ini + IN]. We will not use arrays of dimensions higher than 2, so at this point the remark will suffice that if at all possible we should use vectors instead of matrices in production programs.

The point was made here that we could count the number of operations and would then be able to compare the programs as to their respective speeds. Since counting is quite messy and makes reading of the programs rather boring, it will not be included in the printout of the Pascal programs. The above discussion gives the reader the tools for counting time.

The plan is to discuss only basic programs. They are written in Pascal so that the reader can both understand them and transfer them to ADA for the mainframe computer. It is there that new data structures should be used and Ω counted.

Most of the programs will be iterative and will terminate whenever some value, say, a voltage, "converges," i.e.,

$$|v^{(i)} - v^{(i-1)}| < \epsilon$$

where the superscript denotes the iteration number and ϵ an "accuracy." It will be shown later that some programs converge, but when the preceding inequality is true, the result (here $v^{(i)}$) is not correct and includes an error.

We should therefore not confuse convergence with accuracy and consider accuracy the second but more important of the two requirements (speed was first). The subject, though, is too large to be included here and will be dealt with later.

1.6 EXAMPLE NETWORKS AND NOTES

1.6.1 Networks

As input to our programs we need data as exemplified by the 14-bus network shown in Fig. 1.11 from [FS67]. For the sake of simplicity the following changes are made in this network:

- Whenever two parallel lines connect two buses, e.g., 1 and 2, they will be represented by a single line.
- Transformers are represented by impedances, e.g., between buses 5 and 6.
- A three-winding transformer between buses 4, 7, 8, and 9 is represented as indicated in Fig. 1.11(b).

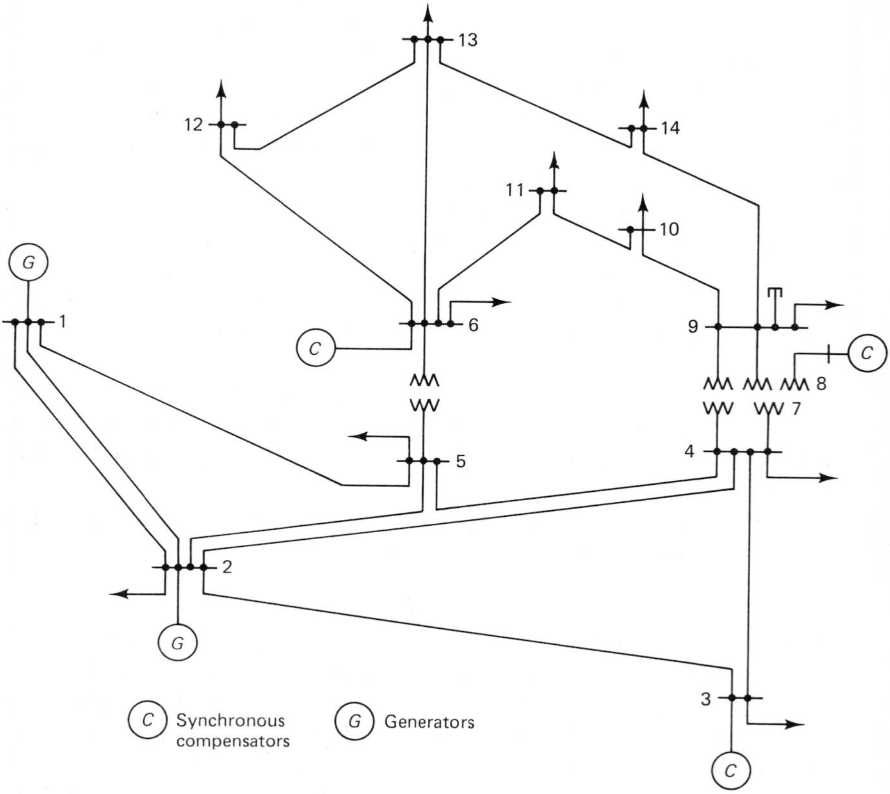

(a) Bus-code diagram

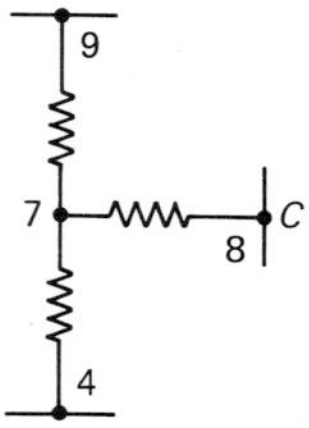

(b) 3-winding transformer equivalent

Figure 1.11 (a) A 14-bus network. (b) Transformer. From [FS67]. Reprinted with permission.

- Synchronous compensators act similarly to static capacitors and will be represented as such. Actually, since line capacitances are considered part of line data, no capacitors need be drawn.
- Note that the transformer between buses 4 and 9 is drawn as a line (impedance).
- One of the generators, the so-called slack bus, is given a voltage in the form of $u_k = 1 + j \cdot 0$ while the others have $u_i' = v_i + j \cdot w_i$. In network of Fig. 1.11 we have $u_1 = 1.06 + j \cdot 0$.
- Capacitive reactance of a line $-j/(\omega C)$ may be represented by $x_c = -j/(2\omega C)$ on each end of the line.
- The impedances are given in the per-unit systems, and so are the powers with generation viewed as negative and load as positive. All buses have some load to supply, and no indication of this is needed.

The network is then redrawn as in Fig. 1.12; its data are summarized in Table 1.1. For economic dispatch (Chapter 6) limits of voltage and power for some buses are shown in Table 1.2a, and the costs of generation are provided in Table 1.2b.

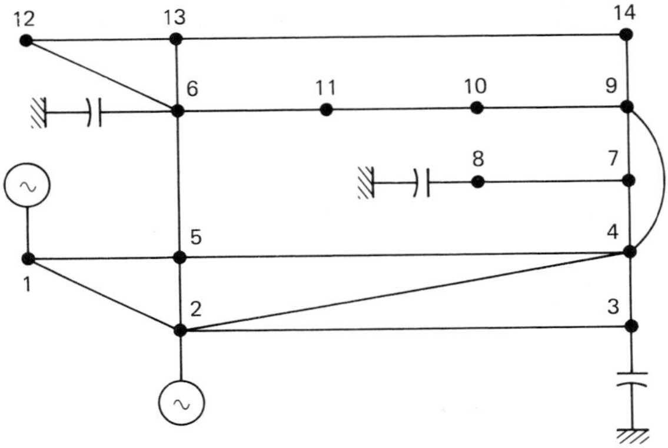

Figure 1.12 Simplified network.

A 5-bus network [SE68] is shown in Fig. 1.13 and its data in Table 1.3. The data for a 7-bus network (derived from the 14-bus network) are shown in Fig. 1.14 and Table 1.4. The data for a 30-bus network, to be used later, are shown in Fig. 1.15 and Table 1.5. Figure 1.16 and Tables 1.6 and 1.7 show other networks. (The 118-bus network is not shown, since its figure would be too large.) The 30, 57 and 118-bus networks can be simplified in the same way as the 14-bus network.

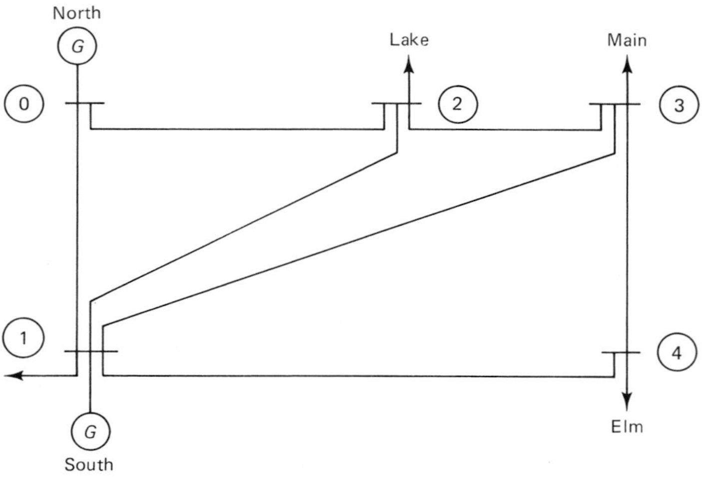

Figure 1.13 Sample system for load-flow solution. From [SE68]. Reprinted with permission.

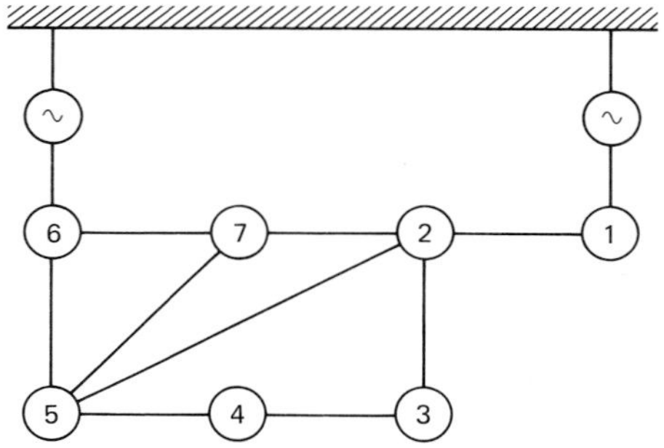

Figure 1.14 A 7-bus network.

1.6.2 Notes

Most of the material in this chapter can be looked up in literature on power systems, in particular and in greater detail in [El71, Gr79, SE68, St62]. Pascal is described in a number of books, e.g., in [Gr81] or [SWP82].

As an exercise, the reader may reduce the number of nodes of the 118-bus network. In this way networks of 70 – 80 and 90 – 100 nodes as well as others in the range of 5 to 118 nodes, can be prepared. The reader may also collect more network data. As mentioned earlier, this book suggests running programs on data of various networks instead of computational examples. The data will therefore come in handy later.

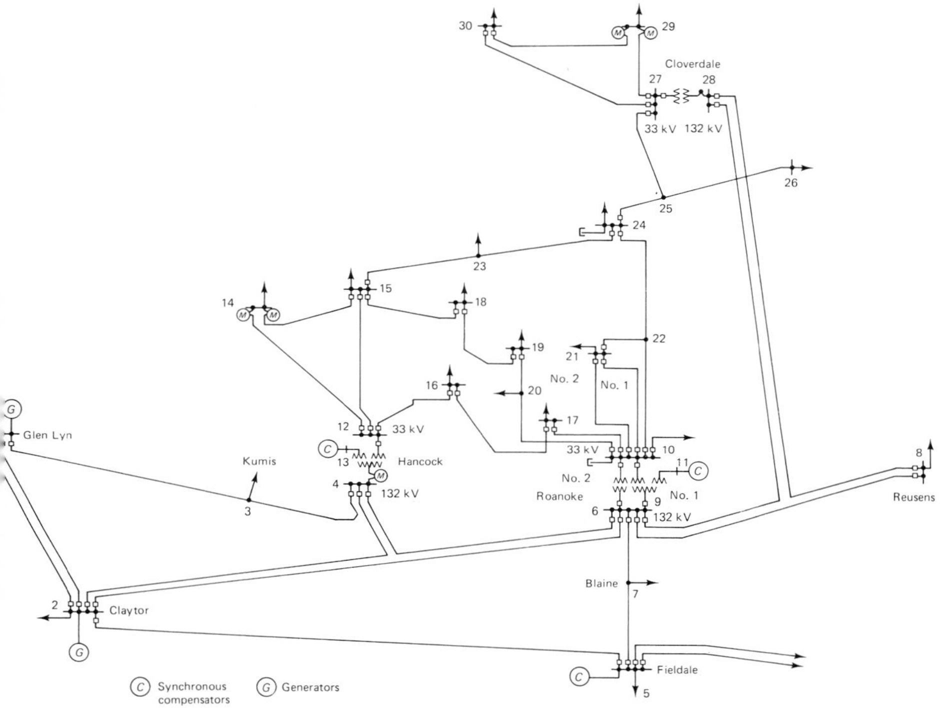

(a) Bus-code diagram

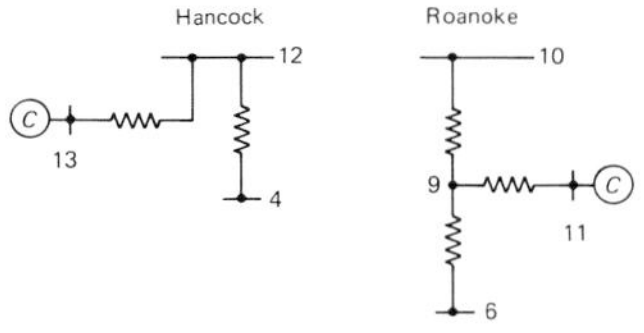

(b) 3-winding transformer equivalents

Figure 1.15 AEP 30-bus test system. From [FS67]. Reprinted with permission.

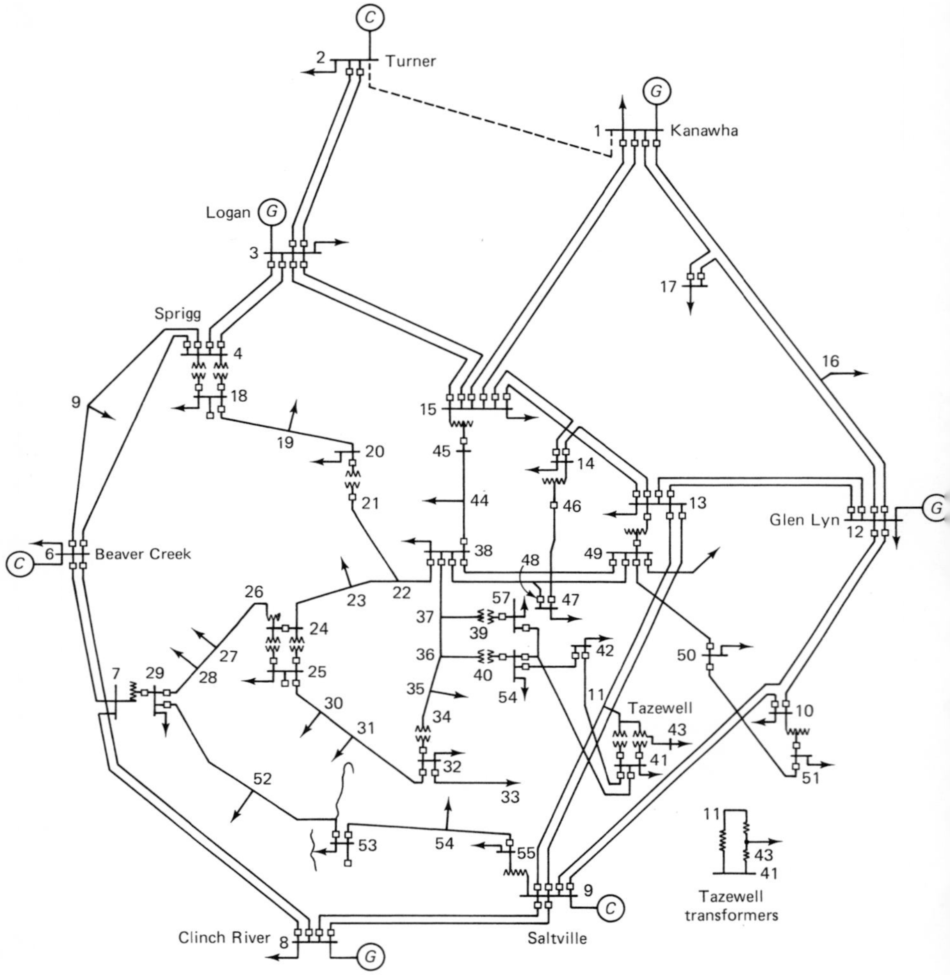

Figure 1.16 AEP 57-bus test system. From [FS67]. Reprinted with permission.

TABLE 1.1(a)* Data of the 14-Bus Network: Impedance and Line-Charging Data

Line designation	Resistance p.u.†	Reactance p.u.†	Line charging p.u.†
1-2	0.01938	0.05917	0.0264
1-5	0.05403	0.22304	0.0246
2-3	0.04699	0.19797	0.0219
2-4	0.05811	0.17632	0.0187
2-5	0.05695	0.17388	0.0170
3-4	0.06701	0.17103	0.0173
4-5	0.01335	0.04211	0.0064
4-7	0	0.20912	0
4-9	0	0.55618	0
5-6	0	0.25202	0
6-11	0.09498	0.19890	0
6-12	0.12291	0.25581	0
6-13	0.06615	0.13027	0
7-8	0	0.17615	0
7-9	0	0.11001	0
9-10	0.03181	0.08450	0
9-14	0.12711	0.27038	0
10-11	0.08205	0.19207	0
12-13	0.22092	0.19988	0
13-14	0.17093	0.34802	0

*From [FS67]. Reprinted with permission.

†Impedance and line-charging susceptance p.u. on a 100000kVA base. Line charging one-half of total charging of line.

TABLE 1.1(b) Operating Conditions

Bus number	Starting bus voltage		Generation		Load	
	Magnitude p.u.	Phase angle deg	MW	MVAr	MW	MVAr
1*	1.06	0	0	0	0	0
2	1.0	0	40	0	21.7	12.7
3	1.0	0	0	0	94.2	19.0
4	1.0	0	0	0	47.8	3.9
5	1.0	0	0	0	7.6	1.8
6	1.0	0	0	0	11.2	7.5
7	1.0	0	0	0	0	0
8	1.0	0	0	0	0	0
9	1.0	0	0	0	29.5	16.6
10	1.0	0	0	0	9.0	5.8
11	1.0	0	0	0	3.5	1.8
12	1.0	0	0	0	6.1	1.6
13	1.0	0	0	0	13.5	5.8
14	1.0	0	0	0	14.9	5.6

*Swing machine

TABLE 1.1(c) Regulated Bus Data

Bus number	Voltage magnitude, p.u.	Minimum MVAr capability	Maximum MVAr capability
2	1.045	−40	50
3	1.010	0	40
6	1.070	−6	24
8	1.090	−6	24

TABLE 1.1(d) Transformer Data

Transformer designation	Tap setting*
4-7	0.978
4-9	0.969
5-6	0.932

*Off-nominal turns ratio, as determined by the actual transformer tap positions and the voltage bases. In the case of nominal turns ratio, this would equal 1.

TABLE 1.1(e)* Static Capacitor Data

Bus number	Susceptance† p.u.
9	0.19

*From [FS67]. Reprinted with permission.
†Susceptance p.u. on a 100000kVA base.

TABLE 1.1(f)

lt	rt	r	x	xc
1	2	.01938	.05917	.0264
1	5	.05403	.22304	.0246
2	3	.04699	.19797	.0219
2	4	.05811	.17632	.0187
2	5	.05695	.17388	.0170
3	4	.06701	.17103	.0173
4	5	.01335	.04211	.0064
4	7	.0	.20912	.0
4	9	.0	.55618	.0
5	6	.0	.25202	.0
6	11	.09498	.19890	.0
6	12	.12291	.25581	.0
6	13	.06615	.13027	.0
7	8	.0	.17615	.0
7	9	.0	.11001	.0
9	10	.03181	.08450	.0
9	14	.12711	.27038	.0
10	11	.08205	.19207	.0
12	13	.22092	.19988	.0
13	14	.17093	.34802	.0

TABLE 1.2(a) Limits of Voltage and Power

Bus	u	p	q
2	1.045	−40.000	50.000
5	1.010	−40.000	40.000
8	1.010	−10.000	40.000
11	1.082	−6.000	24.000
13	1.071	−6.000	24.000

TABLE 1.2(b) Cost of Generation

$$c_1 = 0.0060(p_1^g)^2 + 2.0p_1^g + 140$$
$$c_2 = 0.0075(p_2^g)^2 + 1.5p_2^g + 120$$
$$c_3 = 0.0070(p_3^g)^2 + 1.8p_3^g + 80$$

TABLE 1.3(a) Data of the 5-Bus Network: Impedances and Line Charging for Sample System*

Bus code $p-q$	Impedance z_{pq}	Line charging $y'_{pq}/2$
1-2	$0.02 + j0.06$	$0.0 + j0.030$
1-3	$0.08 + j0.24$	$0.0 + j0.025$
2-3	$0.06 + j0.18$	$0.0 + j0.020$
2-4	$0.06 + j0.18$	$0.0 + j0.020$
2-5	$0.04 + j0.12$	$0.0 + j0.015$
3-4	$0.01 + j0.03$	$0.0 + j0.010$
4-5	$0.08 + j0.24$	$0.0 + j0.025$

*From G.W. Stagg, A.H. El-Abiad: *Computer Methods in Power System Analysis.* © 1968 by McGraw-Hill Book Company, pp. 284, 285 and 286. Reprinted with permission.

TABLE 1.3(b) Data of the 5-Bus Network: Line Admittances and Admittances to Ground for Sample System

Bus code $p-q$	Line admittance y_{pq}
1-2	$5.00000 - j15.00000$
1-3	$1.25000 - j3.75000$
2-3	$1.66667 - j5.00000$
2-4	$1.66667 - j5.00000$
2-5	$2.50000 - j7.50000$
3-4	$10.00000 - j30.00000$
4-5	$1.25000 - j3.75000$

Bus code p	Admittance to ground y_p
1	$0.0 + j0.05500$
2	$0.0 + j0.08500$
3	$0.0 + j0.05500$
4	$0.0 + j0.05500$
5	$0.0 + j0.04000$

TABLE 1.3(c) Scheduled Generation and Loads and Assumed Bus Voltages for Sample System

Bus code	Assumed	Generation		Load	
p	bus voltage	Megawatts	Megavars	Megawatts	Megavars
1	$1.06 + j0.0$	0	0	0	0
2	$1.0 + j0.0$	40	30	20	10
3	$1.0 + j0.0$	0	0	45	15
4	$1.0 + j0.0$	0	0	40	5
5	$1.0 + j0.0$	0	0	60	10

TABLE 1.4 Data of the 7-Bus Network

lt	rt	r	x	xc	Bus	p	q
1	2	0.082	0.192	0.0	1	−.900	−.300
2	3	0.067	0.171	0.0173	2	.478	.039
2	5	0.058	0.176	0.0187	3	.942	.190
2	7	0.013	0.042	0.0064	4	.135	.058
3	4	0.024	0.100	0.01	5	.183	.127
4	5	0.024	0.100	0.01	6	—	—
5	6	0.019	0.059	0.026	7	.076	.016
5	7	0.057	0.174	0.017			
6	7	0.054	0.223	0.025			

TABLE 1.5(a) Data of the 30-Bus Network: Impedance and Line-Charging Data*

Line designation	Resistance p.u.†	Reactance p.u.†	Line charging p.u.†
1-2	0.0192	0.0575	0.0264
1-3	0.0452	0.1852	0.0204
2-4	0.0570	0.1737	0.0184
3-4	0.0132	0.0379	0.0042
2-5	0.0472	0.1983	0.0209
2-6	0.0581	0.1763	0.0187
4-6	0.0119	0.0414	0.0045
5-7	0.0460	0.1160	0.0102
6-7	0.0267	0.0820	0.0085
6-8	0.0120	0.0420	0.0045
6-9	0	0.2080	0
6-10	0	0.5560	0
9-11	0	0.2080	0
9-10	0	0.1100	0
4-12	0	0.2560	0
12-13	0	0.1400	0
12-14	0.1231	0.2559	0
12-15	0.0662	0.1304	0
12-16	0.0945	0.1987	0
14-15	0.2210	0.1997	0
16-17	0.0824	0.1923	0
15-18	0.1070	0.2185	0
18-19	0.0639	0.1292	0
19-20	0.0340	0.0680	0
10-20	0.0936	0.2090	0
10-17	0.0324	0.0845	0
10-21	0.0348	0.0749	0
10-22	0.0727	0.1499	0
21-22	0.0116	0.0236	0
15-23	0.1000	0.2020	0
22-24	0.1150	0.1790	0
23-24	0.1320	0.2700	0
24-25	0.1885	0.3292	0
25-26	0.2544	0.3800	0
25-27	0.1093	0.2087	0
27-28	0	0.3960	0
27-29	0.2198	0.4153	0
27-30	0.3202	0.6027	0
29-30	0.2399	0.4533	0
8-28	0.0636	0.2000	0.0214
6-28	0.0169	0.0599	0.0065

*From [FS67]. Reprinted with permission.

†Impedance and line-charging susceptance p.u. on a 100000kVA base. Line charging one-half of total charging of line.

TABLE 1.5(b) Operating Conditions

Bus number	Starting bus voltage		Generation		Load	
	Magnitude p.u.	Phase angle degrees	MW	MVAr	MW	MVAr
1	1.06	0	0	0	0	0
2	1.0	0	40	0	21.7	12.7
3	1.0	0	0	0	2.4	1.2
4	1.0	0	0	0	7.6	1.6
5	1.0	0	0	0	94.2	19.0
6	1.0	0	0	0	0	0
7	1.0	0	0	0	22.8	10.9
8	1.0	0	0	0	30.0	30.0
9	1.0	0	0	0	0	0
10	1.0	0	0	0	5.8	2.0
11	1.0	0	0	0	0	0
12	1.0	0	0	0	11.2	7.5
13	1.0	0	0	0	0	0
14	1.0	0	0	0	6.2	1.6
15	1.0	0	0	0	8.2	2.5
16	1.0	0	0	0	3.5	1.8
17	1.0	0	0	0	9.0	5.8
18	1.0	0	0	0	3.2	0.9
19	1.0	0	0	0	9.5	3.4
20	1.0	0	0	0	2.2	0.7
21	1.0	0	0	0	17.5	11.2
22	1.0	0	0	0	0	0
23	1.0	0	0	0	3.2	1.6
24	1.0	0	0	0	8.7	6.7
25	1.0	0	0	0	0	0
26	1.0	0	0	0	3.5	2.3
27	1.0	0	0	0	0	0
28	1.0	0	0	0	0	0
29	1.0	0	0	0	2.4	0.9
30	1.0	0	0	0	10.6	1.9

TABLE 1.5(c) Regulated Bus Data

Bus number	Voltage magnitude p.u.	Minimum MVAr capability	Maximum MVAr capability
2	1.045	−40	50
5	1.01	−40	40
8	1.01	−10	40
11	1.082	−6	24
13	1.071	−6	24

TABLE 1.5(d) Transformer Data

Transformer designation	Tap setting*
4-12	0.932
6-9	0.978
6-10	0.969
28-27	0.968

*Off-nominal turns ratio, as determined by the actual transformer-tap positions and the voltage bases. In the case of nominal turns ratio, this would equal 1.

TABLE 1.5(e) Static Capacitor Data

Bus number	Susceptance* p.u.
10	0.19
24	0.043

*Susceptance p.u. on 100000kVA base.

TABLE 1.6(a) Data of the 57-Bus Network: Impedance and Line-Charging Data*

Line designation	Resistance p.u.†	Reactance p.u.†	Line charging p.u.†
1-2	0.0083	0.0280	0.0645
2-3	0.0298	0.0850	0.0409
3-4	0.0112	0.0366	0.0190
4-5	0.0625	0.1320	0.0129
4-6	0.0430	0.1480	0.0174
6-7	0.0200	0.1020	0.0138
6-8	0.0339	0.1730	0.0235
8-9	0.0099	0.0505	0.0274
9-10	0.0369	0.1679	0.0220
9-11	0.0258	0.0848	0.0109
9-12	0.0648	0.2950	0.0386
9-13	0.0481	0.1580	0.0203
13-14	0.0132	0.0434	0.0055
13-15	0.0269	0.0869	0.0115
1-15	0.0178	0.0910	0.0494
1-16	0.0454	0.2060	0.0273
1-17	0.0238	0.1080	0.0143
3-15	0.0162	0.0530	0.0272
4-18	0	0.555	0
4-18	0	0.43	0
5-6	0.0302	0.0641	0.0062
7-8	0.0139	0.0712	0.0097
10-12	0.0277	0.1262	0.0164
11-13	0.0223	0.0732	0.0094
12-13	0.0178	0.0580	0.0302
12-16	0.0180	0.0813	0.0108
12-17	0.0397	0.1790	0.0238
14-15	0.0171	0.0547	0.0074
18-19	0.4610	0.6850	0
19-20	0.2830	0.4340	0
20-21	0	0.7767	0
21-22	0.0736	0.1170	0
22-23	0.0099	0.0152	0
23-24	0.1660	0.2560	0.0042
24-25	0	1.182	0
24-25	0	1.23	0
24-26	0	0.0473	0
26-27	0.1650	0.2540	0
27-28	0.0618	0.0954	0

*From [FS67]. Reprinted with permission.

†Swing machine.

TABLE 1.6(a) (Continued)

Line designation	Resistance p.u.†	Reactance p.u.†	Line charging p.u.†
28-29	0.0418	0.0587	0
7-29	0	0.0648	0
25-30	0.1350	0.2020	0
30-31	0.3260	0.4970	0
31-32	0.5070	0.7550	0
32-33	0.0392	0.0360	0
32-34	0	0.9530	0
34-35	0.0520	0.0780	0.0016
35-36	0.0430	0.0537	0.0008
36-37	0.0290	0.0366	0
37-38	0.0651	0.1009	0.0010
37-39	0.0239	0.0379	0
36-40	0.0300	0.0466	0
22-38	0.0192	0.0295	0
11-41	0	0.7490	0
41-42	0.2070	0.3520	0
41-43	0	0.4120	0
38-44	0.0289	0.0585	0.0010
15-45	0	0.1042	0
14-46	0	0.0735	0
46-47	0.0230	0.0680	0.0016
47-48	0.0182	0.0233	0
48-49	0.0834	0.1290	0.0024
49-50	0.0801	0.1280	0
50-51	0.1386	0.2200	0
10-51	0	0.0712	0
13-49	0	0.1910	0
29-52	0.1442	0.1870	0
52-53	0.0762	0.0984	0
53-54	0.1878	0.2320	0
54-55	0.1732	0.2265	0
11-43	0	0.1530	0
44-45	0.0624	0.1242	0.0020
40-56	0	1.1950	0
56-41	0.5530	0.5490	0
56-42	0.2125	0.3540	0
39-57	0	1.3550	0
57-56	0.1740	0.2600	0
38-49	0.1150	0.1770	0.0030
38-48	0.0312	0.0482	0
9-55	0	0.1205	0

TABLE 1.6(b) Operating Conditions

Bus number	Starting bus voltage		Generation		Load	
	Magnitude p.u.	Phase angle degrees	MW	MVAr	MW	MVAr
1*	1.04	0	0	0	55.0	17.0
2	1.0	0	0	0	3.0	88.0
3	1.0	0	40	0	41.0	21.0
4	1.0	0	0	0	0	0
5	1.0	0	0	0	13.0	4.0
6	1.0	0	0	0	75.0	2.0
4	1.0	0	0	0	0	0
8	1.0	0	450	0	150.0	22.0
9	1.0	0	0	0	121.0	26.0
10	1.0	0	0	0	5.0	2.0
11	1.0	0	0	0	0	0
12	1.0	0	310	0	377.0	24.0
13	1.0	0	0	0	18.0	2.3
14	1.0	0	0	0	10.5	5.3
15	1.0	0	0	0	22.0	5.0
16	1.0	0	0	0	43.0	3.0
17	1.0	0	0	0	42.0	8.0
18	1.0	0	0	0	27.2	9.8
19	1.0	0	0	0	3.3	0.6
20	1.0	0	0	0	2.3	1.0
21	1.0	0	0	0	0	0
22	1.0	0	0	0	0	0
23	1.0	0	0	0	6.3	2.1
24	1.0	0	0	0	0	0
25	1.0	0	0	0	6.3	3.2
26	1.0	0	0	0	0	0
27	1.0	0	0	0	9.3	0.5
28	1.0	0	0	0	4.6	2.3
29	1.0	0	0	0	17.0	2.6
30	1.0	0	0	0	3.6	1.8
31	1.0	0	0	0	5.8	2.9
32	1.0	0	0	0	1.6	0.8
33	1.0	0	0	0	3.8	1.9
34	1.0	0	0	0	0	0
35	1.0	0	0	0	6.0	3.0
36	1.0	0	0	0	0	0
37	1.0	0	0	0	0	0
38	1.0	0	0	0	14.0	7.0

*Swing machine.

TABLE 1.6(b) (Continued)

Bus number	Starting bus voltage: Magnitude p.u.	Starting bus voltage: Phase angle degrees	Generation: MW	Generation: MVAr	Load: MW	Load: MVAr
39	1.0	0	0	0	0	0
40	1.0	0	0	0	0	0
41	1.0	0	0	0	6.3	3.0
42	1.0	0	0	0	7.1	4.4
43	1.0	0	0	0	2.0	1.0
44	1.0	0	0	0	12.0	1.8
45	1.0	0	0	0	0	0
46	1.0	0	0	0	0	0
47	1.0	0	0	0	29.7	11.6
48	1.0	0	0	0	0	0
49	1.0	0	0	0	18.0	8.5
50	1.0	0	0	0	21.0	10.5
51	1.0	0	0	0	18.0	5.3
52	1.0	0	0	0	4.9	2.2
53	1.0	0	0	0	20.0	10.0
54	1.0	0	0	0	4.1	1.4
55	1.0	0	0	0	6.8	3.4
56	1.0	0	0	0	7.6	2.2
57	1.0	0	0	0	6.7	2.0

TABLE 1.6(c) Regulated Bus Data

Bus number	Voltage magnitude p.u.	Minimum MVAr capability	Maximum MVAr capability
2	1.01	−17	50
3	0.985	−10	60
6	0.98	−8	25
8	1.005	−140	200
9	0.98	−3	9
12	1.015	−50	155

TABLE 1.6(d) Static Capacitor Data

Bus number	Susceptance* p.u.
18	0.1
25	0.059
53	0.063

*Susceptance p.u. on a 100000kVA base.

TABLE 1.6(e) Transformer Data

Transformer designation	Tap setting*
4-18	0.97
4-18	0.978
7-29	0.967
9-55	0.94
10-51	0.93
11-41	0.955
11-43	0.958
13-49	0.895
14-46	0.9
15-45	0.955
21-20	1.043
24-25	1.000
24-25	1.000
24-26	1.043
34-32	0.975
39-57	0.98
40-56	0.958

*Off-nominal turns ratio, as determined by the actual transformer-tap positions and the voltage basis. In the case of nominal turns ratio, this would equal 1.

TABLE 1.7(a) AEP 118 Bus Test System:*
Impedance and Line Charging Data†

Line Designation	Resistance Per Unit**	Reactance Per Unit**	Line Charging Per Unit**
1-2	.03030	.09990	.01270
1-3	.01290	.04240	.00541
4-5	.00176	.00798	.00105
3-5	.02410	.10800	.01420
5-6	.01190	.05400	.00713
6-7	.00459	.02080	.00275
8-9	.00244	.03050	.58100
5-8	0	.02670	0
9-10	.00258	.03220	.61500
4-11	.02090	.06880	.00874
5-11	.02030	.06820	.00869
11-12	.00595	.01960	.00251
2-12	.01870	.06160	.00786
3-12	.04840	.16000	.02030
7-12	.00862	.03400	.00437
11-13	.02225	.07310	.00938
12-14	.02150	.07070	.00908
13-15	.07440	.24440	.03134
14-15	.05950	.19500	.02510
12-16	.02120	.08340	.01070
15-17	.01320	.04370	.02220
16-17	.04540	.18010	.02330
17-18	.01230	.05050	.00649
18-19	.01119	.04930	.00571
19-20	.02520	.11700	.01490
15-19	.01200	.03940	.00505
20-21	.01830	.08490	.01080
21-22	.02090	.09700	.01230
22-23	.03420	.15900	.02020
23-24	.01350	.04920	.02490
23-25	.01560	.08000	.04320
25-26	0	.03820	0
25-27	.03180	.16300	.08820
27-28	.01913	.08550	.01080
28-29	.02370	.09430	.01190
17-30	0	.03880	0

*Based on AEP System for Total Loss Formula, June 1962

†From [FS67]. Reprinted with permission.

**Impedance and line-charging susceptance per unit on a 100,000kVA base.

Line charging one-half of total charging of line.

TABLE 1.7(a) (Continued)

Line Designation	Resistance Per Unit**	Reactance Per Unit**	Line Charging Per Unit**
8-30	.00431	.05040	.25700
26-30	.00799	.08600	.45400
17-31	.04740	.15630	.01995
29-31	.01080	.03310	.00415
23-32	.03170	.11530	.05865
31-32	.02980	.09850	.01255
27-32	.02290	.07550	.00963
15-33	.03800	.12440	.01597
19-34	.07520	.24700	.03160
35-36	.00224	.01020	.00134
35-37	.01100	.04970	.00659
33-37	.04150	.14200	.01830
34-36	.00871	.02680	.00284
34-37	.00256	.00940	.00492
37-38	0	.03750	0
37-39	.03210	.10600	.01350
37-40	.05930	.16800	.02100
30-38	.00464	.05400	.21100
39-40	.01840	.06050	.00776
40-41	.01450	.04870	.00611
40-42	.05550	.18300	.02330
41-42	.04100	.13500	.01720
43-44	.06080	.24540	.03034
34-43	.04130	.16810	0.12113
44-45	.02240	.09010	.01120
45-46	.04000	.13560	.01660
46-47	.03800	.12700	.01580
46-48	.06010	.18900	.02360
47-49	.01910	.06250	.00802
42-49	.03575	.01615	.02150
45-49	.06840	.18600	.02220
48-49	.01790	.05050	.00629
49-50	.02670	.07520	.00937
49-51	.04860	.13700	.01710
51-52	.02030	.05880	.00698
52-53	.04050	.16350	.02029
53-54	.02630	.12200	.01550
49-54	.03650	.15000	.01830
54-55	.01690	.07070	.01010
54-56	.00275	.00955	.00366

TABLE 1.7(a) (Continued)

Line Designation	Resistance Per Unit**	Reactance Per Unit**	Line Charging Per Unit**
55-56	.00488	.01510	.00187
56-57	.03430	.09660	.01210
50-57	.04740	.13400	.01660
56-58	.03430	.09660	.01210
51-58	.02550	.07190	.00894
54-59	.05030	.22930	.02990
56-59	.04070	.11225	.01380
55-59	.04739	.21580	.02823
59-60	.03170	.14500	.01880
59-61	.03280	.15000	.01940
60-61	.00264	.01350	.00728
60-62	.01230	.05610	.00734
61-62	.00824	.03760	.00490
59-63	0	.03860	0
63-64	.00172	.02000	.10800
61-64	0	.02680	0
38-65	.00901	.09860	.52300
64-65	.00269	.03020	.19000
49-66	.00900	.04595	.00620
62-66	.04820	.21800	.02890
62-67	.02580	.11700	.01550
65-66	0	.03700	0
66-67	.02240	.10150	.01341
65-68	.00138	.01600	.31900
47-69	.08440	.27780	.03546
49-69	.09850	.32400	.04140
68-69	0	.03700	0
69-70	.03000	.12700	.06100
24-70	.10221	.41150	.05099
70-71	.00882	.03550	.00439
24-72	.04880	.19600	.02440
71-72	.04460	.18000	.02222
71-73	.00866	.04540	.00589
70-74	.04010	.13230	.01684
70-75	.04280	.14100	.01800
69-75	.04050	.12200	.06200
74-75	.01230	.04060	.00517
76-77	.04440	.14800	.01840
69-77	.03090	.10100	.05190
75-77	.06010	.19990	.02489

TABLE 1.7(a) (Continued)

Line Designation	Resistance Per Unit**	Reactance Per Unit**	Line Charging Per Unit**
77-78	.00376	.01240	.00632
78-79	.00546	.02440	.00324
77-80	.01077	.03318	.00769
79-80	.01560	.07040	.00935
68-81	.00175	.02020	.40400
80-81	0	.03700	0
77-82	.02980	.08530	.04087
82-83	.01120	.03665	.01898
83-84	.06250	.13200	.01290
83-85	.04300	.14800	.01740
84-85	.03020	.06410	.00617
85-86	.03500	.12300	.01380
86-87	.02828	.20740	.02225
85-88	.02000	.10200	.01380
85-89	.02390	.17300	.02350
88-89	.01390	.07120	.00967
89-90	.01631	.06515	.01762
90-92	.02540	.08360	.01070
89-92	.00791	.03827	.01179
91-92	.03870	.12720	.01634
92-93	.02580	.08480	.01090
92-94	.04810	.15800	.02030
93-94	.02230	.07320	.00938
94-95	.01320	.04340	.00555
80-96	.03560	.18200	.02470
82-96	.01620	.05300	.02720
94-96	.02690	.08690	.01150
80-97	.01830	.09340	.01270
80-98	.02380	.10800	.01430
80-99	.04540	.20600	.02730
92-100	.06480	.29500	.03860
94-100	.01780	.05800	.03020
95-96	.01710	.05470	.00737
96-97	.01730	.08850	.01200
98-100	.03970	.17900	.02380
99-100	.01800	.08130	.01080
100-101	.02770	.12620	.01640
92-102	.01230	.05590	.00732
101-102	.02460	.11200	.01470
100-103	.01600	.05250	.02680

TABLE 1.7(a) (Continued)

Line Designation	Resistance Per Unit**	Reactance Per Unit**	Line Charging Per Unit**
100-104	.04510	.20400	.02705
103-104	.04660	.15840	.02035
103-105	.05350	.16250	.02040
100-106	.06050	.22900	.03100
104-105	.00994	.03780	.00493
105-106	.01400	.05470	.00717
105-107	.05300	.18300	.02360
105-108	.02610	.07030	.00922
106-107	.05300	.18300	.02360
108-109	.01050	.02880	.00380
103-110	.03906	.18130	.02305
109-110	.02780	.07620	.01010
110-111	.02200	.07550	.01000
110-112	.02470	.06400	.03100
17-113	.00913	.03010	.00384
32-113	.06150	.20300	.02590
32-114	.01350	.06120	.00814
27-115	.01640	.07410	.00986
114-115	.00230	.01040	.00138
68-116	.00034	.00405	.08200
12-117	.03290	.14000	.01790
75-118	.01450	.04810	.00599
76-118	.01640	.05440	.00678

TABLE 1.7(b) Regulated Bus Data*

Bus Number	Voltage Magnitude Per Unit	Minimum Mvar Capability	Maximum Mvar Capability
1	.955	−5	15
4	.998	−300	300
6	.99	−13	50
8	1.015	−300	300
10	1.05	−147	200
12	.99	−35	120
15	.97	−10	30
18	.973	−16	50
19	.962	−8	24
24	.992	−300	300
25	1.05	−47	140
26	1.015	−1000	1000
27	.968	−300	300
31	.967	−300	300
32	.963	−14	42
34	.984	−8	24
36	.98	−8	24
40	.97	−300	300
42	.985	−300	300
46	1.005	−100	100
49	1.025	−85	210
54	.955	−300	300
55	.952	−8	23
56	.954	−8	15
59	.985	−60	180
61	.995	−100	300
62	.998	−20	20
65	1.005	−67	200
66	1.05	−67	200
70	.984	−10	32
72	.98	−100	100
73	.991	−100	100
74	.958	−6	9
76	.943	−8	23
77	1.006	−20	70
80	1.04	−165	280
85	.985	−8	23
87	1.015	−100	1000
89	1.005	−210	300
90	.985	−300	300
91	.98	−100	100
92	.99	−3	9
99	1.01	−100	100

*From [FS67]. Reprinted with permission.

2 Solution of Linear Systems

The *objectives* of this chapter are

1. To review the following methods of solving linear sets: elimination (and factorization), inversion (and Kron's method), orthogonalization, updating, as well as some of the iterative methods.
2. To introduce sparsity and discuss its consequences.
3. To discuss in general roundoff errors and the singular-value decomposition.

2.1 ELIMINATION AND FACTORIZATION

Power system problems involve hundreds or thousands of variables, and it is clearly impossible to exemplify the solution methods using many equations. A system of three equations with three unknowns will be used as an example and then generalized to any number n. The system is

$$\begin{aligned} 1\cdot x_1 + 2\cdot x_2 + 4\cdot x_3 &= 27 \\ 2\cdot x_1 + 2\cdot x_2 + 6\cdot x_3 &= 38 \\ 4\cdot x_1 + 6\cdot x_2 - 3\cdot x_3 &= 7 \end{aligned} \tag{2.1}$$

The general notation is $a_{i,j}$ for the coefficient in row i, column j and b_i for the right-hand side of row i.

Elimination, which probably is familiar from high-school algebra, consists of the following steps:

Eliminate x_1 from the second and third equation: First multiply the first equation by $e = a_{2,1}/a_{1,1} = 2/1 = 2$. This yields for the first equation

$$2 \cdot x_1 + 4 \cdot x_2 + 8 \cdot x_3 = 54$$

Subtracting this from the second equation yields for the second equation

$$0 \cdot x_1 - 2 \cdot x_2 - 2 \cdot x_3 = -16$$

The multiplication of any equation, written, for example, as $a = b$, by a constant and nonzero e does not change its value; neither does subtraction of, say, $c = d$. Thus, $a \cdot e - c = b \cdot e - d$ is as valid as was $a = b$.

Note that $0 \cdot x_1$ means that x_1 does not appear any more in the second equation; it was eliminated.

To eliminate x_1 from the third equation, multiply the first by $e = a_{3,1}/a_{1,1} = 4/1 = 4$ to yield $4 \cdot x_1 + 8 \cdot x_2 + 16 \cdot x_3 = 108$. Next subtract it from the third equation:

$$0 \cdot x_1 - 2 \cdot x_2 - 19 \cdot x_3 = -101$$

The original problem and the same set after eliminating the first column can be rewritten in matrix notation:

$$\begin{bmatrix} 1 & 2 & 4 \\ 2 & 2 & 6 \\ 4 & 6 & -3 \end{bmatrix} * \begin{bmatrix} x_1 \\ x_2 \\ x_3 \end{bmatrix} = \begin{bmatrix} 27 \\ 38 \\ 7 \end{bmatrix}; \quad \begin{bmatrix} 1 & 2 & 4 \\ 0 & -2 & -2 \\ 0 & -2 & -19 \end{bmatrix} * \begin{bmatrix} x_1 \\ x_2 \\ x_3 \end{bmatrix} = \begin{bmatrix} 27 \\ -16 \\ -101 \end{bmatrix}$$

Next, eliminate x_2 from the third equation by first multiplying the second equation by $a_{3,2}/a_{2,2} = 2/2 = 1$, i.e., $0 \cdot x_1 - 2 \cdot x_2 - 2 \cdot x_3 = -16$, and then subtract it from the third, to yield

$$(0 - 0) \cdot x_1 + (-2 + 2) \cdot x_2 + (-19 + 2) \cdot x_3 = -101 + 16$$
$$0 \cdot x_1 + 0 \cdot x_2 - 17 \cdot x_3 = -85$$

The three equations are now

$$\begin{aligned} 1 \cdot x_1 + 2 \cdot x_2 + 4 \cdot x_3 &= 27 \\ 0 \cdot x_1 - 2 \cdot x_2 - 2 \cdot x_3 &= -16 \\ 0 \cdot x_1 + 0 \cdot x_2 - 17 \cdot x_3 &= -85 \end{aligned} \quad \text{or} \quad \begin{bmatrix} 1 & 2 & 4 \\ 0 & -2 & -2 \\ 0 & 0 & -17 \end{bmatrix} * \begin{bmatrix} x_1 \\ x_2 \\ x_3 \end{bmatrix} = \begin{bmatrix} 27 \\ -16 \\ -85 \end{bmatrix}$$

Note that the matrix is now an *upper triangular* matrix **U**. In order to generalize, we would have to use a matrix with more columns and rows, but the result would still be an upper triangular matrix **U**.

The general equations for step i are: Multiply equation i consecutively by $a_{j,i}/a_{i,i}$ where $j = i + 1, i + 2, \ldots, n$ and subtract the resulting equation i from equations j. The new elements of equation j are:

$$a_{j,k} := a_{j,k} - a_{j,i} \cdot \frac{a_{i,k}}{a_{i,i}}; \quad k = 1, 2, \ldots, n \tag{2.2}$$

All elements left of column i are zero, i.e., $a_{j,m} = 0$ and $a_{i,m} = 0$ for $m = 1, 2, \ldots, i - 1$. In our example, while eliminating $a_{3,2}$, both $a_{3,1} = 0$ and $a_{2,1} = 0$, and there was really no need to write $(0 - 0) \cdot x_1$. We see that index k starts "at the diagonal." Note also that for $k = i$, Eq. (2.2) yields

$$a_{j,i} := a_{j,i} - a_{j,i} \cdot \frac{a_{i,i}}{a_{i,i}} = a_{j,i} - a_{j,i} = 0$$

Therefore, the index k of Eq. (2.2) should read $k = i + 1, \ldots, n$.

Having produced the upper triangular matrix **U**, we can calculate all unknown values x_i, $i = n, n - 1, \ldots, 1$ by *back-substitution*. For our case $x_n = x_3$ can be calculated from the last (third) equation as

$$a_{3,3} \cdot x_3 = b_3 \quad \text{or} \quad -17 \cdot x_3 = -85 \quad \text{or} \quad x_3 := 85/17 = 5$$

Next, x_2 can be calculated from the second equation:

$$-2 \cdot x_2 - 2 \cdot x_3 = -16 \quad \text{or} \quad x_2 := \frac{16 - 2 \cdot x_3}{2} = \frac{16 - 10}{2} = 3$$

Finally, x_1 can be calculated from the first equation:

$$x_1 := 27 - 2 \cdot x_2 - 4 \cdot x_3 = 27 - 6 - 20 = 1$$

These steps are called back-substitution because the x_i were computed in the order $i = 3, 2, 1$ or in general $i = n, \ldots, 1$, i.e., backward from n to 1. In the general case, the equation for x_i with $i = n, n - 1, \ldots, 1$ is

$$x_i := \frac{b_i - \Sigma\, a_{i,k} \cdot x_k}{a_{i,i}}; \quad k\Sigma = i + 1, i + 2, \ldots, n$$

Note the following:

1. Since Eq. (2.2) is also applied to the right-hand side **b**, we can add this column to the **A** matrix and perform all operations on the resulting *extended matrix*. In our case,

$$\begin{bmatrix} 1 & 2 & 4 & 27 \\ 2 & 2 & 6 & 38 \\ 4 & 6 & -3 & 7 \end{bmatrix} \rightarrow \begin{bmatrix} 1 & 2 & 4 & 27 \\ 0 & -2 & -2 & -16 \\ 0 & -2 & -19 & -101 \end{bmatrix} \rightarrow \begin{bmatrix} 1 & 2 & 4 & 27 \\ 0 & -2 & -2 & -16 \\ 0 & 0 & -17 & -85 \end{bmatrix}$$

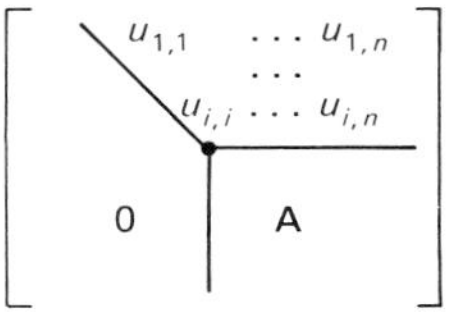

(a)

$$\begin{bmatrix} 1 & 2 & 4 & 27 \\ 0 & -2 & -2 & -16 \\ 4 & 6 & -3 & 7 \end{bmatrix}$$

(b)

$$\begin{bmatrix} 1 & 2 & 4 & 27 \\ 0 & -2 & -2 & -16 \\ 0 & -2 & -19 & -101 \end{bmatrix}$$

(c)

Figure 2.1 The matrix at (a) step i; (b) step 2; (c) step 3.

At stage i, the matrix resembles Fig. 2.1(a). Columns 1 to $i - 1$ are already eliminated, rows 1 to i are already in upper triangular form, and an $(n - i)$-by-$(n - i)$ matrix **A** has yet to be processed.

2. The order of elimination was column 1, column 2, ..., column $n - 1$. This is not the only possible order. We could have viewed the two equations for calculating $a_{3,1}$ and $a_{3,2}$ as starting from Fig. 2.1(b) and calculate for $j = 3$ and $i = 1$:

$$a_{3,1} := a_{3,1} - a_{3,1} \cdot \frac{a_{1,1}}{a_{1,1}} = 4 - 4 \cdot \frac{1}{1} = 0$$

$$a_{3,2} := a_{3,2} - a_{3,1} \cdot \frac{a_{1,2}}{a_{1,1}} = 6 - 4 \cdot \frac{2}{1} = -2$$

$$a_{3,3} := a_{3,3} - a_{3,1} \cdot \frac{a_{1,3}}{a_{1,1}} = -3 - 4 \cdot \frac{4}{1} = -19$$

$$a_{3,4} := a_{3,4} - a_{3,1} \cdot \frac{a_{1,4}}{a_{1,1}} = 7 - 4 \cdot \frac{27}{1} = -101$$

which is the matrix in Fig. 2.1(c). Next, for $i = 2$,

$$a_{3,2} := a_{3,2} - a_{3,2} \cdot \frac{a_{2,2}}{a_{2,2}} = -2 + 2 \cdot \frac{2}{2} = 0$$

$$a_{3,3} := a_{3,3} - a_{3,2} \cdot \frac{a_{2,3}}{a_{2,2}} = -19 + 2 \cdot \frac{2}{2} = -17$$

$$a_{3,4} := a_{3,4} - a_{3,2} \cdot \frac{a_{2,4}}{a_{2,2}} = -101 + 2 \cdot \frac{16}{2} = -85$$

The point is that we can use ordering by rows and eliminate $a_{2,1}$ then $a_{3,1}$, $a_{3,2}$ (as above), then $a_{4,1}$, $a_{4,2}$, $a_{4,3}$, etc. In general, then, in row i we would eliminate $a_{i,1}$, $a_{i,2}$, ..., $a_{i,i-1}$. This ordering will be important.

3. Take as the next example the linear set

$$1.00 \cdot x_1 + 2.00 \cdot x_2 = 2.00 \tag{2.3}$$

$$2.01 \cdot x_1 + 3.99 \cdot x_2 = 4.02 \tag{2.4}$$

This set was derived from a known solution of $x_1 = 1$ and $x_2 = 0.5$ in which $a_{2,2}$ was then changed. If we solve it by elimination, we will run into the following problem. Multiply Eq. (2.3) by 2.01 and subtract the resulting equation from Eq. (2.4) as required by the algorithm. The result is $0.00 \cdot x_1 - 0.03 \cdot x_2 = 4.02 - 4.02 = 0$, which means that $x_2 = 0$. Insert x_2 into Eq. (2.3). This yields $x_1 := 2.0$ with both x's being completely wrong.

The reason for the failure of elimination is that Eq. (2.4) was approximately Eq. (2.3) but multiplied by 2.01. Thus, had we represented the two equations by lines, they would have been nearly parallel. Systems of this type are called *singular* and cannot be solved by elimination.

4. Often, the matrix may be nonsingular, but the elimination process leads to large errors as exemplified below.

Let us assume that we have two x's, $x_1 = 1.00001$ and $x_2 = 0.99999$, and that we use a calculator (or computer) which operates with up to six digits. Using these x's, we can set up the equations

$$0.0001 \cdot x_1 + 2.00 \cdot x_2 = 2.00008 \tag{2.5}$$

$$1.00 \cdot x_1 + 1.00 \cdot x_2 = 2.00 \tag{2.6}$$

The elimination algorithm uses Eq. (2.5) if possible to eliminate x_1 from Eq. (2.6). Here, this is done by multiplying Eq. (2.5) by 10^4 and then subtracting it from Eq. (2.6). Equation (2.6) will be

$$0.00 \cdot x_1 + (1 - 2 \cdot 10^4) \cdot x_2 = 2.0 - 2.00008 \cdot 10^4$$

The obvious approximations $1 - 2 \cdot 10^4 \cong -2 \cdot 10^4$ and $2 - 2.00008 \cdot 10^4 \cong -2.00008 \cdot 10^4$ lead to

$$0 \cdot x_1 - 2 \cdot 10^4 \cdot x_2 \cong -2.00008 \cdot 10^4 \quad \text{or} \quad x_2 := 1.00004$$

Inserting this not entirely wrong x_2 into Eq. (2.5) yields

$$0.0001 \cdot x_1 + 2.00008 = 2.00008 \quad \text{and} \quad x_1 := 0 \tag{2.7}$$

Of course, this is an awfully wrong result. What went wrong? The two lines were not parallel, and we will show later that the problem is in fact easily solved—the set is not singular at all.

What went wrong was that to eliminate x_1 from Eq. (2.6), we had to multiply Eq. (2.5) by 10^4. This number is so much larger than the other numbers that the approximations had to lead to $x_1 := 0$. Note that in Eq. (2.7), we had $\epsilon \cdot x_1 + a = a$ where ϵ is a very small number.

We can generalize this by saying that, if at any stage $a_{i,i} = 0$, we cannot proceed, since elimination then involves a division by zero. Moreover, if $a_{i,i} = \epsilon$, the same will apply, since any number divided by the very small ϵ will swamp all other essential data of the equations.

There is sometimes a rather simple cure for this problem, namely, to exchange the equations. In the case of any $a_{i,i} = 0$, exchanging the equations will result in the new $a_{i,i} \neq 0$; the process is called *pivoting*. This step is essential, and we repeat it for emphasis:

If, at any point in the elimination process, $a_{i,i} = 0$, test all $a_{k,i}$, $k > i$, i.e., all elements of column i below the diagonal. Interchange row i with the row m for which $a_{m,i}$ is not only nonzero but has the largest absolute value of all $a_{k,i}$ tested in the process.

Now, if it is absolutely necessary to interchange rows whenever $a_{i,i} = 0$, it may be beneficial or at least safer to do the same whenever $a_{i,i} = \epsilon$. For instance, reshuffle Eqs. (2.5) and (2.6):

$$1.00 \cdot x_1 + 1.00 \cdot x_2 = 2.00 \tag{2.8}$$

$$0.0001 \cdot x_1 + 2.00 \cdot x_2 = 2.00008 \tag{2.9}$$

Multiplying Eq. (2.8) by 0.0001 and subtracting it from Eq. (2.9) yields $0 \cdot x_1 + 1.9999 \cdot x_2 = 1.99988$ or $1.9999 \cdot x_2 \cong 1.9999$ and $x_2 := 1.00$. The first equation is then $1.00 \cdot x_1 + 1.00 = 2.00$ or $x_1 := 1.00$. The results, $x_1 = 1.00$ and $x_2 = 1.00$, are not so bad considering that we started from 1.00001 and 0.99999, respectively.

The following example shows that we may have to do some more work before attempting to solve a linear set. Consider the system

$$10.00 \cdot x_1 + 2.00 \cdot 10^6 \cdot x_2 = 2.00008 \cdot 10^6 \tag{2.10}$$

$$1.00 \cdot x_1 + 1.00 \cdot x_2 = 2.00 \tag{2.11}$$

If we follow the elimination procedure, no interchanging of equations is required, since $10 > 1$. We thus multiply the first equation by 0.1 and subtract it from the second. This yields for the second $0.0 \cdot x_1 - 2 \cdot 10^5 \cdot x_2 \cong -2.00008 \cdot 10^5$ or $x_2 := 1.00004$ and $x_1 := 0.00$ (from the first equation).

This is just as bad as before, because this is the set Eqs. (2.5) and (2.6) again. Equation (2.10) is Eq. (2.5) multiplied by 10^6; Eqs. (2.6) and (2.11) are identical. The results are wrong again.

As seen, the advice to exchange equations is not satisfactory for all sets. What seems to be wrong with the new set is that Eq. (2.10) has coefficients that are too large for the problem. The advice is therefore to *scale the equations* before solving the linear set. For instance, divide each by its largest element so that the coefficients are roughly of the same size in all equations of the set.

Having shown that elimination requires scaling and pivoting, we next discuss a variant of elimination, namely, *factorization.*

Factorization. A matrix **A** can be decomposed (factored) into a lower (**L**) and an upper (**U**) triangular matrix, i.e., written as

$$\mathbf{A} = \mathbf{L} * \mathbf{U} \tag{2.12}$$

where the diagonal entries of either **L** or **U** are ones. In order to generalize, we first exemplify the procedure on the 3-by-3 set

$$\begin{bmatrix} L_{1,1} & 0 & 0 \\ L_{2,1} & L_{2,2} & 0 \\ L_{3,1} & L_{3,2} & L_{3,3} \end{bmatrix} * \begin{bmatrix} 1 & u_{1,2} & u_{1,3} \\ 0 & 1 & u_{2,3} \\ 0 & 0 & 1 \end{bmatrix} = \begin{bmatrix} a_{11} & a_{12} & a_{13} \\ a_{21} & a_{22} & a_{23} \\ a_{31} & a_{32} & a_{33} \end{bmatrix} = \begin{bmatrix} 1 & 2 & 4 \\ 2 & 2 & 6 \\ 4 & 6 & -3 \end{bmatrix}$$

The first column of **L** can be calculated by multiplying those elements of **L** and **U** which produce the first column of **A**: $L_{1,1}\cdot 1 = 1$, $L_{2,1}\cdot 1 = 2$, $L_{3,1}\cdot 1 = 4$, or $L_{1,1} := 1$, $L_{2,1} := 2$, $L_{3,1} := 4$, which in general is $L_{i,1} := a_{i,1}$; $i := 1, \ldots, n$.

Next, for the remainder of the first row of **A**:

$$L_{1,1}\cdot u_{1,2} = 2;\ L_{1,1}\cdot u_{1,3} = 4 \quad \text{or} \quad u_{1,2} := 2/1 = 2;\ u_{1,3} := 4/1 = 4$$

or in general, for the first row of **U**:

$$u_{1,i} := a_{1,i}/L_{1,1};\quad i := 2, 3, \ldots, n$$

Next, for the remainder of column 2 of **A**:

$$L_{2,1}\cdot u_{1,2} + L_{2,2} = 2, \quad \text{so that} \quad L_{2,2} := 2 - 2\cdot 2 = -2$$

$$L_{3,1}\cdot u_{1,2} + L_{3,2} = 6, \quad \text{so that} \quad L_{3,2} := 6 - 4\cdot 2 = -2;$$

In general, then, for the second column of **L**,

$$L_{i,2} := a_{i,2} - L_{i,1}\cdot u_{1,2};\quad i := 2, \ldots, n$$

Element $u_{2,3}$ derives from the equation for calculating $a_{2,3}$, namely,

$$L_{2,1}\cdot u_{1,3} + L_{2,2}\cdot u_{2,3} = a_{2,3}$$

$$u_{2,3} := \frac{a_{2,3} - L_{2,1}\cdot u_{1,3}}{L_{2,2}} = \frac{6 - 2\cdot 4}{-2} = 1 \tag{2.13}$$

Finally, element $L_{3,3}$ follows the equation

$$L_{3,1}\cdot u_{1,3} + L_{3,2}\cdot u_{2,3} + L_{3,3} = a_{3,3};$$

$$L_{3,3} := a_{3,3} - (L_{3,1}\cdot u_{1,3} + L_{3,2}\cdot u_{2,3}) = -3 - (4\cdot 4 - 2\cdot 1) = -17$$

Had we taken a set larger than for three equations, we could have generalized and written for $k = 1$ to n:

$$L_{i,k} := a_{i,k} - \Sigma\ L_{i,m} \cdot u_{m,k};\quad m\Sigma := 1, 2, \ldots, k - 1 \tag{2.14}$$

$$u_{k,i} := \frac{a_{k,i} - \Sigma\ L_{k,m} \cdot u_{m,i}}{L_{k,k}};\quad m\Sigma := 1, 2, \ldots, k - 1 \tag{2.15}$$

The order in which we proceed is summarized graphically in Fig. 2.2.

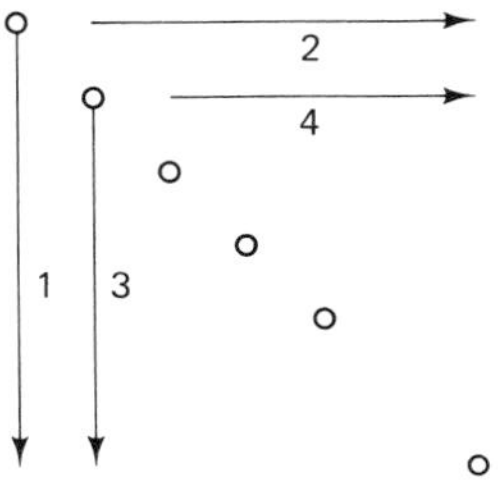

Figure 2.2 Order of factorization.

Suppose we rewrite Eq. (2.13) for $u_{2,3}$, substituting computed values for the u 's and L 's:

$$u_{2,3} := \frac{a_{2,3} - a_{2,1} \cdot a_{1,3}/a_{1,1}}{a_{2,2} - a_{2,1} \cdot u_{1,2}} = \frac{a_{2,3} - a_{2,1} \cdot a_{3,1}/a_{1,1}}{a_{2,2} - a_{2,1} \cdot a_{1,2}/a_{1,1}}$$

It can be seen that instead of performing the operations in the order (col_1, row_1, col_2, row_2, ..., row_{n-1}, $L_{n,n}$), it is entirely correct to sequence them row by row; calculation of $u_{2,3}$ obviously can follow the calculation of $L_{2,1}$, $L_{2,2}$. In elimination, too, we could have computed results by rows: $i = 2, \ldots, n$ applying Eq. (2.16) for $k = 1, \ldots, i - 1$.

$$a_{i,m} := a_{i,m} - \frac{a_{i,k} \cdot a_{k,m}}{a_{k,k}};\quad m := k, \ldots, n \tag{2.16}$$

Equations (2.14) and (2.15) for the L 's and u 's are also true in this case because a sum is zero if taken from i to j such that $j < i$.

The solution of **A** * **x** = **b** by factorization is obtained in two stages:

1. *Factorization*: **A** = **L** * **U**.
2. *Substitution*: If we write the set as **L** * (**U** * **x**) = **b**, then, renaming **U** * **x** as **z**, we have first a forward substitution, **L** * **z** = **b** in which elements z_i are calculated in the order $i = 1, 2, \ldots, n$. Then we have the back-substitution **U** * **x** = **z**.

For instance for the 3-by-3 example we have

$$\begin{bmatrix} 1 & 0 & 0 \\ 2 & -2 & 0 \\ 4 & -2 & -17 \end{bmatrix} * \begin{bmatrix} z_1 \\ z_2 \\ z_3 \end{bmatrix} = \begin{bmatrix} 27 \\ 38 \\ 7 \end{bmatrix} \quad \begin{array}{l} z_1 = 27; \\ 2 \cdot z_1 - 2 \cdot z_2 = 38; \quad 2 \cdot z_2 = 54 - 38; \\ z_2 = 8; \quad 4 \cdot z_1 - 2 \cdot z_2 - 17 \cdot z_3 = 7; \end{array}$$

$$\begin{bmatrix} 1 & 2 & 4 \\ 0 & 1 & 1 \\ 0 & 0 & 1 \end{bmatrix} * \begin{bmatrix} x_1 \\ x_2 \\ x_3 \end{bmatrix} = \begin{bmatrix} 27 \\ 8 \\ 5 \end{bmatrix} \quad \begin{array}{l} 108 - 16 - 17 \cdot z_3 = 7; \quad z_3 := 5 \\ x_3 := 5; \quad x_2 + x_3 = 8; \quad x_2 := 8 - 5 = 3; \\ x_1 + 2 \cdot x_2 + 4 \cdot x_3 = 27; \quad x_1 := 1 \end{array}$$

It is easy now to answer the question whether the factorization is at all required or one should be satisfied with elimination (the two methods were seen to be similar). The amount of work Ω is the same, except that we mostly solve $\mathbf{A} * \mathbf{x} = \mathbf{f}(\mathbf{x})$, i.e., compute each right-hand side only when $\mathbf{x}$ is known. (The solution $\mathbf{x}$ is obtained iteratively.) In this case elimination has to be performed for every new $\mathbf{x}$, but in factorization only the right-hand side changes and since $\mathbf{L}$ and $\mathbf{U}$ remain constant, only $\mathbf{L} * \mathbf{z} = \mathbf{b}$, $\mathbf{U} * \mathbf{x} = \mathbf{z}$ are to be repeated. We will therefore prefer factorization to elimination.

A simple program for the LU factorization, called LU, is Program 2.1a. The results of applying it to Eq. (2.1) are shown in Program 2.1b. The reader interested in a more complete and efficient program is referred to [FM67].

If the matrix is symmetric, then it can be decomposed into

$$\mathbf{A} = \mathbf{L} * \mathbf{L}^{\mathrm{T}} = \mathbf{U}^{\mathrm{T}} * \mathbf{U} \tag{2.17}$$

Write down the equations in detail as in, say,

$$\begin{bmatrix} L_{11} & 0 & 0 \\ L_{21} & L_{22} & 0 \\ L_{31} & L_{32} & L_{33} \end{bmatrix} * \begin{bmatrix} L_{11} & L_{21} & L_{31} \\ 0 & L_{22} & L_{32} \\ 0 & 0 & L_{33} \end{bmatrix} = \begin{bmatrix} a_{11} & a_{12} & a_{13} \\ a_{21} & a_{22} & a_{23} \\ a_{31} & a_{32} & a_{33} \end{bmatrix}$$

Note that for calculating a diagonal element, say, $L_{2,2}$, we have to extract a square root:

$$L_{21}^2 + L_{22}^2 = a_{22} \text{ and } L_{22} := \sqrt{a_{22} - L_{21}^2}$$

Factorization can also be done without the need for extracting square roots. For this multiply $\mathbf{A} = \mathbf{L} * \mathbf{U}$ internally by $\mathbf{I} \equiv \mathbf{D} * \mathbf{D}^{-1}$ where $\mathbf{D}$ is a diagonal matrix and $\tilde{\mathbf{U}}$ is defined as

$$\mathbf{A} = \mathbf{L} * \mathbf{U} = \mathbf{L} * \mathbf{D} * \mathbf{D}^{-1} * \mathbf{U} = \mathbf{L} * \mathbf{D} * \tilde{\mathbf{U}} \tag{2.18}$$

$$\tilde{\mathbf{U}} = \mathbf{D}^{-1} * \mathbf{U} \tag{2.19}$$

For a symmetric set, we have $\mathbf{A} = \mathbf{A}^{\mathrm{T}}$, $\mathbf{L}^{\mathrm{T}} = \mathbf{U}$, $\mathbf{L} = \mathbf{U}^{\mathrm{T}}$, and therefore

$$\tilde{\mathbf{U}}^{\mathrm{T}} * \mathbf{D} * \mathbf{L}^{\mathrm{T}} = \mathbf{U}^{\mathrm{T}} * \mathbf{D}^{-1} * \mathbf{D} * \mathbf{L}^{\mathrm{T}} = \mathbf{L} * \mathbf{D} * \mathbf{D}^{-1} * \mathbf{U} = \mathbf{L} * \mathbf{D} * \tilde{\mathbf{U}}$$

```
program lu(input,output);
const n=3; (* n should be a parameter *)
type vec=array[1..n] of real;
     mat=array[1..n,1..n] of real;
var  i,j,k,m:integer;     (*loop variables*)
     s:real;            (*accumulates the sums*)
     A,L,U: mat;  (*The three matrices of L*U=A *)
     b,z,x:vec;  (*The vectors of L*z=b, U*x=z *)

procedure bside(n:integer; L,U:mat; b:vec; var x,z:vec);
(*Vector x has to be output so it is a var-parameter*)
var h,i,i1,j,m:integer;
    s:real; (* Procedure bside solves A*x=b *)
begin       (* by first solving L*z=b and then U*x=z *)
   for i:=1 to n do
   begin s:=b[i]; i1:=i-1;
      for m:=1 to i1 do s:=s-L[i,m]*z[m] ;
      z[i]:=s/L[i,i] { z[i] is computed according to book}
   end ;
   x[n]:=z[n];h:=n-1 ;
   for i:=1 to h do
   begin i1:=n-i;j:=i1+1;s:=z[i1];
      for m:=n downto j do s:=s-U[i1,m]*x[m];
      x[i1]:=s {x was computed according to book }
   end
end;


procedure ludcmp(n:integer;A:mat;var L,U:mat);
var i,j,k,m:integer;  s:real;
begin  (*This is the LU-Decomposition procedure *)
   for k:=1 to n do
   begin j:=k-1;
     for i:=k to n do
     begin s:=0.0;
       for m:=1 to j do s:=s+L[i,m]*U[m,k];
       L[i,k]:=A[i,k]-s  (*Computing columns of L *)
     end;  u[k,k]:=1.0;
     for i:=k+1 to n do
     begin s:=0.0;
       for m:=1 to j do s:=s+L[k,m]*U[m,i];
       U[k,i]:=(A[k,i]-s)/L[k,k]
     end  (*Computing rows of U *)
   end
end;

procedure primat(n:integer; B:mat);
var i,j:integer;
begin
   for i:=1 to n do
   begin writeln;
    for j:=1 to n do write(B[i,j]:6:1)
   end
end;  (* of printing a matrix *)


procedure privec(n:integer; v:vec);
var i:integer;
begin writeln;
   for i:=1  to n do write(v[i]:6:1)

 end;  (* of printing a vector *)
 (*procedures primat & privec print matrix and vector resp.*)
```

Program 2.1

```
begin (* of the main program *)
    for i:=1 to n do
    begin read(b[i]);
        for j:=1 to n do
        begin
          read(A[i,j]);L[i,j]:=0.0;U[i,j]:=0.0
        end
    end; (* the next call is factorization *)
    ludcmp(n,A,L,U);writeln;
    writeln('Input matrix A and vector b');
    primat(n,A);writeln;privec(n,b);writeln;
    writeln('Matrices L,U and vectors x,z');
    bside(n,L,U,b,z,x);writeln;
    primat(n,L);writeln; primat(n,U); writeln;
    privec(n,z);writeln; privec(n,x)
end.
27 1 2 4
38 2 2 6
7 4 6 -3
```

```
 Input matrix A and vector b

    1.0    2.0    4.0
    2.0    2.0    6.0
    4.0    6.0   -3.0

   27.0   38.0    7.0
 Matrices L,U and vectors x,z

    1.0    0.0    0.0
    2.0   -2.0    0.0
    4.0   -2.0  -17.0

    1.0    2.0    4.0
    0.0    1.0    1.0
    0.0    0.0    1.0

    1.0    3.0    5.0

   27.0    8.0    5.0
```

Program 2.1 (continued)

With $\mathbf{L}^T = \tilde{\mathbf{U}}$, this is an identity, $\mathbf{L} * \mathbf{D} * \mathbf{L}^T = \mathbf{L} * \mathbf{D} * \mathbf{L}^T$. Inserting $\tilde{\mathbf{U}} = \mathbf{L}^T$ into Eq. (2.18) yields

$$\mathbf{A} = \mathbf{L} * \mathbf{D} * \mathbf{L}^T \tag{2.20}$$

With **L** being unit-diagonal this is known as Cholesky's decomposition for symmetric matrices. Since for symmetric matrices (such as frequently occur in power system problems) we compute only **L** and **D**, the amount of work Ω is about halved. Additionally it is proven in [GL81] that this case is simpler to compute, since no pivoting is needed if the matrix is positive-definite (see also Chapter 4).

2.2 MATRIX INVERSION

The classical method to obtain the inverse of a matrix uses determinants.

In selecting a method to be used for matrix inversion, we have to take into account the required computational effort. It might be surprising how large is the effort needed to calculate determinants.

If done by Cramer's rule, a determinant of, say, order 30 is the sum of 30 factorial ($30! = 30 \cdot 29 \cdots 1$) terms, each of which is the product of 30 factors. Thus, we will have to perform about $30 \cdot 30!$ multiplications and additions, which on a machine with a cycle time of 1 μsec (1,000,000 operations per second) would take about 10^{18} years. This is a very large number indeed.

This computational effort is so large that determinants are seldom used for inverting a matrix. Instead let us return to elimination and see how it can be used to compute $\mathbf{A}^{-1}$. Actually, this is done simply by extending the matrix with a unit matrix on its right and performing elimination as previously. Thus we have, for instance,

$$\left[\begin{array}{rrr|rrr} 1 & 2 & 4 & 1 & 0 & 0 \\ 2 & 2 & 6 & 0 & 1 & 0 \\ 4 & 6 & -3 & 0 & 0 & 1 \end{array}\right] \rightarrow \left[\begin{array}{rrr|rrr} 1 & 2 & 4 & 1 & 0 & 0 \\ 0 & -2 & -2 & -2 & 1 & 0 \\ 0 & -2 & -19 & -4 & 0 & 1 \end{array}\right]$$

$$\rightarrow \left[\begin{array}{rrr|rrr} 1 & 2 & 4 & 1 & 0 & 0 \\ 0 & -2 & -2 & -2 & 1 & 0 \\ 0 & 0 & -17 & -2 & -1 & 1 \end{array}\right]$$

If we view the identity matrix as three right-hand sides, we can make one back-substitution for each:

$$-17 \cdot b_{3,1} = -2; \quad b_{3,1} := \frac{2}{17};$$

$$2 \cdot b_{2,1} + 2 \cdot b_{3,1} = 2; \quad b_{2,1} := 1 - \frac{2}{17} = \frac{15}{17};$$

$$b_{1,1} + 2 \cdot b_{2,1} + 4 \cdot b_{3,1} = 1 \text{ or } b_{1,1} := 1 - \frac{30}{17} - \frac{8}{17} = -\frac{21}{17}$$

This completes the first column of $\mathbf{A}^{-1} = \mathbf{B}$.

For the second column:

$$17 \cdot b_{3,2} = 1; \quad b_{3,2} := \frac{1}{17};$$

$$2 \cdot b_{2,2} + 2 \cdot b_{3,2} = -1 \text{ or } b_{2,2} := \frac{-1 - 2/17}{2} = -\frac{19}{34};$$

$$b_{1,2} + 2 \cdot b_{2,2} + 4 \cdot b_{3,2} = 0; \quad b_{1,2} := \frac{38}{34} - \frac{4}{17} = \frac{30}{34}$$

Finally, for column 3:

$$-17 \cdot b_{3,3} = 1; \quad b_{3,3} := -\frac{1}{17};$$

$$2 \cdot b_{2,3} + 2 \cdot b_{3,3} = 0 \text{ or } b_{2,3} := \frac{1}{17};$$

$$b_{1,3} + 2 \cdot b_{2,3} + 4 \cdot b_{3,3} = 0 \text{ or } b_{1,3} = \frac{4}{17} - \frac{2}{17} = \frac{2}{17}$$

To prove that $\mathbf{B} = \mathbf{A}^{-1}$, we check if $\mathbf{A}*\mathbf{B}$ is in fact $\mathbf{I}$.

$$\frac{1}{34} \cdot \begin{bmatrix} 1 & 2 & 4 \\ 2 & 2 & 6 \\ 4 & 6 & -3 \end{bmatrix} * \begin{bmatrix} -42 & 30 & 4 \\ 30 & -19 & 2 \\ 4 & 2 & -2 \end{bmatrix}$$

$$= \frac{1}{34} \cdot \begin{bmatrix} 76-42 & 38-38 & 8-8 \\ 84-84 & 72-38 & 12-12 \\ 180-180 & 120-120 & 28+6 \end{bmatrix} = \begin{bmatrix} 1 & 0 & 0 \\ 0 & 1 & 0 \\ 0 & 0 & 1 \end{bmatrix}$$

If decomposition was used, then from $\mathbf{A} = \mathbf{L} * \mathbf{U}$ we would have $\mathbf{A}^{-1} = \mathbf{U}^{-1} * \mathbf{L}^{-1}$; and since both are triangular, their inversion is easy.

Shipley's method [Br75], which is a modification of the elimination process, can also be used. As will be seen, the matrix is inverted "in place" and at the completion, the negative inverse has replaced the original matrix. The main advantage of this inversion method is that pivoting proceeds in any sequence (but so as not to choose a small or zero diagonal element as the pivot).

The operations below are performed once for each diagonal element $A_{k,k}$:

1. $a := -1/A_{k,k}$
2. $\tilde{A}_{k,k} := a$
3. $\tilde{A}_{m,k} := a \cdot A_{m,k}; \quad m = 1, \ldots, n$ except for $m = k$
4. $\tilde{A}_{k,m} := a \cdot A_{k,m}; \quad m = 1, \ldots, n$ except for $m = k$
5. $\tilde{A}_{j,m} := A_{j,m} + a \cdot A_{j,k} \cdot A_{k,m} = A_{j,m} + \tilde{A}_{j,k} \cdot A_{k,m}; \quad j,m \neq k$

We next calculate the inverse of our matrix (since it is symmetric, step 4 is not needed and $\tilde{A}_{i,j} = \tilde{A}_{j,i}$).

$$\begin{bmatrix} 1 & 2 & 4 \\ 2 & 2 & 6 \\ 4 & 6 & -3 \end{bmatrix}$$

Since $A_{3,3}$ is the largest diagonal element, we choose it and get for $k = 3$

1,2. $a := -1/(-3) = 1/3$; $\tilde{A}_{3,3} := 1/3$
3,4. $\tilde{A}_{m,3} := a \cdot A_{m,3}$ for $m = 1, 2$: $\tilde{A}_{1,3} := 4/3$; $\tilde{A}_{2,3} := 6/3$
5. $A_{j,m} := A_{j,m} + \tilde{A}_{j,3} \cdot A_{3,m}$ for $j, m = 1, 2$:
$\tilde{A}_{1,1} := 3/3 + 4 \cdot 4/3 = 19/3$;
$\tilde{A}_{1,2} := 6/3 + 4 \cdot 6/3 = 30/3$;
$\tilde{A}_{2,2} := 42/3$

After the first pivoting operation, the matrix is $\tilde{\mathbf{A}}$:

$$\tilde{\mathbf{A}} = \frac{1}{3} \cdot \begin{bmatrix} 19 & 30 & 4 \\ 30 & 42 & 6 \\ 4 & 6 & 1 \end{bmatrix}$$

Choose $A_{2,2}$ as the pivot element, so $k = 2$. The steps are now

1,2. $a := -3/42$; $A^{\#}_{2,2} := -3/42$;
3,4. $A^{\#}_{m,2} := -3/42 \cdot \tilde{A}_{m,2}$ for $m = 1, 3$;
$A^{\#}_{1,2} := -3/42 \cdot 30/3 = -30/42$;
$A^{\#}_{3,2} := (-3/42) \cdot (6/3) = -6/42$
5. $A^{\#}_{j,m} := \tilde{A}_{j,m} + A^{\#}_{j,2} \cdot \tilde{A}_{2,m}$ for $j, m = 1, 3$
$A^{\#}_{1,1} := 19/3 - 30/42 \cdot 30/3 = -34/42$;
$A^{\#}_{1,3} := 4/3 - 30/42 \cdot 6/3 = -4/42$;
$A^{\#}_{3,3} := 1/3 - 6/42 \cdot 6/3 = 2/42$

The matrix after the second pivoting is $\mathbf{A}^{\#}$:

$$\mathbf{A}^{\#} = \frac{1}{42} \begin{bmatrix} -34 & -30 & -4 \\ -30 & -3 & -6 \\ -4 & -6 & 2 \end{bmatrix}$$

Finally, with $k = 1$ we have

1,2. $a := 42/34$; $A_{1,1} := 42/34$
3,4. $A_{1,m} := 42/34 \cdot A_{m,1}$ for $m = 2, 3$;
$A_{1,2} := -42/34 \cdot 30/42 = -30/34$;
$A_{1,3} := -42/34 \cdot 4/42 = -4/34$;

5. $A_{j,m} := A^{\#}_{j,m} + A_{j,1} \cdot A_{1,m}$ for $m,j = 2,3$

$A_{2,2} := -3/42 + 30/34 \cdot 30/42 = 19/34;$

$A_{2,3} := -6/42 + 30/42 \cdot 4/42 = -84/(34 \cdot 42) = -2/34;$

$A_{3,3} := 2/42 + 4/34 \cdot 4/42 = 84/(34 \cdot 42) = 2/34$

$$\mathbf{A} = \frac{1}{34} \cdot \begin{bmatrix} 42 & -30 & -4 \\ -30 & 19 & -2 \\ -4 & -2 & 2 \end{bmatrix}$$

We have already verified that this matrix is in fact the inverse of $-\mathbf{A}$. Note that it was calculated with $1/a$ factored each time.

Another method of inversion (Kron's) is used, especially in short-circuit computations where the bus-impedance matrix $\mathbf{Z}$ is required but the bus-admittance matrix $\mathbf{Y}$ is given. We have thus to invert the known matrix $\mathbf{Y}$:

$$\mathbf{Z} = \mathbf{Y}^{-1} \tag{2.21}$$

Suppose we have the block matrix $\mathbf{Z}$ and use a linear set

$$\begin{bmatrix} \mathbf{Z}_1 & \mathbf{Z}_2 \\ \mathbf{Z}_3 & \mathbf{Z}_4 \end{bmatrix} * \begin{bmatrix} \mathbf{x}_1 \\ \mathbf{x}_2 \end{bmatrix} = \begin{bmatrix} \mathbf{c}_1 \\ \mathbf{c}_2 \end{bmatrix} \tag{2.22}$$

If we separate the two equations, we get

$$\mathbf{Z}_1 * \mathbf{x}_1 + \mathbf{Z}_2 * \mathbf{x}_2 = \mathbf{c}_1 \tag{2.23}$$

$$\mathbf{Z}_3 * \mathbf{x}_1 + \mathbf{Z}_4 * \mathbf{x}_2 = \mathbf{c}_2 \tag{2.24}$$

From Eq. (2.24),

$$\mathbf{Z}_4 * \mathbf{x}_2 = \mathbf{c}_2 - \mathbf{Z}_3 * \mathbf{x}_1 \quad \text{or} \quad \mathbf{x}_2 := \mathbf{Z}_4^{-1} * (\mathbf{c}_2 - \mathbf{Z}_3 * \mathbf{x}_1)$$

Substitution into Eq. (2.23) and rearranging yields

$$(\mathbf{Z}_1 - \mathbf{Z}_2 * \mathbf{Z}_4^{-1} * \mathbf{Z}_3) * \mathbf{x}_1 = \mathbf{c}_1 - \mathbf{Z}_2 * \mathbf{Z}_4^{-1} * \mathbf{c}_2$$

The right-hand side is a vector, say, $\mathbf{b}$, so that we again have a set of linear equations, this time $\mathbf{Z} * \mathbf{x} = \mathbf{b}$, where $\mathbf{Z}$ can be represented by Kron's formula:

$$\mathbf{Z}_1 := \mathbf{Z}_1 - \mathbf{Z}_2 * \mathbf{Z}_4^{-1} * \mathbf{Z}_3 \tag{2.25}$$

It is important at this point to note that if $\mathbf{Z}_4$ is very small, then $\mathbf{Z}_4^{-1}$ cannot be calculated accurately by the computer. As a matter of fact, the computer will enter the largest available numbers and keep computing happily ever after, all the time using the wrong values.

Kron's method and its accuracy will be discussed in more detail later.

2.3 ORTHOGONALIZATION

We start with a few definitions:

Two nonzero column vectors $\mathbf{v}_i, \mathbf{v}_j$ are *orthogonal* if their scalar product $\mathbf{v}_i^{\mathrm{T}} * \mathbf{v}_j$ is zero. Vectors $\mathbf{v}_i, \ldots, \mathbf{v}_j$ are mutually orthogonal or form an orthogonal set if for all i, j such that $i \neq j$, we have $\mathbf{v}_i^{\mathrm{T}} * \mathbf{v}_j = 0$.

If $\mathbf{v}$ has n components v_k, then its length or *norm* is

$$||\mathbf{v}|| = \sqrt{v_1^2 + v_2^2 + \cdots + v_n^2} \tag{2.26}$$

If $||\mathbf{v}||$ is 1, then $\mathbf{v}$ is a *normalized* vector.

An orthogonal set which includes only normalized vectors is an *orthonormal* set. A matrix $\mathbf{Q}$ is orthonormal if

$$\mathbf{Q}^{\mathrm{T}} * \mathbf{Q} = \mathbf{Q} * \mathbf{Q}^{\mathrm{T}} = \mathbf{I} \tag{2.27}$$

We will review first the Gram–Schmidt method, since it seems to be little known among power-system engineers. To develop it, denote by $\mathbf{a}_i$ the ith column of an n-by-k matrix $\mathbf{A}$ and calculate a column vector $\mathbf{q}_1$ so that its length is 1:

$$\mathbf{v}_1 := \mathbf{a}_1; \quad \mathbf{q}_1 := \mathbf{v}_1/||\mathbf{v}_1|| = \mathbf{v}_1/r_{1,1}; \text{ where } r_{1,1} \equiv ||\mathbf{v}_1||$$

Next, calculate a new vector $\mathbf{v}_2$ using vectors $\mathbf{a}_2$ and $\mathbf{q}_1$:

$$\mathbf{v}_2 = \mathbf{a}_2 - r_{1,2} \cdot \mathbf{q}_1$$

The scalar $r_{1,2}$ may be chosen so that $\mathbf{v}_2$ is orthogonal to $\mathbf{q}_1$, i.e., that $\mathbf{q}_1^{\mathrm{T}} * \mathbf{v}_2 = \mathbf{q}_1^{\mathrm{T}} * \mathbf{a}_2 - r_{1,2} \cdot (\mathbf{q}_1^{\mathrm{T}} * \mathbf{q}_1) = 0$. The length of $\mathbf{q}_1$ was made 1 so that $\mathbf{q}_1^{\mathrm{T}} * \mathbf{q}_1 = 1$ and therefore

$$r_{1,2} = \mathbf{q}_1^{\mathrm{T}} * \mathbf{a}_2$$

By making $r_{2,2}$ the norm of $\mathbf{v}_2$ we get $\mathbf{q}_2 = \mathbf{v}_2/r_{2,2}$.

For the third column: $\mathbf{v}_3 = \mathbf{a}_3 - r_{2,3} \cdot \mathbf{q}_2 - r_{1,3} \cdot \mathbf{q}_1$. The condition of orthogonality is $\mathbf{q}_1^{\mathrm{T}} * \mathbf{v}_3 = \mathbf{q}_1^{\mathrm{T}} * \mathbf{a}_3 - r_{2,3} \cdot (\mathbf{q}_1^{\mathrm{T}} * \mathbf{q}_2) - r_{1,3} \cdot (\mathbf{q}_1^{\mathrm{T}} * \mathbf{q}_1) = 0$.

Since $\mathbf{q}_1^{\mathrm{T}} * \mathbf{q}_1$ is 1 and $\mathbf{q}_1^{\mathrm{T}} * \mathbf{q}_2$ should be zero, we get that $r_{1,3} = \mathbf{q}_1^{\mathrm{T}} * \mathbf{a}_3$; and in the same way $r_{2,3} = \mathbf{q}_2^{\mathrm{T}} * \mathbf{a}_3$.

The general procedure for $i = 1, 2, \ldots, n$ is therefore

$$\mathbf{v}_i = \mathbf{a}_i - \Sigma r_{j,i} \cdot \mathbf{q}_j; \quad j\Sigma = 1, \ldots, i - 1$$

$$\mathbf{q}_i := \frac{\mathbf{v}_i}{||\mathbf{v}_i||}; \quad r_{i,i} = ||\mathbf{v}_i||; \tag{2.28}$$

$$r_{j,i} = \mathbf{q}_j^{\mathrm{T}} * \mathbf{a}_i \quad \text{for } j = 1, 2, \ldots, i - 1$$

These equations may be rewritten as $\mathbf{a}_i = \Sigma\, r_{j,i} \cdot \mathbf{q}_j + \mathbf{v}_i = \Sigma\, r_{j,i} \cdot \mathbf{q}_j + r_{i,i} \cdot \mathbf{q}_i$; $j\,\Sigma = 1, \ldots, i - 1$:

$$
\begin{aligned}
\mathbf{a}_1 &= r_{1,1} \cdot \mathbf{q}_1 \\
\mathbf{a}_2 &= r_{1,2} \cdot \mathbf{q}_1 + r_{2,2} \cdot \mathbf{q}_2 \\
\mathbf{a}_3 &= r_{1,3} \cdot \mathbf{q}_1 + r_{2,3} \cdot \mathbf{q}_2 + r_{3,3} \cdot \mathbf{q}_3 \\
&\;\;\vdots \\
\mathbf{a}_k &= r_{1,k} \cdot \mathbf{q}_1 + r_{2,k} \cdot \mathbf{q}_2 + r_{3,k} \cdot \mathbf{q}_3 + \cdots + r_{k,k} \cdot \mathbf{q}_k
\end{aligned}
$$

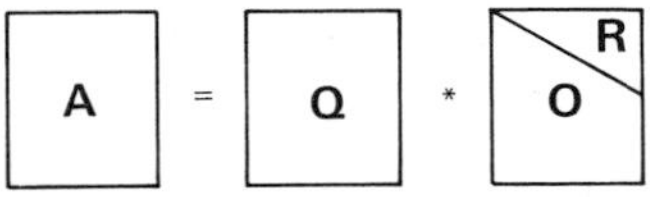

Figure 2.3 Equations in matrix form.

If $\mathbf{a}_i$ is the ith column of an n-by-k matrix $\mathbf{A}$ and $\mathbf{q}_i$ of an n-by-k matrix $\mathbf{Q}$ with orthonormal columns, then $r_{i,j}$ define an upper-triangular (or $\mathbf{R}$ *right*) matrix, and these equations can be rewritten (Fig. 2.3) as

$$\mathbf{A} = \mathbf{Q} * \mathbf{R} \tag{2.29}$$

If $\mathbf{A}$ is a square matrix, then Eq. (2.29) may be viewed as a factorization of the matrix $\mathbf{A}$ (but now so that $\mathbf{Q}$ is an orthonormal matrix).

By premultiplying Eq. (2.29) with $\mathbf{Q}^{\mathrm{T}}$ we get $\mathbf{Q}^{\mathrm{T}} * \mathbf{Q} * \mathbf{R}$ in which $\mathbf{Q}^{\mathrm{T}} * \mathbf{Q} = \mathbf{I}$ because of Eq. (2.27). Thus we can also write

$$\mathbf{Q}^{\mathrm{T}} * \mathbf{A} = \mathbf{R} \tag{2.30}$$

Next we discuss the orthogonalization method of *Givens*.

Orthogonalization viewed as elimination can be effected by premultiplying $\mathbf{A}$ with matrices $\mathbf{G}_{k,j}$ such that $\mathbf{G}_{k,j}$ is a unit matrix, except for $G_{j,j} = G_{k,k} = c$ [for $\cos(\theta)$]; $G_{j,k} = s$ [for $\sin(\theta)$], and $G_{k,j} = -s$. Let us first multiply $\mathbf{G}_{k,j}$ by its transpose:

$$
\begin{array}{r}
\\ \\ j \rightarrow \\ k \rightarrow \\ \\
\end{array}
\begin{bmatrix}
1 & & & & \\
& \ddots & & & \\
& & \overset{\textstyle j \atop \downarrow}{c} & \overset{\textstyle k \atop \downarrow}{-s} & \\
& & s & c & \\
& & & & \ddots \; 1
\end{bmatrix}
*
\begin{bmatrix}
1 & & & & \\
& \ddots & & & \\
& & \overset{\textstyle j \atop \downarrow}{c} & \overset{\textstyle k \atop \downarrow}{s} & \\
& & -s & c & \\
& & & & \ddots \; 1
\end{bmatrix}
= \mathbf{I} \tag{2.31}
$$

If we call the resulting matrix $\mathbf{B}$, we get $B_{j,k} = -s \cdot c + s \cdot c = 0$; then $B_{k,j} = -s \cdot c + s \cdot c = 0$; $B_{j,j} = c^2 + s^2 = 1$ and $B_{k,k} = s^2 + c^2 = 1$. As seen, the result is an identity matrix $\mathbf{I}$ so that we have $\mathbf{G}_{k,j} * \mathbf{G}_{k,j}^{\mathrm{T}} = \mathbf{I}$

and therefore $\mathbf{G}_{k,j}^{-1} = \mathbf{G}_{k,j}^{\mathrm{T}}$. The inverse of $\mathbf{G}$ is its transpose: $\mathbf{G}$ *matrices are orthogonal.*

Note that if we premultiply any matrix $\mathbf{A}$ as in $\mathbf{G}_{k,j} * \mathbf{A} = \mathbf{B}$, we have for any row i except j or k: $B_{i,m} := A_{i,m}$; $m = 1, \dots, n$. Thus premultiplication by $\mathbf{G}_{k,j}$ does not change rows i for which $i \neq k$ and $i \neq j$. The elements in the rows that do change are

$$B_{j,m} := c \cdot A_{j,m} + s \cdot A_{k,m}; \qquad\qquad (2.32)$$
$$B_{k,m} := -s \cdot A_{j,m} + c \cdot A_{k,m}; \quad m = 1, \dots, n$$

In particular, we can make $B_{k,j} = 0$ if we make $c \cdot A_{k,j} = s \cdot A_{j,j}$. Proceeding with $s^2 + c^2 = 1$ or $s^2 + s^2(A_{j,j}/A_{k,j})^2 = s^2 \cdot (A_{k,j}^2 + A_{j,j}^2)/A_{k,j}^2 = 1$ we have that

$$s^2 := \frac{A_{k,j}^2}{A_{k,j}^2 + A_{j,j}^2} \qquad\qquad (2.33)$$

Making $B_{kj} := 0$ amounts to elimination of elements of $\mathbf{A}$.

It is important to order the elimination procedure so that *all* elements below the diagonal are eliminated. The proposed order is to eliminate $A_{2,1}$, $A_{3,1}$, ..., $A_{n,1}$, then $A_{3,2}$, $A_{4,2}$, ..., $A_{n,2}$, i.e., all elements of column 2 below $A_{2,2}$, and so on until $A_{n,n-1}$ is eliminated.

Let us exemplify the method of orthogonalization by the following matrix:

$$\mathbf{A} = \begin{bmatrix} 1 & 2 & 4 \\ 2 & 2 & 6 \\ 4 & 6 & -3 \end{bmatrix}$$

To eliminate $A_{2,1} = 2$, we have to premultiply it by $\mathbf{G}_{2,1}$. The new element is $\tilde{\mathbf{A}}_{2,1} := 2c - s$. If this element is to be 0, then c must be equal to $s/2$. Since $c^2 + s^2 = 1$, we have that $s^2/4 + s^2 = 1$; $5 \cdot s^2/4 = 1$, and therefore $s^2 = 4/5$ and $c^2 = 1/5$. Finally $s = 0.89443$; $c = 0.44721$.

Having calculated s and c, we can compute elements of the new matrix $\mathbf{G}_{2,1} * \mathbf{A}$ (note that row 3 is not changed).

$$\begin{bmatrix} 0.44721 & 0.89443 & 0 \\ -0.89443 & 0.44721 & 0 \\ 0 & 0 & 1 \end{bmatrix} * \begin{bmatrix} 1 & 2 & 4 \\ 2 & 2 & 6 \\ 4 & 6 & -3 \end{bmatrix}$$

$$= \begin{bmatrix} 2.23607 & 2.68327 & 7.15542 \\ 0 & -0.89443 & -0.89446 \\ 4.0 & 6.0 & -3.0 \end{bmatrix}$$

Next, to eliminate $A_{3,1} = 4.0$, we have

$$\begin{bmatrix} c & 0 & s \\ 0 & 1 & 0 \\ -s & 0 & c \end{bmatrix} * \begin{bmatrix} A_{11} & A_{12} & A_{13} \\ A_{21} & A_{22} & A_{23} \\ A_{31} & A_{32} & A_{33} \end{bmatrix}$$

$-A_{1,1} \cdot s + c \cdot A_{3,1} = 0$; $4 \cdot c = 2.23607 \cdot s$; $c = 0.55902 \cdot s$. From this we get $c = 0.48795$, $s = 0.872871$, and

$$\begin{bmatrix} 0.48795 & 0 & 0.872871 \\ 0 & 1 & 0 \\ -0.872871 & 0 & 0.48795 \end{bmatrix} * \begin{bmatrix} 2.23607 & 2.68327 & 7.15542 \\ 0 & -0.89443 & -0.89446 \\ 4.0 & 6.0 & -3.0 \end{bmatrix}$$

$$= \begin{bmatrix} 4.58258 & 6.54653 & 0.872876 \\ 0 & -0.89443 & -0.89446 \\ 0 & 0.585553 & -7.70961 \end{bmatrix}$$

The only element to be yet eliminated is $A_{3,2}$. For it:

$$\mathbf{R} = \begin{bmatrix} 1 & 0 & 0 \\ 0 & c & s \\ 0 & -s & c \end{bmatrix} * \mathbf{A} = \begin{bmatrix} 4.5825 & 6.5465 & 0.8729 \\ 0 & 1.0690 & -3.5742 \\ 0 & 0 & 7.9124 \end{bmatrix}$$

$-s \cdot A_{2,2} + c \cdot A_{3,2} = 0$; $c = s \cdot A_{2,2}/A_{3,2}$, and again $s^2 + 0.8944^2 \cdot s^2/0.5855^2 = s^2 \cdot (1 + 0.8994^2/0.5855^2) = 1$; $s^2 = 0.299995$; $s = 0.5477148$; $c = -s \cdot 0.89443/0.585553 = 0.8366323$.

In all three steps, we have premultiplied by a **G** matrix. This resulted in a *right* triangular matrix **R**:

$$\mathbf{R} = \mathbf{G}_{3,2} * \mathbf{G}_{3,1} * \mathbf{G}_{2,1} * \mathbf{A}; \quad \text{or} \quad \mathbf{A} = (\mathbf{G}_{2,1}^{-1} * \mathbf{G}_{3,1}^{-1} * \mathbf{G}_{3,2}^{-1}) * \mathbf{R} \tag{2.34}$$

In Eq. (2.29) we have $\mathbf{A} = \mathbf{Q} * \mathbf{R}$. Comparing with Eq. (2.34) shows that

$$\mathbf{Q} = \mathbf{G}_{2,1}^{T} * \mathbf{G}_{3,1}^{T} * \mathbf{G}_{3,2}^{T} \tag{2.35}$$

If the equation to be solved is

$$\mathbf{A} * \mathbf{x} = \mathbf{b}; \qquad \mathbf{Q} * \mathbf{R} * \mathbf{x} = \mathbf{b} \tag{2.36}$$

then premultiplying by $\mathbf{Q}^{T}$ leads to

$$\mathbf{R} * \mathbf{x} = \mathbf{Q}^{T} * \mathbf{b} = \mathbf{z} \tag{2.37}$$

which shows that the solution is just a back-substitution of $\mathbf{R} * \mathbf{x} = \mathbf{z}$.

Vector **z** is seen to be

$$\mathbf{z} = (\mathbf{G}_{3,2} * (\mathbf{G}_{3,1} * (\mathbf{G}_{2,1} * \mathbf{b}))) = (\mathbf{G}_{3,2} * \mathbf{G}_{3,1} * \mathbf{G}_{2,1}) * \mathbf{b} \tag{2.38}$$

Comparing Eq. (2.38) with Eq. (2.34) shows that **z** may also be calculated if the transformations included **b** in the first place in the extended matrix.

Returning to solving $\mathbf{A} * \mathbf{x} = \mathbf{b}$ through $\mathbf{R} * \mathbf{x} = \mathbf{Q}^T * \mathbf{b} = \mathbf{z}$, we have to note that for calculating s, c we needed six arithmetic operations and the taking of a square root. In addition, when multiplying, we needed three arithmetic operations for each element in rows j and k.

Next we discuss a modification of Givens' method [Ge73].

Let us factor **A** into the product of a diagonal matrix **D** and an n-by-n matrix **C**, i.e.,

$$\mathbf{A} = \mathbf{D} * \mathbf{C} \tag{2.39}$$

With $C_{i,i} = 1$ and $d_i \equiv A_{i,i}$ we can write for other elements of **C**

$$C_{k,m} = \frac{A_{k,m}}{d_k} \tag{2.40}$$

Instead of the rotation matrix $\mathbf{G}_{j,i}$, we define **F** and **E** such that $\mathbf{G}_{j,i} \equiv \mathbf{F}_{j,i} * \mathbf{E}_{j,i} * \mathbf{D}^{-1}$ where (with only two rows and columns)

$$\mathbf{F}_{j,i} = \begin{bmatrix} f_i & 0 \\ 0 & f_j \end{bmatrix} \tag{2.41}$$

$$\mathbf{E}_{j,i} = \begin{bmatrix} e_i & 1 \\ 1 & e_j \end{bmatrix} \tag{2.42}$$

Inserting $\mathbf{F}_{j,i}$ and $\mathbf{E}_{j,i}$ into the expression for $\mathbf{G}_{j,i}$ yields

$$\begin{bmatrix} f_i & 0 \\ 0 & f_j \end{bmatrix} * \begin{bmatrix} e_i & 1 \\ 1 & e_j \end{bmatrix} * \begin{bmatrix} 1/d_i & 0 \\ 0 & 1/d_j \end{bmatrix}$$

$$= \begin{bmatrix} e_i \cdot f_i/d_i & f_i/d_j \\ f_j/d_i & e_j \cdot f_j/d_j \end{bmatrix} = \begin{bmatrix} c & s \\ -s & c \end{bmatrix}$$

Comparing off-diagonal and diagonal terms yields, respectively,

$$f_i = s \cdot d_j; \quad f_j = -s \cdot d_i$$

$$e_i = \frac{c \cdot d_i}{f_i} = \frac{d_i}{t \cdot d_j}; \quad e_j = \frac{c \cdot d_j}{f_j} = \frac{-d_j}{t \cdot d_i}$$

where $t = \tan(\theta) = s/c$. From equations like $c \cdot A_{j,i} = s \cdot A_{i,i}$ it follows that $t = A_{j,i}/A_{i,i} = (d_j \cdot C_{j,i})/(d_i \cdot C_{i,i})$ and therefore

$$e_j = -\frac{C_{i,i}}{C_{j,i}}; \quad e_i = -\left(\frac{d_i}{d_j}\right)^2 \cdot e_j$$

The sine $s = \sin(\theta)$ can be calculated from Eq. (2.33) as

$$s^2 = \frac{A_{j,i}^2}{A_{i,i}^2 + A_{j,i}^2} = \frac{d_j^2 \cdot C_{j,i}^2}{d_i^2 \cdot C_{i,i}^2 + d_j^2 \cdot C_{j,i}^2}$$

Divide the numerator and denominator by $d_j^2 \cdot C_{j,i}^2$:

$$s^2 = \frac{1}{1 + (d_i/d_j)^2 \cdot (C_{i,i}/C_{j,i})^2} = \frac{1}{1 - e_i \cdot e_j}$$

We thus get for the **F** and **E** matrices

$$e_j := -\frac{C_{i,i}}{C_{j,i}}; \quad e_i := -(d_i/d_j)^2 \cdot e_j \tag{2.43}$$

$$f_i^2 := \frac{d_j^2}{(1 - e_j \cdot e_i)}; \quad f_j^2 := \frac{d_i^2}{(1 - e_i \cdot e_j)} \tag{2.44}$$

To prove that the algorithm is correct, repeat step 1 for $i := 1$, $j := 2$, i.e., eliminate $A_{2,1}$:

$$e_2 := -\frac{C_{1,1}}{C_{2,1}} = -1; \quad e_1 := -\left(\frac{d_1}{d_2}\right)^2 \cdot e_2 = \frac{1}{4}$$

$$f_1^2 := \frac{4}{(1 + 1/4)} = \frac{16}{5}; \quad f_2^2 := \frac{1}{(1 + 1/4)} = \frac{4}{5}$$

Thus we get for $\mathbf{G}_{2,1} * \mathbf{A} = \mathbf{F} * \mathbf{E} * \mathbf{D}^{-1} * \mathbf{A} = \mathbf{F} * \mathbf{E} * \mathbf{C}$:

$$\begin{bmatrix} 4/\sqrt{5} & 0 & 0 \\ 0 & -2/\sqrt{5} & 0 \\ 0 & 0 & -3 \end{bmatrix} * \begin{bmatrix} 1/4 & 1 & 0 \\ 1 & -1 & 0 \\ 0 & 0 & 0 \end{bmatrix} * \begin{bmatrix} 1 & 2 & 4 \\ 1 & 1 & 3 \\ -4/3 & -2 & 1 \end{bmatrix}$$

$$= \begin{bmatrix} 2.236 & 2.6832 & 7.15540 \\ 0 & -0.8944 & -0.89446 \\ 4 & 6 & -3 \end{bmatrix}$$

The same matrix resulted in step 1 of the original method, so that the two methods seem to be equivalent. The advantages of the second method are:

- Since only d^2 values are required, they — and not d — are stored. Thus no taking of square roots is required.
- The particular form of **F** and **E** is such that calculation of an element of any new **C** matrix requires only half the amount of arithmetic of the original method.

Another method of orthogonalization is that of Householder. It differs from that of Givens in that an entire column is treated at once instead of eliminating its elements one by one. The theory of this method is discussed, for instance, in [LH74].

We will transform a vector **v** with indices $1, \ldots, p, \ldots, k, \ldots, m$ with $1 \le p \le m$ and $p \le k$ into an orthogonal vector such that

- If $p > 1$, elements 1 to $p - 1$ are not changed.
- Pivot element p is changed.
- If $p < k - 1$, then elements $p + 1$ to $k - 1$ are not changed.
- If $k \le m$, then elements k through m are eliminated.

Householder's transformation is applied to an m-by-n matrix **A** viewed as n vectors each of dimension m-by-1 as follows (p.54 of [LH74]):

$s := \sigma \cdot (v_p^2 + \Sigma v_i^2)^{1/2}$; $i\Sigma = k, \ldots, m$ and $\sigma =$ sign of v_p.
$h := v_p - s$; $v_p := s$; $b := v_p \cdot h$;
if $b \ne 0$ **and** $n \ne 0$ **then**
for $j := 1$ **to** n **do**
begin $s := (A_{p,j} \cdot h + \Sigma A_{i,j} \cdot v_i)/b$; $i\Sigma = k, \ldots, m$.
$A_{p,j} := A_{p,j} + s \cdot h$;
for $i := 1$ **to** m **do** $A_{i,j} := A_{i,j} + s \cdot v_i$
end;

The programs for Givens' and Householder's algorithms are shown as procedures "Construct–Givens," "Apply Givens" and "Householder" of the SVD program at the end of Chapter 3. This program also includes an explanation of Householder's algorithm.

2.4 SPARSITY

Suppose we have the network in Fig. 2.4(a) numbered as indicated. The corresponding admittance matrix is derived so that $Y_{i,j} \ne 0$ whenever nodes i, j are connected by a branch. These and the diagonal elements $Y_{i,i}$ are indicated in Fig. 2.4(b) by the symbol "×".

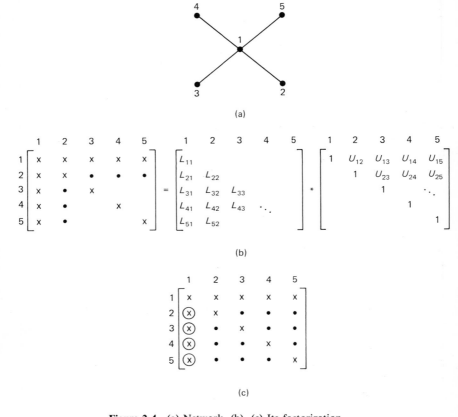

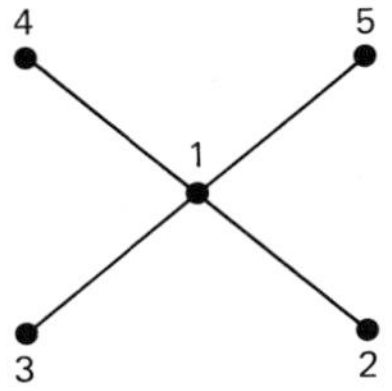

(a)

$$\begin{array}{c|ccccc|}
 & 1 & 2 & 3 & 4 & 5 \\
\hline
1 & \times & \times & \times & \times & \times \\
2 & \times & \times & \bullet & \bullet & \bullet \\
3 & \times & \bullet & \times & & \\
4 & \times & \bullet & & \times & \\
5 & \times & \bullet & & & \times
\end{array}
=
\begin{array}{|ccccc|}
1 & 2 & 3 & 4 & 5 \\
\hline
L_{11} & & & & \\
L_{21} & L_{22} & & & \\
L_{31} & L_{32} & L_{33} & & \\
L_{41} & L_{42} & L_{43} & \ddots & \\
L_{51} & L_{52} & & &
\end{array}
*
\begin{array}{|ccccc|}
1 & 2 & 3 & 4 & 5 \\
\hline
1 & U_{12} & U_{13} & U_{14} & U_{15} \\
 & 1 & U_{23} & U_{24} & U_{25} \\
 & & 1 & & \ddots \\
 & & & 1 & \\
 & & & & 1
\end{array}$$

(b)

$$\begin{array}{c|ccccc|}
 & 1 & 2 & 3 & 4 & 5 \\
\hline
1 & \times & \times & \times & \times & \times \\
2 & \otimes & \times & \bullet & \bullet & \bullet \\
3 & \otimes & \bullet & \times & \bullet & \bullet \\
4 & \otimes & \bullet & \bullet & \times & \bullet \\
5 & \otimes & \bullet & \bullet & \bullet & \times
\end{array}$$

(c)

Figure 2.4 (a) Network. (b), (c) Its factorization

Factorization $\mathbf{Y} = \mathbf{L} * \mathbf{U}$ as shown in Fig. 2.4(b) proceeds as

$$L_{i,1} := Y_{i,1} \quad \text{for } i = 1, \ldots, 5$$

$$U_{1,i} := \frac{Y_{1,i}}{L_{1,1}} \quad \text{for } i = 2, \ldots, 5$$

$$L_{2,2} := Y_{2,2} - L_{2,1} \cdot U_{1,2} \quad \text{and} \quad L_{3,2} := -L_{3,1} \cdot U_{1,2}$$

which is a scalar product of elements in row 3, column 2. In the same way we have $L_{i,2} = -L_{i,1} \cdot U_{1,2}$ for $i = 4$ and 5.

As seen, $L_{3,2}$, $L_{4,2}$, and $L_{5,2}$ are all nonzero despite the fact that originally $Y_{3,2} = Y_{4,2} = Y_{5,2} = 0$. These fill-in elements are indicated in Fig. 2.4(b) by dots.

From equation $L_{2,1} \cdot U_{1,3} + L_{2,2} \cdot U_{2,3} = Y_{2,3}$ $(= 0)$ we have $U_{2,3} = -L_{2,1} \cdot U_{1,3}/L_{2,2}$ and the same rule exists here. We see that any element of **L** or **U** can be computed from a scalar product of its row and column as produced up to this point in the calculation. We can thus produce the entire matrix *in situ* as shown in Fig. 2.4(c).

Figure 2.5(a) is the same network with renumbered nodes. Factorization leads here to Fig. 2.5(b).

Note that whereas Fig. 2.4(c) is completely filled in, the second ordering of nodes does not produce a single fill-in element [Fig. 2.5(b)].

We can simulate this factorization process graphically [GL81] in the following way: Elimination of node i leads to new branches connecting the nodes j and k *if* a connection $j-i-k$ existed originally. Thus for the two networks, the graph transformations are as in Figs. 2.6 and 2.7.

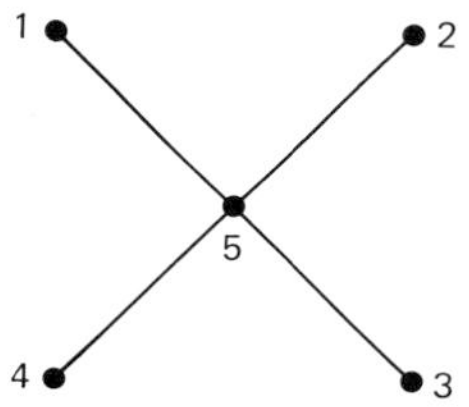

(a)

	1	2	3	4	5
1	x				x
2		x			x
3			x		x
4				x	x
5	(x)	(x)	(x)	(x)	x

(b)

Figure 2.5 Second labeling.

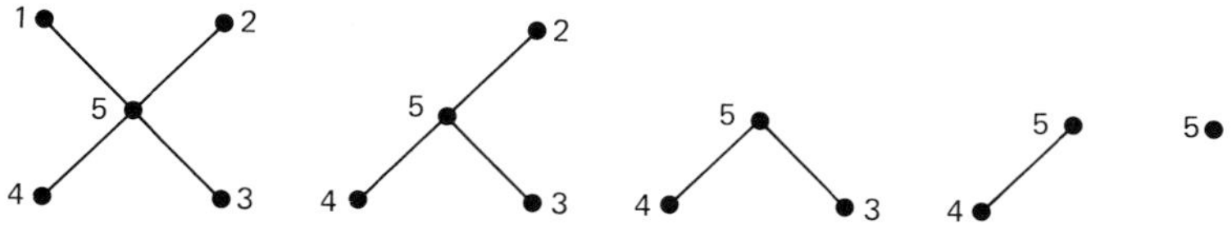

Figure 2.6 Graphical elimination.

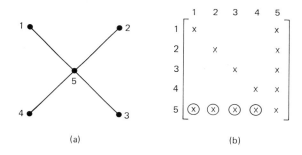

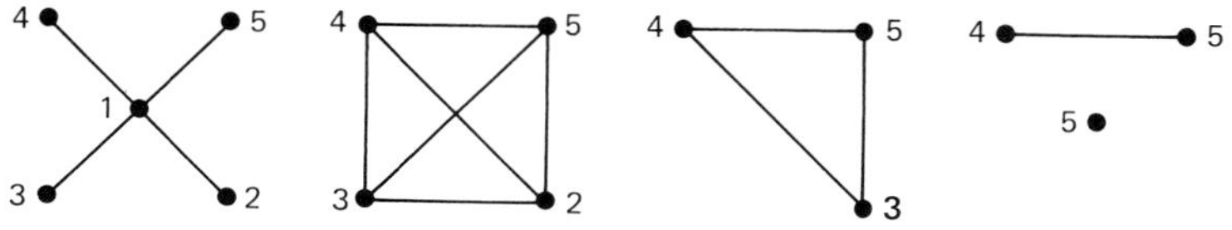

Figure 2.7 Graphical elimination.

Power system networks have, *on the average*, 1000 buses but only 3 lines connected to each bus. Thus, their admittance matrices are extremely sparse: $Y_{i,i}$ and 3 elements $Y_{i,j}$, $j \neq i$, of every row are nonzero, but 996 could be zero! Since memory space still costs money, it is important to *order* the nodes so that when processing the matrix we do not add too many nonzero entries. Inversion always adds nonzero entries and even if **Y** is extremely sparse, $\mathbf{Z} = \mathbf{Y}^{-1}$ is generally full, but in $\mathbf{L} * \mathbf{U}$ decomposition or elimination we may order the nodes so as to minimize *fill-in*. We have seen it very graphically in the two examples above.

The fill-in is undesirable not only because of the additional storage it requires but also because it involves more operations. It is obvious that solving $\mathbf{L} * \mathbf{U} * \mathbf{x} = \mathbf{b}$ in the two cases above will require quite different amounts of time (or numbers of operations).

Let us exemplify this point for the 7-bus network in Fig. 1.14 (repeated in Fig. 2.8 with generators excluded). If we store its admittance matrix in the usual way, we need $7 \cdot 7 = 49$ locations, some of which are zeros. In the "average" case of 1000 nodes, $1000 \cdot 1000 = 1$ million locations are required—or, since the matrix is complex, 4 million locations. An argument could be made that since memory is getting cheaper, it will eventually not be necessary to make efforts to minimize storage. As seen above, this is not so; the amount of wasted storage seems prohibitive under any conditions.

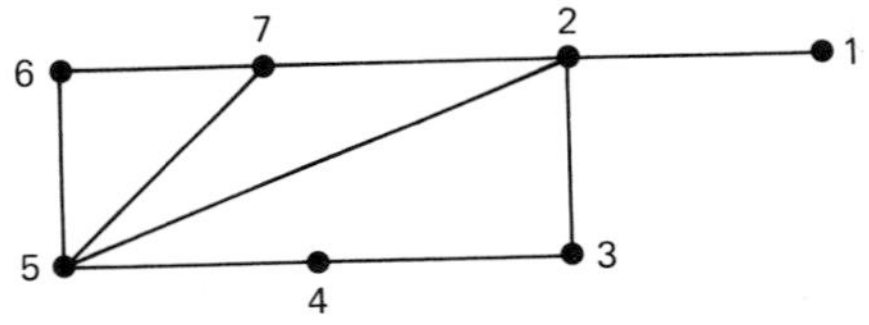

Figure 2.8 The graph of the network.

We do not have to store the zeros. Various storage schemes have been proposed; we will adopt that of [GL81]. In this scheme, the network above will be represented by Table 2.1.

TABLE 2.1 Storing the admittance matrix of network in Fig. 2.8

Admittance Values $g_{i,k} + j \cdot b_{i,k}$																			
2	1	3	5	7	2	4	3	5	2	4	6	7	5	7	2	5	6	0	adj
1	2				6		8		10				14		16			19	ip
1	2				3		4		5				6		7			8	index

To exemplify its use, suppose we need $Y_{2,5}$. Generally to find $Y_{i,j}$, we have to look for j in adj, between ip_i and $\text{ip}_{i+1} - 1$. In our case

$i = 2$, $j = 5$, so that the list is from $ip_2 = 2$ to $ip_3 - 1 = 6 - 1 = 5$, i.e., only four places; $j = 5$ is found in adj_4, and so $Y_{2,5}$ is stored in location 4 of the admittance value list.

Note that this storage is particularly effective when we have to produce scalar products (as was required for $\mathbf{L} * \mathbf{U} = \mathbf{A}$). Thus, to multiply, say, vector $\mathbf{y}_3$ (i.e., the third row of $\mathbf{Y}$) by some vector $\mathbf{x}$ of 7 values, we find the boundaries of $\mathbf{y}_3$ to be 6 and 7, $adj_6 = 2$, $adj_7 = 4$, multiply $Y_{3,2}$ by x_2, $Y_{3,4}$ by x_4, and accumulate these two products. This will obviously be more effective than accumulating $\Sigma\ Y_{3,i} \cdot x_i$, $i\Sigma = 1, \ldots, 7$.

It might seem that the adopted storage scheme lends itself only with difficulty to permutation or renumbering of equations. This is not so. On the contrary, as shown in [GL81], permutation is done with relative efficiency.

We have seen that a reordering can reduce the fill-in considerably and make for more efficient programming. Unfortunately, for a general network, the best reordering can be found only by brute force, and for an average program this would take a very, very long time.

If you cannot achieve the best, you usually strive for second best. In our case, this means that since we cannot find, by theoretical considerations, the best ordering of nodes, we try to get one heuristically (meaning by a method that has a practical rather than a theoretical basis.)

A program called *Optimally Ordered Factorization* (OOF) was developed [TH67,TW67]. It differs from elimination as follows:

- In elimination, elements below the diagonal of column $(i + 1)$ are eliminated only after column (i) has been processed; in OOF the same applies to elements left of the diagonal and factorization proceeds by rows.
- The rows are taken in an order which preserves sparsity as much as possible. For preserving sparsity three ordering "strategies" were suggested [TW67], two of which are:

1. Order the rows before elimination according to an increasing number of nonzero elements in these rows.
2. At each step eliminate that row which has the fewest nonzero elements. Since $\mathbf{L}$ fills in during factorization, this policy is dynamic and normally proceeds so that initially elimination is simulated in order to get the right sequence of row eliminations.

In factorization, policy 2 will be used to reduce fill-in. Load-flow calculations in Chapter 4 will prove this to be effective. In order to arrive at a comparable policy for orthogonalization, the network of Fig. 2.9(a) was solved in [Wa83].* Fill-in was drawn as a dot and a circle put over an eliminated element. In LU factorization the dots were produced by scalar products. In orthogonalization we treat x's and dots as 1's and perform a logical or Boolean OR between rows i and j. From the orthogonalization shown in Fig. 2.9(c) we deduce that

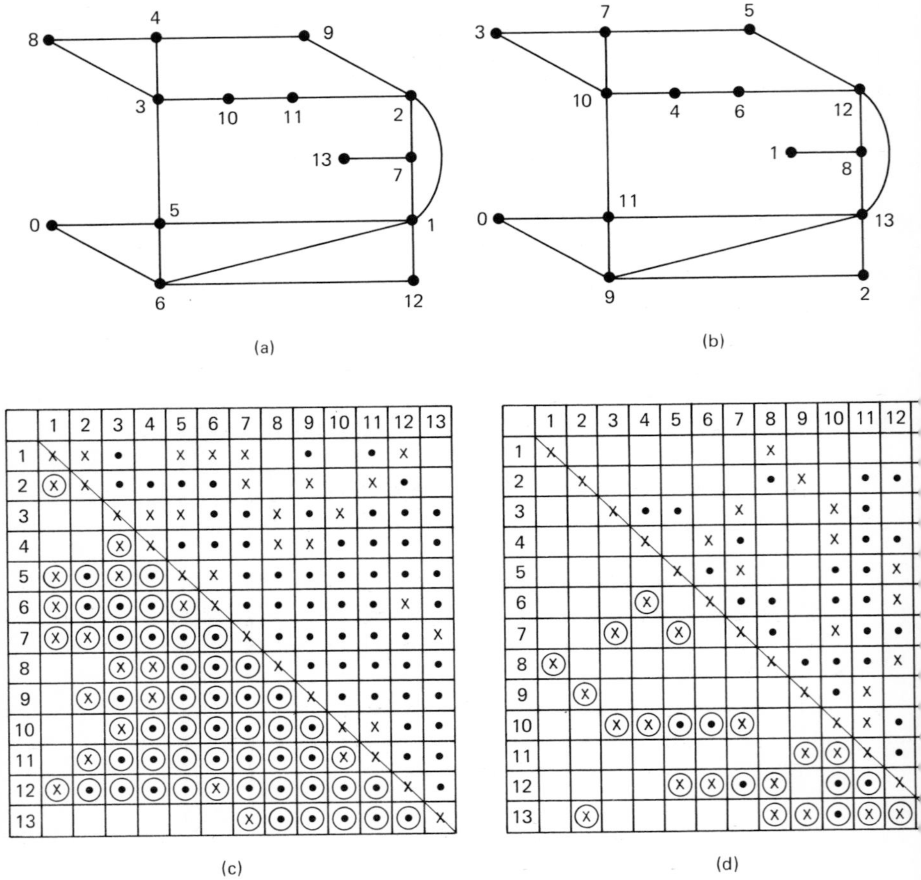

Figure 2.9 (a) The 14-bus network. (b) The renumbered network. (c),(d) Orthogonalization for networks in (a) and (b).

---

* Archiv für Elektrotechnik, **67** (1984) 57–64, Y. Wallach: Orthogonalization for power-system computations. © 1984 Springer-Verlag, Berlin-Heidelberg-New York-Tokyo. Used with permission.

- The closer we get to the lower right-hand corner, the more operations are needed. Thus, $\mathbf{L}_{13,7}$ fills in all elements $A_{13,j}$ for $7 < j < 13$.
- $\mathbf{L}_{5,1}$ enters $A_{1,3}$ as fill-in, and this element generates later $A_{6,3}$, $A_{7,3}$, and $A_{12,3}$, Thus, fill-in contributes (indirectly) to the operations count Ω even if it is in **R**.
- It is obvious that the less linkage, the better. Thus, consecutive numbering of nodes should be discouraged.

These points lead to the following *ordering policy*: Number the nodes in order of increasing number of branches. A number of nodes which have the same number of branches should be numbered in a nonconsecutive order, if possible.

The network in Fig. 2.9(b) is the same as that in Fig. 2.9(a) with the nodes renumbered according to the policy as stated above. The results of orthogonalizing it [Fig. 2.9(d)] seem to justify the stated policy.

The dots in the matrices in Fig. 2.9(c) and (d) show the fill-in. We should count only those belonging to **R**, since **Q** can be produced by multiplying **Q**'s by **b**. For Fig. 2.9(d) we have only 6 new entries for an **R** of $13^2/2 \cong 85$ elements. This low percentage should be even smaller for larger and more sparse matrices.

The above ordering policy is *static*. It will be shown in Chapter 5 that the dynamic policy used for OOF also yields better results if applied to orthogonalization — it may then be called optimally ordered orthogonalization.

2.5 ITERATIVE SOLUTION OF LINEAR EQUATIONS

The solutions of $\mathbf{A} * \mathbf{x} = \mathbf{b}$ in the preceding sections are called *direct*. For some cases of load flow and stability, indirect, so-called iterative, methods [Wa82] are used.

We exemplify these methods by the set of Eqs. (2.45):

$$\begin{aligned}
-20x_1 + x_2 + x_3 + 6x_4 + 2x_5 + x_6 &= -17 \\
x_1 - 20x_2 + 2x_3 + x_4 + 4x_5 + 3x_6 &= -25 \\
x_1 + 2x_2 - 20x_3 + 2x_4 + x_5 + 2x_6 &= -8 \\
6x_1 + x_2 + 2x_3 - 20x_4 + 3x_5 + x_6 &= -60 \\
2x_1 + 4x_2 + x_3 + 3x_4 - 20x_5 + 5x_6 &= -13 \\
x_1 + 3x_2 + 2x_3 + x_4 + 5x_5 - 20x_6 &= -1
\end{aligned} \tag{2.45}$$

We first *normalize* it, that is, divide each equation by the diagonal term. Additionally, we rewrite it and get

$$
\begin{aligned}
x_1 &= 0.85 + 0.05x_2 + 0.05x_3 + 0.30x_4 + 0.10x_5 + 0.05x_6 \\
x_2 &= 1.25 + 0.05x_1 + 0.10x_3 + 0.05x_4 + 0.20x_5 + 0.15x_6 \\
x_3 &= 0.40 + 0.05x_1 + 0.10x_2 + 0.10x_4 + 0.05x_5 + 0.10x_6 \\
x_4 &= 3.00 + 0.30x_1 + 0.05x_2 + 0.10x_3 + 0.15x_5 + 0.05x_6 \\
x_5 &= 0.65 + 0.10x_1 + 0.20x_2 + 0.05x_3 + 0.15x_4 + 0.25x_6 \\
x_6 &= 0.05 + 0.05x_1 + 0.15x_2 + 0.10x_3 + 0.05x_4 + 0.25x_5
\end{aligned} \tag{2.46}
$$

By an iterative solution (in this case, specifically, by the Jacobi method), we mean the following: Let us assume some initial values for x_i, $i = 1, \ldots, 6$, and let us say that all of them are 1. Inserting this vector $\mathbf{x}^{(0)}$ into Eq. (2.46) yields for the new $\mathbf{x}$:

$$
\begin{aligned}
x_1 &= 0.85 + 0.05 + 0.05 + 0.30 + 0.10 + 0.05 = 1.40 \\
x_2 &= 1.25 + 0.05 + 0.10 + 0.05 + 0.20 + 0.15 = 1.80 \\
x_3 &= 0.40 + 0.05 + 0.10 + 0.10 + 0.05 + 0.10 = 0.80 \\
x_4 &= 3.00 + 0.30 + 0.05 + 0.10 + 0.15 + 0.05 = 3.65 \\
x_5 &= 0.65 + 0.10 + 0.20 + 0.05 + 0.15 + 0.25 = 1.40 \\
x_6 &= 0.05 + 0.05 + 0.15 + 0.10 + 0.05 + 0.25 = 0.65
\end{aligned}
$$

We can next insert this $\mathbf{x}$, called $\mathbf{x}^{(1)}$, to get what we will call $\mathbf{x}^{(2)}$ as follows:

$$
\begin{aligned}
x_1 &= 0.85+0.05\cdot1.80+0.05\cdot0.80+0.3\cdot3.65+0.1\cdot1.4+0.05\cdot0.65 = 2.2475 \\
x_2 &= 1.25+0.05\cdot1.40+0.1\cdot0.80+0.05\cdot3.65+0.2\cdot1.4+0.15\cdot0.65 = 1.96 \\
x_3 &= 0.40+0.05\cdot1.40+0.1\cdot1.80+0.10\cdot3.65+0.05\cdot1.4+0.1\cdot0.65 = 1.15 \\
x_4 &= 3.0+0.3\cdot1.40+0.05\cdot1.80+0.1\cdot0.8+0.15\cdot1.4+0.05\cdot0.65 = 3.8325 \\
x_5 &= 0.65+0.1\cdot1.40+0.2\cdot1.80+0.05\cdot0.8+0.15\cdot3.65+0.25\cdot0.65 = 1.90 \\
x_6 &= 0.05+0.05\cdot1.4+0.15\cdot1.80+0.1\cdot0.8+0.05\cdot3.65+0.25\cdot1.4 = 1.0025
\end{aligned}
$$

Each substitution and sweep is called an *iteration*, and its number is used as superscript in the calculation of $\mathbf{x}^{(1)}$, $\mathbf{x}^{(2)}$, $\mathbf{x}^{(3)}$, ... The general formula here is to calculate, for $k = 1, 2, \ldots, n$,

$$x_k^{(i)} = b_k - \Sigma\, a_{k,m}\cdot x_m^{(i-1)}; \quad m\Sigma = 1, 2, \ldots, n \text{ but } m \neq k \tag{2.47}$$

The iterations go on until

$$\Sigma\, r_k^2 < \epsilon \quad \text{or} \quad \max |r_k| < \epsilon; \quad k = 1, \ldots, n \tag{2.48}$$

where

$$r_k = x_k^{(i)} - x_k^{(i-1)} \tag{2.49}$$

The Gauss–Seidel (GS) method differs from that of Jacobi in that whenever $x_k^{(i)}$ is computed, it is used for the calculation of all $x_m^{(i)}$ which follow, i.e., for $m = k + 1, \ldots, n$. Thus, if we again compute $x_1^{(1)} = 1.4$, we get for $x_2^{(1)}$ not 1.8 but $x_2^{(1)} = 1.25 + 0.05 \cdot 1.4 + 0.1 \cdot 1 + 0.05 + 0.2 \cdot 1 + 0.15 \cdot 1 = 1.82$.

Next we use both $x_1^{(1)} = 1.4$ and $x_2^{(1)} = 1.82$ to compute $x_3^{(1)}$, and so on. Iteration 1 will therefore result in

$$x_1 = 0.85 + 0.05 \cdot 1 + 0.05 \cdot 1 + 0.3 \cdot 1 + 0.1 \cdot 1 + 0.05 \cdot 1 = 1.40$$

$$x_2 = 1.25 + 0.05 \cdot 1.4 + 0.1 \cdot 1 + 0.05 \cdot 1 + 0.2 \cdot 1 + 0.15 \cdot 1 = 1.82$$

$$x_3 = 0.40 + 0.05 \cdot 1.4 + 0.1 \cdot 1.82 + 0.1 \cdot 1 + 0.05 \cdot 1 + 0.1 \cdot 1 = 0.90$$

$$x_4 = 3.0 + 0.3 \cdot 1.4 + 0.05 \cdot 1.82 + 0.1 \cdot 0.9 + 0.15 \cdot 1 + 0.05 \cdot 1 = 3.80$$

$$x_5 = 0.65 + 0.1 \cdot 1.4 + 0.2 \cdot 1.82 + 0.5 \cdot 0.9 + 0.15 \cdot 3.8 + 0.25 \cdot 1 = 2.02$$

$$x_6 = 0.05 + 0.05 \cdot 1.4 + 0.15 \cdot 1.82 + 0.1 \cdot 0.9 + 0.05 \cdot 3.8 + 0.25 \cdot 2.02 = 1.18$$

From the point of view of programming, GS is simpler than the Jacobi method. If we calculate and print $\Sigma\, r_k^2$, we will be able to compare *convergence*, i.e., how fast we approach ϵ and therefore how many iterations are required for a given ϵ. For the data of Eq. (2.45), Programs 2.2 and 2.3 were run. Some results obtained from these programs are also shown. Note that $\Sigma\, r^2 = 0.0001$ is achieved in 7 iterations with GS but will require 11 iterations with Jacobi's method.

Let us add a third iterative method which, for reasons made evident later, will be called Fast Gauss–Seidel (FGS). It is different, first, in that FGS is not iterated as $x_1, x_2, \ldots, x_n, x_1, x_2, \ldots$ but rather as $x_1, x_2, \ldots, x_n, x_{n-1}, \ldots, x_2, x_1, x_2, \ldots$. If $x_1, \ldots, x_n$ is called a "down" iteration and $x_n, \ldots, x_1$ an "up" iteration, we have here up-and-down iterations instead of always moving down (as in GS).

In order to introduce FGS, we rewrite Eq. (2.47) as

$$x_k^{(i)} = b_k - \Sigma\, a_{k,c} \cdot x_c = (b_k - \Sigma\, a_{k,j} x_j^{(i)}) - \Sigma\, a_{k,m},\, x_m^{(i-1)};$$

$$c\Sigma = 1, \ldots, n; \quad j\Sigma = k + 1, \ldots, n; \quad m\Sigma = 1, 2, \ldots, k - 1 \tag{2.50}$$

Note that in the first sum, superscript i, but in the second $(i - 1)$, of a previously completed iteration appears. This is so since when computing, say, $x_3^{(i)}$ in GS we use the already computed $x_1^{(i)}$, $x_2^{(i)}$, as well as $x_4^{(i-1)}$, $x_5^{(i-1)}$ and $x_6^{(i-1)}$ known from a previous iteration. Thus if we define two vectors $\mathbf{g}$ and $\mathbf{h}$ through

$$\mathbf{g}^{(i)} = b_k - \Sigma\, a_{k,j} \cdot x_j^{(i)}; \quad j\Sigma = k + 1, \ldots, n \tag{2.51}$$

```
program jac(input,output); (* The Jacobi method of solving sets *)
var i,j,k,n:integer; er,r:real; (* of linear equations A*x=b *)
a:array[1..6,1..6] of real;
b,x,xn:array[1..6] of real;

begin  read(n);          (*All a[i,i] are read in as zeros*)
for i:=1 to n do  (* This makes the calculation simpler *)
begin  read(b[i]);  x[i]:=1.0; (* since the sum is done *)
   for j:=1 to n do read(a[i,j])          (* for all j's *)
end;
writeln('  #     x1      x2      x3     x4      x5     x6    jac');
for k:=1 to 15 do (* 15 iterations  in this particular case *)
begin er:=0.0; (* er will accumulate the sum of squares of r*)
     for i:=1 to n do
     begin xn[i]:=-b[i];
       for j:=1 to n do xn[i]:=xn[i]+a[i,j]*x[j]
     end;
     for i:=1 to n do
     begin
       r:=xn[i]-x[i]; er:=er+r*r; x[i]:=xn[i]
   end; write(k:3);
   for i:=1 to n do write(' ',x[i]:6:4);
   writeln(' e=',er:6:4)
end
end.
6
-0.85 0.00 0.05 0.05 0.30 0.10 0.05
-1.025 0.05 0.00 0.10 0.05 0.20 0.15
-0.40 0.05 0.10 0.00 0.10 0.05 0.10
-3.00 0.30 0.05 0.10 0.00 0.15 0.05
-0.65 0.10 0.20 0.05 0.15 0.00 0.25
-0.05 0.05 0.15 0.10 0.05 0.25 0.00
    #    x1      x2      x3      x4      x5      x6     jac
    1 1.4000 1.5750 0.8000 3.6500 1.4000 0.6500 e=7.8356
    2 2.2362 1.7350 1.1275 3.8212 1.8550 0.9687 e=1.1701
    3 2.3734 1.9569 1.2571 4.1971 2.0924 1.1896 e=0.3312
    4 2.5385 2.0761 1.3577 4.3089 2.2685 1.3209 e=0.1124
    5 2.6073 2.1550 1.4109 4.4075 2.3635 1.4067 e=0.0399
    6 2.6572 2.2005 1.4455 4.4559 2.4251 1.4560 e=0.0143
    7 2.6844 2.2286 1.4654 4.4883 2.4605 1.4865 e=0.0052
    8 2.7016 2.2452 1.4776 4.5067 2.4823 1.5046 e=0.0019
    9 2.7116 2.2553 1.4848 4.5181 2.4952 1.5155 e=0.0007
   10 2.7177 2.2613 1.4892 4.5248 2.5031 1.5221 e=0.0002
   11 2.7214 2.2650 1.4919 4.5289 2.5077 1.5260 e=0.0001
   12 2.7236 2.2671 1.4934 4.5313 2.5106 1.5284 e=0.0000
   13 2.7249 2.2685 1.4944 4.5328 2.5123 1.5298 e=0.0000
   14 2.7257 2.2692 1.4950 4.5337 2.5133 1.5307 e=0.0000
   15 2.7262 2.2697 1.4953 4.5342 2.5139 1.5312 e=0.0000
```

Program 2.2

$$\mathbf{h}^{(i)} = -\Sigma\; a_{k,m} x_m^{(i)}; \quad m\Sigma = 1, 2\ldots, k-1 \tag{2.52}$$

then the GS equation for calculating any $x_k^{(i)}$ is

$$x_k^{(i)} = g_k^{(i-1)} + h_k^{(i)} \tag{2.53}$$

We are now ready for the FGS algorithm. Initially, we prepare $\mathbf{g}^{(0)}$ using $\mathbf{x}^{(0)}$ and make $\mathbf{h} = 0$, i.e., all $h_k := 0$, $k = 1, \ldots, n$. In our case, $g_1^{(0)} = 1.4$; $g_2^{(0)} = 1.75$; $g_3^{(0)} = 0.65$; $g_4^{(0)} = 3.2$; $g_5^{(0)} = 0.9$; $g_6^{(0)} = 0.05$. Note that $g_n = b_n$ and $h_1 = 0$ are independent of $\mathbf{x}$ and therefore will not change at all.

```
program gsa(input,output);
var i,j,k,n:integer; er,r,xn:real;
a:array[1..6,1..6] of real;
b,x:array[1..6] of real;

begin  read(n);
for i:=1 to n do
begin  read(b[i]);  x[i]:=1.0;
   for j:=1 to n do read(a[i,j])
end;
writeln('  #      x1       x2        x3      x4        x5      x6    gas');
for k:=1 to 15 do (* 15 iterations *)
begin er:=0.0;
  for i:=1 to n do
  begin xn:=-b[i];
      for j:=1 to n do xn:=xn+a[i,j]*x[j];
      r:=xn-x[i];  er:=er+r*r; x[i]:=xn
  end; write(k:3);
  for i:=1 to n do write(' ',x[i]:6:4);
  writeln(' e=',er:6:4)
end
end.
6
-0.85 0.00 0.05 0.05 0.30 0.10 0.05
-1.025 0.05 0.00 0.10 0.05 0.20 0.15
-0.40 0.05 0.10 0.00 0.10 0.05 0.10
-3.00 0.30 0.05 0.10 0.00 0.15 0.05
-0.65 0.10 0.20 0.05 0.15 0.00 0.25
-0.05 0.05 0.15 0.10 0.05 0.25 0.00
  #    x1     x2      x3     x4      x5     x6    gas
  1 1.4000 1.5950 0.8795 3.7877 1.9711 1.1294 e=9.2596
  2 2.3636 1.9841 1.3069 4.2911 2.2745 1.3797 e=1.6708
  3 2.5983 2.1620 1.4269 4.4405 2.4246 1.4751 e=0.1551
  4 2.6778 2.2298 1.4696 4.4992 2.4809 1.5105 e=0.0206
  5 2.7084 2.2551 1.4859 4.5215 2.5020 1.5239 e=0.0030
  6 2.7199 2.2646 1.4921 4.5299 2.5100 1.5289 e=0.0004
  7 2.7242 2.2682 1.4944 4.5331 2.5130 1.5308 e=0.0001
  8 2.7259 2.2696 1.4953 4.5343 2.5141 1.5315 e=0.0000
  9 2.7265 2.2701 1.4956 4.5347 2.5145 1.5318 e=0.0000
 10 2.7267 2.2703 1.4957 4.5349 2.5147 1.5319 e=0.0000
 11 2.7268 2.2704 1.4958 4.5349 2.5148 1.5319 e=0.0000
 12 2.7269 2.2704 1.4958 4.5350 2.5148 1.5319 e=0.0000
 13 2.7269 2.2704 1.4958 4.5350 2.5148 1.5319 e=0.0000
 14 2.7269 2.2704 1.4958 4.5350 2.5148 1.5319 e=0.0000
 15 2.7269 2.2704 1.4958 4.5350 2.5148 1.5319 e=0.0000
```

Program 2.3

Having prepared $\mathbf{g}^{(0)}$, $\mathbf{h}^{(0)}$, we compute $x_1^{(1)}$ by applying Eq. (2.53): $x_1^{(1)} = g_1^{(0)} + h_1^{(1)} = 1.4 + 0.0 = 1.4$, which is the same value as computed earlier. Next, instead of computing $x_2^{(1)}$, we start accumulating $\mathbf{h}^{(1)}$ of Eq. (2.52). We get

$$h_2^{(1)} = 0.05 \cdot 1.4 = 0.07; \quad h_3^{(1)} = 0.07; \quad h_4^{(1)} = 0.3 \cdot 1.4 = 0.42$$

$$h_5^{(1)} = 0.1 \cdot 1.4 = 0.14; \quad h_6^{(1)} = 0.07$$

and set $g_1^{(1)} = 0.85$.

Note that g_k includes only terms to the right of the diagonal, h_k to the left of the diagonal. Thus we find that $h_2^{(1)}$ accumulated all the products it will ever have and we compute

$$x_2^{(1)} = g_2^{(0)} + h_2^{(1)} = 1.75 + 0.07 = 1.82$$

i.e., as in GS. We also set $g_2^{(1)} = b_2 = 1.25$.

Again, before computing $x_3^{(1)}$, we accumulate the products of **h** which include x_2. Thus

$$h_3^{(1)} = 0.07 + 0.1\cdot 1.82 = 0.252$$

$$h_4^{(1)} = 0.42 + 0.05\cdot 1.82 = 0.511$$

$$h_5^{(1)} = 0.14 + 0.2\cdot 1.82 = 0.504$$

$$h_6^{(1)} = 0.07 + 0.15\cdot 1.82 = 0.343$$

so that $x_3^{(1)}$ and $g_3^{(1)}$ are: $x_3^{(1)} = 0.252 + 0.65 = 0.902$; $g_3^{(1)} = 0.4$.

We proceed in the same way for $x_4^{(1)}$, $x_5^{(1)}$, $x_6^{(1)}$:

$$h_4^{(1)} = 0.511 + 0.1\cdot 0.902 = 0.601$$

$$h_5^{(1)} = 0.504 + 0.05\cdot 0.903 = 0.549$$

$$h_6^{(1)} = 0.343 + 0.1\cdot 0.902 = 0.433$$

$$x_4^{(1)} = 3.20 + 0.60 = 3.8; \quad g_4^{(1)} = 3.0$$

$$h_5^{(1)} = 0.549 + 0.15\cdot 3.80 = 1.12$$

$$h_6^{(1)} = 0.433 + 0.05\cdot 3.8 = 0.623$$

$$x_5^{(1)} = 0.90 + 1.12 = 2.02; \quad g_5^{(1)} = 0.65$$

$$h_6^{(1)} = 0.623 + 0.25\cdot 2.02 = 1.128$$

$$x_6^{(1)} = 0.05 + 1.13 = 1.18; \quad g_6^{(1)} = 0.05$$

This is the end of the downward sweep, and the reader may convince himself or herself that $\mathbf{x}^{(1)}$ is identical to that computed in GS.

Let us count the required number of multiplications. Since for each x_k we need n multiplications, for each iteration of GS and a dense matrix we need $\Omega = n^2$ multiplications. In FGS, an iteration of one downward sweep, seems to require $\Omega = n^2/2$. Since only the **h**-values (below the diagonal) were computed, *only half of the computational effort* of GS was required! Another and no less important observation is that the situation for the up iteration is identical and symmetric to that at the start of the down iteration. Instead of knowing $\mathbf{g}^{(0)}$ we know all values of $\mathbf{h}^{(1)}$, and instead of accumulating all values of $\mathbf{h}^{(1)}$ we will accumulate $\mathbf{g}^{(2)}$, since the operative equation for the up sweep is

$$x_k^{(i)} = g_k^{(i)} + h_k^{(i-1)} \tag{2.54}$$

The calculation of x's in iteration (2) proceeds therefore as follows:

$$g_5 = 0.65 + 0.25\cdot 1.18 = 0.945$$

$$x_5 = 0.945 + 1.12 = 2.065; \quad h_5 = 0$$

$$g_4 = 3.0 + 0.05\cdot 1.18 + 0.15\cdot 2.065 = 3.37$$

$$g_3 = 0.4 + 0.1 \cdot 1.18 + 0.05 \cdot 2.065 = 0.62$$

$$g_2 = 3.0 + 0.05 \cdot 1.18 + 0.15 \cdot 2.065 = 1.84$$

$$g_1 = 0.85 + 0.05 \cdot 1.18 + 0.1 \cdot 2.065 = 1.1155$$

$$x_4 = 3.37 + 0.60 = 3.97; \quad h_4 = 0$$

$$g_3 = 0.62 + 0.1 \cdot 3.97 = 1.017$$

$$g_2 = 1.84 + 0.05 \cdot 3.97 = 2.04$$

$$g_1 = 1.1155 + 0.3 \cdot 3.97 = 2.31$$

$$x_3 = 1.017 + 0.252 = 1.269; \quad h_3 = 0$$

$$g_2 = 2.04 + 0.1 \cdot 1.269 = 2.17$$

$$g_1 = 2.31 + 0.05 \cdot 1.269 = 2.37$$

$$x_2 = 2.17 + 0.07 = 2.24; \quad h_2 = 0$$

$$g_1 = 2.37 + 0.05 \cdot 2.24 = 2.482; \quad x_1 = 2.482$$

[All have superscript (2).]

Iteration 1 started by preparing vector $\mathbf{g}^{(0)}$. Since all elements of $\mathbf{g}^{(2)}$ were computed above, iteration 3 can be started. In the upward-sweep, only g's were updated, so that again only half the Ω of GS was needed. The conclusion is therefore that *FGS with the* **g** *and* **h** *vectors requires only half of the computational effort of GS.*

The convergence of the Jacobi and the GS method is discussed in [DB74], that of FGS in [Fo65]. It is found that in most linear cases the convergence of FGS is better than that of GS. On the other hand, convergence (or accuracy) of these methods is not known in power system calculations, since they are nonlinear anyway. We can, though, compare Ω of factorization to that of FGS. In factorization, we need $n^3/3$ for $\mathbf{A} = \mathbf{L} * \mathbf{U}$, and $n^2/2$ for both forward and backward substitution. Thus

$$\Omega_{\text{fact}} \cong \frac{n^3}{3} + n^2$$

FGS requires n^2 operations for each double iteration and will be faster if its number of iterations is less than $(n + 3)/3$. This holds for dense matrices; for sparse matrices, because of fill-in, only test results are of any value.

2.6 UPDATING METHODS

For some computations we are given the admittance matrix $\mathbf{Y}$ and its inverse $\mathbf{Z} = \mathbf{Y}^{-1}$. We are required to calculate the inverse $\tilde{\mathbf{Z}}$ of a slightly different $\tilde{\mathbf{Y}}$:

$$\tilde{\mathbf{Z}} = \tilde{\mathbf{Y}}^{-1} \tag{2.55}$$

Matrix **Y** is extremely sparse, but since **Z** is dense, inversion requires $\Omega \cong n^3$. The storage space for **Z** is $\Psi \cong 0.5n^2$. [We have n^2 elements, but if the matrix is symmetric ($Z_{i,j} = Z_{j,i}$), only about half of them have to be stored.]

The procedure for updating is that of Sherman–Morrison. We start its development by defining a *fundamental* matrix

$$\mathbf{F}_c = \mathbf{I} - c\cdot\mathbf{w} * \mathbf{v}^{\mathrm{T}} \tag{2.56}$$

where **I** is the identity matrix, c is a scalar constant, and **w**, **v** are two (column) vectors. Suppose we multiply two such matrices, $\mathbf{F}_c$ and $\mathbf{F}_d$, which differ only in the scalar:

$$\begin{aligned}\mathbf{F}_c * \mathbf{F}_d &= (\mathbf{I} - c\cdot\mathbf{w} * \mathbf{v}^{\mathrm{T}}) * (\mathbf{I} - d\cdot\mathbf{w} * \mathbf{v}^{\mathrm{T}}) \\ &= (\mathbf{I} - c\cdot\mathbf{w} * \mathbf{v}^{\mathrm{T}} - d\cdot\mathbf{w} * \mathbf{v}^{\mathrm{T}} + c\cdot d\cdot\mathbf{w} * \mathbf{v}^{\mathrm{T}} * \mathbf{w} * \mathbf{v}^{\mathrm{T}})\end{aligned}$$

The product $\mathbf{v}^{\mathrm{T}} * \mathbf{w}$ is a scalar and as such can be factored out of the last product so that it is $[c\cdot d\cdot(\mathbf{v}^{\mathrm{T}} * \mathbf{w})] \cdot \mathbf{w} * \mathbf{v}^{\mathrm{T}}$ and all terms except **I** include the matrix $\mathbf{w} * \mathbf{v}^{\mathrm{T}}$. Thus

$$\mathbf{F}_c * \mathbf{F}_d = \mathbf{I} - [c + d - c\cdot d\cdot(\mathbf{v}^{\mathrm{T}} * \mathbf{w})]\cdot(\mathbf{w} * \mathbf{v}^{\mathrm{T}})$$

Let us make the scalar in the brackets equal to zero. For this, d must be such that $d - c\cdot d\cdot(\mathbf{v}^{\mathrm{T}} * \mathbf{w}) = -c$ or $d(1 - c\cdot\mathbf{v}^{\mathrm{T}} * \mathbf{w}) = -c$ or

$$d := \frac{c}{c\cdot\mathbf{v}^{\mathrm{T}} * \mathbf{w} - 1} \tag{2.57}$$

Since for such d we have $\mathbf{F}_c * \mathbf{F}_d = \mathbf{I}$, we see that $\mathbf{F}_d = \mathbf{F}_c^{-1}$. Thus, in order to invert matrix $\mathbf{F}_c$, we calculate d from Eq. (2.57) and $\mathbf{F}_d = \mathbf{I} - d\cdot\mathbf{w} * \mathbf{v}^{\mathrm{T}}$ is the inverse of $\mathbf{F}_c$ or

$$(\mathbf{I} - c\cdot\mathbf{w} * \mathbf{v}^{\mathrm{T}})^{-1} = \mathbf{I} - d\cdot\mathbf{w} * \mathbf{v}^{\mathrm{T}} \tag{2.58}$$

Let us derive the Sherman–Morrison formula from Eq. (2.58). Assume that a single element $A_{i,j}$ is changed, i.e., $A_{i,j} := A_{i,j} - e$. We can say that this change can also be represented by changing **A**:

$$c\cdot\mathbf{w} * \mathbf{v}^{\mathrm{T}} = 1\cdot[0,\ldots,0,\overset{\overset{i}{\downarrow}}{1},0,\ldots,0]^{\mathrm{T}} * [0,\ldots,0,\overset{\overset{j}{\downarrow}}{e},0,\ldots,0]$$

$$\tilde{\mathbf{A}} = \mathbf{A} - c\cdot\mathbf{w} * \mathbf{v}^{\mathrm{T}}; \quad c = 1$$

This can be rewritten as $\tilde{\mathbf{A}} = \mathbf{A} * (\mathbf{I} - \mathbf{A}^{-1} * \mathbf{w} * \mathbf{v}^{\mathrm{T}}) = \mathbf{A} * (\mathbf{I} - \mathbf{z} * \mathbf{v}^{\mathrm{T}})$, where we have defined a new vector $\mathbf{z} = \mathbf{A}^{-1} * \mathbf{w}$.

Matrix $(\mathbf{I} - \mathbf{z} * \mathbf{v}^{\mathrm{T}})$ is a fundamental matrix, so that with $\mathbf{B} \equiv \mathbf{A}^{-1}$ we can compute the new inverse as follows:

$$\tilde{\mathbf{A}}^{-1} = (\mathbf{I} - \mathbf{z} * \mathbf{v}^{\mathrm{T}})^{-1} * \mathbf{A}^{-1} = \left[\mathbf{I} - \frac{\mathbf{z} * \mathbf{v}^{\mathrm{T}}}{\mathbf{v}^{\mathrm{T}} * \mathbf{z} - 1}\right] * \mathbf{A}^{-1}$$

$$\tilde{\mathbf{A}}^{-1} = \mathbf{A}^{-1} - \mathbf{A}^{-1} * \left[\frac{\mathbf{w} * \mathbf{v}^{\mathrm{T}} * \mathbf{A}^{-1}}{\mathbf{v}^{\mathrm{T}} * \mathbf{A}^{-1} * \mathbf{w} - 1}\right]$$

$$\tilde{\mathbf{A}}^{-1} = \mathbf{B} - \mathbf{B} * \frac{(\mathbf{w} * \mathbf{v}^{\mathrm{T}} * \mathbf{B})}{(\mathbf{v}^{\mathrm{T}} * \mathbf{B} * \mathbf{w} - 1)}; \quad \mathbf{B} \equiv \mathbf{A}^{-1} \tag{2.59}$$

If applied to every element (i, j) of the known matrix **B**, Eq. (2.59) represents the Sherman–Morrison formula.

Kron's method may be viewed as adding a link between nodes p and q (Fig. 2.10), or making four changes in the **Y** matrix (to be called **A**).

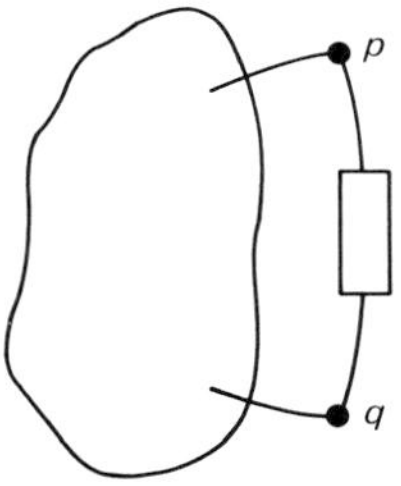

Figure 2.10 Adding a link to a network.

$$A_{pp} := A_{pp} + e; \; A_{qq} := A_{qq} + e; \; A_{pq} := A_{qp} := A_{pq} - e$$

We could apply the Sherman–Morrison formula four times—once for each of the changes—but we can also use the following formula to account for all four changes at once:

$$\tilde{\mathbf{A}} = \mathbf{A} - \mathbf{w} * \mathbf{v}^{\mathrm{T}} = \mathbf{A} - [0,\ldots,\underset{\uparrow p}{0,1},0,\ldots,\underset{\uparrow q}{-1},\ldots] * [0,\ldots,\underset{\uparrow p}{e},\ldots,\underset{\uparrow q}{-e},\ldots]^{\mathrm{T}}$$

$$\tilde{\mathbf{A}} = \mathbf{A} * (\mathbf{I} - \mathbf{A}^{-1} * \mathbf{w} * \mathbf{v}^{\mathrm{T}})$$

The vector $\mathbf{z} = \mathbf{A}^{-1} * \mathbf{w}$ is now such that its ith element is $z_i := A_{i,p}^{-1} - A_{i,q}^{-1}$, which shows that we have to subtract some columns in Kron's algorithm [Eq. (3.19)].

The inverse according to Eq. (2.59) is again:

$$\tilde{\mathbf{A}}^{-1} := \mathbf{A}^{-1} - \frac{\mathbf{z} * \mathbf{v}^{\mathrm{T}} * \mathbf{A}^{-1}}{\mathbf{v}^{\mathrm{T}} * \mathbf{z} - 1}$$

but now

$$\mathbf{v}^{\mathrm{T}} * \mathbf{A}^{-1} = e \cdot \mathbf{z}^{\mathrm{T}}; \quad \mathbf{v}^{\mathrm{T}} * \mathbf{z} = -e \cdot (2 \cdot A_{p,q}^{-1} - A_{p,p}^{-1} - A_{q,q}^{-1})$$

Inserting both equations yields $\tilde{\mathbf{A}}^{-1} := \mathbf{A}^{-1} + d \cdot \mathbf{z} * \mathbf{z}^{\mathrm{T}}$ where

$$d := \frac{e}{e \cdot (A_{p,p}^{-1} + A_{q,q}^{-1} - 2 \cdot A_{p,q}^{-1}) + 1} = \frac{1}{A_{p,p}^{-1} + A_{q,q}^{-1} - 2 \cdot A_{p,q}^{-1} + 1/e}$$

The last is element $1/\bar{z}$ of Kron's method as will be described later.

Another approach to calculate $\mathbf{Z} = \mathbf{Y}^{-1}$ was suggested in [TFC73] for the case of a symmetric matrix $\mathbf{Y}$. Factor first:

$$\mathbf{Y} = \mathbf{L} * \mathbf{D} * \mathbf{L}^{\mathrm{T}}$$

Insertion will yield for the identity matrix $\mathbf{I}$

$$\mathbf{I} = \mathbf{Y} * \mathbf{Z} = \mathbf{L} * \mathbf{D} * \mathbf{L}^{\mathrm{T}} * \mathbf{Z} = \mathbf{L} * \mathbf{D} * \mathbf{W}$$

Matrix $\mathbf{W}$ may be calculated through

$$\mathbf{W} \equiv \mathbf{L}^{\mathrm{T}} * \mathbf{Z} = (\mathbf{L} * \mathbf{D})^{-1} \tag{2.60}$$

Defining $\mathbf{U}$ as a strictly upper-triangular matrix (zeros on the diagonal)

$$\mathbf{U} = \mathbf{I} - \mathbf{L}^{\mathrm{T}} \tag{2.61}$$

leads to a recursive formula for $\mathbf{Z}$:

$$\mathbf{W} + \mathbf{U} * \mathbf{Z} = \mathbf{L}^{\mathrm{T}} * \mathbf{Z} + (\mathbf{I} - \mathbf{L}^{\mathrm{T}}) * \mathbf{Z} = \mathbf{Z}$$

that is,

$$\mathbf{Z} = \mathbf{W} + \mathbf{U} * \mathbf{Z} \tag{2.62}$$

Matrix $\mathbf{Z}$ of Eq. (2.62) is computed according to

$$Z_{i,j} := \Sigma\, U_{i,m} \cdot Z_{m,j}; \quad m\Sigma = i + 1, \ldots, n \tag{2.63}$$

for $i = n, n - 1, \ldots, 1$ and $j = n, n - 1, \ldots, i$.

The form of Eq. (2.62) is such that only diagonal elements of $\mathbf{W}$ have to be used:

$$Z_{i,i} = A_{i,i} + W_{i,i} \tag{2.64}$$

This is the basic algorithm advocated in [TFC73], but as published, it has a problem with programming: Since both $Z_{m,j}$ and $Z_{j,m}$ are needed, programming Eq. (2.63) requires an instruction of the form

```
if m > j then Z[i, j] := Z[i, j] + Z[j, m] * U[i, m]
        else Z[i, j] := Z[i, j] + Z[m, j] * U[i, m];
```

inside the loops on i, j, and m.

The above **if**-statement will slow down the program considerably, since it will appear for every i, j, and m or n, $(n - 1)$, $(n - i - 1)$ times, altogether $0.5\cdot(n)\cdot(n-1) \cong 0.5\cdot n^2$ times.

The computational procedure may be improved if Eq. (2.63) is rewritten as

$$Z_{i,j} = \Sigma\, U_{i,m} * Z_{m,j} + \Sigma\, U_{i,k} * Z_{j,k}; \qquad (2.65)$$
$$m\Sigma = i+1,\ldots,j; \qquad k\Sigma = j+1,\ldots,n$$

This will reduce time, simplify the program (no **if** required), and, if the triangular matrices **U** and **Z** are stored as vectors, also reduce storage.

Suppose again that an admittance y_{pq} (Fig. 2.10) is removed ($e = -y_{pq}$) or inserted ($e = y_{pq}$) between buses p, q of a network. Only four elements of **Y** change.

$$\tilde{Y}_{pq} = \tilde{Y}_{qp} = Y_{pq} + e; \quad \tilde{Y}_{pp} = Y_{pp} - e; \quad \tilde{Y}_{qq} = Y_{qq} - e$$

We have already seen how to update the inverse. For updating the factorization, rewrite matrix $\tilde{\mathbf{Y}}$ as

$$\tilde{\mathbf{Y}} = \mathbf{Y} + c\cdot\mathbf{a} * \mathbf{a}^{\mathrm{T}} \qquad (2.66)$$

where $c = -2\cdot e$, column vector **a** has all zeros except $1/\sqrt{2}$ in position a_p and $-1/\sqrt{2}$ in position q. Vector **a** has thus length $||\mathbf{a}|| = 1$.

If we calculate a vector **b** from $\mathbf{L} * \mathbf{b} = \mathbf{a}$ and insert into Eq. (2.66), then

$$\tilde{\mathbf{Y}} = \mathbf{L} * \mathbf{D} * \mathbf{L}^{\mathrm{T}} + c\cdot\mathbf{L} * \mathbf{b} * \mathbf{b}^{\mathrm{T}} * \mathbf{L}^{\mathrm{T}} \qquad (2.67)$$
$$= \mathbf{L} * (\mathbf{D} + c\cdot\mathbf{b} * \mathbf{b}^{\mathrm{T}}) * \mathbf{L}^{\mathrm{T}}$$

The matrix in parentheses will be called **E** and factored (with $\tilde{\mathbf{L}}$, $\tilde{\mathbf{D}}$ being new matrices)

$$\mathbf{E} = \mathbf{D} + c\cdot\mathbf{b} * \mathbf{b}^{\mathrm{T}} = \tilde{\mathbf{L}} * \tilde{\mathbf{D}} * \tilde{\mathbf{L}}^{\mathrm{T}} \qquad (2.68)$$

Inserting into Eq. (2.67) yields

$$\tilde{\mathbf{Y}} = (\mathbf{L} * \tilde{\mathbf{L}}) * \tilde{\mathbf{D}} * [\tilde{\mathbf{L}}^{\mathrm{T}} * \mathbf{L}^{\mathrm{T}}] = \mathbf{L}^{\#} * \tilde{\mathbf{D}} * (\mathbf{L}^{\#})^{\mathrm{T}} \qquad (2.69)$$
$$\mathbf{L}^{\#} = \mathbf{L} * \tilde{\mathbf{L}}$$

Eq (2.69) is the required factorized form of $\tilde{\mathbf{Y}}$.

The calculation of **b**, **E**, $\tilde{\mathbf{L}}$, and $\tilde{\mathbf{D}}$ can be considerably simplified [Gea74]* if one notices that

---

* Reprinted from Gill et al., "Methods for Modifying Matrix Factorizations," *Mathematics of Computation*, Volume 28, April 1974, pp 505-35, courtesy of the American Mathematical Society.

$$E_{i,i} = d_i + c \cdot b_i \cdot b_i; \quad E_{i,j} = c \cdot b_i \cdot b_j; \quad i \neq j \tag{2.70}$$

For the first column, this yields

$$E_{1,1} = \tilde{d}_1 = d_1 + c \cdot b_1^2$$
$$E_{i,1} = \tilde{L}_{i,1} \cdot \tilde{d}_i = c \cdot (b_i \cdot b_1) = b_i \cdot (c_1 \cdot d_1); \quad i = 2, \ldots, n$$

with c_1 defined through $c_1 = c \cdot b_1 / \tilde{d}_1$.

Writing out Eq. (2.70) in detail, we get for the remaining diagonal and nondiagonal elements of **E**:

$$E_{i,i} = d_i + \tilde{c} \cdot b_i^2 = \tilde{d}_i + \Sigma\, \tilde{d}_m \cdot (\tilde{L}_{i,m})^{2;} \quad m\Sigma = 1, \ldots, i - 1$$
$$E_{i,j} = c \cdot b_i \cdot b_j = d_j \cdot \tilde{L}_{i,j} + \Sigma\, \tilde{d}_m \cdot \tilde{L}_{i,m} \cdot \tilde{L}_{j,m}; \quad i \neq j; \ m\Sigma = 1, \ldots, j - 1$$

The last expression leads to

$$\tilde{d}_j \cdot \tilde{L}_{i,j} = c \cdot b_i \cdot b_j - \Sigma\, \tilde{d}_m \cdot \tilde{L}_{i,m} \cdot \tilde{L}_{j,m}; \quad m\Sigma = 1, \ldots, j - 1 \tag{2.71}$$

Define h_j and c_j through $h_j = \Sigma\, \tilde{d}_m \cdot c_m^2$; $c_j = b_j \cdot (c - h_j)/\tilde{d}_j$. It can be verified that for any i, the following sequence holds:

$$j = 1{:} \ c_1 = c \cdot \frac{b_1}{\tilde{d}_1}; \quad \tilde{d}_1 \cdot \tilde{L}_{i,1} = c \cdot b_i \cdot b_1 = c_i \cdot \tilde{d}_1 \cdot b_i; \quad L_{i,1} = b_i \cdot c_1$$

$$j = 2{:} \ c_2 = b_2 \cdot (c - \tilde{d}_1 \cdot c_1^2) \cdot \tilde{d}_2;$$

$$\tilde{d}_2 \cdot \tilde{L}_{i,2} = b_2 \cdot \left(c - \frac{\tilde{d}_1 \cdot \tilde{L}_{i,1} \cdot \tilde{L}_{2,1}}{b_i} \right) \cdot b_i = b_i \cdot c_2 \cdot \tilde{d}_2; \quad \tilde{L}_{i,2} = b_i \cdot c_2$$

and so on. Since for any j

$$h_j = (\Sigma\, \tilde{d}_m \cdot c_m^2) + d_{j-1} \cdot c_{j-1}^2$$
$$= h_{j-1} + \tilde{d}_{j-1} \cdot c_{j-1}^2; \quad m\Sigma = 1, \ldots, j - 2$$

h_j can be accumulated recursively. Inserting into Eq. (2.71) yields, for $m\Sigma = 1, \ldots, j - 1$,

$$\tilde{d}_j = d_j + c \cdot b_j^2 - \Sigma\, \tilde{d}_m \cdot (L_{jm})^2$$
$$= d_j + c \cdot b_j^2 - \Sigma\, \tilde{d}_m \cdot (b_j \cdot c_m)^2 = d_j + b_j^2 \cdot (c - h_j)$$

Updating of **L** starts with $\tilde{d}_1$, c_1, h_1, $\tilde{L}_{i,1}$ and proceeds for $j = 2, \ldots, n$:

$$h_j = h_{j-1} + d_{j-1} \cdot c_{j-1}^2; \quad \tilde{d}_j = d_j + b_j^2 \cdot (c - h_j);$$

$$c_j = b_j \cdot \frac{c - h_{j-1}}{d_j}$$

$$\tilde{L}_{i,j} = b_i \cdot c_j; \quad i = j + 1, \ldots, n$$

The most time-consuming part seems to be $\mathbf{L}^{\#} = \mathbf{L} * \tilde{\mathbf{L}}$, since normally it requires about $n^3/6$ operations. As shown in [Gea74], the matrices are special and the algorithm can proceed as follows:

Define initially $c_1 = c$; $\mathbf{w}^{(1)} = \mathbf{a}$

For $j = 1, 2, \ldots, n$ compute

$$b_j = w_j^{(j)}; \quad \tilde{d}_j = d_j + c_j \cdot b_j^2; \quad \beta_j = c_j \cdot \frac{b_j}{\tilde{d}_j}; \quad c_{j+1} = c_j \cdot \frac{d_j}{\tilde{d}_j}$$

and, by an inner loop on $i = j + 1, \ldots, n$,

$$w_i^{(j+1)} = w_i^{(j)} - b_j \cdot L_{i,j}; \quad L_{i,j}^{\#} = L_{i,j} + \beta_j \cdot w_i^{(j+1)}$$

Most of the operations are inside the inner loop, in which four operations are required. Thus

$$\Omega = 4 \cdot [(n-1) + (n-2) + \cdots + 2 + 1] = 4 \cdot (n-1) \cdot \frac{n}{2} \cong 2 \cdot n^2$$

and altogether $\Omega \cong 2 \cdot n^2 + n^2 + 1.5n^2 = 4.5 \cdot n^2$.

This is much lower than the n^3 operations required normally for dense matrices. For sparse matrices a comparable reduction by a factor of n can be expected, because in producing $\mathbf{L}^{\#}$ or in equations involving β_j in the algorithm above, zeros need not be multiplied.

The admittance matrix $\mathbf{Y}$ can be factored also as in

$$\mathbf{Y} = \mathbf{Q} * \mathbf{R} \tag{2.72}$$

where $\mathbf{R}$ is a right (upper) triangular and $\mathbf{Q}$ an orthogonal matrix. With $\mathbf{Z} = \mathbf{Y}^{-1}$ we have

$$\mathbf{I} = \mathbf{Y} * \mathbf{Z} = \mathbf{Q} * \mathbf{R} * \mathbf{Z}$$

Similarly to [TFC73], insertion results in

$$\mathbf{Q} + (\mathbf{I} - \mathbf{R}) * \mathbf{Z} = \mathbf{Q} + \mathbf{Z} - \mathbf{R} * \mathbf{R}^{-1} * \mathbf{Q} = \mathbf{Z}$$

or

$$\mathbf{Q} + \mathbf{U} * \mathbf{Z} = \mathbf{Z}; \quad \mathbf{U} = \mathbf{I} - \mathbf{R} \tag{2.73}$$

Equation (2.73) is almost identical to Eq. (2.62).

Next we discuss a method [Dea76] for updating $\mathbf{Q}$ and $\mathbf{R}$.*

Equation (2.66) is first rewritten (with $v_i = \sqrt{c} \cdot a_i$) as

$$\tilde{\mathbf{Y}} = \mathbf{Y} + \mathbf{v} * \mathbf{v}^{\mathrm{T}} \tag{2.74}$$

---

* Reprinted from J. W. Daniel et al., "Reorthogonalization and Stable Algorithms for Updating the Gram–Schmidt OR-Factorization," *Mathematics of Computation*, Vol. 30, pp. 772-95, courtesy of the American Mathematical Society.

The Gram–Schmidt algorithm accumulates matrices **Q** and **R** so that if at stage k, vector **v** is added to already orthogonal vectors $\mathbf{q}_i$, for $i = 1, 2, \ldots, k$ of **Q**, then $\mathbf{q}_{k+1}$, ρ, **r** can be calculated as

$$\mathbf{r} = \mathbf{Q}^{\mathrm{T}} * \mathbf{v}$$

$$\tilde{\mathbf{v}} = (\mathbf{I} - \mathbf{Q} * \mathbf{Q}^{\mathrm{T}}) * \mathbf{v}$$

$$\rho = ||\mathbf{v}||$$

$$\mathbf{q}_{k+1} = \frac{\tilde{\mathbf{v}}}{\rho}$$

Since $\rho \cdot \mathbf{q}_{k+1} = \tilde{\mathbf{v}} = (\mathbf{I} - \mathbf{Q} * \mathbf{Q}^{\mathrm{T}}) * \mathbf{v} = \mathbf{v} - \mathbf{Q} * \mathbf{Q}^{\mathrm{T}} * \mathbf{v} = \mathbf{v} - \mathbf{Q} * \mathbf{r}$, it is seen that matrix **Q** concatenated with vector **v** is

$$(\mathbf{Q}, \mathbf{v}) = (\mathbf{Q}, \mathbf{q}_{k+1}) * \begin{bmatrix} \mathbf{I} & \mathbf{r} \\ \mathbf{0}^{\mathrm{T}} & \rho \end{bmatrix}$$

Equation (2.74) yields for this case

$$\tilde{\mathbf{Y}} = \mathbf{Q} * \mathbf{R} + \mathbf{v} * \mathbf{v}^{\mathrm{T}} = (\mathbf{Q}, \mathbf{v}) * \begin{bmatrix} \mathbf{R} \\ \mathbf{v}^{\mathrm{T}} \end{bmatrix}$$

$$= (\mathbf{Q}, \mathbf{q}_{k+1}) * \begin{bmatrix} \mathbf{I} & \mathbf{r} \\ \mathbf{0}^{\mathrm{T}} & \rho \end{bmatrix} * \begin{bmatrix} \mathbf{R} \\ \mathbf{v}^{\mathrm{T}} \end{bmatrix}$$

$$= (\mathbf{Q}, \mathbf{q}_{k+1}) * \left(\begin{bmatrix} \mathbf{R} \\ \mathbf{0}^{\mathrm{T}} \end{bmatrix} + \begin{bmatrix} \mathbf{r} \\ \rho \end{bmatrix} * \mathbf{v}^{\mathrm{T}} \right)$$

The preceding yields $\tilde{\mathbf{Y}}$ already in the form $\tilde{\mathbf{Y}} = \tilde{\mathbf{Q}} * \tilde{\mathbf{R}}$ with $\tilde{\mathbf{Q}} = (\mathbf{Q}, \mathbf{q}_{k+1})$ as an orthogonal matrix. On the other hand, $\tilde{\mathbf{R}}$ is not upper triangular as exemplified for a 4-by-3 matrix:

$$\begin{bmatrix} R_{11} + r_1 v_1 & R_{12} + r_1 v_2 & R_{13} + r_1 v_3 \\ r_2 v_1 & R_{22} + r_2 v_2 & R_{23} + r_2 v_3 \\ r_3 v_1 & r_3 v_2 & R_{33} + r_3 v_3 \\ \rho v_1 & \rho v_2 & \rho v_3 \end{bmatrix} = \begin{bmatrix} \mathbf{R} \\ 0 \end{bmatrix} + \begin{bmatrix} r_1 \\ r_2 \\ r_3 \\ \rho \end{bmatrix} * [v_1, v_2, v_3]$$

It was suggested [Dea76] to eliminate ρ, r_n, ..., r_2 by n transformations of Givens:

$$\mathbf{G} * (\mathbf{r}, \rho)^{\mathrm{T}} = \mathbf{G}_{12} * \mathbf{G}_{23} * \cdots * \mathbf{G}_{n,n+1} * (\mathbf{r}, \rho)^{\mathrm{T}} = (\mathbf{x}, 0)^{\mathrm{T}}$$

The same must be applied to $[\mathbf{R}, \mathbf{0}]^{\mathrm{T}}$, and the result is an upper Hessenberg matrix as exemplified by the following 5-by-5 case:

$$\mathbf{G}_{21} * \mathbf{G}_{32} * \mathbf{G}_{43} * \mathbf{G}_{54} * \begin{bmatrix} x & x & x & x \\ 0 & x & x & x \\ 0 & 0 & x & x \\ 0 & 0 & 0 & x \\ 0 & 0 & 0 & 0 \end{bmatrix} = \begin{bmatrix} x & x & x & x & x \\ x & x & x & x & x \\ 0 & x & x & x & x \\ 0 & 0 & x & x & x \\ 0 & 0 & 0 & x & x \end{bmatrix}$$

Elements x are $s_i \cdot$x with s_i the sines of $\mathbf{G}_{j,i}$. A third step is thus needed, to annihilate these elements, by Householder's rotation matrices, $\mathbf{H}_{2,1}, \ldots, \mathbf{H}_{n,n+1}$. As a result of steps 2 and 3, we have

$$\tilde{\mathbf{Y}} = \mathbf{Q}^{\#} * \mathbf{R}^{\#} \tag{2.75}$$

where $(\mathbf{Q}^{\#}, q_{k+1}^{\#}) = \tilde{\mathbf{Q}} * \mathbf{G}^{\mathrm{T}} * \mathbf{H}^{\mathrm{T}}$ and $\mathbf{R}^{\#} = \mathbf{H} * \mathbf{G} * \tilde{\mathbf{R}}$.

The algorithm requires $\Omega = 8 \cdot m \cdot m + 3 \cdot n^2$, which is an order of magnitude less than n^3 used earlier. This Ω can yet be reduced if square-root-free rotations and an ordering policy are used.

To sum up: In some cases updating methods are an order of magnitude faster and — as will be shown in Section 3.3 — lead to more accurate results than some of the direct methods. They will be used repeatedly in the text.

2.6 ON ERRORS

Errors occurred whenever we had to divide by a very small number. In elimination the remedy was to scale and exchange equations. In Kron's method the denominator is small if we subtract two nearly equal quantities 1 and $c \cdot \mathbf{v}^{\mathrm{T}} * \mathbf{w}$. (If they were exactly equal, we would have had to divide by zero, and no meaningful result would have been produced at all.) In this case, the remedy is not to divide at all, and we can achieve this by using the updating method.

The errors just mentioned are indicative of an entire class of problems which have to do with subtracting nearly equal quantities, the so-called cancellation error.

Suppose we take a simpler case, that of calculating the two roots of $x^2 - 68x + 1 = 0$. Since $\sqrt{34 \cdot 34 - 1} = \sqrt{1155} = 33.985291$ (on a pocket calculator), $x_1 = 67.985291$ and $x_2 = 0.014709$. If we only carry five digits, the square root is 33.985 and

$$x_1 := 67.985; \quad x_2 := 0.015$$

so that we have only two nonzero digits in x_2. We get a rather inaccurate x_2.

In this case too the reason for inaccuracy was that x_2 was calculated by subtracting two nearly equal quantities: $x_2 = 34 - 33.985$. There is a simple remedy for this problem, namely, to compute x_2 from $x_1 \cdot x_2 = 1$ or $x_2 = 1.0/67.985 = 0.0147089 \cong 0.014709$, which is as accurate as x_1.

In power system problems we have large, sparse sets of linear equations, and the approach above cannot be used. We have seen that scaling, pivoting, or updating can reduce the errors. In other cases all we can do is estimate and possibly warn that large errors exist.

Let us return to linear equations. Recall that the *length* or *norm* of vector **x** is defined as

$$||\mathbf{x}|| = \sqrt{x_1^2 + x_2^2 + \cdots + x_n^2} = \sqrt{\mathbf{x}^{\mathrm{T}} * \mathbf{x}}$$

Two-dimensional and n-dimensional vectors obey the rules

$$||c \cdot \mathbf{x}|| = |c| \cdot ||\mathbf{x}|| \quad \text{for all scalars } c \text{ and vectors } \mathbf{x}$$

$$||\mathbf{x} + \mathbf{y}|| \le ||\mathbf{x}|| + ||\mathbf{y}|| \quad \text{for all vectors } \mathbf{x} \text{ and } \mathbf{y}$$

$$||\mathbf{x}^{\mathrm{T}} * \mathbf{y}|| \le ||\mathbf{x}|| \cdot ||\mathbf{y}|| \quad \text{for all vectors } \mathbf{x} \text{ and } \mathbf{y}$$

The second rule is the *triangle inequality*.

Next we define, for n-by-n matrices **A** and **B**, the norm

$$||\mathbf{A}|| = \max\left(\frac{||\mathbf{A} * \mathbf{x}||}{||\mathbf{x}||}\right); \quad \text{provided } ||\mathbf{x}|| \ne 0 \tag{2.76}$$

and the rules (corresponding to those for vectors)

$$||c \cdot \mathbf{A}|| = |c| \cdot ||\mathbf{A}||; \qquad ||\mathbf{A} + \mathbf{B}|| \le ||\mathbf{A}|| + ||\mathbf{B}||$$

From the definition of $||\mathbf{A}||$ in Eq. (2.76) it follows that

$$||\mathbf{A} * \mathbf{x}|| \le ||\mathbf{A}|| \cdot ||\mathbf{x}|| \tag{2.77}$$

If we replace vector **x** by a matrix **B**, this will lead to

$$||\mathbf{A} * \mathbf{B}|| \le ||\mathbf{A}|| \cdot ||\mathbf{B}||$$

We are now ready to deal with the following problem. Given that

$$\mathbf{A} * \mathbf{x} = \mathbf{b} \tag{2.78}$$

is to be solved, if **b** is changed into $\mathbf{b} + \delta\mathbf{b}$, perhaps because of inaccurate measurements, calculate the resulting $\delta\mathbf{x}$ in

$$\mathbf{A} * (\mathbf{x} + \delta\mathbf{x}) = \mathbf{b} + \delta\mathbf{b} \tag{2.79}$$

Subtracting Eq. (2.78) from Eq. (2.79) yields

$$\mathbf{A} * \delta\mathbf{x} = \delta\mathbf{b} \quad \text{or} \quad \delta\mathbf{x} = \mathbf{A}^{-1} * \delta\mathbf{b}$$

Using Eq. (2.77) we find that $||\delta\mathbf{b}|| \leq ||\mathbf{A}||\cdot||\delta\mathbf{x}||$, and $||\delta\mathbf{x}|| \leq ||\mathbf{A}^{-1}||\cdot||\delta\mathbf{b}||$. Division by $||\mathbf{x}||$ shows that for a relative perturbation (change)

$$\frac{||\delta\mathbf{x}||}{||\mathbf{x}||} \leq \frac{||\mathbf{A}^{-1}||\cdot||\delta\mathbf{b}||}{||\mathbf{x}||} \tag{2.80}$$

From Eqs. (2.78) and (2.77) we have that

$$||\mathbf{b}|| = ||\mathbf{A} * \mathbf{x}|| \leq ||\mathbf{A}||\cdot||\mathbf{x}||$$

We can insert $||\mathbf{x}||$ from this equation into Eq. (2.80), and the relation $\leq$ will hold even more:

$$||\mathbf{x}|| \geq \frac{||\mathbf{b}||}{||\mathbf{A}||}; \qquad \frac{||\delta\mathbf{x}||}{||\mathbf{x}||} \leq (||\mathbf{A}||\cdot||\mathbf{A}^{-1}||)\cdot\frac{||\delta\mathbf{b}||}{||\mathbf{b}||}$$

The factor in the parentheses is the *condition number* cond(**A**) of the matrix **A**, so that

$$\frac{||\delta\mathbf{x}||}{||\mathbf{x}||} \leq \text{cond}(\mathbf{A})\cdot\frac{||\delta\mathbf{b}||}{||\mathbf{b}||} \tag{2.81}$$

It is seen to be the proportionality factor between the relative change of **b** to the resulting relative change of **x**.

Suppose now that **A** instead of **b** is changed ("perturbed"). Then $(\mathbf{A} + \delta\mathbf{A}) * (\mathbf{x} + \delta\mathbf{x}) = \mathbf{b}$ will hold and if $\mathbf{A} * \mathbf{x} = \mathbf{b}$ is subtracted, also: $\mathbf{A} * \delta\mathbf{x} + \delta\mathbf{A} * (\mathbf{x} + \delta\mathbf{x}) = \mathbf{0}$. From this it follows that $\delta\mathbf{x} = -\mathbf{A}^{-1} * \delta\mathbf{A} * (\mathbf{x} + \delta\mathbf{x})$ and from inequality Eq. (2.77) that (with signs disregarded)

$$||\delta\mathbf{x}|| \leq ||\mathbf{A}^{-1}||\cdot||\delta\mathbf{A}||\cdot||\mathbf{x} + \delta\mathbf{x}||$$

Recalling the definition of cond(**A**), we can rewrite this as

$$\frac{||\delta\mathbf{x}||}{||\mathbf{x} + \delta\mathbf{x}||} \leq \text{cond}(\mathbf{A})\cdot\frac{||\delta\mathbf{A}||}{||\mathbf{A}||} \tag{2.82}$$

In this case, too, we see that if **A** is changed by $\delta\mathbf{A}$, the relative change in **x** is proportional to the change in **A** and the proportionality factor is

$$\text{cond}(\mathbf{A}) = ||\mathbf{A}||\cdot||\mathbf{A}^{-1}||$$

It might be argued that Eqs. (2.81) and (2.82) are not what we want to know, since they only yield a bound for the relative perturbation of **x** when either **A** or **b** is changed. Still, the preceding can be interpreted as that the solution of $\mathbf{A} * \mathbf{x} = \mathbf{b}$ yields not **x** but, say, $\tilde{\mathbf{x}}$ such that

$$(\mathbf{A} + \delta\mathbf{A}) * \tilde{\mathbf{x}} = \mathbf{b} \tag{2.83}$$

The value of $\tilde{\mathbf{x}}$ is thus the absolutely correct solution of Eq. (2.83), and the error bound of **x** can be found by using Eq. (2.81) or (2.82).

Let us take a closer look at cond(**A**). It bounds the ratio of the relative *uncertainty* in the solution **x** to that of **b** or of **A**. If cond(**A**) is 1, then $||\delta\mathbf{x}||$ bears the same ratio to $||\mathbf{x}||$ that $||\delta\mathbf{b}||$ does to $||\mathbf{b}||$, but if, say, cond(**A**) $= 10^6$, then $||\delta\mathbf{x}||/||\mathbf{x}||$ will be a million times $||\delta\mathbf{b}||/||\mathbf{b}||$. If cond(**A**) is relatively small, **A** is well conditioned; but if it is relatively large, then **A** is ill conditioned (with respect to solving $\mathbf{A} * \mathbf{x} = \mathbf{b}$). All we have to do, in order to estimate the error of the computation, is to calculate cond(**A**).

That is easier said than done. Since cond(**A**) includes the norm of $\mathbf{A}^{-1}$, we would have to invert **A**, and this means going from bad to worse. Therefore, we better try to compute cond(**A**) in a different way.

Recall first that orthogonalization factored **A** into $\mathbf{A} = \mathbf{Q} * \mathbf{R}$ where **R** was a right triangular and **Q** an orthonormal matrix such that $\mathbf{Q} * \mathbf{Q}^T = \mathbf{I}$ or $\mathbf{Q}^{-1} = \mathbf{Q}^T$. By a singular-value decomposition (SVD) it can also be orthogonalized according to

$$\mathbf{A} = \mathbf{T} * \mathbf{S} * \mathbf{V}^T \tag{2.84}$$

where **T** and **V** are orthonormal and **S** is a diagonal matrix. Because $\mathbf{T}^T * \mathbf{T} = \mathbf{I}$ and $\mathbf{V}^T * \mathbf{V} = \mathbf{I}$, if we premultiply Eq. (2.84) by $\mathbf{T}^T$ and postmultiply it by **V**, we get

$$\mathbf{T}^T * \mathbf{A} * \mathbf{V} = \mathbf{S} \tag{2.85}$$

which is in the form normally given. **S** is diagonal, and its elements, the singular values s_i of **A**, can, according to Theorem (3.1) of [FM67], be ordered, i.e.,

$$s_1 \geq s_2 \geq \cdots \geq s_r \geq s_{r+1} = \cdots = s_n = 0$$

where r is the rank of **A**. In particular, if **A** is nonsingular,

$$s_1 \geq s_2 \geq \cdots \geq s_n > 0$$

From now on if not stated otherwise we take the case of the nonsingular matrix for which none of the singular values is zero.

For any vector **x** or matrix **X** we have

$$||\mathbf{Q}||\cdot||\mathbf{x}|| = ||\mathbf{x}|| \quad \text{or} \quad ||\mathbf{Q}||\cdot||\mathbf{X}|| = ||\mathbf{X}|| \tag{2.86}$$

since for an orthonormal matrix $||\mathbf{Q}|| = 1$. From Eqs. (2.84) and (2.86) it follows that with **T** and **V** being orthonormal matrices, $||\mathbf{A}|| = ||\mathbf{S}||$.

Since by Eq. (2.76), $||\mathbf{A}|| = \max(||\mathbf{A} * \mathbf{x}||/||\mathbf{x}||)$ for any nonzero vector **x**, we have $||\mathbf{S}|| = \max(||\mathbf{S} * \mathbf{x}||/||\mathbf{x}||)$. With **x** being a unit vector $\mathbf{e}_1$ and with s_1 the largest absolute value of s's, we have

$$\begin{bmatrix} s_1 & & & \\ & \cdot & & \\ & & \cdot & \\ & & & \cdot \\ & & & & s_n \end{bmatrix} * \begin{bmatrix} 1 \\ 0 \\ \cdot \\ \cdot \\ \cdot \\ 0 \end{bmatrix} = \begin{bmatrix} s_1 \\ 0 \\ \cdot \\ \cdot \\ \cdot \\ 0 \end{bmatrix}; \quad \begin{array}{l} ||\mathbf{S}|| = s_1 \\ ||\mathbf{A}|| = ||\mathbf{S}|| = s_1 \end{array} \tag{2.87}$$

Since **S** is a diagonal matrix, so is $\mathbf{S}^{-1}$, and its elements are $1/s_i$. Thus, in a manner similar to the preceding,

$$||\mathbf{A}^{-1}|| = ||\mathbf{S}^{-1}|| = \frac{1}{s_n}$$

where s_n is the smallest of the s_i's. The result is

$$\boxed{\text{cond}(\mathbf{A}) = \frac{s_1}{s_n}} \tag{2.88}$$

The errors are proportional to the ratio of the largest to the smallest singular value.

The calculation of **S** for a given **A** is discussed and programmed in Chapter 3. A way of *estimating* cond(**A**) follows.

Assume that $\mathbf{A} * \mathbf{x} = \mathbf{b}$ has been solved by a direct method. The solution $\mathbf{x}^{(1)}$ will be inaccurate because of the inevitable roundoff error. The residual, $\mathbf{r}^{(1)} = \mathbf{b} - \mathbf{A} * \mathbf{x}^{(1)}$, will not be a zero vector. Suppose we also define the *error* vector

$$\mathbf{e}^{(1)} = \mathbf{x} - \mathbf{x}^{(1)} \tag{2.89}$$

where **x** is the correct solution. Insertion of Eq. (2.89) into $\mathbf{A} * \mathbf{e}^{(1)}$ yields $\mathbf{A} * \mathbf{e}^{(1)} = \mathbf{A} * \mathbf{x} - \mathbf{A} * \mathbf{x}^{(1)} = \mathbf{b} - \mathbf{A} * \mathbf{x}^{(1)} = \mathbf{r}^{(1)}$. It is tempting to say that all that is required to get the absolutely correct result is to solve

$$\mathbf{A} * \mathbf{e}^{(1)} = \mathbf{r}^{(1)} \tag{2.90}$$

and then insert $\mathbf{e}^{(1)}$ into Eq. (2.89):

$$\mathbf{x} = \mathbf{e}^{(1)} + \mathbf{x}^{(1)} \tag{2.91}$$

Unfortunately, it is precisely Eq. (2.90) that we cannot solve; otherwise, we could have solved $\mathbf{A} * \mathbf{x} = \mathbf{b}$ in the first place more accurately. What we may assume is that **x** (let us now call it $\mathbf{x}^{(2)}$) of Eq. (2.91) is a better approximation to **x** than $\mathbf{x}^{(1)}$ was. We can proceed according to *such iterative improvements* of $\mathbf{x}^{(i)}$. Additionally, note the following:

1. The original system $\mathbf{A} * \mathbf{x} = \mathbf{b}$ was probably solved using $\mathbf{L} * \mathbf{U}$ decomposition. Equation (2.90) can thus be written as

$$\mathbf{L} * \mathbf{U} * \mathbf{e}^{(i)} = \mathbf{r}^{(i)}$$

and solved in two steps as previously discussed in this chapter:

$$\mathbf{L} * \mathbf{z} = \mathbf{r}^{(i)}; \qquad \mathbf{U} * \mathbf{e}^{(i)} = \mathbf{z}$$

The computation of $\mathbf{r}$ requires $n^2 + n$, that of $\mathbf{e}$ only n, and the back-substitutions only n^2. Altogether $\Omega \cong 2n^2$ instead of $\Omega \cong n^3/3$ are required — an order-of-magnitude reduction.
2. The computation of $\mathbf{r}^{(i)} = \mathbf{b} - \mathbf{A} * \mathbf{x}^{(i)}$ involves subtraction of nearly equal quantities and so cancellation may take place. It is therefore advisable to compute $\mathbf{r}^{(i)}$ using double precision and round off the results only when finished. There is no reason for higher precision work while correcting $\mathbf{x}^{(i)}$.
3. The convergence of the process can be proved by using an approximation to $\mathbf{A}$, say $\tilde{\mathbf{A}}$, such that $\tilde{\mathbf{A}} * \mathbf{x}^{(i)} \cong \mathbf{b}$. Then

$$\mathbf{r}^{(1)} = \mathbf{b} - \mathbf{A} * (\tilde{\mathbf{A}}^{-1} * \mathbf{b}) = (\mathbf{I} - \mathbf{A} * \tilde{\mathbf{A}}^{-1}) * \mathbf{b}$$

$$\mathbf{r}^{(2)} = \mathbf{b} - \mathbf{A} * (\mathbf{x}^{(1)} + \mathbf{e}^{(1)})$$

$$= (\mathbf{I} - \mathbf{A} * \tilde{\mathbf{A}}^{-1}) * \mathbf{b} - \mathbf{A} * \mathbf{e}^{(1)}$$

$$\mathbf{r}^{(2)} = (\mathbf{I} - \mathbf{A} * \tilde{\mathbf{A}}^{-1}) * \mathbf{b} - \mathbf{A} * \tilde{\mathbf{A}}^{-1} * \mathbf{r}^{(1)}$$

$$\mathbf{r}^{(2)} = (\mathbf{I} - \mathbf{A} * \tilde{\mathbf{A}}^{-1}) * \mathbf{b} - \mathbf{A} * \tilde{\mathbf{A}}^{-1} * (\mathbf{I} - \mathbf{A} * \tilde{\mathbf{A}}^{-1}) * \mathbf{b}$$

$$= (\mathbf{I} - \mathbf{A} * \tilde{\mathbf{A}}^{-1})^2 * \mathbf{b}$$

or in general $\mathbf{r}^{(i)} = (\mathbf{I} - \mathbf{A} * \tilde{\mathbf{A}}^{-1})^i * \mathbf{b}$.

The process will converge if all eigenvalues of $\mathbf{I} - \mathbf{A} * \tilde{\mathbf{A}}^{-1}$, $|\lambda| < 1$. The convergence of the process is linear, and

$$\mathbf{x}^{(i)} = \mathbf{x}^{(1)} + \mathbf{e}^{(1)} + \mathbf{e}^{(2)} + \cdots + \mathbf{e}^{(i)} \cong \mathbf{x} \quad \text{for } i \to \infty$$

Next we define the round-off unit u. For that we need to remind ourselves of how a digital computer works.

First we define correct decimals and significant digits. The number of *digits* does not include the leading zeros; the number of *decimals* does. Thus 0.0123 has three digits and four decimals. Suppose now that we know the approximate value of $a = 0.0123 \pm 0.00006$ or that the number is between $0.0122\underline{4}$ and $0.0123\underline{6}$. Obviously, it has four correct decimals, but only two *significant* digits, since we are only sure of 0.012. Since $0.012d$ is represented by 0.012 if $d < 0.005$, and by 0.013 if $d \geq 0.0005$, then if the error in $\tilde{a}$ does not exceed 0.5×10^{-t} it is said to have *t correct decimals*.

The digits in $\tilde{a}$ greater than 10^{-t} are called *significant digits*. Thus if $\tilde{a} = 0.0123 \pm 0.00004$, we see that in $\tilde{a} = a \pm \epsilon$ we have $|\epsilon| = 0.4 \cdot 10^{-4}$ or, since $0.4 \cdot 10^{-4} < 0.5 \cdot 10^{-4}$, $t = 4$. In $\tilde{a} = 0.0123 \pm 0.00006$ we have $|\epsilon| = 0.6 \cdot 10^{-4} = 0.06 \cdot 10^{-3} < 0.5 \cdot 10^{-3}$, and $t = 3$.

Having determined the number of correct decimals, it is easy to decide on the number of significant digits: In the first case it was 3, in the second only 2. Note that the error was $|\epsilon| < 0.5 \times 10^{-t}$.

Decimal numbers are either rounded or chopped; for example 0.3456 if rounded to 3 digits would yield 0.346, but if chopped, only 0.345. Since numbers in a computer are usually in *floating-point* representation, as

$$a = m \cdot 10^q; \quad 0.1 \le |m| < 1; \quad q = \text{integer}$$

where m is the *mantissa* and q the *exponent*, only the mantissa is chopped or rounded. In the computer, a is represented as $\tilde{a} = \tilde{m} \cdot 10^q$, where $\tilde{m}$ is rounded off to t digits (t = precision of the machine, q its range). Thus if we assume rounding

$$|\tilde{m} - m| = |\epsilon| \le 0.5 \cdot 10^{-t}$$

The magnitude of the relative error (with $m \ge 0.1$) is at most

$$\frac{\tilde{a} - a}{a} = \frac{\tilde{m} \cdot 10^q - m \cdot 10^q}{m \cdot 10^q}$$

$$= \frac{\tilde{m} - m}{m} \le \frac{0.5 \cdot 10^{-t}}{m} < 0.5 \cdot 10^{(1-t)}$$

As we see, every real number can be represented with a relative error which does not exceed a *round-off unit* u:

$$u = 0.5 \cdot \beta^{(1-t)}$$

where β is the base (radix) of the system (normally $\beta = 2$). Note that u is known for a given computer (it normally lies between 10^{-15} and 10^{-6}).

The main point is that [DB74], if $\mathbf{A}$ is not too ill conditioned then we can estimate cond($\mathbf{A}$) from

$$\boxed{\text{cond}(\mathbf{A}) \le \frac{1}{n \cdot u} \frac{\|\delta \mathbf{x}^{(1)}\|}{\|\mathbf{x}^{(2)}\|}} \tag{2.92}$$

Recall Eqs. (2.89) to (2.91) and the algorithm following them. We may compute $\mathbf{x}^{(1)}$ and then for $i = 2, 3, \ldots$

$$\mathbf{r}^{(i)} = \mathbf{b} - \mathbf{A} * \mathbf{x}^{(i)}; \quad \mathbf{L} * (\mathbf{U} * \delta\mathbf{x}^{(i)}) = \mathbf{r}^{(i)}; \quad \mathbf{x}^{(i+1)} = \mathbf{x}^{(i)} + \delta\mathbf{x}^{(i)}$$

where $\mathbf{r}^{(i)}$ is computed with double precision.

We will have to solve the load-flow equations, which are nonlinear. In this case we compute $\Delta\mathbf{x}$ instead of $\mathbf{x}$ and cannot directly use the preceding algorithm, since the right-hand side is a function of $\mathbf{x}$. We therefore suggest using the method of iterative-improvements, as described earlier, in the following way:

(a) Solve for $\mathbf{x}$ iteratively from

$$\mathbf{L} * \mathbf{U} * \Delta\mathbf{x} = \mathbf{f}(\mathbf{x})$$

(b) Occasionally keep the right-hand side constant and calculate $\mathbf{x}_2$, $\mathbf{x}_3$, ... by iterative improvements, i.e., from

$$\mathbf{r}_i = \mathbf{b} - \mathbf{L} * \mathbf{U} * \delta\mathbf{x}_i$$

$$\mathbf{L} * (\mathbf{U} * \delta\mathbf{x}_i) = \mathbf{b} - \mathbf{r}_i$$

$$\mathbf{x}_{i+1} = \mathbf{x}_i + \delta\mathbf{x}_i$$

with $\mathbf{r}_i$ computed with double precision. Following the computation of a new $\mathbf{x}_{i+1}$, test if $n \cdot u \cdot \text{cond}(\mathbf{A})$ is small enough, say, less than 0.1. This test can be made by checking if

$$\frac{||\delta\mathbf{x}_i||}{||\mathbf{x}_{i+1}||} \leq 0.1$$

If the test is positive, proceed with (a) until $||\Delta\mathbf{x}|| < \epsilon$. If the test is negative, say, three or four times, the problem is probably ill conditioned [FM67].

2.8 NOTES

Most of the material of Chapter 2 can be looked up in [DB74]. For the methods of Kron and Shipley see [Br75] and for orthogonalization [No69]. There are many publications on sparsity. Error treatment follows that of [FM67] and [DB74]. The material on singular-value decomposition is from [LH73], a text recommended for further reading, especially since it will be used repeatedly in the following chapters.

As exercises, it is suggested that the reader write a program corresponding to any of the algorithms discussed—except that no sparsity should be assumed. (This will be done anyway in the following chapters.) For data, the networks described in Chapter 1 can be used.

3 Short-Circuit Calculations

The *objectives* of this chapter are

1. To calculate the bus impedance matrix and introduce "diakoptics."
2. To show how $\mathbf{L} * \mathbf{D} * \mathbf{L}^{\mathrm{T}}$ factorization can be used to calculate (symmetrical) short-circuit currents.
3. To introduce the method of symmetrical components and exemplify its use.
4. To discuss the singular-value decomposition (SVD) and its possible application in short-circuit calculations. (Readers interested only in *using* SVD may skip this section.)

3.1 THE BUS-IMPEDANCE MATRIX

The three-bus network of Chapter 1 is redrawn in Fig. 3.1 with the following remarks:

- No AC or complex quantities are used. This simplifies the equations.
- The nodes are numbered so that 0 is the common ground node. The branches carry letters with a to e representing lines, f and h representing the two generators, g representing the load.

- The following vectors are defined:

Bus voltage:	$\mathbf{u}$	=	$[u_1, u_2, u_3]^T$
Injected current:	$\mathbf{i}$	=	$[i_f, i_g, i_h]^T$
Line current:	$\mathbf{i}_L$	=	$[i_a, i_b, i_c, i_d, i_e]^T$
Line voltage:	$\mathbf{u}_L$	=	$[u_a, u_b, u_c, u_d, u_e]^T$

- Line impedances z_i or admittances y_i can be arranged as diagonal matrices. Thus, the *line admittance matrix* is

$$\mathbf{Y}_L = \text{diag}\,[y_a, y_b, y_c, y_d, y_e]$$

- The network can be solved using the loop currents i_1 to i_5. The equations on the left lead to those on the right:

$i_1 z_f + (i_1 - i_2) z_a = 0;$	$(z_a + z_f) i_1 - z_a i_2 = 0$
$(i_2 - i_1) z_a + i_2 z_e + (i_2 - i_3) z_c = 0;$	$-z_a i_1 + (z_a + z_e + z_c) i_2 - z_c i_3 = 0$
$(i_3 - i_2) z_c + (i_3 - i_4) z_g = 0;$	$-z_c i_2 + (z_c + z_g) i_3 - z_g i_4 = 0$
$(i_4 - i_3) z_g + i_4 \cdot z_d + (i_4 - i_5) z_b = 0;$	$-z_g \cdot i_3 + (z_g + z_d + z_b) i_4 - z_b \cdot i_5 = 0$
$(i_5 - i_4) z_b + i_5 z_h = 0;$	$-z_b i_4 + (z_b + z_h) i_5 = 0$

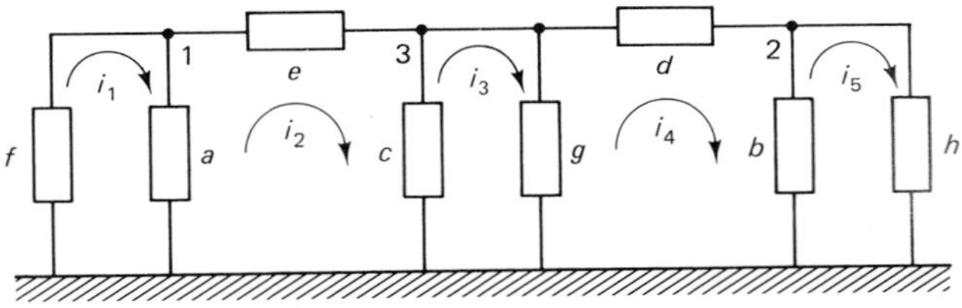

Figure 3.1 The 3-bus network.

In terms of a loop-current vector $\mathbf{i}_l$ and a loop impedance matrix $\mathbf{Z}_l$, these equations can be written as

$$\mathbf{Z}_l * \mathbf{i}_l = \mathbf{0} \tag{3.1}$$

Note that $Z_{j,k}$ is the negative of the common impedance of loop currents i_j and i_k and that $\mathbf{Z}_l$ is a symmetric matrix. Also, since there are five equations for the five unknowns $\mathbf{i}_l = [i_1, i_2, i_3, i_4, i_5]^T$, the system can be solved for $\mathbf{i}_l$. The branch currents and voltages can then be calculated, for example, as $i_a = i_2 - i_1$ and $u_1 = i_a \cdot z_a$.

Another way to solve the problem is to use the node, or bus voltage vector $\mathbf{u}$ as the set of unknowns. Currents i_f, i_h are given by the generator power (p/u) and i_g by the load power. Kirchhoff's current laws lead then to only three instead of five equations.

$$-i_f + u_1 y_a + (u_1 - u_3)y_e = 0$$

$$(u_2 - u_3)y_d + u_2 y_b - i_h = 0$$

$$(u_3 - u_1)y_e + (u_3 - u_2)y_d + u_3 y_c - i_g = 0$$

$$\begin{bmatrix} y_a + y_e & 0 & -y_e \\ 0 & y_b + y_d & -y_d \\ -y_e & -y_d & y_c + y_d + y_e \end{bmatrix} * \begin{bmatrix} u_1 \\ u_2 \\ u_3 \end{bmatrix} = \begin{bmatrix} i_f \\ i_h \\ i_g \end{bmatrix}$$

$$\mathbf{Y}_b * \mathbf{u} = \mathbf{i} \tag{3.2}$$

Network equations (3.1) and (3.2) are based either on loop currents or on node (bus) voltages; for the sake of lower computational effort Ω, the smaller set should be chosen. Let us calculate the computational effort.

The topology of the network is adequately described by a graph in which every impedance is replaced by a line (or branch). The graph in Fig. 3.2 corresponds, then, to the network in Fig. 3.1. It is a *connected* graph because there is a path from every node to every other node, and it is a *directed* graph, since arrows were added to it.

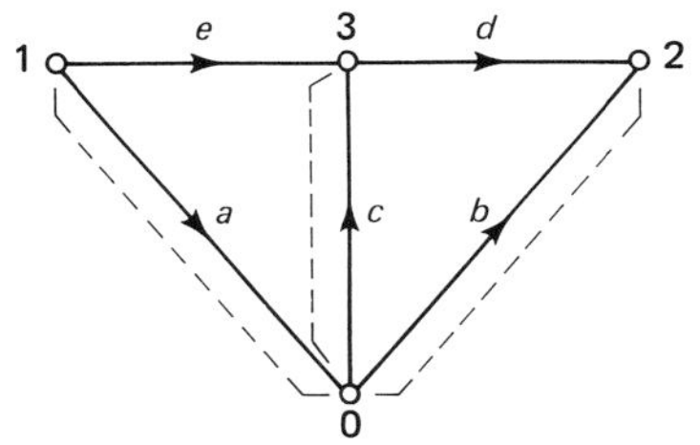

Figure 3.2 The graph of Fig 3.1.

If *all* nodes are connected so that *no loop* is formed, a *tree* of the network results. More than one tree can be drawn for a given network; one is shown for the 3-bus network in Fig. 3.3. It connects (by solid lines) all nodes.

Note that each link (dashed lines in Fig. 3.3) completes exactly one loop and that the number of tree lines and links together is the original number of branches: $b = t + l$.

The tree has to start somewhere, say, at node 0, and the first tree line 0 to 1 would make $t = 1$. Moving to each additional node adds 1 to t, so that altogether with $n + 1$ nodes (from 0 to n), we have

$$t = n$$

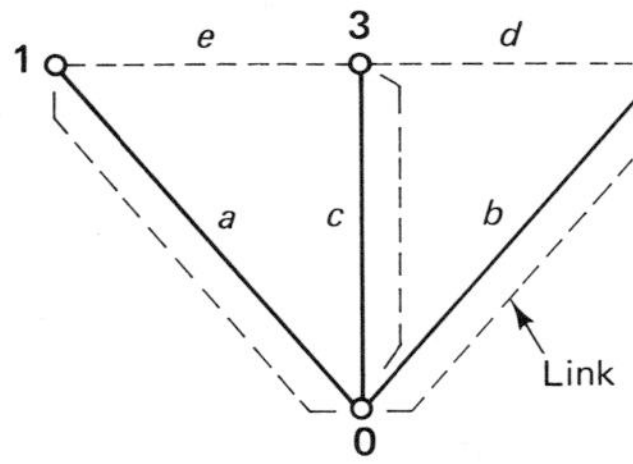

Figure 3.3 A tree for Fig 3.1.

Inserting each link produces a loop by closing a part of the tree. Thus, the number of loop equations for a current circulating through each loop is equal to the number of links $l = b - t = b - n$. In our case $n = 3$ and $b = 8$, so that the number of loop currents is $l = 8 - 3 = 5$.

The number of node equations to be solved is n (here 3). The number of loop equations is that of links l, but if each node has a generator or load connected to it, n loops have to be added and $l = b$. For the networks mentioned in Section 1.6, these numbers are summarized in Table 3.1.

TABLE 3.1 Number of loop (b) and node (n) equations.

b	9	20	41	77	179
n	6	13	29	56	117

Since in all cases $b > n$, this means that the node-voltage or the $\mathbf{Y}_b$ system leads to smaller sets to be solved. From now on we will use only this system.

The solution of Eq. (3.2) is the vector of bus-voltages $[u_1, u_2, u_3]^T$.

The line voltages $\mathbf{u}_L$ can be computed from the bus voltages as follows:

$$\begin{bmatrix} u_a \\ u_b \\ u_c \\ u_d \\ u_e \end{bmatrix} = \begin{bmatrix} 1 & 0 & 0 \\ 0 & 1 & 0 \\ 0 & 0 & 1 \\ 0 & -1 & 1 \\ 1 & 0 & -1 \end{bmatrix} * \begin{bmatrix} u_1 \\ u_2 \\ u_3 \end{bmatrix}$$

With the previous definitions, this becomes $\mathbf{u}_L = \mathbf{A} * \mathbf{u}_b$, where $\mathbf{A}$ is the so-called *incidence matrix* of b rows and n columns. For branch k, node m, $A_{k,m} = +1$ if the arrow points from k to m and $A_{k,m} = -1$ if it points from m to k.

The vector of injected currents can be calculated as,

$$\begin{bmatrix} y_a & & & & \\ & y_b & & & \\ & & y_c & & \\ & & & y_d & \\ & & & & y_e \end{bmatrix} * \begin{bmatrix} u_1 \\ u_2 \\ u_3 \\ u_3 - u_2 \\ u_1 - u_3 \end{bmatrix} = \begin{bmatrix} i_1 - i_2 \\ i_4 - i_5 \\ i_2 - i_3 \\ i_4 \\ i_2 \end{bmatrix} \tag{3.3}$$

To calculate $\mathbf{Y}_b$ of Eq. (3.2), we compute the product

$$\mathbf{Y}_b = \mathbf{A}^{\mathrm{T}} * \mathbf{Y}_L * \mathbf{A} \tag{3.4}$$

(by a two-step process)

$$\mathbf{B} \equiv \mathbf{Y}_L * \mathbf{A} := \begin{bmatrix} y_a & & & & \\ & y_b & & & \\ & & y_c & & \\ & & & y_d & \\ & & & & y_e \end{bmatrix} * \begin{bmatrix} 1 & 0 & 0 \\ 0 & 1 & 0 \\ 0 & 0 & 1 \\ 0 & -1 & 1 \\ 1 & 0 & -1 \end{bmatrix} = \begin{bmatrix} y_a & 0 & 0 \\ 0 & y_b & 0 \\ 0 & 0 & y_c \\ 0 & -y_d & y_d \\ y_e & 0 & -y_e \end{bmatrix}$$

$$\mathbf{A}^{\mathrm{T}} * \mathbf{B} = \begin{bmatrix} 1 & 0 & 0 & 0 & 1 \\ 0 & 1 & 0 & -1 & 0 \\ 0 & 0 & 1 & 1 & -1 \end{bmatrix} * \begin{bmatrix} y_a & 0 & 0 \\ 0 & y_b & 0 \\ 0 & 0 & y_c \\ 0 & -y_d & y_d \\ y_e & 0 & -y_e \end{bmatrix}$$

$$= \begin{bmatrix} y_a + y_e & 0 & -y_e \\ 0 & y_b + y_d & -y_d \\ -y_e & -y_d & y_c + y_d + y_e \end{bmatrix}$$

which is the bus-admittance matrix $\mathbf{Y}_b$ of Eq. (3.2). (In the future, index b will be dropped.)

The bus-admittance matrix can also be computed as follows: Figure 3.4 depicts a portion of a power system. Bus k is connected through a transmission line to bus m. The transmission line is represented by the impedance $z' = r_{km} + jx_{km}$ or the corresponding series admittance and two shunt admittances. They are, respectively,

$$y'_{s(k,m)} = \frac{1}{r_{km} + jx_{km}}; \quad y'_{c(k)} = 1 / jx_c \tag{3.5}$$

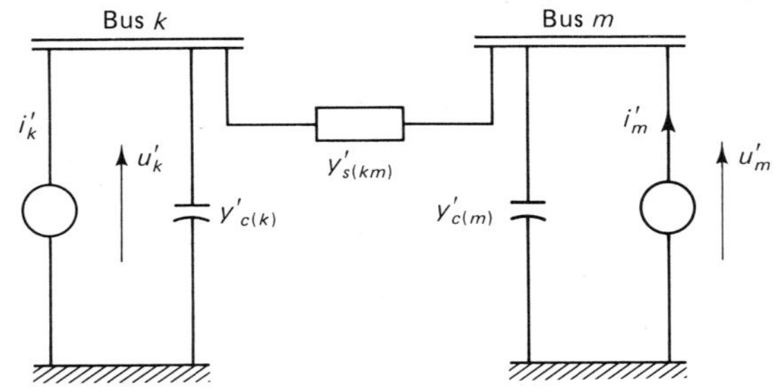

Figure 3.4 Two buses connected by a line.

where r_{km} and x_{km} are the known (positive) resistance and reactance of the line, respectively, and x_c represents half of the lines' capacitive reactance, i.e., $\omega C/2$. The current flowing into bus k is denoted i_k'. The (complex) voltage of bus k is u_k'. A similar notation applies to bus m.

The current flowing through line $k-m$ is obviously the voltage difference times the line admittance:

$$i_{km}' = \frac{u_k' - u_m'}{r_{km} + jx_{km}} = (u_k' - u_m')\cdot y_{s(km)}' \tag{3.6}$$

The charging of the line is represented by two identical reactances $\omega C/2$. The current through $y_{c(k)}'$ to ground is $u_k'\cdot y_{c(k)}'$. Hence the current leaving bus k is given by the sum of these two components.

$$i_k' = u_k'\cdot y_{c(k)}' + (u_k' - u_m')\cdot y_{s(km)}' \tag{3.7}$$

where the first summand denotes the shunt and the second the line current. Reordering yields

$$i_k' = u_k'\cdot(y_{c(k)}' + y_{s(k,m)}') + u_m'\cdot(-y_{s(k,m)}')$$

Let the network consist of $n + 1$ buses, numbered $0, \ldots, n$. Then by Kirchhoff's current law, the total current leaving any node k is, by generalization of Eq. (3.7),

$$i_k' = u_k'\cdot\Sigma\,(y_{c(m)}' + y_{s(km)}') + \Sigma\, u_m'\cdot(-y_{s(km)}'); \tag{3.8}$$

$$m\Sigma = 0, \ldots, n \text{ but } m\Sigma \neq k$$

If buses k and m are not connected, then $y_{s(km)}' = 0$ and $y_{c(m)}' = 0$. Hence, only buses directly connected to bus k contribute to the above sums.

Let us rename the negative series admittance $y_{s(km)}'$ of the line connecting buses k and m as the *mutual admittance*, y_{km}':

$$y_{km}' = -y_{s(km)}' \tag{3.9}$$

The sum of all admittances y'_{km} of lines connected to bus k, plus all (capacitive) charge admittances $y'_{c(m)}$ of bus k, is called the *self-admittance* y'_{kk}, i.e.,

$$y'_{kk} = \Sigma\,(y'_{c(m)} - y'_{km}); \quad m\Sigma = 0, \ldots, n \tag{3.10}$$

and this time the case $m = k$ is included in the sum.

We can separate the real and imaginary parts of any admittance y'_{km} as in $y'_{km} = g_{km} + jb_{km}$.

Normally, we are not given the admittance but the impedance, $z'_{km} = r_{km} + jx_{km}$; but since $y' = 1/z'$, we can calculate the mutual admittance $-y'_{s(km)}$ of line $k-m$:

$$g_{km} + jb_{km} = \frac{-1}{r_{km} + jx_{km}} = \frac{-r_{km} + jx_{km}}{r_{km}^2 + x_{km}^2} \tag{3.11}$$

Separating the real and imaginary parts on the right and comparing the two sides of Eq. (3.11) yields

$$\begin{aligned} g_{km} &= \frac{-r_{km}}{r_{km}^2 + x_{km}^2} < 0; \quad k \neq m \\ b_{km} &= \frac{x_{km}}{r_{km}^2 + x_{km}^2} > 0; \quad k \neq m \end{aligned} \tag{3.12}$$

The shunt admittance $y'_{c(m)}$ is purely capacitive and can be written as $y'_{c(m)} = 1/(jx_{c(m)}) = -j/x_{c(m)}$. Insertion into Eq. (3.10) for the self-admittance yields

$$y'_{kk} = g_{kk} + jb_{kk} = \Sigma\, y'_{c(m)} - \Sigma y'_{km} = -j\,\Sigma\,\frac{1}{x_{c(m)}} - \Sigma\,(g_{km} + jb_{km})$$

and comparison of the two sides:

$$g_{kk} = -\Sigma\, g_{km} = \Sigma\,\frac{r_{km}}{r_{km}^2 + x_{km}^2} > 0; \quad m\Sigma \neq k$$

$$b_{kk} = -\Sigma\left(\frac{1}{x_{c(m)}} + b_{km}\right) = -\Sigma\left(\frac{1}{x_{c(m)}} + \frac{x_{km}}{r_{km}^2 + x_{km}^2}\right) < 0 \tag{3.13}$$

A problem exists in that the data are given in a form exemplified in Table 1.4 and a program should set them up in the form given in Section 2.4 for sparse matrices. Such a program is described next.

The mutual admittance of line $i-k$ from Table 1.4 is computed as follows. Line $1-2$ will serve as an example. It had appeared in Table 1.4 as $r = 0.082$, $x = 0.192$ and therefore $g_{12} + j\cdot b_{12} = 1/(0.082 + j\cdot 0.192) = (82 - j\cdot 192)\cdot 10^{-3}/(82^2 + 192^2)10^{-6}$; $g_{1,2} = 1.88$, $b_{1,2} = -4.40$. These values for all lines are shown in Tables 3.3 and 3.4 as nondiagonal terms. Summing up all admittances $-g_{k,i} - j \cdot b_{k,i}$ which are connected to bus k and adding all capacitances $j \cdot x_c$ connected to the same bus k yields $y_{k,k}$ (Table 3.2), e.g., for bus 2: $g_{2,2} = g_{2,1} + g_{2,3} + g_{2,5} + g_{2,7} = 1.88 + 1.99 + 1.69 + 6.73 = 12.29$ and $b_{2,2} = -4.40 - 5.07 - 5.13 - 21.72 + 0.0173 + 0.0187 + 0.0064 = -36.32 + 0.042 = -36.2776$, which is rounded here to -36.28.

TABLE 3.2 Self admittances, as computed.

Bus No.	1	2	3	4	5	6	7
$g_{k,k}$	1.88	12.29	4.26	4.54	10.61	5.98	9.46
$-b_{k,k}$	4.40	36.28	14.50	18.90	35.07	19.45	31.14

The resulting matrices **G** and **B** are shown in Tables 3.3 and 3.4.

TABLE 3.3 The G matrix of the 7-bus network.

$$\begin{bmatrix} 1.88 & -1.88 & & & & & \\ -1.88 & 12.29 & -1.99 & & -1.69 & & -6.73 \\ & -1.99 & 4.26 & -2.27 & & & \\ & & -2.27 & 4.54 & -2.27 & & \\ & -1.69 & & -2.27 & 10.61 & -4.95 & -1.70 \\ & & & & -4.95 & 5.98 & -1.03 \\ & -6.73 & & & -1.70 & -1.03 & 9.46 \end{bmatrix}$$

TABLE 3.4 The B matrix for the 7-bus network.

$$\begin{bmatrix} 4.40 & -4.40 & & & & & \\ -4.40 & 36.28 & -5.07 & & -5.13 & & -21.72 \\ & -5.07 & 14.50 & -9.46 & & & \\ & & -9.46 & 18.90 & -9.46 & & \\ & -5.13 & & -9.46 & 35.07 & -15.35 & -5.19 \\ & & & & -15.35 & 19.45 & -4.24 \\ & -21.72 & & & -5.19 & -4.24 & 31.14 \end{bmatrix}$$

TABLE 3.5 Storage of the Y matrix for the 7-bus network.

	1	2	3	4	5	6	7	8
g[k,m]	-1.8813	-1.8813	-1.9864	-1.6890	-6.7253	-1.9864	-2.2693	-2.2693
b[k,m]	4.4049	4.4049	5.0697	5.1252	21.7279	5.0697	9.4554	9.4554
adj[j]	2	1	3	5	7	2	4	3

	9	10	11	12	13	14	15
	-2.2693	-1.6890	-2.2693	-4.9453	-1.7020	-4.9453	-1.0257
	9.4554	5.1252	9.4554	15.3566	5.1926	15.3566	4.2359

ip[i]	1	2	6	8	10	14

g[k,k]	1.8813	12.2819	4.2557	4.5386	10.6056	5.9711	9.4530
b[k,k]	-4.4049	-36.2853	-14.4977	-18.8907	-35.0580	-19.5415	-31.1080

The admittance matrix would be stored as in Table 3.5.

To get, say, $B_{2,5}$ from Table 3.5, we find that first ip[2] = 2 and ip[3] − 1 = 5. The search for adj[k] = 5 from j = 2 to j = 5 yields j = 4 and so $B_{2,5}$ = 5.1252.

Program 3.1 ("indata") produces these tables, using input as given in the Tables of Section 1.6.

The development of any program is a complex and iterative process. For instance, array *ll* of indata is not needed, but in the first attempt, it made the program simpler. (As an exercise, the reader may rewrite the program without using array *ll*.) What follows is the description of the program as it was finally written—not the first, unsuccessful attempts made. Note in particular the comments in the program.

The number of lines is unknown, and therefore an integer "sen" is attached to every input row and is zero in the last row. Thus, the rows include "sen lt rt r x xc" with lt ≡ left, rt ≡ right and all of them zero in the last row. After a row is read, it is processed by the procedure proline (i, j) where i, j are running indices.

Initially all diagonal elements of **b**, or diab[k] are set to zero, since their value, the sum of all b_m of lines connected to bus k, will be accumulated, with the accumulation starting from zero. Then the first row is read and processed. When reading the second row "2 to 3," the problem is that node 1 is also connected to bus 2 and "2 to 1" should precede "2 to 3." In the same way, when row "5 to 6" is read, nodes "5 to 2" and "4 to 5" should be taken care of. This is done with the loop on jj.

This completes the calculation of the bus-admittance matrix, which includes all admittances y_{km} of lines connected to bus k. The current leaving bus k is therefore,

$$i_k' = \Sigma\, u_k' \cdot y_{km}' = \Sigma\, [(v_k + jw_k)\cdot(g_{km} + jb_{km})]; \quad m\Sigma = 0, \ldots, n$$

where we have split the (complex) voltage u_k' into its two components:

```
program indata(input,output); (* Input of network data and   *)
var i,j,jj,j1,m,k,lt,nbus,rt,sen:integer;(*it up as required*)
BB,BC,GG,r,rp,rs,x,xc,xp,xs,zsq:real;
adj,ip,ll:array[0..200] of integer;
g,b.diag,diab:array[0..200] of real;

procedure prt(var jj,m:integer);
var k:integer;    (*This procedure prints data *)
begin           (*limited because of row length *)
   for k:=jj to m do write('  ',k:6); writeln;
   for k:=jj to m do write('  ',g[k]:6:4);writeln;
   for k:=jj to m do write('  ',b[k]:6:4);writeln;
   for k:=jj to m do write('  ',adj[k]:6); writeln
end;

procedure proline (var i,j:integer);
begin  (* Calculates g,b and diagonal g,b's *)
rp:=1000*r; xp:=1000*x; rs:=1000*rp; xs:=1000*xp;
adj[j]:=rt; ll[j]:=i; zsq:=rp*rp+xp*xp;
GG:=rs/zsq; BB:=-xs/zsq; g[j]:=-GG; b[j]:=-BB;
diag[lt]:=diag[lt]+GG;diag[rt]:=diag[rt]+GG;
BC:=BB+xc; diab[lt]:=diab[lt]+BC; diab[rt]:=diab[rt]+BC;
end; (*of procedure proline *)

begin read(nbus);
for k:=1 to nbus do diag[k]:=0.0;          (*Accumulate diagonal *)
for k:=1 to nbus do diab[k]:=0.0;                 (* g's and b's *)
i:=1; j:=1; readln(sen,lt,rt,r,x,xc);           (*read a line and*)
proline(i,j); readln(sen,lt,rt,r,x,xc);            (* the second*)
repeat                          (* m is for search, i and ip are *)
    m:=j;   i:=i+1; ip[i]:=j+1;                    (* for table *).
    for jj:=1 to m do         (*This loop searches the adjacency*)
    if adj[jj]=i then        (*table for element connected to i.*)
          (*Their values are copied into position j, with ll *)
                      (* "remembering" which was the left node *)
    begin j:=j+1; adj[j]:=ll[jj]; ll[jj]:=i;
          g[j]:=g[jj]; b[j]:=b[jj]
    end;
    repeat(*All lines connected to bus i are read and processed*)
       j:=j+1 ; proline(i,j); (*One line was prepared ahead of *)
       readln(sen,lt,rt,r,x,xc);        (*the big while-loop , so *)
    until lt<>i;(*that readln is at the end. When the all-zero *)
until sen=0;               (* line occurs, processing is finished*)
ip[i]:=1;
jj:=1; m:=8; prt(jj,m); writeln;
jj:=9; m:=15; prt(jj,m); writeln; writeln;
for j1:=1 to nbus-1 do write('  ',ip[j1]:8); writeln;
for j1:=1 to nbus do write('  ',diag[j1]:6:4); writeln;
for j1:=1 to nbus do write('  ',diab[j1]:6:4)
end.
```

Program 3.1

$$u_k' = v_k + jw_k$$

It will be shown later that, for calculations of voltages and short-circuit currents, the inverse $\mathbf{Z} = \mathbf{Y}^{-1}$ is required. We therefore need this *bus-impedance* matrix **Z**. One way to calculate it would be by factorization of **Y** into $\mathbf{L} * \mathbf{U}$ and subsequent use of $\mathbf{Y}^{-1} = \mathbf{U}^{-1} * \mathbf{L}^{-1}$. Since factorization was discussed in Chapter 2 for dense matrices and will be discussed in detail for sparse matrices in Chapter 4, it will be assumed here that both **L** and **U** matrices are known.

Another way is to invert **Y**, but since a sparse **Y** produces a dense **Z**, Gaussian elimination, as described in Section 2.2, is replaced by Kron's formula [Eq. (2.25)]:

$$\mathbf{Z}_1 := \mathbf{Z}_1 - \mathbf{Z}_2 * \mathbf{Z}_4^{-1} * \mathbf{Z}_3; \qquad \mathbf{Z} = \begin{bmatrix} \mathbf{Z}_1 & \mathbf{Z}_2 \\ \mathbf{Z}_3 & \mathbf{Z}_4 \end{bmatrix}$$

Kron's method and a step-by-step method of collecting **Z** can be based on updating. It can also be derived in terms of electric networks as follows.

If the network is drawn as in Fig. 3.5(a), i.e., with all n buses outside, then it consists only of the connecting lines and is thus completely passive.

Assuming that **Z** is known, we may write $\mathbf{v} = \mathbf{Z} * \mathbf{i}$ (in the rest of this section we use dc quantities and thus v instead of u). If only a single voltage v_k is applied, then:

$$v_k = Z_{k,1} \cdot i_1 + Z_{k,2} \cdot i_2 + \cdots + Z_{k,k} \cdot i_k + \cdots + Z_{k,n} \cdot i_n \tag{3.14}$$

Since all currents except i_k are zero, Eq. (3.14) yields

$$Z_{k,k} = \frac{v_k}{i_k}$$

Generally, if voltage v_k is applied to node m, then $i_m \neq 0$ and

$$Z_{k,m} = \frac{v_k}{i_m} \tag{3.15}$$

Let us take the case of adding an impedance z to the ground or 0-bus [Fig. 3.5(b)]. Since $v_k = i_k \cdot z$, we find by inserting it into Eqs. (3.14) and (3.15) that $Z_{k,k} = z$ and $Z_{m,k} = Z_{k,m} = 0$.

We generalize this by saying that if $\mathbf{Z}_{\text{old}}$ was an "old" matrix, the "new" matrix has an additional column k and row k of zeros and a diagonal term z. It is thus as follows:

$$\mathbf{Z}_{\text{new}} = \begin{bmatrix} \mathbf{Z}_{\text{old}} & \mathbf{0} \\ \mathbf{0}^{\mathrm{T}} & z \end{bmatrix}; \quad \begin{matrix} \mathbf{0}^{\mathrm{T}} = [0, 0, \ldots, 0] \\ \leftarrow \text{row } k \end{matrix} \tag{3.16}$$

Next, suppose that the new branch with impedance z is connected to a branch m already included in the network [Fig. 3.5(c)]. For this, case 2, we have that v_k is v_m plus voltage drop on z or

$$v_k = v_m + i_k \cdot z =$$

$$Z_{m,1} i_1 + Z_{m,2} i_2 + \cdots + Z_{m,m}(i_k + i_m) + \cdots + Z_{m,n} i_n + i_k \cdot z$$

$$v_k = (Z_{m,1} i_1 + Z_{m,2} i_2 + \cdots + Z_{m,m} i_m + \cdots + Z_{m,n} i_n) \tag{3.17}$$

$$+ (Z_{m,m} + z) i_k;$$

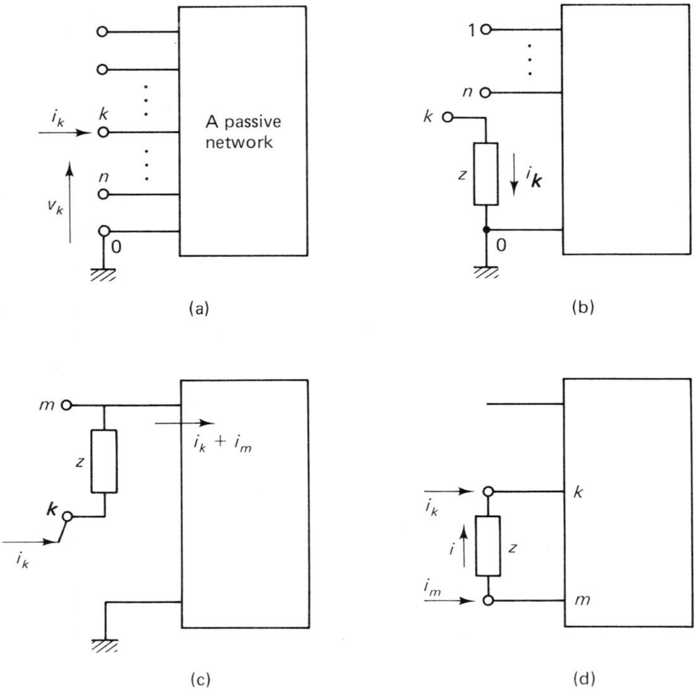

Figure 3.5 (a) Basic network configuration. (b) Connecting a line to ground. (c) Adding a line to an included node. (d) Adding a line between two included nodes.

We can see this too as a modification of $\mathbf{Z}_{\text{old}}$:

$$\mathbf{Z}_{\text{new}} = \begin{bmatrix} \mathbf{Z}_{\text{old}} & \mathbf{z} \\ \mathbf{z}^{\text{T}} & (z + Z_{m,m}) \end{bmatrix}; \quad \mathbf{z}^{\text{T}} = [Z_{m,1}, Z_{m,2}, \ldots, Z_{m,n}] \tag{3.18}$$

This time, we have to add a row and column $\mathbf{z}$ to the old matrix. From Eq. (3.17) and Fig. 3.5(c), it follows that the new diagonal element $Z_{k,k} = v_k / i_k = Z_{m,m} + z$.

Finally, as case 3 consider the closing of a loop by adding z between existing nodes k and m [Fig. 3.5(d)]. The equation for node 1 is

$$v_1 = Z_{1,1} \cdot i_1 + Z_{1,2} \cdot i_2 + \cdots + Z_{1,k} \cdot (i_k + i) + Z_{1,m} \cdot (i_m - i) + \cdots + Z_{1,n} \cdot i_n$$

Rearranging this equation yields

$$v_1 = (Z_{1,1} \cdot i_1 + \cdots + Z_{1,k} \cdot i_k + Z_{1,m} \cdot i_m + \cdots + Z_{1,n} \cdot i_n) + (Z_{1,k} - Z_{1,m}) \cdot i$$

and similarly for all indices except k and m. For index m we have

$$v_m = v_k + z \cdot i =$$

$$Z_{k,1} i_1 + \cdots + Z_{k,k}(i_k + i) + Z_{k,m} \cdot (i_m - i) + \cdots + Z_{k,n} i_n + z \cdot i$$

On the other hand, we can also write in general

$$v_m = Z_{m,1} \cdot i_1 + Z_{m,2} \cdot i_2 + \cdots$$
$$+ Z_{m,k} \cdot (i_k + i) + Z_{m,m} \cdot (i_m - i) + \cdots + Z_{m,n} \cdot i_n$$

Subtracting these two equations yields

$$0 = (Z_{k,1} - Z_{m,1}) \cdot i_1 + \cdots + (Z_{k,k} - Z_{m,k}) \cdot i_k + (Z_{m,k} - Z_{m,m}) \cdot i_m$$
$$+ \cdots + (Z_{k,n} - Z_{m,n}) \cdot i_n + (Z_{k,k} + Z_{m,m} - 2 \cdot Z_{k,m} + z) \cdot i$$

In matrix form all this can be written as

$$\left[\begin{array}{c|c} & Z_{k,1} - Z_{m,1} \\ & Z_{k,2} - Z_{m,2} \\ \mathbf{Z}_{\text{old}} & \vdots \\ \hline (Z_{k,1} - Z_{m,1}) \cdots (Z_{k,n} - Z_{m,n}) & \bar{z} \end{array}\right] * \left[\begin{array}{c} i_1 \\ i_2 \\ \\ \hline i \end{array}\right] = \left[\begin{array}{c} v_1 \\ v_2 \\ \\ \hline 0 \end{array}\right] \tag{3.19}$$

where

$$\bar{z} = Z_{k,k} + Z_{m,m} - 2 \cdot Z_{k,m} + z \tag{3.20}$$

If we denote by $\mathbf{z}^{\mathrm{T}}$ the row vector

$$\mathbf{z}^{\mathrm{T}} = [(Z_{k,1} - Z_{m,1}), (Z_{k,2} - Z_{m,2}), \ldots, (Z_{k,n} - Z_{m,n})]$$

then Kron's formula can be applied to Eq. (3.19)

$$\mathbf{Z}_{\text{new}} := \mathbf{Z}_{\text{old}} - \frac{\mathbf{z} * \mathbf{z}^{\mathrm{T}}}{\bar{z}} \tag{3.21}$$

Note that in this case, Eq. (3.21) reduces the matrix to its original size (that of $\mathbf{Z}_{\text{old}}$). The reason for this is that we have not added a new node but only linked two existing nodes. In the two previous cases, one node was added and the matrix size correspondingly increased by 1.

To summarize: The **Z** matrix can be built as a sequence of modifications — cases 1, 2, and 3. The sequence should start from the reference node.

We will exemplify the algorithm by Program 3.2 (kinv) using the network in Fig. 3.6(a).

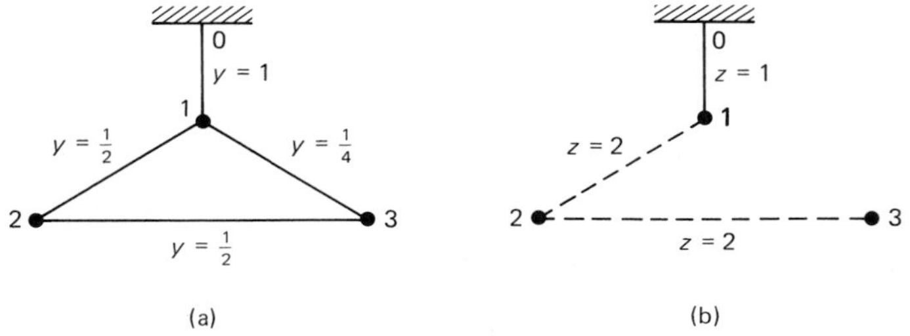

Figure 3.6 (a) An example. (b) Partially connected network.

Connecting branch $0-1$ leads to a matrix of a single element $\mathbf{Z} = 1$ [Program 3.2(b)]. Adding branch $1-2$ should be viewed as belonging to case 2, since node 1 is already part of the tree. The matrix is therefore as in Program 3.2(c). In the same way, adding branch $2-3$ will extend the matrix by a row and a column [Fig. 3.6(b) and the matrix of Program 3.2(d)]. Finally, the addition of branch $1-3$ closes a loop so that this is case 3. The matrix size increases to 4 and then is reduced to size 3 again as in Program 3.2(e).

We next add the multiplication of the matrix by its inverse in order to show that these formulas indeed will produce $\mathbf{Z}$.

$$\frac{1}{4} \cdot \begin{bmatrix} 1 & 1 & 1 \\ 1 & 2.5 & 2 \\ 1 & 2 & 3 \end{bmatrix} * \begin{bmatrix} -7 & 2 & 1 \\ 2 & -4 & 2 \\ 1 & 2 & -3 \end{bmatrix} = \frac{1}{4} \cdot \begin{bmatrix} -4 & 0 & 0 \\ 0 & -4 & 0 \\ 0 & 0 & -4 \end{bmatrix}$$

Program 3.2 is the program for Kron's inversion (kinv) of a dc network. It consists of three procedures: zer, bran, and Kron for cases 1, 2, and 3, respectively. It reads the same data as indata (sen, lt, rt, r, x, and xc) but disregards r and xc. The **if** statement marked "main-if" activates one of the three cases depending on the data just read. Function "prt" prints the bus-impedance matrix as it is computed. Function f identifies the permutations, so that if the network of Fig. 3.6(a) was read in the order 1, 3 and 2, the array "per" will be 1, 3 and 2. Thus, when adding line $3-2$, the program adds column 3 to column 2 identified as columns 2 and 3.

An important observation on Kron's method concerns accuracy.*

* Y. Wallach, "On Power System Simulation Studies," *Transactions of the Society for Computer Simulation*, Volume 1, Number 2, pp. 133-153. Copyright © (1984) by Simulation Councils, Inc. Used with permission.

```
program prog(input,output);
var n:integer;


procedure kinv(var n:integer); (* Kron's inversion method *)
type index=0..9;
     mat=array[index,index] of real;
var i,j,m1,m,lt,ltn,rt,rtn,sen:integer;r,x,xc:real;
    y,z,zn:mat;con:array[index] of boolean;
    per:array[index] of integer;

function f(kk:integer):integer; (*This function produces node *)
var ii,kn:integer; (* number according to the permutation *)
begin
   for ii:=1 to m do
      if per[ii]=kk then kn:=ii;
   f:=kn;
end;

procedure zer; (* adds a column and row of zeros *)
var i:integer; (* with index m+1 to the z-matrix *)
begin per[m1]:=rt;
    for i:=1 to m do
    begin
      z[i,m1]:=0.0; z[m1,i]:=0.0;
    end; (* Adds a corner element, sets m and con *)
    z[m1,m1]:=x;m:=m1;con[rt]:=true;
end;

procedure bran; (* Adds column and row m+1 for *)
var i:integer; (*a new branch equal to the *)
begin per[m1]:=rt; (* impedances z[i,lt], etc. *)
   ltn:=f(lt);
   for i:=1 to m do
   begin
      z[i,m1]:=z[i,ltn];  z[m1,i]:=z[ltn,i]
   end;
   z[m1,m1]:=x+z[ltn,ltn];m:=m1;con[rt]:=true;
end;

procedure Kron;
var i,j:integer;  zpr:real;
begin  (* Prepares zpr according to Eq. 3-31 *)
   ltn:=f(lt); rtn:=f(rt);
   zpr:=z[ltn,ltn]+z[rtn,rtn]-2*z[ltn,rtn]+x;
   for i:=1 to m do
   begin (* This loop adds a row and column, Eq. 3-32 *)
      z[i,m1]:=z[i,ltn]-z[i,rtn];
      z[m1,i]:=z[i,m1]
   end;
   for i:=1 to m do
   for j:=1 to m do
   begin (*Reduces matrix back to size m, Eq. 3-33 *)
     z[i,j]:=z[i,j]-z[i,m1]*z[j,m1]/zpr;
   end;
end;
```

Program 3.2(a).

```
    procedure prt(var m:integer); (* for printing the matrix *)
    var i,j,k:integer;
    begin writeln; writeln;
       writeln; writeln('prt',m);
       for i:=1 to m do
       begin writeln;
             for j:=1 to m do
             write('    ',z[i,j]:8:6);
       end
    end;

 begin m:=0;
    for i:=1 to n do con[i]:=false;
    readln(sen,lt,rt,x);
    while sen<>0 do
    begin m1:=m+1;
      if lt=0 then  (* MAIN "IF" *)
       begin
          zer; prt(m)
       end
      else if (con[lt] and con[rt]) then
       begin
          Kron; prt(m)
       end
      else
          begin
             bran; prt(m)
          end;
       readln(sen,lt,rt,x);
    end; (* of the while loop *)
 end;


 begin
    n:=3; kinv(n)
 end.
 1 0 1 1.0
 1 1 2 2.0
 1 2 3 2.0
 1 1 3 4.0
 0 0 0 0.0
```

Program 3.2(a) (cont.)

```
prt            1

     1.000000
```

Program 3.2(b).

```
prt              2

    1.000000    1.000000
    1.000000    3.000000
```

Program 3.2(c).

```
prt              3

    1.000000    1.000000    1.000000
    1.000000    3.000000    3.000000
    1.000000    3.000000    5.000000
```

Program 3.2(d).

```
prt              3

    1.000000    1.000000    1.000000
    1.000000    2.500000    2.000000
    1.000000    2.000000    3.000000
```

Program 3.2(e).

Suppose we form the **Z** matrix of the network in Fig. 3.7 by Kron's algorithm in the following sequence:

Connecting line $0-1$ produces a 1-by-1 matrix of $Z = 0.4$, adding line $0-2$ extends it to a 2-by-2 matrix, and closing line $1-2$ leads to the 3-by-3 matrix

$$\begin{bmatrix} 0.4 & 0 & -0.4 \\ 0 & 0.5999 & -0.5999 \\ -0.4 & -0.5999 & 1 \end{bmatrix}$$

Kron's formula reduces this to

$$Z_{1,1} = 0.4 - 0.4^2 = 0.4 - 0.16 = 0.24$$

$$Z_{2,2} = 0.5999 - 0.5999^2 = 0.24$$

$$Z_{1,2} = 0.4 \cdot 0.5999 = 0.23996$$

We can simulate the opening of line $1-2$ by saying that a line with $z = -0.0001$ was connected between nodes 1 and 2. The denominator of Kron's method is

$$\mathbf{Z}_4 \equiv \bar{z} := Z_{1,1} + Z_{2,2} - 2 \cdot Z_{1,2} + z = -0.0000001$$

Notice that seven significant figures were lost in $\bar{z}$, since only one remains. This leads to completely irrelevant results for $Z_{1,1}$ and $Z_{2,2}$.

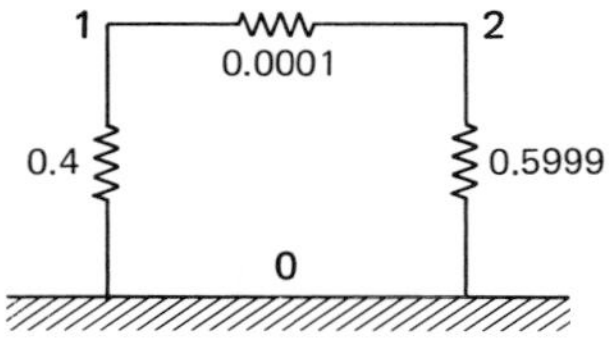

Figure 3.7 Impedances.

With a hand calculator, the following results were obtained:

$$Z_{1,1} := 4000; \qquad Z_{2,2} := 0.4796$$

instead of 0.4 and 0.59999 as in the matrix

$$\begin{bmatrix} 0.4 & 0 \\ 0 & 0.59999 \end{bmatrix}$$

Thus, whenever the denominator in Kron's method is very small, the cancellation errors will be very large and another method must be used. In Section 3.5 we will suggest use of updating if serious cancellation errors occur.

3.2 DIAKOPTICS

The 14-bus network of [FS67], with nodes renamed by letters A to N, is shown in Fig. 3.8. Its *incidence matrix* **A** is shown in Fig. 3.9 with + and − symbolizing +1 and −1, respectively.

Let us compute the *primitive* diagonal admittance matrix $\mathbf{Y}_L$. If the impedance of branch k is z_k, then the corresponding nonzero diagonal element of $\mathbf{Y}_L$ is

$$Y_{k,k} = \frac{1}{z_k} \tag{3.22}$$

As we have seen in Eq. (3.4), the admittance matrix can be calculated by multiplying

$$\mathbf{Y} = \mathbf{A}^{\mathrm{T}} * \mathbf{Y}_L * \mathbf{A}$$

The size of **Y** is n-by-n (here 14-by-14). As was shown earlier, the diagonal elements of **Y** in row/column k equal the negative sum of the rest of the row elements. We can therefore write down the **Y** matrix also by inspection.

Let the admittance of the element in row j, column k (line $j-k$), be $y_{j,k} = -1/z_{j,k}$. For instance, according to Kirchhoff's current law for node D,

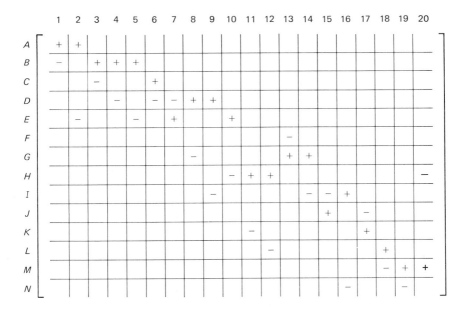

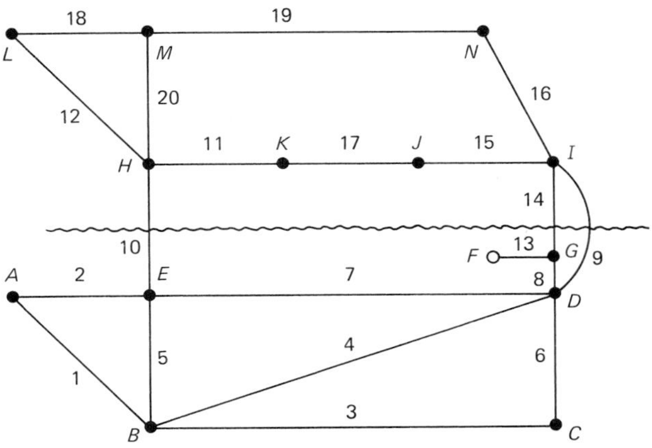

Figure 3.8 Renamed 14-bus network.

	1	2	3	4	5	6	7	8	9	10	11	12	13	14	15	16	17	18	19	20
A	+	+																		
B	−		+	+	+															
C			−			+														
D				−		−	−	+	+											
E		−			−		+			+										
F													−							
G								−					+	+						
H										−	+	+								−
I									−					−	−	+				
J															+		−			
K											−						+			
L												−						+		
M																		−	+	+
N																−			−	

Figure 3.9 The incidence matrix.

$$(v_d - v_c)\cdot y_{dc} + (v_d - v_b)\cdot y_{db} + (v_d - v_e)\cdot y_{de} + (v_d - v_g)\cdot y_{dg} + i_{di} = 0$$

in which the y_{dd} is next defined as $y_{dc} + y_{db} + y_{de} + y_{dg}$ or generally $y_{k,k} = \Sigma\,(1/z_{j,k})$. Thus, if we denote $y_{k,k}$, $k = 1, \ldots, n$, by d's we get, for the 14-bus network, the matrix in Fig. 3.10.

	A	B	C	D	E	F	G	H	I	J	K	L	M	N
A	d	y			y									
B	y	d	y	y	y									
C		y	d	y										
D		y	y	d	y		y		y					
E	y	y		y	d			y						
F						d	y							
G				y		y	d		y					
H					y			d			y	y	y	
I				y			y		d	y				y
J									y	d	y			
K								y		y	d			
L								y				d	y	
M								y				y	d	y
N									y				y	

Figure 3.10 Admittance matrix.

The main point can be made if we artificially "tear" ("diakoptics" is Greek for tearing) the network in Fig. 3.8 along the indicated line (in the process tearing branches 9, 10, and 14). We can then write the equations as

$$\begin{bmatrix} \mathbf{Y}_r & \mathbf{A}_t \\ \mathbf{A}_t^{\mathrm{T}} & -\mathbf{Z}_t \end{bmatrix} * \begin{bmatrix} \mathbf{v} \\ \mathbf{i}_t \end{bmatrix} = \begin{bmatrix} \mathbf{i} \\ \mathbf{0} \end{bmatrix} \tag{3.23}$$

where indices r and t indicate "remains" and "torn," respectively, and $\mathbf{A}$ is an incidence matrix as defined earlier. For the network in Fig. 3.8 we then get the matrix in Fig. 3.11.

It is important for the reader to calculate this matrix and note then the following points:

- The $\mathbf{Y}_r$ matrix is *block-diagonal* with the blocks corresponding to the tearing as indicated. In Fig. 3.8 nodes A to G form one block, and nodes H to N another block. The same division occurs in Fig. 3.11. Had we divided the network into k subnetworks, $\mathbf{Y}_r$ would have been divided into k submatrices (diagonal blocks).
- Each block is symmetric, since $y_{i,j} = y_{j,i}$, for any i and j.
- The elements of the incidence matrix $\mathbf{A}$ can be written by inspection, e.g., since branch 9 joins nodes D and I, we have $A_{D,9} = -1$ and $A_{I,9} = +1$.

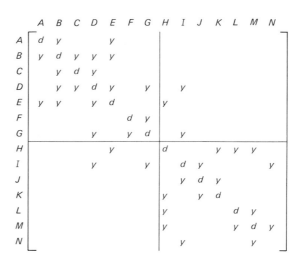

	A	B	C	D	E	F	G	H	I	J	K	L	M	N	9	10	14				
A	d	y			y														v_A		i_A
B	y	d	y	y	y														v_B		i_B
C		y	d	y															v_C		i_C
D		y	y	d	y		y								−				v_D		i_D
E	y	y		y	d											−			v_E		i_E
F						d	y												v_F		i_F
G				y		y	d										−		v_G		i_G
H								d			y	y	y			+			v_H		i_H
I									d	y				y	+		+	*	v_I	=	i_I
J									y	d	y								v_J		i_J
K								y		y	d								v_K		i_K
L								y				d	y						v_L		i_L
M								y				y	d	y					v_M		i_M
N									y				y	d					v_N		i_N
9				−					+						$-z_9$				i_9		0
10					−			+								$-z_{10}$			i_{10}		0
14							−		+								$-z_{14}$		i_{14}		0

Figure 3.11 Re-formed admittance matrix.

- Admittances of the torn branches did not appear in $\mathbf{Y}_r$, but they reenter the equations for currents, e.g., for i_D:

  $$-y_{D,B}\cdot v_B - y_{D,C}\cdot v_C + y_{D,D}\cdot v_D - y_{D,E}\cdot v_E - y_{D,G}\cdot v_G - 1\cdot i_9 = i_D$$

  in which current $y_{D,D}\cdot v_D$ is supplied to the node, the other currents flow out of node D. Generally, $i_p = 0$ except that if a current is injected (by a generator or load), then $i_p \neq 0$.
- For the last three nodes we have

  $$z_9 \cdot i_9 = v_I - v_D$$
  $$z_{10}\cdot i_{10} = v_H - v_E$$
  $$z_{14}\cdot i_{14} = v_I - v_G$$

  which are obviously correct. The number of these equations will equal that of the torn branches, since for each branch k which connects nodes a and b, we have $z_k\cdot i_k = v_a - v_b$.

Matrix $\mathbf{Y}_r$ is block-diagonal. Therefore we can write the main equation Eq. (3.2) in bordered, block diagonal (BBD) form, which for, say, four blocks (four subnetworks) would be as in

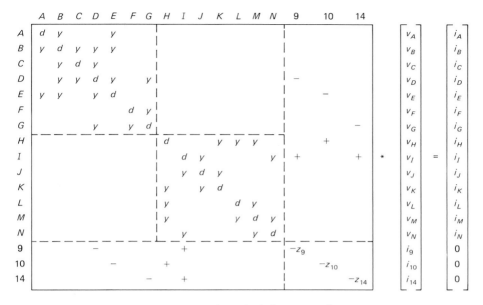

$$\begin{bmatrix} \mathbf{Y}_1 & \mathbf{0} & \mathbf{0} & \mathbf{0} & \mathbf{A}_1 \\ \mathbf{0} & \mathbf{Y}_2 & \mathbf{0} & \mathbf{0} & \mathbf{A}_2 \\ \mathbf{0} & \mathbf{0} & \mathbf{Y}_3 & \mathbf{0} & \mathbf{A}_3 \\ \mathbf{0} & \mathbf{0} & \mathbf{0} & \mathbf{Y}_4 & \mathbf{A}_4 \\ \mathbf{A}_1^T & \mathbf{A}_2^T & \mathbf{A}_3^T & \mathbf{A}_4^T & \mathbf{Y}_5 \end{bmatrix} * \begin{bmatrix} \mathbf{v}_1 \\ \mathbf{v}_2 \\ \mathbf{v}_3 \\ \mathbf{v}_4 \\ \mathbf{v}_5 \end{bmatrix} = \begin{bmatrix} \mathbf{i}_1 \\ \mathbf{i}_2 \\ \mathbf{i}_3 \\ \mathbf{i}_4 \\ \mathbf{i}_5 \end{bmatrix} \tag{3.24}$$

The impedance matrix is the inverse of the BBD matrix and can be calculated by elimination. We can eliminate $\mathbf{A}_1^T$ by subtracting from it $\mathbf{A}_1^T * \mathbf{Y}_1^{-1} * \mathbf{Y}_1 \equiv \mathbf{A}_1^T$. If we do this, then block $\mathbf{Y}_5$ should also be changed into

$$\mathbf{Y}_5 := \mathbf{Y}_5 - \mathbf{A}_1^T * \mathbf{Y}_1^{-1} * \mathbf{A}_1 = \mathbf{Y}_5 - \mathbf{E}_1; \quad \mathbf{E}_1 \equiv \mathbf{A}_1^T * \mathbf{Y}_1^{-1} * \mathbf{A}_1$$

Other elements of row 5 are not affected because of zeros in row 1.

In the same way we can form blocks $\mathbf{E}_2$, $\mathbf{E}_3$, and $\mathbf{E}_4$:

$$\mathbf{E}_2 := \mathbf{A}_2^T * \mathbf{Y}_2^{-1} * \mathbf{A}_2;$$

$$\mathbf{E}_3 := \mathbf{A}_3^T * \mathbf{Y}_3^{-1} * \mathbf{A}_3;$$

$$\mathbf{E}_4 := \mathbf{A}_4^T * \mathbf{Y}_4^{-1} * \mathbf{A}_4$$

Note that formation of all p blocks $\mathbf{E}_q$, $q = 1, \ldots, p$; can proceed simultaneously and independently.

Since all $\mathbf{E}_q$ must be subtracted from $\mathbf{Y}_5$, we have

$$\mathbf{Y}_5 := \mathbf{Y}_5 - \mathbf{E}_1 - \mathbf{E}_2 - \mathbf{E}_3 - \mathbf{E}_4$$

The general equation allows definition of $\mathbf{E}_k$ and $\mathbf{F}_k$ as

$$\mathbf{E}_k := \mathbf{A}_k^T * \mathbf{Y}_k^{-1} * \mathbf{A}_k = \mathbf{A}_k^T * \mathbf{F}_k; \quad \mathbf{F}_k \equiv \mathbf{Y}_k^{-1} * \mathbf{A}_k \tag{3.25}$$

Premultiply $\mathbf{F}_k$ by $\mathbf{Y}_k$ and solve it by factorization:

$$(\mathbf{Y}_k = \mathbf{L}_k * \mathbf{U}_k); \quad \mathbf{Y}_k * \mathbf{F}_k = \mathbf{A}_k \tag{3.26}$$

$$\mathbf{L}_k * (\mathbf{U}_k * \mathbf{F}_k) = \mathbf{L}_k * \mathbf{H}_k = \mathbf{A}_k; \quad \mathbf{U}_k * \mathbf{F}_k = \mathbf{H}_k \tag{3.27}$$

for matrix $\mathbf{F}_k$. According to our definition of $\mathbf{E}_k$ and $\mathbf{F}_k$ in Eq. (3.25), we can next compute $\mathbf{E}_k$

$$\mathbf{E}_k = \mathbf{A}_k^T * \mathbf{F}_k \tag{3.28}$$

and this simply means that columns of $\mathbf{E}_k$ are combinations of columns of $\mathbf{F}_k$. We have thus calculated the new $\mathbf{Y}_5$.

The next step is to use the new $\mathbf{Y}_5$ and to solve

$$\mathbf{Y}_5 * \mathbf{v}_5 = \mathbf{i}_5$$

by factorization or elimination. If we use elimination, then this amounts to transforming $\mathbf{Y}_5$ into an upper-triangular matrix $\mathbf{U}_5$, and since then the entire matrix of Eq. (3.24) is upper triangular, the set is solved by back-substitution: $\mathbf{v}_5 := \mathbf{Y}_5^{-1} * \mathbf{i}_5$.

For each of the other blocks $j = 1, \ldots, 4$, the equation $\mathbf{Y}_j * \mathbf{v}_j + \mathbf{A}_j * \mathbf{v}_5 = \mathbf{i}_j$ has to be solved. The solution is therefore a sequence of back-substitutions:

$$\mathbf{v}_j := \mathbf{Y}_j^{-1} * (\mathbf{i}_j - \mathbf{A}_j * \mathbf{v}_5); \quad j = 4, \ldots, 1$$

On the other hand, if $\mathbf{Y}_k$ was factored into the product $\mathbf{L} * \mathbf{U}$, the solution would be:

$$\mathbf{v}_5 := (\mathbf{L}_k * \mathbf{U}_k)^{-1} * \mathbf{i}_5; \qquad \mathbf{L}_5 * \mathbf{U}_5 * \mathbf{v}_5 = \mathbf{i}_5$$

$$\mathbf{L}_k * \mathbf{U}_k * \mathbf{v}_k = \mathbf{i}_k - \mathbf{A}_k * \mathbf{v}_5; \quad k = 4, \ldots, 1$$

A different solution of Eq. (3.23) is normally advocated. Rewrite first these equations as

$$\mathbf{A}_t^{\mathrm{T}} * \mathbf{v} - \mathbf{Z}_t * \mathbf{i}_t = \mathbf{0} \tag{3.29}$$

$$\mathbf{Y}_r * \mathbf{v} + \mathbf{A}_t * \mathbf{i}_t = \mathbf{i} \tag{3.30}$$

From Eq. (3.30), we have $\mathbf{v} = \mathbf{Y}_r^{-1} * (\mathbf{i} - \mathbf{A}_t * \mathbf{i}_t)$, which, if inserted into Eq. (3.29) yields:

$$\mathbf{A}_t^{\mathrm{T}} * \mathbf{Y}_r^{-1} * \mathbf{i} - \mathbf{A}_t^{\mathrm{T}} * \mathbf{Y}_r^{-1} * \mathbf{A}_t * \mathbf{i}_t - \mathbf{Z}_t * \mathbf{i}_t = \mathbf{0}$$

$$(\mathbf{Z}_t + \mathbf{A}_t^{\mathrm{T}} * \mathbf{Y}_r^{-1} * \mathbf{A}_t) * \mathbf{i}_t = \mathbf{A}_t^{\mathrm{T}} * \mathbf{Y}_r^{-1} * \mathbf{i} \tag{3.31}$$

$$\mathbf{v} = \mathbf{Y}_r^{-1} * \mathbf{i} - \mathbf{Y}_r^{-1} * \mathbf{A}_t * \mathbf{i}_t = \mathbf{x}_r - \mathbf{F} * \mathbf{i}_t \tag{3.32}$$

where $\mathbf{F} \equiv \mathbf{Y}_r^{-1} * \mathbf{A}_t$ and $\mathbf{F}$ consists of block submatrices $\mathbf{F}_k$ as defined earlier.

It would be very inefficient to solve for $\mathbf{v}$ and $\mathbf{i}_t$ using $\mathbf{Y}_r^{-1}$ as in the two equations above. This is because $\mathbf{Y}_r^{-1}$ is dense even if $\mathbf{Y}_r$ is very sparse. Factorization is suggested instead.

The algorithm is then as follows (with subscript k denoting a block):

1. Factor $\mathbf{Y}_r$ into $\mathbf{L}$ and $\mathbf{U}$ (or $\mathbf{L}$ and $\mathbf{D}$):

   $$\mathbf{Y}_r = \mathbf{L}_k * \mathbf{U}_k; \quad k = 1,2,\ldots$$

2. Solve for $\mathbf{x}_i$ the system

   $$\mathbf{Y}_r * \mathbf{x}_i = \mathbf{i}$$

   (Use the $\mathbf{L}_k$, $\mathbf{U}_k$ matrices for forward and back-substitution.)
3. Solve for $\mathbf{F}$ in the same way, the second part of Eq. (3.25), i.e., $\mathbf{Y}_r * \mathbf{F} = \mathbf{A}_t$
4. Solve for $\mathbf{i}_t$ Eq. (3.31) in the form

$$(\mathbf{Z}_t + \mathbf{A}_t^{\mathrm{T}} * \mathbf{F}) * \mathbf{i}_t = \mathbf{A}_t^{\mathrm{T}} * \mathbf{x}_r$$

Finally, subtract the two parts of Eq. (3.32), i.e.,

$$\mathbf{v} = \mathbf{x}_r - \mathbf{F} * \mathbf{i}_t$$

A few remarks follow:

- The algorithm is applicable if the matrix $\mathbf{Z}_t + \mathbf{A}_t^{\mathrm{T}} * \mathbf{F}$ in step 4 is nonsingular ($\mathbf{Z}_t$, however, may be singular).
- We assumed throughout that there is no mutual coupling between the torn branches and the remaining subsystems.
- Since $\mathbf{A}_t$ has only k nonzero columns, $\mathbf{F}$ will also have k nonzero columns. This sparsity can be exploited.

Still another algorithm of diakoptics is advocated in [ARB77]. It uses a so-called $\mathbf{Z}_{\mathrm{cut}}$ matrix, which is calculated by substituting a single node for every subnetwork. All branches which are to be cut are retained and the network connects these "supernodes." The two algorithms mentioned earlier can obviously be used for such supernodes.

This completes the discussion of how to solve a BBD system of equations as produced by artificial tearing.

Suppose we have a good decomposition of matrix $\tilde{\mathbf{A}}$ in BBD form with the exception of a small number of nonzero elements, which "spoil" the decomposition. The algorithms previously discussed can still be used as follows. The matrix $\tilde{\mathbf{A}}$ may be written as $\mathbf{A} + \mathbf{B}$ where $\mathbf{A}$ is in true BBD form, and $\mathbf{B}$ consists of the previously mentioned elements. It is therefore natural to ask whether a solution to $(\mathbf{A} + \mathbf{B}) * \tilde{\mathbf{x}} = \mathbf{b}$ can be obtained with few operations given $\mathbf{A}^{-1}$. This process has a simple graphic interpretation. Figure 3.12 shows the graph of an "almost BBD" matrix. If the lines $9-10$ and $2-4$ were removed, the resulting matrix would be in a perfect BBD form. These branches are artificially "torn." The removed links form the *separating set* S.

If the matrix $\mathbf{B}$ of the torn elements is of low rank, say r, where $r < n$, then it can always be expressed in the form:

$$\mathbf{B} = \mathbf{V} * \mathbf{W}^{\mathrm{T}} \tag{3.33}$$

where $\mathbf{V}$ and $\mathbf{W}$ are n-by-r and r-by-n. Often the matrices $\mathbf{V}$ and $\mathbf{W}$ can be derived very simply from $\mathbf{B}$ for instance when $\mathbf{B}$ has only one nonzero element b_{ij}; then $\mathbf{V}$ may be taken as an n-vector with $v_i = 1$ and $v_k = 0$ for $k \neq i$ and $\mathbf{W}$ as an n-vector with $w_k = 1$ and $w_m = 0$ for $m \neq j$.

Matrices $\mathbf{V}$ and $\mathbf{W}$ are now vectors and Eq. (3.33) shows that the Sherman–Morrison equation as formulated in Chapter 2 may be applied:

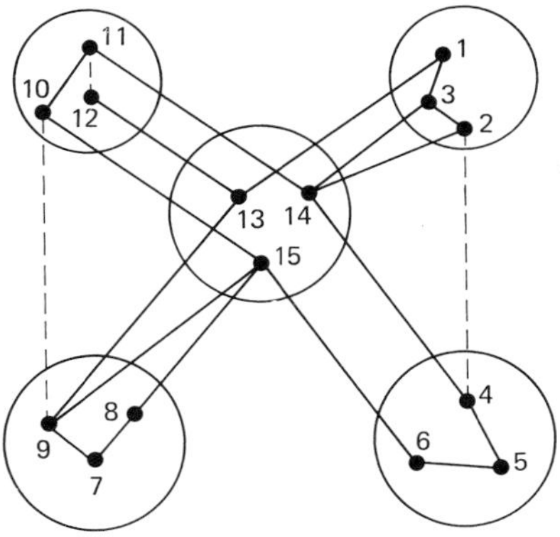

Figure 3.12 An "almost BBD" network.

$$\tilde{\mathbf{A}}^{-1} = (\mathbf{A} + \mathbf{v} * \mathbf{w}^{\mathrm{T}})^{-1} \tag{3.34}$$
$$= \mathbf{A}^{-1} - \mathbf{A}^{-1} * \mathbf{v} * (\mathbf{I} + \mathbf{w}^{\mathrm{T}} * \mathbf{A}^{-1} * \mathbf{v})^{-1} * \mathbf{w}^{\mathrm{T}} * \mathbf{A}$$

The advantage of Eq. (3.34) over direct inversion of $\mathbf{A} + \mathbf{B}$ is that the inversion of $\mathbf{I} + \mathbf{w}^{\mathrm{T}} * \mathbf{A}^{-1} * \mathbf{v}$ is often very easy. For the example cited above, $\mathbf{w}^{\mathrm{T}} * \mathbf{A}^{-1} * \mathbf{v}$ consists only of one nonzero element, and the inversion is trivial. It can be seen that Eq. (3.34) may be used for the solution of a system of linear equations since

$$\tilde{\mathbf{A}}^{-1} * \mathbf{b} = \mathbf{A}^{-1} * \mathbf{b} - [\mathbf{A}^{-1} * \mathbf{v} * (\mathbf{I} + \mathbf{w}^{\mathrm{T}} * \mathbf{A}^{-1} * \mathbf{v})^{-1} * \mathbf{w}^{\mathrm{T}} * \mathbf{A}] * \mathbf{b}$$

and given $\mathbf{A}^{-1}$ the process of solving $\tilde{\mathbf{A}} * \mathbf{x} = \mathbf{b}$ breaks into the following stages:

(a) Compute $\mathbf{y} = \mathbf{A}^{-1} * \mathbf{b}$ (and n-vector).
(b) Compute $\mathbf{z} = \mathbf{w}^{\mathrm{T}} * \mathbf{A}$ (an r-vector).
(c) Solve the linear system $(\mathbf{I} + \mathbf{w}^{\mathrm{T}} * \mathbf{A}^{-1} * \mathbf{v}) * \mathbf{u} = \mathbf{z}$ for $\mathbf{u}$ (an r-vector).
(d) Compute $\mathbf{s} = \mathbf{v} * \mathbf{u}$ (an n-vector).
(e) Compute $\mathbf{t} = \mathbf{A}^{-1} * \mathbf{s}$ (an n-vector).
(f) The final result is given by $\mathbf{x} = \mathbf{y} - \mathbf{t}$.

It may be added that a matrix in BBD form may be reduced to a block-diagonal form by means of Eq. (3.34), if all links connecting S with the other sets are "torn." When the separating set S is small, the number of operations necessary to include the effect of those links [i.e., the operations implied by Eq. (3.34)] is likewise small. This again stresses the importance of a small separating set.

Useful applications of Eq. (3.34) are to be found in Chapter 5 of [No69].

3.3 SYMMETRIC FAULT (SHORT-CIRCUIT) CURRENTS

As already mentioned, we calculate the values of voltages and currents during short-circuit, "faulted" conditions primarily in order to coordinate the setting of relays and to make an intelligent choice of circuit breakers. Faults should be detected and contingencies minimized.

The time constants are such that sinusoidal steady-state values may be used. In the case of an asymmetrical fault (e.g., the most common short of a line to ground) this means that phasors can be used; but because the fault is not symmetric, the method of *symmetrical components* will be used. To make the presentation gradual, asymmetrical faults are treated later.

Other simplifications which will not affect the accuracy too much are as follows:

- As already mentioned, short-circuit currents are so much larger than the steady-state values that we entirely disregard the latter. This leads to the definition of the problem as that of computing the current vector **i** from

$$\mathbf{Z} * \mathbf{i} = \mathbf{u} \tag{3.35}$$

  where **Z** is the bus-impedance matrix and **u** represents the voltages. Note that the admittance matrix is known and $\mathbf{Z} = \mathbf{Y}^{-1}$ is to be computed.
- The transformers can be represented as single series impedances (magnetization branch removed), and the shunt capacitances of the lines can be neglected.
- We will ignore resistances and perform DC analysis. This means that in general, a current is computed from

$$\mathrm{i} = \frac{\mathrm{ju}}{\mathrm{jx}} = \frac{\mathrm{u}}{\mathrm{x}}$$

  This may lead to larger errors, but the change to complex quantities is very simple and the reader may do it if he or she feels this is needed. Some computer languages will allow a simple changeover. Because of i = u/x, we will in this section again use v instead of u to designate the voltage and x instead of the impedance z.
- The circuit, outside of the fault, is symmetric and may be represented as in Fig. 3.13(a). The driving voltages may all be assumed to have the same magnitude (1.0) and angle (90°) so that they can be united

into a single source connecting the ground or neutral to the 0 node of the "box."

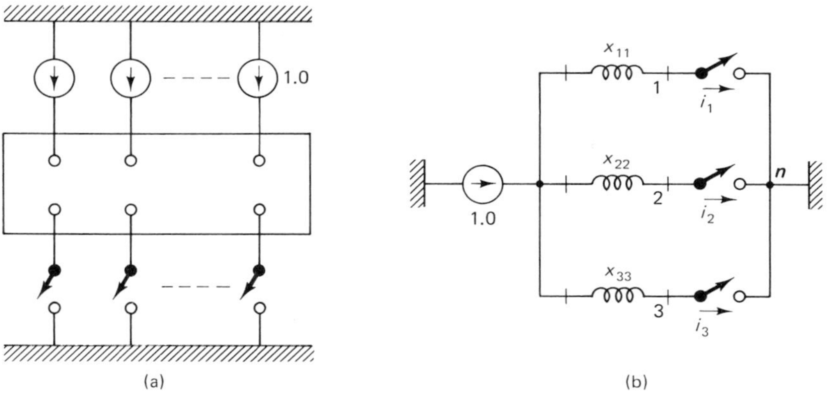

Figure 3.13 (a) Unfaulted network. (b) Switches for simulations.

- The nodes which may be faulted are also separated from the network. As a matter of fact, as long as their impedance to ground (on a per-phase basis) is the load impedance, such impedance is so large that the (load) current is assumed to be zero. It is precisely the substitution of a small reactance for the load reactance that leads to a fault and will be studied. The current will be determined by the network and fault reactance, as well as the type of connection.

If all these assumptions are made and the **Z** matrix computed, Eq. (3.35) for a 3-bus system would be written

$$\begin{bmatrix} x_{1,1} & x_{1,2} & x_{1,3} \\ x_{2,1} & x_{2,2} & x_{2,3} \\ x_{3,1} & x_{3,2} & x_{3,3} \end{bmatrix} * \begin{bmatrix} i_1 \\ i_2 \\ i_3 \end{bmatrix} = \begin{bmatrix} 1.0 \\ 1.0 \\ 1.0 \end{bmatrix}$$

and pictured as in Fig. 3.13(b) where reactances $x_{i,j}$, $i \neq j$, are not shown for lack of space. The short-circuit currents are those flowing through the imaginary switches. Before the study begins, they are all zero: $i_1 = i_2 = i_3 = 0$.

Suppose that switch $k = 2$ is closed. The current flowing from ground, through the generator, network, switch 2, and back to ground is calculated from Kirchhoff's voltage law:

$$x_{2,1} \cdot i_1 + x_{2,2} \cdot i_2 + x_{2,3} \cdot i_3 = 1.0$$

or in general

$$x_{k,k} \cdot i_k + \Sigma x_{j,k} \cdot i_k = 1.0; \quad j\,\Sigma = 1, 2, \ldots, n \text{ but } k \neq j$$

Since all currents except i_2 (or in general i_k) are approximated by zero, we have for a fault (short) in node k:

$$i_k = \frac{1.0}{x_{k,k}} \tag{3.36}$$

With bus 2 shorted, the voltage across switch 1 is $v_{1,n}$ and thus Kirchhoff's voltage law is

$$1.0 - v_{1,n} = x_{1,1} \cdot i_1 + x_{1,2} \cdot i_2 + x_{1,3} \cdot i_3$$

Insertion of i_2 from Eq. (3.36) and $i_1 = i_3 = 0$ yields

$$v_{1,n} = 1.0 - x_{1,2}/x_{2,2}$$

We can generalize and write for this case

$$\begin{bmatrix} x_{1,1} & x_{1,2} & x_{1,3} \\ x_{2,1} & x_{2,2} & x_{2,3} \\ x_{3,1} & x_{3,2} & x_{3,3} \end{bmatrix} * \begin{bmatrix} 0 \\ i_2 \\ 0 \end{bmatrix} = \begin{bmatrix} 1.0 - v_{1,n} \\ 1.0 \\ 1.0 - v_{3,n} \end{bmatrix} \tag{3.37}$$

and

$$v_{n,m} = 1 - \frac{x_{k,m}}{x_{k,k}} \tag{3.38}$$

The current flowing through a branch j,m with reactance x is therefore

$$i_{j,m} = \frac{v_{j,n} - v_{m,n}}{x} = \frac{(1 - x_{k,j}/x_{k,k}) - (1 - x_{k,m}/x_{k,k})}{x} \tag{3.39}$$

Equations (3.36) to (3.39) are all that is needed to calculate the fault currents.

Note that in order to calculate $i_{j,m}$, both reactances $x_{k,m}$ and $x_{k,j}$ were required. Since the matrix is symmetric, we see that $x_{m,k}$, $x_{j,k}$, as well as $x_{k,k}$ were required. Thus, with bus k faulted, all currents can be computed, if the entire column k of matrix **X** is retained. Since we usually calculate faults for every possible node, the entire **X** matrix would have to be computed and stored. This is not exactly true, since with **X** being symmetric, only half (upper or lower triangle plus the diagonal) would be needed. Still, for n nodes this number is $1 + 2 + 3 + \cdots + n = n \cdot (n + 1)/2$.

This can be an extremely large number; for $n = 1000$ buses, it would top half a million. The way out of this is to reduce the network outside the area of interest into "equivalent" nodes. The short-circuit analysis is carried out for the retained part with the equivalent network accounting for the rest. This will be done in Chapter 7.

Let us exemplify the calculation of faults on the network of Fig. 3.6. Its **Z** matrix was already calculated in Section 3.1, and is also repeated in Fig. 3.14.

$$Z = \begin{bmatrix} 1 & 1 & 1 \\ 1 & 2.5 & 2 \\ 1 & 2 & 3 \end{bmatrix}$$

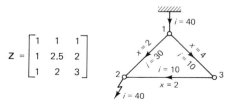

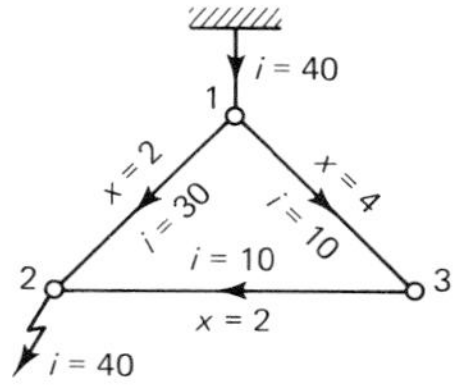

Figure 3.14 **Z**-bus matrix and current distribution.

We will assume that a three-phase fault occurred on bus 2. Thus, if the base MVA is s = 100 MVA, we have

$$i_{\text{fault}} = \frac{100}{2.5} = 40 \text{ p.u.}$$

The current distribution is

$$i_{1-2} = 40 \cdot \frac{Z_{2,2} - Z_{1,2}}{x_{1-2}} = 40 \cdot \frac{2.5 - 1}{2} = \frac{60}{2} = 30 \text{ p.u.}$$

$$i_{1-3} = 40 \cdot \frac{Z_{3,2} - Z_{1,2}}{x_{1-3}} = 40 \cdot \frac{2 - 1}{4} = 10 \text{ p.u.}$$

$$i_{2-3} = 40 \cdot \frac{Z_{3,2} - Z_{2,2}}{x_{2-3}} = 40 \cdot \frac{2 - 2.5}{2} = -10 \text{ p.u.}$$

Note that we have computed currents of bus 2 using column 2 of the **Z** bus matrix.

There are two problems associated with using Kron's method, namely, the large storage space required and the low accuracy attained in some cases. A more accurate calculation of currents will therefore be developed next. The problem of storage and equivalents will be discussed in Chapter 7.

To repeat, the following are reasons for trying another method:

- Matrix **Y** is sparse, but matrix **Z** is dense and may require over $n^2/2$ of storage space.
- The number of operations to obtain **Z** from **Y** is of the order of n^3 and has to be repeated for every faulted line.
- The accuracy in some fault calculations was shown to be very low.

Because of the first two reasons, it was proposed [TFC73]* not to invert the symmetric matrix **Y** but to factor it as

$$\mathbf{Y} = \mathbf{L} * \mathbf{D} * \mathbf{L}^{\mathrm{T}} \qquad (3.40)$$

This factorization for computing matrix **Z** was discussed in Section 2.6. We repeat equations (2.60), (2.61), (2.62):

$$\mathbf{W} = \mathbf{D}^{-1} * \mathbf{L}^{-1}; \quad \mathbf{U} = \mathbf{I} - \mathbf{L}^{\mathrm{T}} \qquad (3.41)$$

$$\mathbf{Z} = \mathbf{W} + \mathbf{U} * \mathbf{Z} \qquad (3.42)$$

Let us exemplify the use of these equations for the purely reactive network in Fig. 3.15. If we apply factorization, we get the **Y**, **L**, and **D** matrices of Eq. (3.43). (We have used an "optimum" ordering, so that quite a number of elements remain zero.)

$$
\begin{array}{c}
 \\
1 \\ 2 \\ 3 \\ 4 \\ 5 \\ 6 \\ 7
\end{array}
\begin{array}{c}
\begin{array}{ccccccc}
1 & 2 & 3 & 4 & 5 & 6 & 7
\end{array} \\
\left[
\begin{array}{ccccccc}
1 & -1 & & & & & \\
-1 & 2 & -\frac{1}{4} & & & & -\frac{3}{4} \\
& -\frac{1}{4} & 1 & -\frac{3}{4} & & & \\
& & -\frac{3}{4} & 4 & -\frac{13}{4} & & \\
& & & -\frac{13}{4} & 4 & -\frac{3}{4} & \\
& & & & -\frac{3}{4} & 1 & -\frac{1}{4} \\
& -\frac{3}{4} & & & & -\frac{1}{4} & 1
\end{array}
\right] ;
\end{array}
\qquad (3.43)
$$

$$
\begin{array}{c}
1 \\ 2 \\ 3 \\ 4 \\ 5 \\ 6 \\ 7
\end{array}
\begin{array}{c}
\begin{array}{ccccccc}
1 & 2 & 3 & 4 & 5 & 6 & 7
\end{array} \\
\left[
\begin{array}{ccccccc}
1 & & & & & & \\
-1 & 1 & & & & & \\
& \frac{i}{2} & 1 & & & & \\
& & -\frac{3}{5} & 1 & & & \\
& & & -\frac{65}{71} & 1 & & \\
& & & & -\frac{71}{97} & 1 & \\
& \frac{1}{2} & \frac{1}{5} & \frac{3}{71} & \frac{39}{291} & -1 & 1
\end{array}
\right] ;
\end{array}
\begin{array}{c}
1 \\ 2 \\ 3 \\ 4 \\ 5 \\ 6 \\ 7
\end{array}
\begin{array}{c}
\begin{array}{ccccccc}
1 & 2 & 3 & 4 & 5 & 6 & 7
\end{array} \\
\left[
\begin{array}{ccccccc}
1 & & & & & & \\
& 1 & & & & & \\
& . & \frac{5}{4} & & & & \\
& & . & \frac{71}{20} & & & \\
& & & . & 1.025 & & \\
& & & & . & 0.45 & \\
. & . & . & . & . & . & 1.514
\end{array}
\right]
\end{array}
$$

Matrix **U** is simply the transposed **L** matrix with zeros on the diagonal. Matrix **L**$^{-1}$ is lower triangular with 1s on the diagonal and **D**$^{-1}$ is diagonal with elements $1/D_{i,i}$, so that the diagonal elements of **W** are

$$W_{i,i} := 1/D_{i,i} \qquad (3.44)$$

If all this is inserted into Eq. (3.42), we get the following expression:

* K. Takahashi, J. Fagan, M. Chen, "Formation of a Sparse Bus-Impedance Matrix," PICA-Conference 1973, pp. 63-69. © 1973 IEEE. Used with permission.

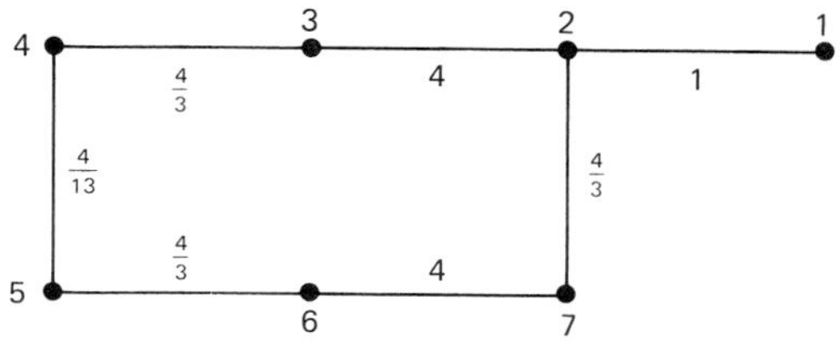

Figure 3.15 A network.

$$\mathbf{Z} = \begin{bmatrix} W_{11} & & & & & & \\ & W_{22} & & & & & \\ & & W_{33} & & & & \\ & & & W_{44} & & & \\ & & & & W_{55} & & \\ & & & & & W_{66} & \\ & & & & & & W_{77} \end{bmatrix} + \begin{bmatrix} 0 & L_{21} & L_{31} & L_{41} & L_{51} & L_{61} & L_{71} \\ & 0 & L_{32} & L_{42} & L_{52} & L_{62} & L_{72} \\ & & 0 & L_{43} & L_{53} & L_{63} & L_{73} \\ & & & 0 & L_{54} & L_{64} & L_{74} \\ & & & & 0 & L_{65} & L_{75} \\ & & & & & 0 & L_{76} \\ & & & & & & 0 \end{bmatrix} * \mathbf{Z}$$

From this expression we write for elements of $\mathbf{Z}$ (note that the calculation has to proceed in the following order):

$$Z_{7,7} := W_{7,7}; \quad Z_{6,7} := L_{7,6} \cdot Z_{7,7}; \quad Z_{6,6} := W_{6,6} + L_{7,6} \cdot Z_{6,7};$$

$$Z_{5,7} := L_{6,5} \cdot Z_{6,7} + L_{7,5} \cdot Z_{7,7}; \quad Z_{5,6} := L_{6,5} \cdot Z_{6,6} + L_{5,7} \cdot Z_{6,7};$$

$$Z_{5,5} := W_{5,5} + L_{6,5} \cdot Z_{5,6} + L_{5,7} \cdot Z_{5,7};$$

and so on.

Let us return to fault calculations. The beauty of the method proposed in [TFC73] is not only in using a sparse **L** (instead of a dense **Z**) matrix but also in that only elements needed for the calculation (and a few additional terms) are to be calculated. To remind the reader: If node k is shorted, the fault current flowing through branch $m-k$ is

$$i_{m,k} = \frac{X_{k,j} - X_{k,m}}{X_{k,k} \cdot x}$$

As seen, we need only the diagonal ($X_{k,k}$) and those off-diagonal terms of **X** which are actually connected to the shorted node k. The main point is that if we denote by **U** the matrix $\mathbf{I} - \mathbf{L}^{\mathrm{T}}$, then we have

The following property concerning the generation of new nonzero off-diagonal terms:

If term (p, i) where $p < i$ is a nonzero term in **U**, and term (p, j) where $p > j$ is also a nonzero term in **U**, then the term (i, j) or (j, i) is a nonzero term in **U**. Figure 3.16 indicates the relationship graphically. Note that nonzero terms may assume the value of zero.

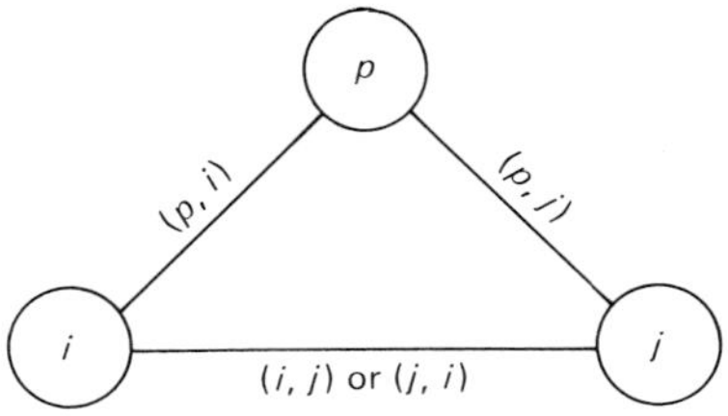

Figure 3.16 Connections.

Considering the above property, one can easily realize that in order to determine the branch elements or off-diagonal terms it is enough to calculate, by the following [Eq. (3.45)], only such terms (p, q) that are located at the positions of nonzero terms of **U**.

$$Z_{pq} = \Sigma\, U_{pk} \cdot Z_{kq} \quad \text{for } p < q \text{ and } k > p \tag{3.45}$$

where the summation is taken for only such k that $U_{pk} \neq 0$.

The calculation given by Eq. (3.45) is restricted to the backward solution. It is concluded that if U_{pk} is a nonzero term, we have already calculated either Z_{kq} or Z_{qk} (see that $Z_{kq} = Z_{qk}$) because pq is a nonzero term.

For the node elements or the diagonal terms (p, p) of the **Z** matrix, Eq. (3.42) yields

$$Z_{pp} = W_{pp} + \Sigma\, U_{pk} \cdot Z_{kp} \tag{3.46}$$

where we can also mention that for $U_{pk} \neq 0$, $p < k$, we have already solved the terms $Z_{kp} = Z_{pk}$.

By carrying out the computations given by Eqs. (3.45) and (3.46) with $p = n$ to $p = 1$ in the backward manner, all specific terms of the matrix can successively be determined. Thus, the terms which are generated by the sparse **Z** matrix method can fill the data requirement for the **Z** matrix information needed for the usual short circuit calculation.*

We have thus achieved the objectives by:

- Factorization of matrix **Y**. We will use for it the program of Chapter 4.
- Computing only those elements of **Z** which are required by a given fault. For this we may use Equations (3.40) to (3.46).

---

* K. Takahashi, J. Fagan, M. Chen, "Formation of a Sparse Bus-Impedance Matrix," PICA-Conference 1973, pp. 63–69. © 1973 IEEE. Used with permission.

3.4 ASYMMETRIC FAULTS

Most of the faults are not symmetrical, three-phase faults. The most frequent is the single line-to-ground short brought about by a flashover or simply by a broken wire touching ground. Since in that case one phase has an impedance of zero, but the other two of practically infinity, the fault current is carried only in the shorted phase. The other two phases provide only load currents which we have decided to neglect. We thus have a rather asymmetric fault: one phase carries a very large current, the other two, negligible currents. Other asymmetric cases result for a double line-to-ground and a line-to-line (two-phase) fault. It is therefore imperative to study asymmetric (or *unbalanced*) faults.

The method most commonly used is that of *symmetrical components*, as published by C. L. Fortescue in 1918.

The basic approach is to represent an asymmetric three-phase system by three symmetrical systems: the positive (superscript +), negative (superscript −), and zero (superscript 0) systems. To derive them, we first draw a symmetric system of three vectors (actually phasors) as in Fig. 3.17(a). The vectors are assumed to be displaced by 120° with phase b following a and c following b [this corresponds to a counterclockwise rotation in Fig. 3.17(a)].

Next, define a phasor a† of unit length which, when multiplying any vector, shifts it by +120°, i.e.,

$$a = 1\cdot\epsilon^{j120} = \cos(120°) + j\cdot\sin(120°) = -0.5 + j\cdot 0.866 \quad (3.47)$$

Multiplying twice by a corresponds to a shift of 240°, i.e., $a^2 = a\cdot a = \epsilon^{-j120} = -0.5 - j\cdot 0.866$

Obviously a^3 leads back to the starting position, and so

$$a^3 + a^2 + a = 1 + a + a^2 = 0$$

since the three vectors form a symmetric system [Fig. 3.17(a)] for which the sum is obviously zero. Also, $a^4 = a$ and

$$a - a^2 = (-0.5 + j\cdot\sqrt{3}/2) - (-0.5 - j\cdot\sqrt{3}/2) = j\cdot\sqrt{3}$$

If the time axis coincides with phasor v_a, we have

$$v_b^+ = \epsilon^{j240}\cdot v_a^+ = a^2\cdot v_a^+; \qquad v_c^+ = \epsilon^{j120}\cdot v_a^+ = a\cdot v_a^+$$

and *the sum is zero*: $v_a^+\cdot(1 + a^2 + a) = v_a^+\cdot 0 = 0$.

A negative system would have the phase sequence reversed so that it passes the time axis as v_a, v_c, and then v_b. Thus

† Letter a denotes both the phasor a' and phase a. They are easily differentiated by their context.

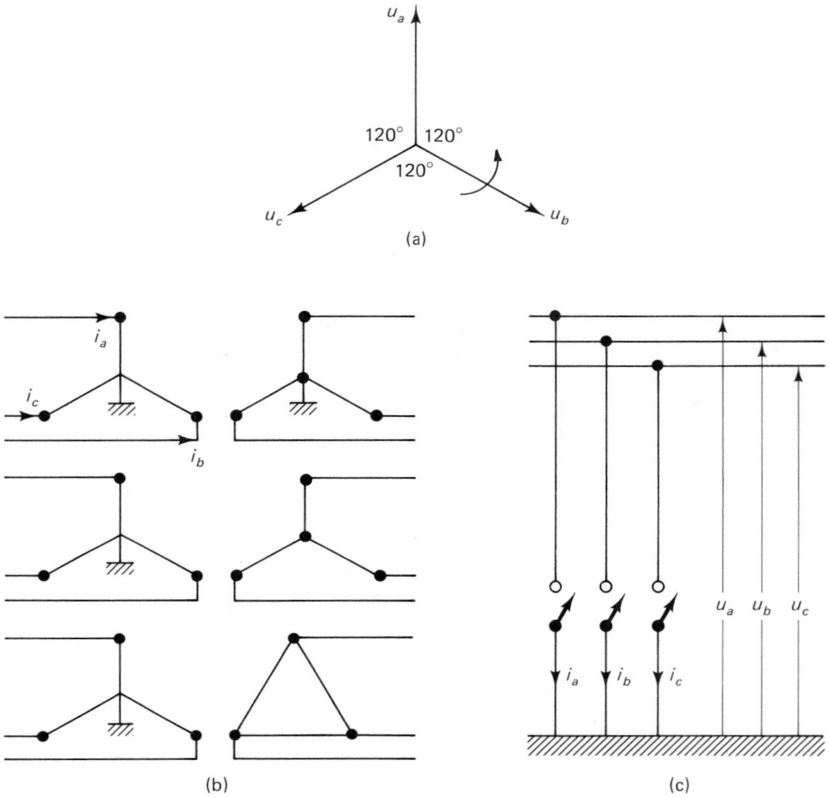

Figure 3.17 (a) Phasors. (b) Connections. (c) A faulted network.

$$v_b^- = a \cdot v_a^-; \qquad v_c^- = a^2 \cdot v_a^-$$

and the sum $v_a^- + v_b^- + v_c^- = (1 + a + a^2) \cdot v_a^- = 0$.

A zero sequence consists of three identical phasors $v_a^0 = v_b^0 = v_c^0$ and therefore *their sum is not zero*.

If we are given the three sequences i.e. the phasors v_a^+, v_a^- and v_a^0, then summation produces the phase quantities

$$\begin{aligned} v_a &= v_a^+ + v_a^- + v_a^0 \\ v_b &= v_b^+ + v_b^- + v_b^0 = a^2 \cdot v_a^+ + a \cdot v_a^- + v_a^0 \\ v_c &= v_c^+ + v_c^- + v_c^0 = a \cdot v_a^+ + a^2 \cdot v_a^- + v_a^0 \end{aligned} \tag{3.48}$$

and we have expressed all three phasors of the unbalanced system by the three symmetrical systems given by v_a^+, v_a^-, v_a^0 and phasor a.

To reverse the transformation and calculate v_a^+, v_a^-, and v_a^0 from the known unbalanced system v_a, v_b, v_c, we first add the last three equations:

$$v_a + v_b + v_c = v_a^+(1 + a^2 + a) + v_a^-(1 + a + a^2) + 3v_a^0$$
$$= 0 + 0 + 3v_a^0$$

In the same way,

$$v_a + a \cdot v_b + a^2 \cdot v_c$$
$$= v^+ + v^- + v^0 + a^3 v^+ + a^2 v^- + av^0 + a^3 v^+ + av^- + a^2 v^0$$
$$= v^+ \cdot (1 + 1 + 1) + v^- \cdot (1 + a^2 + a) + v^0 \cdot (1 + a + a^2) = 3 \cdot v^+$$
$$v_a + a^2 \cdot v_b + a \cdot v_c$$
$$= v^+ + v^- + v^0 + av^+ + a^3 v^- + a^2 v^0 + a^2 v^+ + a^3 v^- + av^0$$
$$= v^+ \cdot (1 + a + a^2) + v^- \cdot (1 + 1 + 1) + v^0 \cdot (1 + a^2 + a) = 3 \cdot v^-$$

Since subscript a appears on all phasors, we have slightly changed the notation and used v^+, v^-, and v^0 for v_a^+, v_a^- and v_a^0, respectively.

As seen the transformation consists of:

$$v^0 = \frac{v_a + v_b + v_c}{3}$$
$$v^- = \frac{v_a + a^2 v_b + av_c}{3} \tag{3.49}$$
$$v^+ = \frac{v_a + av_b + a^2 v_c}{3}$$

Given v_a, v_b, and v_c, these three equations yield v^0, v^-, and v^+.

Next, let us reflect upon the impedances of the network. Since normal conditions mean actually a positive system, the per-phase representation yields in fact a $\mathbf{Z}^+$ matrix. Also, because impedances do not depend on the sequence (of voltages or currents), $\mathbf{Z}^-$ is identical to $\mathbf{Z}^+$.

The only difference between them is that since generators produce a symmetric positive sequence of voltages, the $\mathbf{Z}^-$ network is passive.

The story is more complicated for the zero network, because of transformer connections. Figure 3.17(b) shows three connections of transformers: In each, the primary is a grounded-star; the secondary is connected in grounded-star, ungrounded-star, and delta network, respectively.

Assume next an unbalanced system of three currents i_a, i_b, and i_c. The current

$$i^0 = \frac{i_a + i_b + i_c}{3}$$

which is not zero, will flow from neutral to ground. In the first case of Fig. 3.17(b), i^0 flows both in the primary and secondary circuit. In the second case, there can be no zero current, since there is no path along which it can flow. Since for any phase of the transformer $n_1 \cdot i_1 \cong n_2 \cdot i_2$, we find for the primary

$$3i^0 = i_{a,1} + i_{b,1} + i_{c,1} = \frac{n_2}{n_1} \cdot (i_{a,2} + i_{b,2} + i_{c,2}) = \frac{3 \cdot n_2 \cdot i_2^0}{n_1} = 0$$

No "zero-sequence" current flows into the primary of the transformer, and since an impedance can be viewed as v_{line}/i_{line}, we get for $\mathbf{Z}^0$ an infinite impedance.

In case 3, no zero component exists in the secondary line currents, but i^0 can flow in the primary. It is then transformed (by n_2/n_1 and a phase shift) into the secondary winding and flows around the delta-connected secondary.

The values of $\mathbf{Z}^+$, $\mathbf{Z}^-$, and $\mathbf{Z}^0$ for various types of equipment and different connections are given in [WE33], to which we refer the reader. For now we assume that $\mathbf{Z}^+$, $\mathbf{Z}^-$, and $\mathbf{Z}^0$ are given and proceed to the calculation of different fault types. For this we assume imaginary terminals at the point of the fault [Fig. 3.17(c)], so that normally the three "switches" are open, the three voltages v_a, v_b, and v_c form a symmetric positive sequence, and the three fault currents $i_a = i_b = i_c = 0$. Suppose first that switch a is closed; this is the case of a *line-to-ground fault.* For this case the conditions are

$$v_a = 0; \quad i_b = i_c = 0 \tag{3.50}$$

The currents of the symmetrical components are

$$\left.\begin{aligned} i^0 &= \frac{i_a + i_b + i_c}{3} = \frac{i_a}{3} \\ i^+ &= \frac{i_a + ai_b + a^2 i_c}{3} = \frac{i_a}{3} \\ i^- &= \frac{i_a + a^2 i_b + ai_c}{3} = \frac{i_a}{3} \end{aligned}\right\} \tag{3.51}$$

$$v_a = v^+ + v^- + v^0 = 0 \tag{3.52}$$

For the three currents i^0, i^+, and i^- to be identical, the three networks are connected in series. Equation (3.52) then expresses Kirchhoff's voltage law for the interconnection of the three networks in a serial loop.

For a *double fault to ground,* switches c and b in Fig. 3.17(c) are closed so that the conditions are

$$v_b = v_c = 0; \quad i_a = 0 \tag{3.53}$$

This yields

$$v^0 = v^+ = v^- = \frac{v_a}{3}; \quad i_a = i^0 + i^+ + i^- = 0 \tag{3.54}$$

This case can be represented with the three networks connected in parallel so that their voltage drops are identical and then at the junction, Eq. (3.54) is also true for the currents.

For a *line-to-line* fault, we may remove the ground in Fig. 3.17(c) and close the switches b and c. The conditions and values are therefore

$$i_a = 0; \quad i_b = -i_c; \quad v_b = v_c \tag{3.55}$$

$$3i^0 = 0 + i_b + i_c = 0; \quad i^0 = 0$$

$$3i^+ = i_a + a\cdot i_b + a^2 i_c = 0 + a\cdot i_b - a^2\cdot i_b = (a - a^2)\cdot i_b \tag{3.56}$$

$$3i^- = i_a + a^2 i_b + a i_c = 0 + a^2\cdot i_b - a\cdot i_b = (a^2 - a)i_b = -3i^+$$

Since $i^0 = 0$, it follows that v^0 is 0 too. Furthermore,

$$3v^+ = v_a + av_b + a^2 v_c = v_a + (a + a^2)v_b \tag{3.57}$$

$$3v^- = v_a + a^2 v_b + av_c = v_a + (a^2 + a)v_b = 3v^+$$

All conditions are satisfied if the zero network is removed and the other two networks connected in parallel.

Finally, in the case of a three-phase short (without ground), the system is the symmetric, positive sequence and all we have to do is remove the negative and zero sequences and short the positive network.

The example from Chapter IV of [WE33]* will next be recalculated for the single-line-to-ground fault [Fig.3.18(a)]. No current-distribution factors will be used. If one of the sequence networks, say, the positive [Fig. 3.18(b)], is supplied with current of 1 pu through the shorted node 3, then its distribution throughout the network can be calculated as follows: First replace parallel branches by single lines and drop j throughout. Then write the set of equations for the loop currents i_1, i_2, i_3:

$$42.5\cdot(i_1 - i_3) + 6\cdot(i_1 - i_2) = v; \quad 48.5\cdot i_1 - 6\cdot i_2 - 42.5\cdot i_3 = v$$

$$6\cdot(i_2 - i_1) + 11\cdot(i_2 - i_3) + 16\cdot i_2 = 0; \quad -6\cdot i_1 + 33\cdot i_2 - 11\cdot i_3 = 0$$

$$42.5\cdot(i_3 - i_1) + 11\cdot(i_3 - i_2) + 40\cdot i_3 = 0; \quad 42.5\cdot i_1 + 11\cdot i_2 - 93\cdot 5\cdot i_3 = 0$$

* C. F. Wagner and R. D. Evans, *Symmetrical Components*, Copyright 1933 by McGraw-Hill Book Company, Inc. Used with permission.

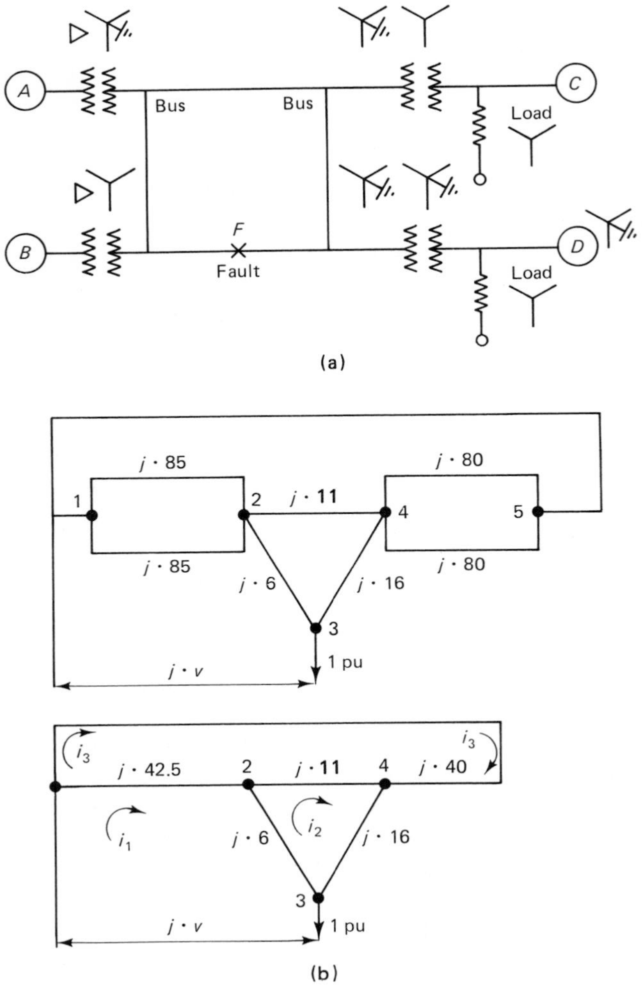

Figure 3.18 (a),(b) A faulted network.

If this system is triangulated by the Gauss elimination procedure, the following results:

$$i_1 - 0.124 \cdot i_2 - 0.875 \cdot i_3 = 0.0206 \cdot v$$

$$i_2 - 0.504 \cdot i_3 = 0.0038 \cdot v$$

$$48.12 \cdot i_3 = 0.9378 \cdot v$$

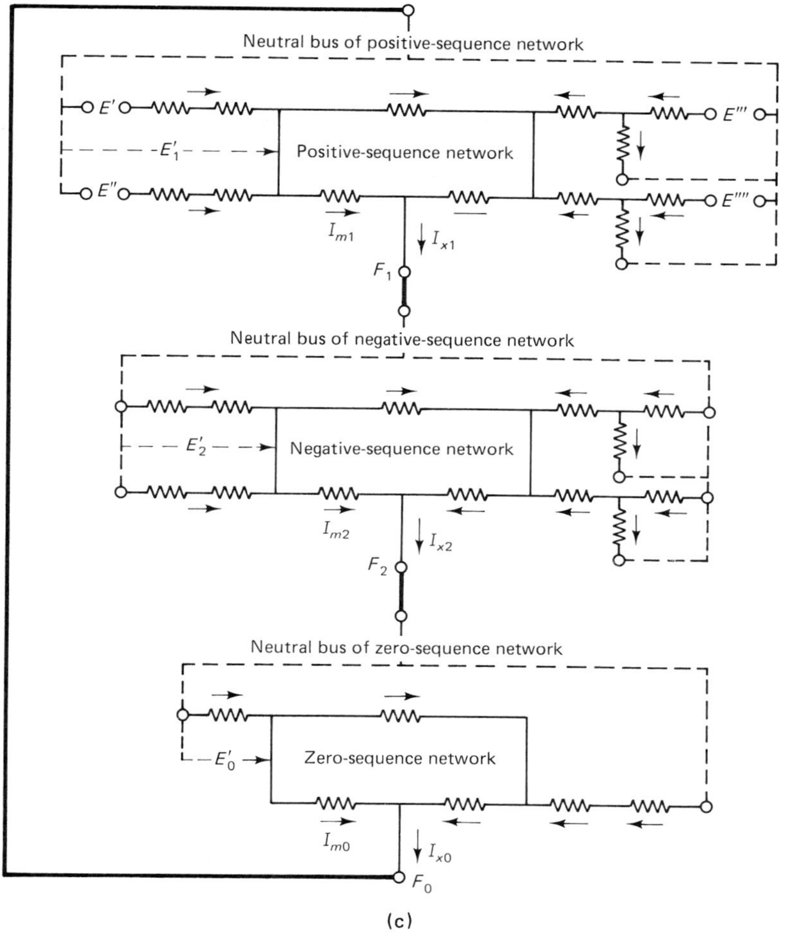

Figure 3.18 (c) Connecting the networks.

These are three equations, and if we assume $i_1 = 1$, they yield: $v = 25.42$, $i_2 = 2.594$, $i_3 = 4.954$.

The "equivalent reactance" is obviously

$$x^+ := v/i_1 = v = 25.41942$$

since a current i^+ flowing through this x^+ will produce exactly v. In the same way, elimination will produce

$$x^- = 25.13; \quad x^0 = 29.15$$

For a single-line-to-ground fault the three networks are connected in series, so that with $u = j \cdot 38{,}100$ volts, $i^+ = i^- = i^0 := 38{,}100/(25.42 + 25.13 + 29.15) = 477$ amp.

In each of the three sequence networks, current i_1 is not 1 but 477 amp and because the network is assumed to be linear, the other currents change correspondingly. The currents of the three sequences and the line currents [Eq. (3.48) for currents] for every reactance can next be calculated. Then, for every sequence, the sequence voltages are

$$u_i = u_i^s - \Sigma\, i^s \cdot x^s$$

where s is $+$, $-$, or 0 and $u_i^- = u_i^0 = 0$. Equations (3.48) result now in the phase or line voltages.

The calculation of current distribution replaced each of the networks by an "equivalent" reactance. Such replacements are needed repeatedly in various calculations. A more general way of calculating "equivalents" is discussed in Chapter 8.

3.5 SINGULAR VALUE DECOMPOSITION

There is a connection between singular values and eigenvalues. We start with eigenvalues since they are better known. An eigenvalue λ and eigenvector $\mathbf{x}$ of matrix $\mathbf{A}$ are a scalar and a vector such that

$$\mathbf{A} * \mathbf{x} = \lambda \cdot \mathbf{x} \tag{3.58}$$

Eigenvalues of a matrix $\mathbf{A}$ could be calculated from $\det(\mathbf{A} - \lambda \cdot \mathbf{I}) = 0$ (where "det" denotes determinant). This way is very inefficient, and we will mention another later. Note here that if $\mathbf{A}$ is triangular, so is $\mathbf{A} - \lambda \cdot \mathbf{I}$ and (with Π denoting a product)

$$\det(\mathbf{A} - \lambda \cdot \mathbf{I}) = \Pi\, d_{i,i;} \quad i\,\Pi = 1, \ldots, n$$

where $d_{i,i}$ is the ith diagonal term of $\mathbf{A} - \lambda \cdot \mathbf{I}$.

A similarity transformation of matrix $\mathbf{A}$ is defined by $\mathbf{M} * \mathbf{A} * \mathbf{M}^{-1}$ where we assume that $\mathbf{M}$ is nonsingular.

Introduce next vector $\mathbf{z} = \mathbf{M} * \mathbf{x}$ or equivalently $\mathbf{x} = \mathbf{M}^{-1} * \mathbf{z}$. Insertion of this $\mathbf{x}$ into Eq. (3.58) yields $\mathbf{A} * \mathbf{M}^{-1} * \mathbf{z} = \lambda \cdot \mathbf{M}^{-1} * \mathbf{z}$. Premultiplication by $\mathbf{M}$ shows that

$$\mathbf{M} * \mathbf{A} * \mathbf{M}^{-1} * \mathbf{z} = \lambda \cdot \mathbf{M} * \mathbf{M}^{-1} * \mathbf{z}$$

or

$$\mathbf{B} * \mathbf{z} = \lambda \cdot \mathbf{z}; \qquad \mathbf{B} \equiv \mathbf{M} * \mathbf{A} * \mathbf{M}^{-1} \tag{3.59}$$

$\mathbf{B}$ is seen to be similar to $\mathbf{A}$ and to have the same eigenvalue λ (but a different eigenvector $\mathbf{z} = \mathbf{M} * \mathbf{x}$.) Thus, similarity transformations do not change the eigenvalues. Finally, assuming that $\mathbf{M} \equiv \mathbf{Q}^T$ where $\mathbf{Q}$ is an orthonormal matrix, we have that $\mathbf{B} = \mathbf{Q}^T * \mathbf{A} * \mathbf{Q}$ has the same eigenvalues as $\mathbf{A}$.

Suppose we partition $\mathbf{Q}$ and $\mathbf{A}$ as follows:

$$\mathbf{Q} = \begin{bmatrix} 1 & \mathbf{0} \\ \mathbf{0} & \mathbf{H} \end{bmatrix}; \quad \mathbf{A} = \begin{bmatrix} A_{1,1} & \mathbf{v}^T \\ \mathbf{v} & \mathbf{A}_1 \end{bmatrix}$$

The product matrix B has the form

$$\mathbf{B} \equiv \mathbf{Q}^T * \mathbf{A} * \mathbf{Q} = \begin{bmatrix} A_{1,1} & \mathbf{v}^T * \mathbf{H} \\ \mathbf{H}^T * \mathbf{v} & \mathbf{H}^T * \mathbf{A}_1 * \mathbf{H} \end{bmatrix}$$

If matrix $\mathbf{H}$ is a *Householder matrix* (Chapter 2), then the last $(n - 2)$ elements of vector $\mathbf{H}^T * \mathbf{v}$ are zero. Since $(\mathbf{v}^T * \mathbf{H})^T = \mathbf{H}^T * \mathbf{v}$, this means that the last $(n - 2)$ elements of row 1 are also zero. The matrix $\mathbf{B}$ therefore has the form

$$\begin{bmatrix} \times & \times & 0 & \cdots & 0 \\ \times & \times & \times & \cdots & \times \\ 0 & \ddots & & & \\ \vdots & & \ddots & & \\ 0 & \times & & & \times \end{bmatrix} \tag{3.60}$$

Next we introduce zeros into the last $(n - 3)$ elements of column and row 2 of the matrix in Eq. (3.60). Repeating this procedure $(n - 2)$ times produces a *tridiagonal* matrix.

Summary: We apply $(n - 2)$ times the similarity transformation

$$\mathbf{Q}^T * \mathbf{A} * \mathbf{Q}$$

and produce a tridiagonal matrix which has the same eigenvalues as had $\mathbf{A}$.

For the singular-value decomposition, we first use the orthogonalization

$$\mathbf{B} = \mathbf{Q}_1 * \mathbf{A} * \mathbf{H}_2$$

to eliminate elements $B_{i,1}$, $i = 2, \ldots, m$ by $\mathbf{Q}_1$, and elements $B_{1,k}$, $k = 3, \ldots$ by $\mathbf{H}_2$. If we proceed in this way, we get an n-by-n *bidiagonal* matrix $\mathbf{B}$

$$\begin{bmatrix} \mathbf{B} \\ \mathbf{0} \end{bmatrix} = \mathbf{Q}_n (\ldots((\mathbf{Q}_1 * \mathbf{A}) * \mathbf{H}_2 \cdots \mathbf{H}_n) = \mathbf{Q}^T * \mathbf{A} * \mathbf{H} \tag{3.61}$$

$$\mathbf{B} = \begin{bmatrix} d_1 & e_2 & & \\ & d_2 & \ddots & \\ & & \ddots & e_n \\ & & & d_n \end{bmatrix}$$

where $\mathbf{Q}^T$ and $\mathbf{H}$ are defined as the products of the $\mathbf{Q}_i$ and $\mathbf{H}_i$ matrices, respectively. The zero matrix has dimension $(m - n)$ by n, $m > n$.

Application of Eq. (3.61) does not change the eigenvalues or singular values. The second step is thus to calculate these values starting from a tridiagonal or bidiagonal matrix.

The so-called QR algorithm for computing eigenvalues of a tridiagonal matrix $\mathbf{A}$ starts by defining $\mathbf{P}_1 \equiv \mathbf{A}$. We next calculate iteratively for $k = 1, 2, \ldots$ the sequence $\mathbf{P}_k$:

$$\mathbf{Q}_k * (\mathbf{P}_k - \sigma_k \cdot \mathbf{I}) = \mathbf{R}_k; \quad \mathbf{P}_{k+1} = \mathbf{R}_k * \mathbf{Q}_k^T + \sigma_k \cdot \mathbf{I}_n \tag{3.62}$$

The first produces the orthonormal $\mathbf{Q}_k$ and triangular $\mathbf{R}_k$ matrix; the second uses these for calculating the next $\mathbf{P}$ in sequence.

Inserting $\mathbf{R}_k$ into the equation for $\mathbf{P}_{k+1}$ yields

$$\begin{aligned} \mathbf{P}_{k+1} &= \mathbf{Q}_k * (\mathbf{P}_k - \sigma_k \cdot \mathbf{I}) * \mathbf{Q}_k^T + \sigma_k \cdot \mathbf{I}_n \\ &= \mathbf{Q}_k * \mathbf{P}_k * \mathbf{Q}_k^T - \sigma_k \cdot \mathbf{Q}_k * \mathbf{Q}_k^T + \sigma_k \cdot \mathbf{I}_n \end{aligned}$$

but since $\mathbf{Q}_k$ is orthonormal ($\mathbf{Q}_k * \mathbf{Q}_k^T = \mathbf{I}$), we have

$$\mathbf{P}_{k+1} = \mathbf{Q}_k * \mathbf{P}_k * \mathbf{Q}_k^T \tag{3.63}$$

This proves that all matrices $\mathbf{P}_k$ have the same eigenvalues as $\mathbf{P}_1 \equiv \mathbf{A}$.

The *shift parameter* σ is normally chosen as an eigenvalue of the 2-by-2 submatrix at the lower right-hand end. In our case we have first to calculate this submatrix for $\mathbf{B}^T * \mathbf{B}$ where $\mathbf{B}$ is the bidiagonal matrix $\mathbf{B}$ of Eq. (3.61).

$$\begin{bmatrix} \ddots & & & \\ & e_{n-1} & d_{n-1} & 0 \\ & 0 & e_n & d_n \end{bmatrix} * \begin{bmatrix} \ddots & \\ e_{n-1} & 0 \\ d_{n-1} & e_n \\ 0 & d_n \end{bmatrix} = \begin{bmatrix} \ddots & & \\ & e_{n-1}^2 + d_{n-1}^2 & e_n \cdot d_{n-1} \\ & e_n \cdot d_{n-1} & e_n^2 + d_n^2 \end{bmatrix}$$

The determinant of this 2-by-2 matrix $-\lambda\mathbf{I}$ is set equal to zero: $(e_{n-1}^2 + d_{n-1}^2 - \lambda)\cdot(e_n^2 + d_n^2 - \lambda) - (e_n \cdot d_{n-1})^2 = 0$ or $a \cdot c - b = 0$. Since

$$c \equiv e_n^2 + d_n^2 - \lambda \tag{3.64}$$

and $a \cdot c - b = c^2 - c^2 + a \cdot c - b = c^2 + (a - c)\cdot c - b = 0$, we have

$$c^2 + (e_{n-1}^2 + d_{n-1}^2 - \lambda - e_n^2 - d_n^2 + \lambda)\cdot c - b = 0$$

$$c^2 + (d_{n-1}^2 - d_n^2 + e_{n-1}^2 - e_n^2)\cdot c - (e_n\cdot d_{n-1})^2 = 0$$

$$f \equiv \frac{-(d_{n-1}^2 - d_n^2 + e_{n-1}^2 - e_n^2)}{2\cdot e_n\cdot d_{n-1}}; \qquad g \equiv \frac{c}{e_n\cdot d_{n-1}}$$

This yields $(g\cdot e_n\cdot d_{n-1})^2 - 2\cdot e_n\cdot d_{n-1}\cdot f\cdot c - (e_n\cdot d_{n-1})^2 = 0$ or $g^2 - 2\cdot f\cdot g - 1 = 0$. Its root with the smallest magnitude is $g = 1/t$, where $t = -f \pm \sqrt{1 + f^2}$ (+ for $f < 0$ and − for $f \geq 0$).

Since from Eq. (3.64) $\lambda = e_n^2 + d_n^2 - g\cdot e_n\cdot d_{n-1}$ we complete the transformation by computing the shift factor σ (or λ):

$$\sigma = d_n^2 + e_n\cdot\left(e_n - \frac{d_{n-1}}{t}\right) \tag{3.65}$$

Let us show what SVD, i.e., $\mathbf{A} = \mathbf{T} * \mathbf{S} * \mathbf{V}^{\mathrm{T}}$, represents. Since $\mathbf{S}^{\mathrm{T}} * \mathbf{S} = (\mathbf{T}^{\mathrm{T}} * \mathbf{A} * \mathbf{V})^{\mathrm{T}} * (\mathbf{T}^{\mathrm{T}} * \mathbf{A} * \mathbf{V}) = \mathbf{V}^{\mathrm{T}} * \mathbf{A}^{\mathrm{T}} * \mathbf{T} * \mathbf{T}^{\mathrm{T}} * \mathbf{A} * \mathbf{V}$ and $\mathbf{T} * \mathbf{T}^{\mathrm{T}} = \mathbf{I}$, we have for the diagonal matrix $\mathbf{S}^{\mathrm{T}} * \mathbf{S}$ with elements s_i^2 that

$$\mathbf{S}^{\mathrm{T}} * \mathbf{S} = \mathbf{V}^{\mathrm{T}} * (\mathbf{A}^{\mathrm{T}} * \mathbf{A}) * \mathbf{V}$$

Since $\mathbf{V}^{\mathrm{T}} * \mathbf{V} = \mathbf{I}$, it follows that pre- and postmultiplication of any matrix $\mathbf{B}$ by $\mathbf{V}^{\mathrm{T}}$ and $\mathbf{V}$, respectively, is a similarity transformation which does not change the eigenvalues λ_i of $\mathbf{B}$. From the equation above it therefore follows that s_i^2 are eigenvalues of $\mathbf{A}^{\mathrm{T}} * \mathbf{A}$ and that the singular values of $\mathbf{A}$ are the nonnegative square roots of the eigenvalues of $\mathbf{A}^{\mathrm{T}} * \mathbf{A}$.

The SVD algorithm will repeatedly calculate orthogonal matrices $\mathbf{T}$ and $\mathbf{V}$ such that the product $\mathbf{V}_k^{\mathrm{T}} * (\mathbf{B}_k^{\mathrm{T}} * \mathbf{B}_k - \sigma_k\cdot\mathbf{I})$ and $\mathbf{B}_{k+1} = \mathbf{T}_k^{\mathrm{T}} * \mathbf{B}_k * \mathbf{V}_k$ are upper triangular and upper bidiagonal, respectively. This is done using Givens' rotation matrices $\mathbf{G}_{i,j}$ as introduced in Chapter 2. For example, if we multiply $\mathbf{G}_{2,1} * \mathbf{B}$, we eliminate $B_{2,1}$ but introduce a nonzero in $B_{1,3}$. Postmultiplying this matrix by $\mathbf{G}_{3,2}^{\mathrm{T}}$ will yield

$$\begin{bmatrix} B_{11} & B_{12} & B_{13} & \\ 0 & B_{22} & B_{23} & \\ & 0 & B_{33} & B_{34} \\ \undersetEquation{}{} \end{bmatrix} \begin{bmatrix} 1 & & \\ & c & -s \\ & s & c \end{bmatrix} = \begin{bmatrix} B_{11} & C_{12} & C_{13} & \\ 0 & C_{22} & C_{23} & \\ 0 & C_{32} & C_{33} & B_{34} \end{bmatrix}$$

where $C_{1,3}$ has to be eliminated. The cosine and sine are thus computed from $C_{1,3} = -s\cdot B_{1,2} + c\cdot B_{1,3} = 0$; $s^2 + c^2 = s^2 + (s\cdot B_{1,2}/B_{1,3})^2 = 1$. Note that a nonzero $C_{3,2} = s\cdot B_{3,3}$ is introduced and has to be eliminated next. The process is graphically shown in Fig. 3.19.

Note that the first column of $(\mathbf{B}^{\mathrm{T}} * \mathbf{B} - \sigma\cdot\mathbf{I})$ is

$$[d_1^2 - \sigma,\ d_i\cdot e_2,\ 0, \ldots, 0]^{\mathrm{T}} \tag{3.66}$$

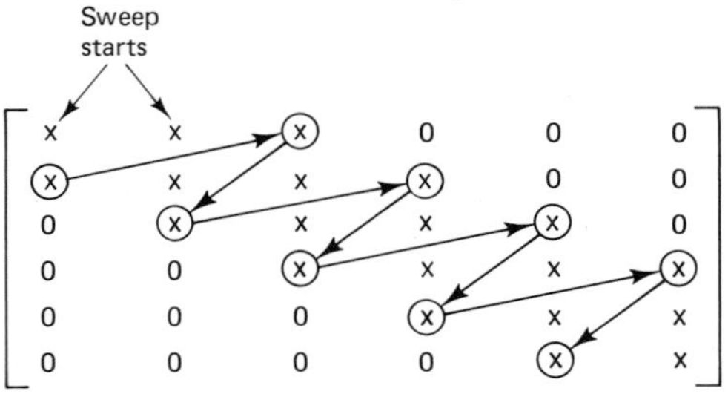

Figure 3.19 The chasing pattern of the second stage. C. L. Lawson, R. T. Hanson: "Solving Least Squares Problems," © 1974 by Prentice-Hall, Inc., Fig. 18.1, p. 115. Used with permission.

with σ as in Eq. (3.65). This is used in determining the cosine and sine values.

Collecting all rotations of a single sweep for, say, a 5-by-5 matrix, results in

$$\mathbf{S} = \mathbf{G}_{5,4} * \mathbf{G}_{4,3} * \mathbf{G}_{3,2} * \mathbf{G}_{2,1} * \mathbf{B} * \mathbf{G}_{3,2}^{\mathrm{T}} * \mathbf{G}_{4,2}^{\mathrm{T}} * \mathbf{G}_{5,3}^{\mathrm{T}} \qquad (3.67)$$

$$= \tilde{\mathbf{T}}^{\mathrm{T}} * \mathbf{B} * \tilde{\mathbf{V}}$$

$$\tilde{\mathbf{T}}^{\mathrm{T}} \equiv (\mathbf{G}_{5,4} * \mathbf{G}_{4,3} * \mathbf{G}_{3,2} * \mathbf{G}_{2,1}); \quad \tilde{\mathbf{V}} \equiv (\mathbf{G}_{5,3} * \mathbf{G}_{4,2} * \mathbf{G}_{3,2}) \qquad (3.68)$$

The main point is that **B** was bidiagonal, but the process reduces the super diagonal terms. If any such term e_i becomes negligible, then **B** splits into two bidiagonal matrices and each is processed separately. The process is repeated until all superdiagonal elements $e_{i,k}$, $k = i + 1$, are negligible.

Recall that from Eq. (3.61) we have $\mathbf{A} = \mathbf{Q} * \mathbf{B} * \mathbf{H}^{\mathrm{T}}$. Inserting Eq. (3.67) yields $\mathbf{A} = (\mathbf{Q} * \tilde{\mathbf{T}}) * \mathbf{S} * (\tilde{\mathbf{V}}^{\mathrm{T}} * \mathbf{H}^{\mathrm{T}})$, so that we get as the final result

$$\mathbf{A} = \mathbf{T} * \mathbf{S} * \mathbf{V}^{\mathrm{T}}; \quad \mathbf{T} \equiv \mathbf{Q} * \tilde{\mathbf{T}}; \quad \mathbf{V} \equiv \mathbf{H} * \tilde{\mathbf{V}} \qquad (3.69)$$

This is the SVD result we set out to get. **S** is a diagonal matrix with $s_1, \ldots, s_n$ being the singular values of **A**.

In the case that **A** is an m-by-n matrix with $m > n$, an $(m - n)$-by-n zero matrix is attached to **S** as in Eq. (3.70).

$$\mathbf{S} \rightarrow \begin{bmatrix} \mathbf{S} \\ \mathbf{O} \end{bmatrix} \qquad (3.70)$$

We next develop the equations for Householder and Givens transformations as used in the pseudoprogram at the end of Section 2.3.

Given is vector $\mathbf{v} = [v_1, \ldots, v_{p-1}, v_p, v_{p+1}, \ldots, v_{l-1}, v_l, \ldots, v_m]^T$

Define vector $\mathbf{u} = [0, \ldots, 0, u_p, 0, \ldots, 0, v_l, \ldots, v_m]^T$ such that

$$u_p = v_p - s \quad \text{and} \quad s = -\sqrt{v_p^2 + \sum_{i=l}^{m} v_i^2} \tag{3.71}$$

and matrix

$$\mathbf{Q} = \mathbf{I}_m + \mathbf{u}{*}\mathbf{u}^T/b \quad \text{where } b = s \cdot u_p \tag{3.72}$$

Next we can prove that

$$b = -0.5 \cdot ||u||^2 \tag{3.73}$$

$$\begin{aligned} ||u||^2 &= u_p^2 + \sum_{j=l}^{m} v_j^2 = (v_p - s)^2 + \Sigma = (v_p^2 + \Sigma) - 2v_p s + s^2 \\ &= s^2 - 2v_p s + s^2 = 2s^2 - 2v_p s \\ &= -2s(v_p - s) = -2su_p = -2b \qquad \text{Q.E.V.} \end{aligned}$$

We can also prove that for a symmetric $\mathbf{Q}$ (i.e., $\mathbf{Q}^T = \mathbf{Q}$), matrix $\mathbf{Q}$ is orthonormal, that is $\mathbf{Q}^T * \mathbf{Q} = \mathbf{I}$:

$$\begin{aligned} \mathbf{Q}^T * \mathbf{Q} &= (\mathbf{I} + \mathbf{u} * \mathbf{u}^T/b)(\mathbf{I} + \mathbf{u} * \mathbf{u}^T/b) \\ &= \mathbf{I} + \frac{2}{b}\mathbf{u} * \mathbf{u}^T + \frac{\mathbf{u} * (\mathbf{u}^T * \mathbf{u}) * \mathbf{u}^T}{b^2} \end{aligned}$$

The scalar in parentheses is $||\mathbf{u}||^2 = -2b$ so that

$$\mathbf{Q}^T * \mathbf{Q} = \mathbf{I} + \frac{2}{b}\mathbf{u} * \mathbf{u}^T - \frac{2}{b}\mathbf{u} * \mathbf{u}^T = \mathbf{I} \quad \text{Q.E.V}$$

Finally, the algorithm for calculating $\mathbf{y} = \mathbf{Q} * \mathbf{v}$ is developed.

$$\begin{aligned} \mathbf{u}^T * \mathbf{v} &= [0, \ldots, 0, u_p, 0, \ldots, 0, v_l, \ldots, v_m] * \mathbf{v} \\ &= u_p \cdot v_p + \sum_{j=l}^{m} v_j^2 = u_p \cdot v_p + s^2 - v_p^2 \\ &= (v_p - s) \cdot v_p + s^2 - v_p^2 \\ &= -s \cdot v_p + s^2 = s \cdot (s - v_p) = -s \cdot u_p \end{aligned}$$

$$\mathbf{u}^T * \mathbf{v} = -s \cdot u_p \tag{3.74}$$

Using Eq. (3.72) we have

$$\mathbf{u}^T * \mathbf{v} = -b$$

and therefore

$$\mathbf{y} = \mathbf{Q} * \mathbf{v} = \left(\mathbf{I} + \frac{\mathbf{u} * \mathbf{u}^{\mathrm{T}}}{b}\right) * \mathbf{v}$$

$$\mathbf{y} = \mathbf{v} + \frac{1}{b}\mathbf{u} * (\mathbf{u}^{\mathrm{T}} * \mathbf{v}) = \mathbf{v} - \mathbf{u} \tag{3.75}$$

The elements of vector $\mathbf{y}$ are:

$y_i = v_i$ for $i = 1, \ldots, p - 1$ (since $u_i = 0$)

$y_p = s$ (since $y_p = v_p - u_p = v_p - v_p + s = s$)

$y_i = v_i$ for $i = p + 1, \ldots, l - 1$ (since $u_i = 0$)

$y_i = 0$ for $i = l, \ldots, m$ (since $v_i - u_i = v_i - v_i = 0$)

The algorithm for calculating $\mathbf{Q} * \mathbf{C}$ where

$$\mathbf{C} = {}_{m}\Big[\qquad\qquad\Big]^{v} = [\mathbf{c}_1, \mathbf{c}_2, \ldots, \mathbf{c}_v] \tag{3.76}$$

is as follows:

Since $\mathbf{Q} = \mathbf{I} + \mathbf{u} * \mathbf{u}^{\mathrm{T}}/b$ we can compute $\tilde{\mathbf{c}}_j = \mathbf{Q} * \mathbf{c}_j$; $j = 1, \ldots, v$ as follows:

$$t_j := \mathbf{u}^{\mathrm{T}} * \mathbf{c}_j \,/\, b; \quad j = 1, \ldots, v \tag{3.77}$$

$$\tilde{\mathbf{c}}_j := \mathbf{c}_j + t_j \cdot \mathbf{u}; \quad j = 1, \ldots, v \tag{3.78}$$

This can be formalized in five steps of

Algorithm H1 (h, p, l, m, v: *integer*; v:vector; C:matrix);

1. $s := sqrt(v_p * v_p + \Sigma v_i^2$ for $i\Sigma = l, \ldots, m)$;
2. **if** $v_p > 0$ **then** $s := -s$;
3. $h := v_p - s$; (* h stores our u_p *)
   $v_p := s$; (* v_p stores our s *)
4. $b := v_p * h$; (* b was $s * u_p$ or here $v_p * h$ *)
   (* We assume, neither b nor v is zero *)
5. **for** $j := 1$ **to** v **do** (* for each column j of matrix c *) **begin**
   $s := (h * C_{p,j} + \sum_{i=l}^{m} C_{i,j} \cdot v_i) \,/\, b$; (* was t_j in Eq. (3.77) *)
   $C_{p,j} := C_{p,j} + s * h$;
   for $i := l$ **to** m **do** $C_{i,j} := C_{i,j} + s * v_i$;

   end;

Note: Computation of $s = \sqrt{v_p^2 + \Sigma v_i^2} = \sqrt{\Sigma w^2}$ can be made more accurate by computing it through:

$$\sqrt{w_l^2 + \cdots + w_m^2} = t \cdot \sqrt{(w_l/t)^2 + \cdots + (w_m/t)^2}$$

with

$$t = \max\{|w_i|, i = l, \ldots, m \text{ and } i = p\}$$

In *constructing Givens rotations*, we will need $r = \sqrt{v_1^2 + v_2^2}$. To avoid unnecessary under- or over-flow, we compute:

$$x = \max(|v_1|, |v_2|); \quad u = \min(|v_1|, |v_2|)$$

and then

$$r = x\sqrt{1 + u^2/x^2} = \sqrt{x^2 + u^2}$$

which is the r as defined since x, u are either v_1, v_2 or v_2, v_1 (which is the same).

The rotation is:

$$\begin{bmatrix} c & s \\ -s & c \end{bmatrix} * \begin{bmatrix} v_1 \\ v_2 \end{bmatrix} = \begin{bmatrix} cv_1 + sv_2 \\ cv_2 - sv_1 \end{bmatrix}$$

For the second to vanish, we have $c \cdot v_2 = s \cdot v_1$ and therefore $s^2 + c^2 = c^2 + c^2 v_2^2/v_1^2 = c^2(v_1^2 + v_2^2)/v_1^2 = c^2 \cdot r^2/v_1^2 = 1$. The values are: $c = v_1/r$ and $s = v_2/r$. The first element is: $v_1^2/r + v_2^2/r = r^2/r = r$.

Suppose that we define Cons(x, u, c, s, r) as follows:

$$w := u/x;$$
$$q := \sqrt{1 + w \cdot w}; \quad c := 1/q; \quad s := w \cdot c;$$
$$r := |x| \cdot q$$

Case 1: $|v_1| > |v_2|$ or $x = v_1$, $u = v_2$ and the computation yields:

$$w = v_2/v_1;$$
$$q = \sqrt{1 + v_2^2/v_1^2} = \sqrt{v_1^2 + v_2^2}\,/v_1 = r/v_1$$
$$c = v_1/r;$$
$$s = (v_2/v_1) \cdot (v_1/r) = v_2/r$$
$$r = |v_1| \cdot (\sqrt{1 + v_2^2/v_1^2})/v_1$$

Case 2: $|v_2| > |v_1|$ or $x = v_2$, $u = v_1$ but we call $C(u, x, s, c, r)$. Then:

$$w = x/u;$$

$$q = \sqrt{1 + x^2/u^2} = (\sqrt{u^2 + x^2})/u;$$

$$c = u/\sqrt{1 + \cdots} = v_1/r$$

$$s = (x/u) \cdot (u/r) = x/r = v_2/r;$$

$$r = |v_1| \cdot r/v_1 = r$$

Case 3: $v_1 = 0$ and $v_2 = 0$. Here we set: $c = 1$, $s = 0$ and $r = 0$.

In *applying the Givens rotation* we will save a location if we do it as follows:

$$w := c * v_1 + s * v_2;$$

$$v_2 := c * v_2 - s * v_1;$$

$$v_1 := w;$$

All these equations are used in Program 3.3.

Program 3.3 is a Pascal transcription of the Fortran program* of [LH77]. It prints the matrices **A**, **B**, **V**, $\mathbf{T}^{\mathrm{T}} * \mathbf{B}$, and the diagonal elements of **S** — the singular values of **A**. For the 7-bus network of Chapter 1, theses results appear in Program 3.3b. It is hoped that the comments included are sufficient to show that it corresponds to the material previously discussed.

The SVD procedure will be used as a basic algorithm in Chapter 5. Here we can use it to address the question of whether diakoptics will decrease or increase the errors. To solve this problem, the 30-bus network was processed in stages, as a 7-, 11-, 17-, 22-, and 30-bus network. The 7-, 11-, and a 17-bus network are shown in Fig. 3.20. The data were those of Chapter 1 (indata), except that only x values were used. Since our procedure does not include a warning statement, a library subroutine was chosen.

Table 3.6 shows the singular values of these 7-, 11-, 22-, and 30-bus systems. Note that in all cases $s_n \cong 0.0$ (actually 0.0...1), but since the condition number is s_1/s_n and s_1 increases with the size of the matrix, the *conclusion* seems to be that *diakoptics will decrease the roundoff error.* This conclusion is reinforced by Table 3.7, which shows [Wa83] the singular values of the 14-, 30-, 57-, and 118-bus systems of Chapter 1. The ratio s_1/s_n increases with the size of the network, and so does the condition number. (Diakoptics will also be useful for parallel processing, which we discuss in Chapter 5.)

---

* C. L. Lawson, R. J. Hanson, *Solving Least Squares Problems*, p. 115 © 1974 by Prentice-Hall, Inc. Used with permission.

```
program sivd(input,output);
    constant vector_length = 10;
type
    index = 1..vector_length;
    vector = array[index] of real;
    matrix = array[index] of vector;
    StorageArray = array [1..3] of vector;
    var eps : real; S : StorageArray;
    A,B : matrix; i,j,mm,nn,nb : integer;

procedure Print(M : matrix; col : integer);
var i,j : integer;
begin {Print}
    for j := 1 to mm do
    begin
        for i := 1 to col do
        write (M[i][j]:10:5,' ');
        writeln(' ')
    end;
    writeln(' ')
end; (* of print.

Given an m-by-n matrix A and an m-by-nb matrix B, this procedure
calculates the singular values of A and other quantities needed
in solving the least-squares problem.
Matrix A is first reduced to bidiagonal form, as indicated in
Eq.(3.61). The nonzero elements of B replace the corresponding
elements of A in storage. The same transformations are applied
to b at the same time and are not saved. The resulting vector
replaces b in storage. The right-hand transformations of Eq.(3.61)
are stored in the upper triangle of A (not needed anymore) and in
a vector h.
After the bi-diagonalization, the two arrays q and e are stored so
that location e[1] is used as working storage of the QR-algorithm.
The calculation of the matrix V of Eq.(3.68) is initiated by
forming the products H*H***H in Eq.(3.70). This computation is
organized so that the resulting product_matrix occupies the first
n rows of A, and no auxiliary storage is required.
The QR-algorithm is then applied to B (represented by vectors
 q and e). As each rotation is produced, it is multiplied by
the partial product already stored in A for forming V in Eq.3.70.
Similarly, the other rotations are multiplied by a vector stored
in b in order to form matrix T_up_t. of Eq.(3.68).
At termination of the QR-algorithm, the numbers stored in vector e
(except e[1]) will be small. The numbers stored in vector q must
next be made non-negative and sorted. This processing of matrix A
completes the calculation of matrix A in Eq.(3.70).Applying these
permutations to vector b produces T_up_t*b. in Eq.(3.71).
The procedure below scans initially matrix A for zero columns. If
such columns are found , they are put on the right-side of matrix
which then has the same number of zero-singular values. *)

procedure SingularValueDecomposition(var A,B:matrix;
var S:StorageArray;mm,nn,nb : integer; eps:real);
var
    k,l,m,n,kk,np1,ns,nsp1,i,j : integer;
    t : real; Ipass : boolean; U : vector; V : matrix; (*
```

Program 3.3(a)

```
A single sweep of the QR_Bidiagonal_Decomposition algorithm is ne
described. It first tests the off-diagonal elements e[i] against
a given accuracy eps. If abs(e[i])<eps then the largest of such
indices is stored as l and the algorithm terminates. Otherwise
the algorithm sets l:=1 and proceeds to compute the shift
parameters of Eq.(3.65). Next the algorithm determines and applie
the right and left rotations of Eq.(3.67) and terminates with the
elements of the transformed matrix B = T_up_t*B*V replacing B.
The algorithm could be summarized as follows:
for i:=n downto 2 do
if abs(e[i])<eps then
begin l := i; return end;
l:=1;
Compute sigma by means of Eq.(3.64) to (3.65).
for i:=2 to n do
begin
   e[1] := q[1]-sigma/q[1]; z := e[2];
   Construct_Givens(e[i-1],z,c,s,e[i-1]);
   Apply_Givens(c,s,q[i-1],e[i]);
   for j :=1 to k do Apply-Givens(c,s,w[j,i-1],w[j,i]);
   z := s*q[i];  q[i] := c*q[i];
   Construct_Givens(q[i-1],z,c,s,q[i-1]);
   Apply_Givens(c,s,e[i],q[i]);
   for j := 1 to p do Apply_Givens(c,s,g[i-1,j],g[i,j]);
   if i<>n then
   begin
      z := s*e[i+1]; e[i+1] := c*e[i+1];
   end;
end;
By repeated application of this algorithm to a bi_diagonal matrix
B, a sequence of bidiagonal matrices with elements e[2],...,e[n]
and q[1],...,q[n] are produced. *)

procedure QR_Bidiagonal_Decomposition (var Ipass:boolean;
var Q,E:vector;  nn,nrv,ncc:integer;  eps:real; var V,C:matrix);
var Wntv, Havers, Fail : boolean;
   ap,j,lp1,ll,l,i,ii,k,kk,Nqrs,n10,n : integer;
   t,g,h,x,y,z,f,cs,sn : real;

procedure Last; (* This procedure orders the singular values*)
var i,j : integer; t : real; (*after they have been computed*)
begin
   for i := 2 to n do
   begin
      t := Q[i-1]; k := i-1; j := i;
      while (j<=n) and (t<Q[j]) do
      begin
         t := Q[j]; k := j; j := j+1
      end;
      if k <> i-1 then
      begin
         Q[k] := Q[i-1]; Q[i-1] := t;
         if Havers then
         begin
            for j := 1 to ncc do
            begin
               t := C[j][i-1];
```

Program 3.3(a) (cont.)

```
                C[j][i-1]:= C[j][k];
                C[j][k] := t
             end
          end;
          if Wntv then
          for j := 1 to nrv do
          begin
             t := V[i-1][j];
             V[i-1][j] := V[k][j];
             V[k][j] := t
          end
       end
    end;
    if Fail then Ipass := false
end;{Last}

procedure Construct_Givens(v1,v2:real; var c,s,r:real);
procedure Cons(v1,v2:real;var c,s,r:real);
var q,w : real;
begin {Cons}
    w := v2/v1; q := sqrt(1+w*w); c := 1/q;
    if v1 < 0 then c := -c;
    s := w*c; r := abs(v1)*q
end;{Cons}
begin{Construct_Givens}
    if (v1 <> 0) or (v2 <> 0) then
       if abs(v1) > abs(v2) then
           Cons(v1,v2,c,s,r)
       else Cons(v2,v1,s,c,r)
    else begin c := 1; s := 0; r := 0 end
end;{Construct_Givens}

procedure Apply_Givens(c,s : real; var z1,z2 : real);
var w : real;
begin {Apply_Givens}
    w := z1 * c + z2 * s;
    z2 := -z1 * s + z2 * c; z1 := w
end;{Apply_Givens}

begin (*of QR-Bidiagonal_Decomposition - one sweep *)
    n := nn;
    Ipass := true;
    if n>0 then
    begin
       n10 := 10*n; Wntv := nrv > 0;
       Havers := ncc > 0; Fail := false;
       Nqrs := 0; E[1] := 0;
       for kk := 1 to n do
       begin
          k := n+1-kk;
          repeat (* Test for splitting. First test if q[k]<eps *)
             if k <> 1 then (* next we make E[k]=0*)
                if abs(Q[k]) < eps then
                begin
                   cs:=0; sn:=-1;
                   for ii := 2 to k do
                   begin
                      i := k+1-ii;
```

Program 3.3(a) (cont.)

```
                f := -sn*E[i+1];
                E[i+1] := cs*E[i+1];
                Construct_Givens(Q[i],f,cs,sn,Q[i]);
                (*To make element i,k zero*)
                if Wntv then (*accumulate the V's*)
                for j := 1 to nrv do
                Apply_Givens(cs,sn,V[i][j],V[k][j]);
            end (* The matrix is now bidiagonal *)
        end; (* and of lower order since e[k]=0 *)
    ll := 1;
    while ll <= k do
    begin
        l := k+1-ll;
        if abs(E[l]) > eps then
            if abs(Q[l-1]) > eps then
                ll := ll + 1
            else
            begin (* cancelling e[l] for l>1 *)
                cs:=0; sn:=-1;
                i:=1; f:=1;
                while (i<=k) and (abs(f)>=eps) do
                begin
                    f := -sn * E[i]; E[i] := cs*E[i];
                    if abs(f)>eps then
                    begin
                        Construct_Givens(Q[i],f,cs,sn,Q[i]);
                        if Havers then
                        for j := 1 to ncc do
                        Apply_Givens(cs,sn,C[j][i],C[j][l-1]
                        i := i + 1
                    end;
                    ll := k+1
                end
            end
        else ll := k+1
    end; (* Next is a test for convergence *)
    z := Q[k];
    if l<>k then
    begin (* Shift from bottom 2_by_2 minor of B_up_t*b
        x := Q[l]; y:=Q[k-1];
        g := E[k-1]; h:=E[k];
        f := ((y-z)*(y+z)+(g-h)*(g+h))/(2*h*y);
        g := sqrt(1+f*f);
        if f>= 0
        then t := f+g
        else t := f-g;
        f := ((x-z)*(x+z)+h*(y/t-h))/x;
        cs:=1; sn:=1; (* The next QR-sweep *)
        lp1 := l + 1;
        for i := lp1 to k do
        begin
            g := E[i]; y := Q[i]; h := sn*g; g := cs*g;
            Construct_Givens(f,h,cs,sn,E[i-1]);
            f := x*cs+g*sn; g := -x*sn+g*cs;
            h := y*sn; y := y*cs;
            if Wntv then (* Accumulate right rotations V *
            for j:= 1 to nrv do
            Apply_Givens(cs,sn,V[i-1][j],V[i][j]);
```

Program 3.3(a) (cont.)

```
                    Construct_Givens(f,h,cs,sn,Q[i-1]);
                    f := cs*g+sn*y; x := cs*y-sn*g;
                    if Havers then (*Apply left_to_right rotations *
                    for j := 1 to ncc do
                    Apply_Givens(cs,sn,C[j][i-1],C[j][i])
                 end;
                 E[1] := 0; E[k] := f; Q[k] := x;
                 Nqrs := Nqrs + 1;
              end
              else Nqrs := N10 + 10
           until Nqrs > N10;
           if Nqrs = N10+1 then Fail := true;
           if z < 0 then (*Cutoff for convergence failure*)
           begin  (* Nqrs is normally 2*n *)
              Q[k] := -z;
              if Wntv then
              for j := 1 to nrv do
              V[k][j]:=-V[k][j]
           end (* Convergence tested *)
        end; (* Next, Q[k] is made non_negative *)
        if n <> 1 then
        begin
           i := 2;
           while i <= n do
           if Q[i] <= Q[i-1] then i := i+1
           else begin
              i := n+10;
              Last (* This is the ordering algorithm *)
           end;
           if (i=n+1) and Fail then Ipass := false;
        end;
     end
end;{QR-Bidiagonal_Decomposition}

procedure Householder(make_transf : boolean;  p,l,m,
number_of_vectors_to_transform : integer;
var v:vector; var vectors:matrix; var u_sub_p : real);

(*This function takes as input make_trans,p,l,m,number_
of_vectors_to_transform, and vectors V. The variable
make_trans indicates whether or not the Householder
transformation needs to be constructed or just applied.
If make_trans is true, the procedure Construct_House
(which constructs the transformation) is performed.
p,l and m are as defined in chapter ten of [LH68].
If number_of_vectors_to_transform is a positive
integer, the main body of the function Householder
computes the Householder transformation. In order to
compute the Householder transformation, we need
the vector u. This vector is computed in Construct_House.
Components l through m of u are  stored in v[l] through v[m]
and u[p] is stored in u_sub_p. All other components of the m_
vectors u are zero. In order to apply the Householder trans
formation, multiply the vector to be transformed by
 (I[m]+inner_product of(u,u_up_T))/(v[p]*u_sub_p).
v[p] should have been computed in Construct_House.
All the m_vectors to be transformed are stored in
the array called vector. All the transformed vectors
```

Program 3.3(a) (cont.)

```
are stored in the array vectors and passed back to
the main program as variable parameters. Vector u is also
passed back in the vector v as variable parameters and u[p]
is passed back directly as a result of the function *)
var
   b,s : real; nop : boolean; j,i : integer;

procedure Construct_House(var nop : boolean);
(*This procedure constructs the Householder
transformation. The algorithm used is steps 1
through 4 on page 57 of [LH68].*)
var j:integer; t,t_inv : real;
begin {*Construct_House*}
   t := abs(v[p]); (* Next we compute T for Eq.(3.71) *)
   for j:=1 to m do if t<abs(v[j]) then t:=abs(v[j]);
   if t>0 then
   begin (* First we compute the sum_of_squares *)
   t_inv := 1.0/t; s := sqr(v[p]*t_inv);
   for j := 1 to m do s := s+sqr(v[j]*t_inv);
   t := t*sqrt(s); (* T was s in Eq.(3.71). *)
   if v[p] > 0 then t := -t; (* sign of s *)
   u_sub_p := v[p] - t; (* Defining u[p] and y[p] *)
   v[p] := t  (* stored as v[p] *)
end
else nop := true
end;{*Construct_House*}

begin (*Householder. Check first condition for no_operations*)
   nop := (p<0) or (p>=1) or (1>m);
   if (not nop) and make_transf then Construct_House(nop);
   if not nop then (* nop could have resulted from Construct*)
   begin
      b := v[p] * u_sub_p;
      if b*number_of_vectors_to_transform <> 0 then
      for j:=1 to number_of_vectors_to_transform do
      begin
         s:=0;
         for i := 1 to m do s:= s+vectors[j][i]*v[i];
         s:= s+vectors[j][p]*u_sub_p; s := s/b;
         vectors[j][p]:=vectors[j][p]+s*u_sub_p;
         for i := 1 to m do vectors[j][i]:=
         vectors[j][i]+s*v[i]
      end
   end
end;{*Householder*}

begin{SingularValueDecomposition}
   n := nn;
   if (n>0) and (mm>0) then
   begin
      for j := n downto 1 do
      begin
         i := 1;
         while (i<=mm) and (abs(A[j][i])< eps) do i:=i+1;
         if (abs(A[j][i])<eps) and (i=mm+1) then
         begin (* If column j is all 0, exchange it with column n*)
            if j <> n then (*Next is the exchange*)
            for i := 1 to mm do A[j][i] := A[n][i];
```

Program 3.3(a) (cont.)

```
        A[n][1] := j; n := n-1;
      end
   end;
   ns := 0; (*If n=0 then matrix A is all 0 and the entire*)
   if n <> 0 then (*SVD computation could be skipped *)
   begin
      i := 1; m := mm;
      while (i<=n) and (i<m) do
      if abs(A[i][i])<eps then
      begin
         j := 1;
         while j <= n do
         if A[j][i] >= eps then
         begin
            i := i + 1; j := n + 10;
         end
         else j := j+1;
         if j = n+1 then
         begin
            if nb>0 then (*row i is 0. Exchange rows i and m.*)
            for j := 1 to nb do
            begin
               t := B[j][i];
               B[j][i] := B[j][m];
               B[j][m] := t
            end; (* Next finish the exchange *)
            for j := 1 to n do A[j][i] := A[j][m];
            if m<=n then
            for j:= 1 to n do A[j][m] := 0;
            m := m-1
         end
         else i := i+1
      end
      else i:= i+1;
This is where the SVD_algorithm begins. Its steps:
 Reduce the matrix to upper bidiagonal form with Householder's
 transformations: H(n)*   *H(1)*A*Q(1)*   *Q(n-2)=(D_up_t,0)**t
 where D is upper bidiagonal.
 Apply H(n),...,H(1) to b. Here H(n)*   *H(1)*B replaces B in memory.
 The matrix product W=Q[1]*   *Q[n-2] overwrites the first n rows of A.
 An SVD is computed on D.The resulting S-values are nonnegative and
 nonincreasing.
 With proper definitions, T_up_t*B overwrites B, while V overwrites
 the first n rows and columns of A. *)
      if m<n
      then l := m
      else l := n;
The following loop reduces A to upper bidiagonal and also
plies the premultiplying transformations to B. *)
      for j := 1 to l do
      begin
         if j<m then
         begin
            for k := 1 to n-j do V[k] := A[j+k];
            Householder(true,j,j+1,m,n-j,A[j],V,t);
            for k := 1 to n-j do A[j+k] := V[k];
            Householder(false,j,j+1,m,nb,A[j],B,t);
         end;
```

Program 3.3(a) (cont.)

```
                if j<n-1 then
                begin
                   k := 1;
                   while k<=n do
                   begin
                      U[k] := A[k][j]; k := k+1;
                   end;
                   for k:= j+1 to m do
                   for kk := 1 to n do
                   V[k-j][kk] := A[kk][k];
                   Householder(true,j+1,j+2,n,m-j,U,V,S[3][j]);
                   k := 1;
                   while k <= n do
                   begin
                      A[k][j] := U[k]; k := k+1
                   end;
                   for k:=j+1 to m do
                   for kk := 1 to n do
                   A[kk][k] := V[k-j][kk]
                end (*Next copy the bidiagonal matrix into array *)
             end; (* S for applying the QRBD-algorithm *)
             if n <> 1 then
             for j:= 2 to n do
             begin
                S[1][j] := A[j][j];
                S[2][j] := A[j][j-1]
             end;
             S[1][1] := A[1][1]; ns := n;
             if m<n then
             begin
                ns := m+1;
                S[1][ns] := 0;
                S[2][ns] := A[m+1][m]
             end;

    (*Construct the product matrix W=Q[1]*   *Q[1] in array A. *)
             for k := 1 to n do
             begin
                i := n+1-k;
                if i<n-1 then
                begin
                   kk := 1;
                   while kk<=n do
                   begin
                      U[kk] := A[kk][i]; kk := kk+1
                   end;
                   for kk := 1 to n-i do V[kk] := A[i+kk];
                   Householder(false,i+1,i+2,n,n-i,U,V,S[3][i]);
                   kk := 1;
                   while kk<=n do
                   begin
                      A[kk][i]:=U[kk]; kk := kk+1
                   end;
                   for kk:=1 to n-i do A[i+kk] := V[kk];
                end;
                for j:= 1 to n do A[j][i] := 0;
                A[i][i] := 1
             end;
```

Program 3.3(a) (cont.)

```
(*Compute the SVD of the bidiagonal matrix *)
            QR_Bidiagonal_Decomposition(Ipass,S[1],S[2],
               ns,n,nb,eps,A,B)

         end;
         if (n=0) or (Ipass=true) then
         begin
            if ns<n then
            begin
               nsp1 := ns+1;
               for j:=nsp1 to n do S[1][j] := 0
            end;
            if n<>nn then
            begin
               np1 := n + 1;
(*Move record of permutations and store zeros *)
               for j:= np1 to nn do
               begin
                  S[1][j] := A[j][1];
                  for i := 1 to n do A[j][i] := 0
               end; (*Permute rows and zero singular values *)
               for k:= np1 to nn do
               begin
                  i := trunc(S[1][k]);
                  S[1][k] := 0;
                  for j := 1 to nn do
                  begin
                     A[j][k] := A[j][i];
                     A[j][i] := 0
                  end;
                  A[k][i] := 1
               end
            end
         end
         else writeln ('convergence failure')
      end
   end;{SingularValueDecomposition}


   begin {prog}
      read(mm,nn,nb,eps);
      for j:=1 to nn do
         for i := 1 to mm do read(A[j][i]);
      for j := 1 to nb do
         for i := 1 to mm do read(B[i][j]);
      writeln ('The matrix A = US(transpose(V)) is');
      Print(A,nn);
      writeln('The input matrix B (Ax => B) is');
      Print(B,nb);

      SingularValueDecompostion(A,B,S,mm,nn,nb,eps);

      writeln ('The matrix V is');
      Print(A,nn);
      writeln('The matrix transpose(U)B is');
      Print(B,nb);
      writeln('The singular values of A are');
      for j := 1 to mm do writeln (S[1][j]:10:5)
   end.
```

Program 3.3(a) (cont.)

```
The matrix A = US(transpose(V)) is
   4.40000    -4.40000    -5.07000         0.0         0.0         0.0
  -4.40000    36.28000    14.50000    -9.46000    -5.13000   -21.72000
       0.0    -5.07000    -9.46000    18.90000    -9.46000         0.0
       0.0         0.0         0.0    -9.46000         0.0         0.0
       0.0    -5.13000         0.0         0.0    35.07000    -5.19000
       0.0   -21.72000         0.0         0.0    -5.19000    31.14000

The output matrix B (Ax => B) is
   1.00000         0.0         0.0         0.0         0.0         0.0
       0.0     1.00000         0.0         0.0         0.0         0.0
       0.0         0.0     1.00000         0.0         0.0         0.0
       0.0         0.0         0.0     1.00000         0.0         0.0
       0.0         0.0         0.0         0.0     1.00000         0.0
       0.0         0.0         0.0         0.0         0.0     1.00000

The matrix V is
  -0.06489     0.02324    -0.05859     0.34629    -0.89343     0.27145
   0.73096    -0.16720     0.06075    -0.30871    -0.32730    -0.48128
   0.22724    -0.00650     0.43713    -0.48459    -0.01360     0.72265
  -0.18411    -0.08999    -0.76194    -0.58808    -0.13013     0.12118
   0.00910     0.96791     0.02302    -0.18863    -0.09151    -0.13630
  -0.61308    -0.16282     0.46980    -0.41053    -0.26299    -0.37310

The matrix transpose(U)B is
  -0.08011     0.77656    -0.16218     0.02998    -0.00428    -0.60276
   0.02279    -0.17903    -0.26038     0.02228     0.93302    -0.16914
  -0.10897     0.22601    -0.75769     0.28651    -0.07721     0.52432
   0.48236    -0.38874    -0.28739     0.50263    -0.26210    -0.46074
  -0.83850    -0.25199     0.06730     0.42618    -0.05728    -0.20970
  -0.21315    -0.31499    -0.49466    -0.69444    -0.22696    -0.27731

The singular values of A are
  58.09097
  38.20646
  25.15777
  11.06825
   2.88849
   1.65073
```

Program 3.3(b)

TABLE 3.6 Singular values of various networks

7-bus	0.8091	0.4231	0.3469	0.3138	0.1865	0.0572	0.0001				
11-bus	1.5265	0.7630	0.6967	0.4192	0.3375	0.2658	0.1902	0.0959	0.0526	0.0372	0.0000
22-bus	1.7491	1.2363	0.9002	0.7856	0.7456	0.5319	0.4821	0.4208	0.4136	0.3704	0.2844
	0.2505	0.1865	0.1572	0.1317	0.1015	0.0898	0.0830	0.0498	0.0407	0.0353	0.0000
30-bus	2.1336	1.7791	1.3946	1.3013	1.2398	0.9912	0.9188	0.7781	0.7483	0.6946	
	0.5346	0.4877	0.4354	0.4144	0.3961	0.3634	0.2977	0.2615	0.2329	0.1975	
	0.1817	0.1327	0.1147	0.1013	0.0923	0.0824	0.0573	0.0444	0.0301	0.0000	

TABLE 3.7 Singular values of various networks.

Buses	14	30	57	118
s_1	3796	11813	19962	336,356
s_n	4.55	0.51	0.24	0.04

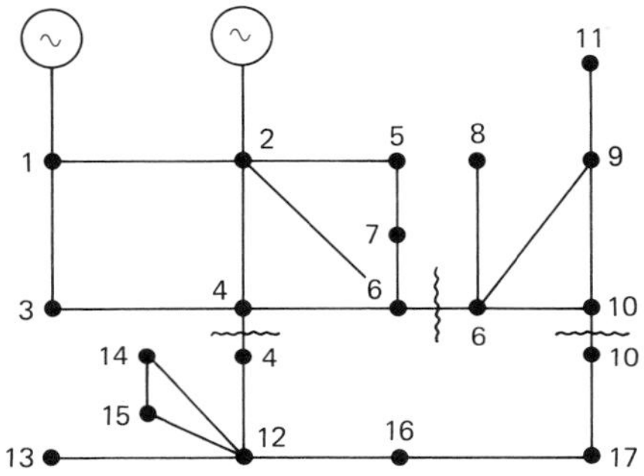

Figure 3.20 Partial network.

3.6 NOTES AND A PROJECT

3.6.1 Notes

The material on short-circuit calculations can be found in [Br75, El71, Gr79, Ha80, SE68, St62, and WE33]. The method actually suggested is based on [TFC73] and the updating part on [Gea74].

A short-circuit program should be based on factorization as discussed in Section 2.6, and on updating methods [Eqs. (2.60) to (2.64)]. The question is how to reduce the errors for cases like those shown in Fig. 3.7. This is easily done by using the updating methods of Section 2.6. For the original network of Fig. 3.7, the **Y** matrix is

$$\mathbf{Y} = \begin{bmatrix} 10{,}002.5 & -10{,}000 \\ -10{,}000 & 10{,}001.67 \end{bmatrix}$$

and the **L** and **D** matrices can be computed as follows:

$$\mathbf{L} = \begin{bmatrix} 1 & 0 \\ -0.9997501 & 1 \end{bmatrix}$$

$$d_1 = 10{,}002.5$$

$$d_2 = 4.17$$

Opening of line $1-2$ is reflected by $\tilde{\mathbf{Y}} = \mathbf{Y} + c \cdot \mathbf{a} * \mathbf{a}^{\mathrm{T}}$ with $c = 20{,}000$ and $\mathbf{a}^{\mathrm{T}} = [1/\sqrt{2}\ ,\ -1/\sqrt{2}\ ]$. Therefore **b** and **E** are

$$\mathbf{b} = \mathbf{L}^{-1} * \mathbf{a} = \begin{bmatrix} 1 & 0 \\ 0.9997501 & 1 \end{bmatrix} * \begin{bmatrix} 1/\sqrt{2} \\ 1/\sqrt{2} \end{bmatrix} = \frac{1}{\sqrt{2}} \cdot \begin{bmatrix} 1 \\ -0.0002499 \end{bmatrix}$$

$$\mathbf{E} = \mathbf{D} - 20{,}000 * \mathbf{b} * \mathbf{b}^{\mathrm{T}} = \begin{bmatrix} 2.5 & 2.4999 \\ 2.4999 & 4.17 \end{bmatrix}$$

This **E** is next factored into $\tilde{\mathbf{L}} * \mathbf{D} * \tilde{\mathbf{L}}^{\mathrm{T}}$ with $L_{2,1} = 0.9996$, $d_1 = 2.5$, and $d_2 = 1.67$. The new $\mathbf{L}^{\#}$ is

$$\mathbf{L}^{\#} = \mathbf{L} * \tilde{\mathbf{L}} = \begin{bmatrix} 1 & 0 \\ -0.99997501 & 1 \end{bmatrix} * \begin{bmatrix} 1 & 0 \\ 0.9996 & 1 \end{bmatrix}$$

$$= \begin{bmatrix} 1 & 0 \\ -0.00015 & 1 \end{bmatrix}$$

and **D** remains as it was. Next we compute $w_1 = 1/d_1 = 0.4$, and $w_2 = 1/1.67 = 0.5999$, and set up the recursive equation

$$\begin{bmatrix} Z_{1,1} & Z_{1,2} \\ Z_{1,2} & Z_{2,2} \end{bmatrix} = \begin{bmatrix} 0.4 & 0 \\ 0 & 0.5999 \end{bmatrix} + \begin{bmatrix} 0 & 0.00015 \\ 0 & 0 \end{bmatrix} * \begin{bmatrix} Z_{1,1} & Z_{1,2} \\ Z_{2,1} & Z_{2,2} \end{bmatrix}$$

From it we get first $Z_{2,2} = 0.5999$, then $Z_{1,2} = Z_{2,1} \cong 0$, and finally $Z_{1,1} = 0.4$. The new matrix is a diagonal matrix with $Z_{1,1} = 0.4$ and $Z_{2,2} = 0.5999$, as it should be [We84].

We discussed errors at length, and this invites the following criticism:

Since short-circuit studies involve the solution of linear systems, the computational error is due to roundoff in the triangularization. It seems that the issue of the numerical errors is rather insignificant, since the error introduced by the assumption of linearity for the nonlinear network may involve considerably more severe errors.

The treatment of roundoff errors was still worthwhile, however, because the conclusions supported the use of the method proposed in

[TFC73] anyway and *updating reduces the number of operations and hence the time to a very large degree* (see [Gea74]), in addition to reducing the error.

3.6.2 Project

An efficient factorization program will be described in Chapter 4. If the reader assumes its availability, he or she can additionally write a program for updating $\mathbf{L} * \mathbf{D} * \mathbf{L}^{\mathrm{T}}$ and combine it with factorization into a short-circuit program, test it out on the networks of Chapter 1, and add input/output. The result would be a complete short-circuit program.

4 Load Flow

The *objectives* of this chapter are

1. To define the problem as that of solving a large, sparse set of nonlinear algebraic equations.
2. To show how linearization—the Newton – Raphson method—leads to a number of algorithms.
3. To develop a program which can be the basis for decoupled, optimally ordered factorization.

4.1 DEFINITION OF THE PROBLEM

4.1.1 Basic Equations

Load-flow calculations deal with steady-state equations of a power network. They are needed for planning, optimization, and also as part of stability calculations.

Load-flow equations are nonlinear and algebraic. They are nonlinear because they express powers as a function of voltages. They are algebraic rather than differential because they describe the steady-state instead of the transient behavior of the network. Their coefficients (admittances) are constant.

The complex power injected into bus k by a generator is

$$p_k + j\cdot q_k = u_k'\cdot i_k'' = u_k'\cdot\Sigma\, u_m''\cdot y_{km}''; \quad m\Sigma = 0, \ldots, n \tag{4.1}$$

where $y_{km}' = g_{km} + j\cdot b_{km}$ and therefore $y_{km}'' = g_{km} - j\cdot b_{km}$. Inserting for the injected power $p_k + jq_k = (v_k + jw_k) \cdot \Sigma\, [(v_m - jw_m) \cdot (g_{km} - jb_{km})]$, and separating the real and imaginary parts yields

$$p_k = v_k\cdot\Sigma\, (v_m g_{km} - w_m b_{km}) + w_k\cdot\Sigma\, (w_m g_{km} + v_m b_{km}); \tag{4.2}$$

$$q_k = w_k\cdot\Sigma\, (v_m g_{km} - w_m b_{km}) - v_k\cdot\Sigma\, (w_m g_{km} + v_m b_{km}); \tag{4.3}$$

$$m\Sigma = 0, \ldots, n$$

Defining (for the sake of brevity)

$$S(k) = \Sigma\, (v_m g_{km} - w_m b_{km}); \quad m\Sigma = 0, \ldots, n \tag{4.4}$$

$$Z(k) = \Sigma\, (w_m g_{km} + v_m b_{km}); \quad m\Sigma = 0, \ldots, n \tag{4.5}$$

and substituting into Eqs. (4.2) and (4.3) yields

$$p_k = v_k\cdot S(k) + w_k\cdot Z(k); \qquad q_k = w_k\cdot S(k) - v_k\cdot Z(k) \tag{4.6}$$

This system of equations will be called <u>R1</u>.

Another useful Cartesian representation (to be called <u>R2</u>) may be derived from Eqs. (4.6) by multiplying p_k and q_k by the voltages (and recalling that $u^2 = v^2 + w^2$) as follows:

$$\frac{p_k\cdot v_k + q_k\cdot w_k}{u_k^2} = S(k); \qquad \frac{p_k\cdot w_k - q_k\cdot v_k}{u_k^2} = Z(k) \tag{4.7}$$

In polar coordinates

$$u_k' = u_k\cdot\exp(j\theta_k); \qquad y_{k,m}' = y_{k,m}\cdot\exp(j\psi_{k,m}) \tag{4.8}$$

Separating the real and imaginary parts and substituting into Eq. (4.1) yields the following system of equations (to be called the <u>P</u> system, for "polar"):

$$p_k = u_k\cdot\Sigma\, u_m\cdot y_{km}\cdot\cos(-\theta_k + \theta_m + \psi_{km}); \quad m\Sigma = 0, \ldots, n \tag{4.9}$$

$$q_k = u_k\cdot\Sigma\, u_m\cdot y_{km}\cdot\sin(-\theta_k + \theta_m + \psi_{km}); \quad m\Sigma = 0, \ldots, n \tag{4.10}$$

It is seen that the systems (P), (R1), and (R2) express the injected powers (the real and imaginary parts thereof, also referred to as active and reactive powers) *as functions of the nodal voltages.* These functions are quadratic in v_k, w_k, or u_k, and since we usually know the powers and seek the voltages, we conclude that these equations are algebraic but nonlinear.

We express other quantities also as functions of voltage. For instance, the *line flows*, i.e., the active and reactive powers flowing through a transmission line k – m from bus k to bus m equal, respectively,

$$p_{km} = -[v_k\cdot(v_k - v_m) + w_k\cdot(w_k - w_m)]\cdot g_{km} \tag{4.11}$$
$$+ [v_k\cdot(w_k - w_m) - w_k\cdot(v_k - v_m)]\cdot b_{km}$$

$$\begin{aligned} q_{km} = {} & [v_k \cdot (v_k - v_m) + w_k \cdot (w_k - w_m)] \cdot b_{km} \\ & + [v_k \cdot (w_k - w_m) - w_k \cdot (v_k - v_m)] \cdot g_{km} \\ & - (v_k^2 + w_k^2) \cdot y_{c(km)} \end{aligned} \tag{4.12}$$

Note that this expression includes the powers of both the series and the shunt admittances.

4.1.2 Definition of the Load-Flow Problem

Let $\{p_k, q_k, v_k, w_k\}$ with k from 0 to n be the set of $n + 1$ four-vectors of variables, where the ith vector is associated with the ith bus. A load-flow (LF) problem, in general, can be defined as follows:

Given 2(n + 1) of these quantities, determine the remaining 2(n + 1) quantities.

To this end, regard any of the sets $\underline{R}$ as a system of $2(n + 1)$ equations, where the unknowns are the $2(n + 1)$ quantities to be determined, and solve for these unknowns. (A similar problem may be posed in polar coordinates, set $\underline{P}$.)

The classification of the variables as given and unknown is not ours to make. For example, let the voltages of all buses be known and the injected powers sought. Thus $\{v_k, w_k\}$ are given and $\{p_k, q_k\}$ are sought. The solution of this "load-flow" problem follows trivially the substitution into $\underline{R1}$ or $\underline{R2}$. Note, however, that this is an exceptionally simple case; normally $\{p_k, q_k\}$ may be given and $\{v_k, w_k\}$ sought. In this case $\underline{R1}$ or $\underline{R2}$ form a set of algebraic nonlinear equations—a situation which characterizes all practical load-flow problems.

The load-flow problems encountered in actual practice are of mixed type; different known and unknown quantities are associated with different buses. Many types of buses are discussed in literature [El71], of which only three will be mentioned here:

1. Generation buses. At these p_k and u_k can be controlled and are regarded as given quantities whereas q_k and θ_k depend on the behavior of the entire network and are thus unknown. The generation buses will be numbered from 1 to n^g.
2. Load buses. At these the power consumption, i.e., p_k and q_k, are assumed to be known (from statistics, measurements, etc.) and v_k and w_k are to be calculated. Load buses will be numbered from $n^g + 1$ to n so that their number is $n^c = n - n^g$.
3. Slack or swing bus. At this bus v_k and w_k are assumed to be known. The introduction of this bus into the power network is dictated by theoretical considerations and will be discussed later. For

the moment note that the (single) slack bus has index 0 so that only types 1 and 2 for $k = 1, \ldots, n$ are present.

Under these assumptions, the load-flow problem seems to read in polar coordinates as follows:

Given $\{p_k, u_k = \sqrt{v_k^2 + w_k^2}\}$; $k = 0, \ldots, n^g$ and $\{p_k, q_k\}$; $k = n^g + 1, \ldots, n$,

determine $\{q_k, \theta_k\}$; $k = 0, \ldots, n^g$, and $\{u_k, \theta_k\}$ for $k = n^g + 1, \ldots, n$.

Since the voltage of the slack bus is known, there are $2 \cdot (n + 1) = 2 \cdot (n^g + n^c + 1)$ equations in the $\underline{P}$-system but only $2 \cdot (n^c + n^g)$ unknowns. We drop therefore index $k = 0$ and define the problem as that of solving the set of $n + n^c$ equations (4.9) and (4.10):

$$p_k = u_k \cdot \Sigma\, u_m \cdot y_{km} \cdot \cos(\theta_k - \theta_m - \psi_{km}); \tag{4.13}$$

$$k = 1, \ldots, n; \quad m\Sigma = 0, \ldots, n$$

$$q_k = u_k \cdot \Sigma\, u_m \cdot y_{km} \cdot \sin(\theta_k - \theta_m - \psi_{km}); \tag{4.14}$$

$$k = n^g + 1, \ldots, n; \quad m\Sigma = 0, \ldots, n$$

for the unknowns $\{u_k\}$, $k = n^g + 1, \ldots, n$, and $\{\theta_k\}$, $k = 1, \ldots, n$. Having determined the unknown u_k, θ_k, the values of $\{q_k\}$, $k = 1, \ldots, n^g$, can be computed directly from Eq. (4.10).

Similar modifications may be introduced in $\underline{R1}$. It consists of $2 \cdot (n + 1)$ equations in $2(n^c + n^g) + n^g$ unknowns, namely, $\{v_k, w_k\}$, $k = 1, \ldots, n$, and $\{q_k\}$, $k = 1, \ldots, n^g$. Since for all n^g generators $u_k^2 = v_k^2 + w_k^2$ and u_k are known values, we may augment $\underline{R1}$ by these equalities.

Finally, the number of equations can be reduced by again dropping equations and unknowns q_k for $k = 1, \ldots, n^g$. The transformed problem is now the following:

Solve for $2 \cdot n$ unknowns $\{v_k, w_k\}$, $k = 1, \ldots, n$, the system of $2 \cdot n$ equations:

$$\begin{aligned} p_k &= v_k \cdot S(k) + w_k \cdot Z_k; \quad k = 1, \ldots, n \\ q_k &= w_k \cdot S(k) - v_k \cdot Z(k); \quad k = n^g + 1, \ldots, n \\ u_k^2 &= v_k^2 + w_k^2; \quad k = 1, \ldots, n^g \end{aligned} \tag{4.15}$$

A similar procedure can be carried out for $\underline{R2}$ so that

$$\frac{p_k v_k + q_k w_k}{v_k^2 + w_k^2} = S(k); \quad k = 1, \ldots, n$$

$$\frac{p_k w_k - q_k v_k}{v_k^2 + w_k^2} = Z(k); \quad k = n^g + 1, \ldots, n \tag{4.16}$$

$$v_k^2 + w_k^2 = u_k^2; \quad k = 1, \ldots, n^g$$

The Slack Bus. The systems as presented are still not ready for solving LF. Although in each case the number of unknowns equals the number of equations, the systems are not well posed, in the sense that, as defined above, they allow an infinite number of solutions or none at all.

Consider Eq. (4.13). It is readily seen that the unknown angles θ appear only in the form of differences $\theta_k - \theta_m$. Thus, the change of variables $\tilde{\theta}_k = \theta_k - \theta$, where θ is an arbitrary constant, leaves the equations unchanged. The resulting u_ks are therefore defined up to a rotation. However, if θ_0 is assigned an arbitrary fixed value, Eq. (4.13) has more equations than variables and can be solved only if one of the equations is deleted.

It is customary to choose a generator bus s, set $\theta = \theta_s$ (thus assuming phase angle 0 at this bus), and delete the equation $p_s = \ldots$ for this s. This particular bus, which we will number 0, is called the *slack* or *swing bus*. Since the voltage $u_0 \cdot \exp(\theta_0)$ is specified, index k of Eq. (4.13) ranged from 1 to n (rather than from 0 to n).

The three sets may be solved by various methods (to be presented later) and yield a set of voltages at all buses of the network. These in turn determine the real power of the slack bus via Eq. (4.13) for $k = 0$. It is thus seen that this power could not have been fixed beforehand, because such predetermination of p_0 may disagree with the result given by the rest of the network. Therefore, the original set of equations may not possess any solution. In short, we may not impose an arbitrary set of real powers at all buses; one of these powers must remain unspecified. This is precisely the power injected at the slack bus.

To clarify the situation further, consider the "degenerate" power system in Fig. 4.1. (This system has no claim to reality and is analyzed here solely for the purpose of illustrating the foregoing discussion.)

Let us assume that power consumption at bus 2 is $p_2 = -1$, $q_2 = 1$, that reference voltage at bus 1 is $1 + j \cdot 0$, and that the real injection of the generator at bus 1 equals $p_1 = 3$. The voltage $u_2' = v_2 + j \cdot w_2$ has to be computed.

The calculation is as follows: $i' = \Delta u' \cdot y' = (1 - u_2') \cdot (1 + j)$;

$$p_2 + j \cdot q_2 = u_2' \cdot i_2'' = (v_2 + j \cdot w_2) \cdot [(1 - v_2 + w_2) - j \cdot (1 - v_2 - w_2)]$$

$$= [v_2 + w_2 - (v_2^2 + w_2^2)] + j \cdot [w_2 - v_2 + (v_2^2 + w_2^2)]$$

Equating the real and imaginary parts on both sides yields

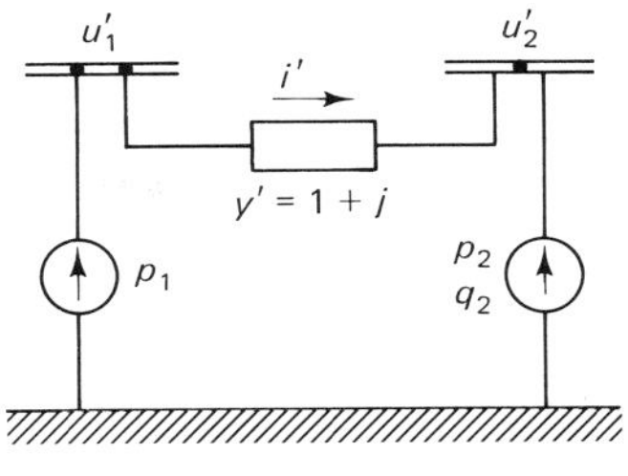

Figure 4.1 A degenerate system.

$$p_2 = -1 = v_2 + w_2 - (v_2^2 + w_2^2);$$

$$q_2 = +1 = -v_2 + w_2 + (v_2^2 + w_2^2)$$

Hence, $w_2 = 0$, $v_2 = (1 \pm \sqrt{5})/2$. The objective of the load-flow solution has thus been achieved, without recourse to p_1. Moreover, $i' = (1 \pm \sqrt{5})\cdot(1 - j)/2$, and $p_1 + jq_1 = u_1' \cdot i''= (1 \pm \sqrt{5})(2 + j)/2$, which lead to $p_1 = (1 \pm \sqrt{5})/2$; $q_2 = (1 \pm \sqrt{5})/2$. It is seen that the initial set of data was incompatible.

It may be asked whether we could not have chosen an arbitrary value of θ so that p_1 as obtained from the preceding computation equals the preassigned value $p_1 = 3$. The answer is negative. The equations do not depend on θ, and thus any choice of θ should yield the same $p_1 = (1 \pm \sqrt{5})/2$.

To sum up: The injected power of the slack bus should be left unspecified.

A Special Case of Load Flow. An often-discussed case of load flow occurs when no generator buses exist in the system except for the slack bus. Under this assumption every bus has its p and q specified. This type of problem appears, for example, in solving for transient stability, where LF is part of the calculation. It is also used in contingency analysis, which seeks to foresee the results of a change in a network structure. If it can be assumed that as a result of this change the outputs of the generators and the loads change very little, then the problem of determining the voltages after the change, given the powers before the change, reduces to this special case of LF.

Apart from its usefulness in many applications, this type of LF exhibits symmetry (all buses but the slack bus are of the same type). Furthermore, it turns out that its system of equations becomes well posed if two equations — one of the p type and another of the q type—are deleted and the real and imaginary part of some voltage are fixed. The slack bus is therefore left out completely with both its p and q equations gone and its voltage a constant. The symmetry of the system is thus preserved. The reason why two equations have to be deleted rather than one is that the law of conservation of energy applies to reactive as well as to real power. For both, a degree of freedom must be left to balance the generated, consumed, and lost powers.

4.1.3 General Solutions

Let us next rewrite once more the three possible formulations of the load-flow problem.

P: Solve, for $k = 1, \ldots, n$ (but not $k = 0$),

$$p_k = u_k \cdot \Sigma\, u_m \cdot y_{km} \cos(\theta_k - \theta_m - \psi_{km});\quad m\Sigma = 0 \ldots, n \tag{4.17}$$

$$q_k = u_k \cdot \Sigma\, u_m \cdot y_{km} \sin(\theta_k - \theta_m - \psi_{km});\quad m\Sigma = 0, \ldots, n \tag{4.18}$$

The unknown values are u_k for the load, q_k for the generator, and θ_k for all buses. Note that these are nonlinear equations because of the transcendental sine and cosine functions.

R1: Solve, for $k = 1, \ldots, n$,

$$p_k = v_k \cdot \Sigma\,(v_m g_{km} - w_m b_{km}) - w_k \cdot \Sigma\,(w_m g_{km} + v_m b_{km});$$

$$q_k = w_k \cdot \Sigma\,(v_m g_{km} - w_m b_{km}) - v_k \cdot \Sigma\,(w_m g_{km} + v_m b_{km});$$

The unknown values are the voltages v_k, w_k of all buses (except the slack bus 0). These are nonlinear, algebraic equations, since products of voltages, e.g., $v_k \cdot v_m$, occur.

R2: Solve, for $k = 1, \ldots, n$,

$$\frac{p_k v_k + q_k w_k}{v_k^2 + w_k^2} = \Sigma\,(v_m g_{km} - w_m b_{km});\quad m\Sigma = 0, \ldots, n$$

$$\frac{p_k w_k - q_k v_k}{v_k^2 + w_k^2} = \Sigma\,(w_m g_{km} + v_m b_{km});\quad m\Sigma = 0, \ldots, n$$

The nonlinearity appears in the "diagonal" terms with u_k^2.

In all three cases we can transfer all terms to one side and have thus to solve a vector function $\mathbf{r}$ of *residuals*,

$$\mathbf{r}(\mathbf{x}) = \mathbf{0} \tag{4.19}$$

where the components of $\mathbf{x}$ are the voltages (their real and imaginary parts in the case of R1 and R2 and their moduli and angles for P).

The function $\mathbf{r}$ has $2n$ components, i.e., there are $2n$ equations r_i, $i = 1, \ldots, 2n$ for some $2n$ unknowns x_i, $i = 1, \ldots., 2n$.

Before we discuss the solution of these equations, let us briefly take up the simpler case of a single nonlinear equation $f(x) = 0$. There are a number of methods to solve this equation; we will discuss one of the more popular.

The Newton – Raphson method.

Suppose we have an approximation x_1 such that $f(x_1) \cong 0$. If we had $f(x_1) = 0$, then x_1 would have been the solution. As seen in Fig. 4.2, x_1 is only an approximation and $f(x_1) \equiv f_1 \neq 0$.

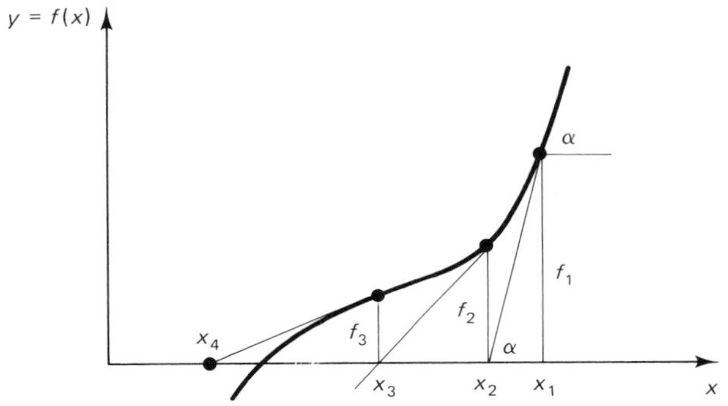

Figure 4.2 A scalar function.

Next, draw a slope through point (x_1, f_1) which crosses the x-axis at point x_2. This point is clearly a better approximation than x_1. Let us calculate it.

The slope $\tan(\alpha)$ is $f_1/(x_1 - x_2)$ from the triangle in Fig. 4.2. It also is the derivative $g_1 \equiv df/dx$ at point (x_1, f_1). Thus $g_1 = f_1/(x_1 - x_2)$ or $x_1 - x_2 = f_1/g_1$ and, finally,

$$x_2 = x_1 - \frac{f_1}{g_1}$$

The value of x_2 is such that $f(x_2) = f_2$ is still not zero and we have to *iterate* further, i.e., use x_2 to calculate x_3, etc., until we are close enough to the solution and to $f(x) \cong 0$. In every iteration, then, $x_{i+1} := x_i - f_i/g_i$.

For power systems f is a vector function $\mathbf{r}$ and the derivative g is replaced by the Jacobian matrix $\mathbf{J(x)}$ with elements i, k defined as

$$J_{i,k} \equiv J(\mathbf{x})_{i,k} = \frac{\partial r_i}{\partial x_k}$$

i.e., element (i, k) of matrix $\mathbf{J}$ results from differentiating function r_i partially to unknown x_k and inserting the present values of $\mathbf{x}$.

No division by a matrix is possible; instead, we use multiplication by the inverse of $\mathbf{J}$, written as $\mathbf{J}^{-1}$. Thus, instead of $x_{i+1} := x_i - f_i/g_i$ we have

$$\mathbf{x}_{i+1} := \mathbf{x}_i - \mathbf{J}_i^{-1} * \mathbf{r}_i$$

This is more conveniently solved as follows. Rewrite the equation as $\mathbf{J}_i^{-1} * \mathbf{r}_i = \mathbf{x}_i - \mathbf{x}_{i+1}$ and multiply both sides by $\mathbf{J}_i$. Since $\mathbf{J}_i * \mathbf{J}_i^{-1}$ is a unity matrix $\mathbf{I}$ and $\mathbf{I} * \mathbf{r} = \mathbf{r}$ for any vector $\mathbf{r}$, we

$$\mathbf{J}_i * (\mathbf{x}_i - \mathbf{x}_{i+1}) = \mathbf{r}_i \tag{4.20}$$

This is a set of linear equations in the unknown vector $\mathbf{x}_{i+1}$. It is solved as follows:

Given an approximation $\mathbf{x}_i$, insert it into the equations defining $\mathbf{r}_i$ and $\mathbf{J}_i$ and then *solve numerically* the linear set Eq. (4.20) for $\mathbf{x}_{i+1}$. Next, use this $\mathbf{x}_{i+1}$ as an approximation to compute a better value $\mathbf{x}_{i+2}$ and proceed until you are satisfied that the *problem converges*, i.e., that the changes $\mathbf{x}_i - \mathbf{x}_{i+1}$ are small enough.

As seen, the Jacobian matrix plays an important role. For system R1, straightforward differentiation shows that the Jacobian has the elements

$$\begin{aligned}
\frac{\partial p_k}{\partial v_k} &= 2v_k g_{kk} + \Sigma\,(v_m g_{km} - w_m b_{km}); \quad m \neq k \\
\frac{\partial p_k}{\partial w_k} &= 2w_k g_{kk} + \Sigma\,(w_m g_{km} + v_m b_{km}); \quad m \neq k \\
\frac{\partial q_k}{\partial v_k} &= -2v_k b_{kk} - \Sigma\,(w_m g_{km} + v_m b_{km}) - v_k \cdot \Sigma\, y_{km}; \quad m \neq k \\
\frac{\partial q_k}{\partial w_k} &= -2w_k b_{kk} + \Sigma\,(v_m g_{km} - w_m b_{km}) - w_k \cdot \Sigma\, y_{km}; \quad m \neq k
\end{aligned} \tag{4.21}$$

where all sums have $m\Sigma = 1, \ldots, n$ except $m = k$ (as indicated). For subscript $h \neq k$ we have

$$\begin{aligned}
\frac{\partial p_k}{\partial v_h} &= v_k g_{kh} + w_k b_{kh} \\
\frac{\partial p_k}{\partial w_h} &= -v_k b_{kh} + w_k g_{kh} \\
\frac{\partial q_k}{\partial v_h} &= w_k g_{kh} - v_k b_{kh} \\
\frac{\partial q_k}{\partial w_h} &= -w_k b_{kh} - v_k g_{kh}
\end{aligned} \tag{4.22}$$

(Observe the regular structure of these derivatives.)

$$\frac{\partial u_k^2}{\partial v_k} = 2v_k \tag{4.23}$$

$$\frac{\partial u_k^2}{\partial w_k} = 2w_k$$

For system R2 we have

$$\frac{\partial p_k}{\partial v_k} = g_{kk} + \frac{2q_k v_k w_k - p_k(v_k^2 - w_k^2)}{u_k^4}$$

$$\frac{\partial p_k}{\partial w_k} = -b_{kk} + \frac{2p_k v_k w_k - q_k(v_k^2 - w_k^2)}{u_k^4} \tag{4.24}$$

$$\frac{\partial q_k}{\partial v_k} = b_{kk} + \frac{2q_k v_k w_k - p_k(v_k^2 - w_k^2)}{u_k^4}$$

$$\frac{\partial q_k}{\partial w_k} = g_{kk} + \frac{2p_k v_k w_k - q_k(v_k^2 - w_k^2)}{u_k^4}$$

To bring out the symmetry of the off-diagonal elements, we write them as follows:

$$\frac{\partial p_k}{\partial v_h} = g_{kh} \qquad \frac{\partial p_k}{\partial w_h} = -b_{kh} \tag{4.25}$$

$$\frac{\partial q_k}{\partial v_h} = b_{kh} \qquad \frac{\partial q_k}{\partial w_h} = g_{kh}$$

It can be seen that the Jacobian of R2 is much simpler than that of R1; in particular its off-diagonal part ($k \neq h$) is constant and independent of **v** and **w**, so that its formation does not require any arithmetic operations (as opposed to R1).

The general expressions in polar coordinates for power at bus i, Eqs. (4.1), are repeated with $\psi_{k,m} = 0$ and $\theta_{i,j} \equiv \theta_i - \theta_j$. Since

$$u_j'\cdot y_{ij}'' = u_j\cdot[\cos(\theta_j) + j\sin(\theta_j)]\cdot(g_{ij} - jb_{ij})$$

we have

$$p_i = u_i\cdot\Sigma\, u_j\cdot[g_{ij}\cdot\cos(\theta_{ij}) + b_{ij}\cdot\sin(\theta_{ij})] \tag{4.26}$$

$$q_i = u_i\cdot\Sigma\, u_j\cdot[g_{ij}\cdot\sin(\theta_{ij}) - b_{ij}\cdot\cos(\theta_{ij})]$$

Separating case $i = j$ from the sum for p_i yields

$$p_i = u_i^2\cdot g_{ii} + u_i\cdot\Sigma\, u_j\cdot[g_{ij}\cdot\cos(\theta_{ij}) + b_{ij}\cdot\sin(\theta_{ij})]; \quad j\Sigma \neq i$$

For $i \neq j$, then,

$$\frac{\partial p_i}{\partial \theta_j} = u_i \cdot u_j \cdot \frac{\partial [g_{ij} \cdot \cos(\theta_{ij}) + b_{ij} \cdot \sin(\theta_{ij})]}{\partial \theta_j}$$

Since

$$\cos(\theta_{ij}) \equiv \cos(\theta_i - \theta_j) = \cos(\theta_i) \cdot \cos(\theta_j) + \sin(\theta_i) \cdot \sin(\theta_j)$$

$$\sin(\theta_{ij}) \equiv \sin(\theta_i - \theta_j) = \sin(\theta_i) \cdot \cos(\theta_j) - \cos(\theta_i) \cdot \sin(\theta_j)$$

we have to differentiate

$$g_{ij} \cdot [\cos(\theta_i) \cdot \cos(\theta_j) + \sin(\theta_i) \cdot \sin(\theta_j)] + b_{ij} \cdot [\mathit{sin}\ (\theta_i) \cdot \cos(\theta_j) - \cos(\theta_i) \cdot \sin(\theta_j)]$$

Differentiation yields

$$g_{ij} \cdot [\mathit{sin}\ (\theta_i) \cdot \cos(\theta_j) - \cos(\theta_i) \cdot \sin(\theta_j)] - b_{ij} \cdot [\sin(\theta_i) \cdot \sin(\theta_j) + \cos(\theta_i) \cdot \cos(\theta_j)]$$

$$= g_{ij} \cdot \sin(\theta_i - \theta_j) - b_{ij} \cdot \cos(\theta_i - \theta_j) = g_{ij} \cdot \sin(\theta_{ij}) - b_{ij} \cdot \cos(\theta_{ij})$$

This was true for $i \neq j$. Next, for $i = j$,

$$\frac{\partial p_i}{\partial \theta_i} = u_i \cdot u_j \cdot \frac{\partial [g_{ij} \cdot \cos(\theta_{ij}) + b_{ij} \cdot \sin(\theta_{ij})]}{\partial \theta_i}; \quad j\Sigma = 1, \ldots, n$$

Using the $\cos(\theta_{ij})$ and $\sin(\theta_{ij})$ identities above, we obtain

$$\partial [g_{ij} \cdot \cos(\theta_{ij}) + b_{ij} \cdot \sin(\theta_{ij})] / \partial \theta_i$$

$$= g_{ij} \cdot [\sin(\theta_j) \cdot \cos(\theta_i) - \cos(\theta_j) \cdot \sin(\theta_i)] + b_{ij} \cdot [\cos(\theta_j) \cdot \cos(\theta_i) + \sin(\theta_j) \cdot \sin(\theta_i)]$$

$$= g_{ij} \cdot \sin(\theta_{ji}) + b_{ij} \cdot \cos(\theta_{ji}) = b_{ij} \cdot \cos(\theta_{ij}) - g_{ij} \cdot \sin(\theta_{ij})$$

Thus,

$$\frac{\partial p_i}{\partial \theta_j} = u_i \cdot u_j \cdot [g_{ij} \cdot \sin(\theta_{ij}) - b_{ij} \cdot \cos(\theta_{ij})] \tag{4.27}$$

$$\frac{\partial p_i}{\partial \theta_i} = u_i \cdot u_j \cdot [b_{ij} \cdot \cos(\theta_{ij}) - g_{ij} \cdot \sin(\theta_{ij})]$$

Differentiation yields also:

$$\frac{\partial p_i}{\partial u_i} = u_i^2 \cdot b_{ii} - q_i \tag{4.28}$$

Similarly, for the q's:

$$\frac{\partial q_i}{\partial \theta_j} = u_i \cdot u_j \cdot [g_{ij} \cdot \sin(\theta_{ij}) - b_{ij} \cdot \cos(\theta_{ij})]; \quad i \neq j$$

$$\frac{\partial q_i}{\partial \theta_i} = u_i \cdot u_j \cdot \Sigma\, [g_{ij} \cdot \sin(\theta_{ij}) - b_{ij} \cdot \cos(\theta_{ij})]; \quad i = j \tag{4.29}$$

$$\frac{\partial q_i}{\partial u_i} = -u_i^2 \cdot b_{ii} + q_i; \quad j\Sigma = 1, \ldots, n$$

This completes the calculation of the Jacobian.

Equation $\mathbf{r(x)} = \mathbf{0}$ is solved by repeatedly solving $\Delta\mathbf{r} = \mathbf{J} * \Delta\mathbf{x}$.

Elements of $\mathbf{J}$ are those of equations (4.27) to (4.29). They show that matrix $\mathbf{J}$ and the set $\mathbf{J} * \Delta\mathbf{x} = \Delta\mathbf{r}$ can be written as

$$\begin{bmatrix} \Delta\mathbf{p} \\ \Delta\mathbf{q} \end{bmatrix} = \begin{bmatrix} \mathbf{J}_{1,1} & \mathbf{J}_{1,2} \\ \mathbf{J}_{2,1} & \mathbf{J}_{2,2} \end{bmatrix} * \begin{bmatrix} \Delta\boldsymbol{\theta} \\ \Delta\mathbf{u} \end{bmatrix} \begin{bmatrix} \Delta\mathbf{u} \end{bmatrix} \tag{4.30}$$

Note that since the voltage u_k is known for all generators $k = 1$ to n^g, there are only n^c equations for $\partial q_i / \partial u_j$. Thus, the size of the submatrices $\mathbf{J}_{1,1}$, $\mathbf{J}_{1,2}$, $\mathbf{J}_{2,1}$, and $\mathbf{J}_{2,2}$ is n-by-n, n-by-n^c, n^c-by-n, and n^c-by-n^c, respectively, and that of the entire matrix is $(n + n^c)$-by-$(n + n^c)$. Since in sets R̲ it was $2n$-by-$2n$ and $n > n^c$, we have here an advantage for the polar definition: The matrix is smaller. The equation $\mathbf{J} * \Delta\mathbf{x} = \mathbf{r}$ for the network in Fig. 4.3 may serve as an illustration.

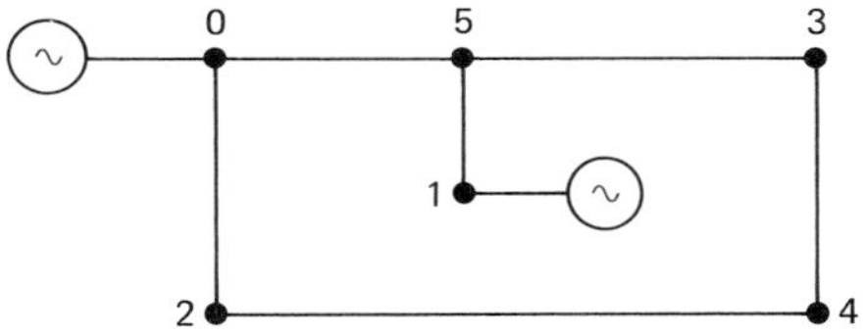

Figure 4.3 A network.

$$\begin{bmatrix} \Delta p_1 \\ \Delta p_2 \\ \Delta p_3 \\ \Delta p_4 \\ \Delta p_5 \\ \Delta q_2 \\ \Delta q_3 \\ \Delta q_4 \\ \Delta q_5 \end{bmatrix} = \begin{bmatrix} x & 0 & 0 & 0 & x & 0 & 0 & 0 & y \\ 0 & x & 0 & x & 0 & y & 0 & y & 0 \\ 0 & 0 & x & x & x & 0 & y & y & y \\ 0 & x & x & x & 0 & y & y & y & 0 \\ x & 0 & x & 0 & x & 0 & y & 0 & y \\ 0 & z & 0 & z & 0 & c & 0 & c & 0 \\ 0 & 0 & z & z & z & 0 & c & c & c \\ 0 & z & z & z & 0 & c & c & c & 0 \\ z & 0 & z & 0 & z & 0 & c & 0 & c \end{bmatrix} * \begin{bmatrix} \Delta\theta_1 \\ \Delta\theta_2 \\ \Delta\theta_3 \\ \Delta\theta_4 \\ \Delta\theta_5 \\ \Delta u_2 \\ \Delta u_3 \\ \Delta u_4 \\ \Delta u_5 \end{bmatrix}$$

$$x,\ y,\ c \neq 0.$$

Since the slack bus has number 0, we have $n^g = 1$, $n^c = 4$, and $n = 5$. In rectangular coordinates $\mathbf{J}$ would be 10-by-10 because node 1 is a generator. In polar coordinates, $\mathbf{J}$ is 9-by-9. (The more nodes in a network, the sparser is the matrix $\mathbf{J}$, but even for $n = 5$ we have 45 nonzero elements out of $9 \cdot 9 = 81$.)

4.2 THE ALGORITHMS

4.2.1 The Newton–Raphson Method

Whether one uses the polar or the rectangular system, the equation $\mathbf{r}(\mathbf{x}) = \mathbf{0}$ is to be solved by repeatedly solving

$$\mathbf{J} * \Delta\mathbf{x} = \Delta\mathbf{r}$$

This is a set of linear equations, so that the Newton–Raphson method may proceed as follows: Given an initial approximation $\mathbf{x}_0$ and a convergence accuracy ϵ, do the following:

(a) Compute the vector of residuals $\Delta\mathbf{r}$ using the current value of $\mathbf{x}$.
(b) If the largest component of this vector is smaller in absolute value than some predetermined ϵ, stop. Otherwise, proceed.
(c) Form the elements of the Jacobian.
(d) Solve $\mathbf{J} * \Delta\mathbf{x} = \Delta\mathbf{r}$ for $\Delta\mathbf{x}$.
(e) Compute the new vector of unknowns $\mathbf{x}$ through $\mathbf{x} := \mathbf{x} + \Delta\mathbf{x}$
(f) Return to step (a).

Not every system $\mathbf{J} * \Delta\mathbf{x} = \Delta\mathbf{r}$ can be solved; if matrix $\mathbf{J}$ is *singular*, no inverse matrix $\mathbf{J}^{-1}$ exists and $\mathbf{J} * \Delta\mathbf{x} = \Delta\mathbf{r}$ cannot be solved. To make the condition of nonsingularity clear, the problem was defined [WE67]* in rectangular coordinates, but with the voltage defined through

$$u_k = v_k + j \cdot v_{n+k}; \qquad u_k^2 = v_k^2 + v_{n+k}^2$$

The equations are now

$$r_k = \Sigma\,(g_{ki} \cdot v_i + b_{ki} \cdot v_{n+1}) + g_{k0} + \frac{p_k \cdot v_k - q_k \cdot v_{n+k}}{u_k^2}$$

$$r_{n+k} = \Sigma\,(b_{ki} \cdot v_i - g_{ki} \cdot v_{n+1}) + b_{k0} - \frac{q_k \cdot v_k + p_k \cdot v_{n+k}}{u_k^2}$$

The Jacobian consists here of admittance matrices $\mathbf{G}$ and $\mathbf{B}$ and diagonal matrices $\mathbf{D}$ and $\mathbf{T}$ such that

$$\mathbf{J} = \mathbf{J}_0 + \tilde{\mathbf{J}} = \begin{bmatrix} \mathbf{G} & \mathbf{B} \\ \mathbf{B} & -\mathbf{G} \end{bmatrix} + \begin{bmatrix} \mathbf{D} & \mathbf{T} \\ -\mathbf{T} & \mathbf{D} \end{bmatrix}$$

Matrices $\mathbf{D}$ and $\mathbf{T}$ change with every iteration according to

---

* Y. Wallach, R. Even, "Application of Newton's Method to Load-Flow Calculations," *Proc. IEEE*, Vol. 114, 1967, pp. 372–74. Used with permission.

$$d_i := \frac{-[p_i \cdot (v_i^2 - v_{n+i}^2) - 2 \cdot q_i \cdot v_i \cdot v_{n+1}]}{(v_i^2 + v_{n+i}^2)^2}$$

$$t_i := \frac{-[q_i \cdot (v_i^2 - v_{n+i}^2) + 2 \cdot p_i \cdot v_i \cdot v_{n+1}]}{(v_i^2 + v_{n+i}^2)^2}$$

Since only $\tilde{\mathbf{J}}$ changes at each iteration step, the iteration number was omitted, and a method for deriving the inverse of $\mathbf{J}$ from $\mathbf{J}_0^{-1}$ in m steps (p. 79 of [Ho53]) can be employed in the following way: At the ith step the $(i - 1)$th matrix $\mathbf{J}_{i-1}$ is modified by adding the ith row of $\tilde{\mathbf{J}}$ giving

$$\mathbf{J}_i = \mathbf{J}_{i-1} + \mathbf{e}_i * \mathbf{w}_i$$

where $\mathbf{e}_i$ is the ith column of the unit matrix of order m and $\mathbf{w}_i$ is the ith row of $\tilde{\mathbf{J}}$ so that $\mathbf{J}_m = \mathbf{J}$ and therefore

$$\mathbf{J}_{i-1} - \frac{(\mathbf{J}_{i-1}^{-1} * \mathbf{e}_i) \cdot (\mathbf{w}_i * \mathbf{J}_{i-1}^{-1})}{1 + \mathbf{w}_i \cdot \mathbf{J}_{i-1}^{-1} * \mathbf{e}_i}$$

$$= \mathbf{J}_{i-1} - \frac{\mathbf{c}_i * \mathbf{w}_i * \mathbf{J}_{i-1}^{-1}}{1 + \mathbf{w}_i * \mathbf{c}_i^{(i-1)}}$$

where $\mathbf{c}_i^{(i-1)}$ is the ith column of $\mathbf{J}_{i-1}^{-1}$. It is seen that all m columns of $\mathbf{J}_{i-1}^{-1}$ change in the ith step, according to

$$\mathbf{c}_j := \mathbf{c}_j - c_i^{(i-1)} \cdot [\mathbf{w}_i * \mathbf{c}_j^{(i-1)}]/[1 + \mathbf{w}_i * \mathbf{c}_i^{(i-1)}] \qquad (4.31)$$

Newton's process converges if the residuals r_k have continuous first derivatives in the neighborhood of a solution, if $\mathbf{J}$ is nonsingular there, and if the initial approximation is close enough to the solution (pp. 132–138 of [Ho53]). In the case of load flow, it is clear that the first partial derivatives of the r_ks are always continuous, and since the normalized node voltages are always near $1 - j \cdot 0$, this may serve as a good initial approximation.

Next, we show that $\mathbf{J}_0$ is nonsingular. $\mathbf{J}_0^{-1}$ can be written as

$$\begin{bmatrix} \mathbf{G}^{-1} - \mathbf{G}^{-1} * \mathbf{B} * \mathbf{Q}^{-1} * \mathbf{B} * \mathbf{G} & \mathbf{G}^{-1} * \mathbf{B} * \mathbf{Q} \\ (\mathbf{G}^{-1} * \mathbf{B} * \mathbf{Q})^{\mathrm{T}} & -\mathbf{Q}^{-1} \end{bmatrix} = \mathbf{J}_0^{-1}$$

where $\mathbf{Q} = \mathbf{G} + \mathbf{B} * \mathbf{G}^{-1} * \mathbf{B}$

Thus $\mathbf{J}_0^{-1}$ exists if $\mathbf{G}^{-1}$ and $\mathbf{Q}^{-1}$ exist. But $\mathbf{G}$, being the admittance matrix of a purely resistive network, is positive definite and therefore nonsingular. Matrix $\mathbf{B}$ is the admittance matrix of a purely reactive network and therefore symmetric and nonsingular.

It will now be proved that $\mathbf{M} = \mathbf{B} * \mathbf{G}^{-1} * \mathbf{B}$ is positive definite. To do this, compute with $\mathbf{x}$ and $\mathbf{y}$ two row vectors:

$$\mathbf{x} * \mathbf{G}^{-1} * \mathbf{x}^{\mathrm{T}} = \mathbf{x} * \mathbf{B}^{-1} * \mathbf{M} * \mathbf{B}^{-1} * \mathbf{x}^{\mathrm{T}} = \mathbf{y} * \mathbf{M} * \mathbf{y}^{\mathrm{T}} \qquad (4.32)$$

We had $\mathbf{G}^{-1}$ and now have $\mathbf{y} = \mathbf{x} * \mathbf{B}^{-1}$. Since $\mathbf{G}$ is positive definite, Eq. (4.32) shows that so is $\mathbf{M}$. Thus $\mathbf{Q}$, being a sum of two positive-definite matrices, is positive definite and therefore nonsingular. The existence of $\mathbf{J}_0^{-1}$ is therefore proved.

Equation (4.31) shows that $\mathbf{J}^{-1}$ exists if, for every i,

$$\mathbf{w}_i * \mathbf{c}_i^{(i-1)} \neq -1 \tag{4.33}$$

a condition which can be easily checked at each step leading to the inversion of $\mathbf{J}$. Therefore Eq. (4.33) is the condition for nonsingularity.

Having proved the condition for nonsingularity, we next deal with the *speed of convergence.* As such, reference [He64] proves that the convergence of the Newton–Raphson method is quadratic and that the Gauss–Seidel method which we will use later has linear convergence. The difference is that letting the error at iteration i be ϵ_i we have for these two cases

$$\epsilon_{i+1} = k_q \cdot \epsilon_i^2; \qquad \epsilon_{i+1} = k_n \cdot \epsilon_i$$

If both $k_q = 0.8$ and $k_n = 0.8$, we get for quadratic and linear convergence Table 4.1. For $\epsilon_1 = 1.6$ we see that quadratic convergence "runs away," with the error increasing instead of decreasing. This shows that quadratic convergence is better if and only if we *start with a good approximation*.

TABLE 4.1 Convergence.

k_n:	0.8	0.64	0.51	0.41	0.33
k_q:	0.8	0.51	0.33		
k_n:	1.6	1.28	1.02	0.82	0.66
k_q:	1.6	2.05	3.56		

To be able to start close enough to the solution, it was proposed in [TH67] to "Set the voltage magnitudes, where given, to their given values and set other voltage magnitudes equal to that of the slack node. The use of a per unit system is assumed. All angles are set equal to the slack node angle. This will be referred to as a *flat* voltage start", and one Gauss–Seidel iteration is made to assure a favorable start.

Even if we start with a relatively good approximation of the Jacobian and notwithstanding the fact that even under more general conditions ([OR70], Chapter 10) convergence of the Newton–Raphson method is quadratic, this does not mean that the time is shorter than that obtained with linear methods. The reason is that each iteration may take much more time than that of the Gauss–Seidel method and the overall time is the number of iterations times Ω per iteration.

The number of operations in steps (a) to (f) may be approximated as follows:

For known u and θ values, $\Delta\mathbf{r}$ of step (a) requires a simple insertion if we replace $\cos(\delta)$ by $1 - 0.5 \cdot \delta^2 + \delta^4/24$ and $\sin(\delta)$ by $\delta - \delta^3/6$ (the first three or two terms of their Taylor expansion). This is justified by the fact that δ is rather small and, in order to save time, may be calculated by the steps

```
desq := delta * delta;                cosn := 1.0 - 0.5 * desq;
sinn := delta * (1.0 - desq/6.0);     cosn := cosn + desq * desq/24.0;
```

(with $\Omega = 9$). For generators Δq_k does not have to be computed. In this case only $\cos(\delta)$ is required, so $\Omega = 6$. For all $2n^g + n^c = n + n^g$ we therefore need $\Omega = 9 \cdot n + 6 \cdot n^g = 6 \cdot (1.5 \cdot n + n^g)$. This Ω is proportional to n; we say that the computational effort is of the order of n and write $O(n)$. Step (c) uses equations (4.27) to (4.30) and requires also $O(n)$. Step (b) can be done while keeping $\Delta \mathbf{r}$ in the register so that it requires even less computational effort. Step (e) requires $\Omega = 2 \cdot n + n^g$, and (f) is a simple branch statement. Only (d) seems to require more than the time of $O(n)$.

The solution of a linear m-by-m dense system requires $2 \cdot m^3/3$ operations, which for $m \cong 1000$ would be prohibitively high, about 667 million operations. Fortunately, the matrices of power networks are extremely sparse, and, as already shown, proper reordering will minimize both the fill-in and Ω. The amount of computational effort required by such optimally ordered factorization (*OOF*) can only be found by simulation (Section 4.3) but is much lower than $2 \cdot m^3/3$; otherwise the Newton method could hardly be applied for power system network calculations.

Another disadvantage lies in the storage requirement of the Newton–Raphson method. While GS requires only about as much space as is necessary for storing the usually sparse admittance matrix, the Newton–Raphson method requires storage for $\mathbf{J}^{-1}$ or $\mathbf{L} * \mathbf{U}$, which may not be sparse at all. Even if the factorization is used, the phenomenon of fill-in (described earlier) may require excessive memory space.

4.2.2 Modifications

To alleviate the difficulties, first the Newton–Raphson procedure is modified so that fewer matrix inversions or factorizations are needed. One such modification due to Shamanski ([OR70, p.316] or Householder [Ho53]) has proven effective in reducing the number of inversions while retaining fast convergence. The main idea is to invert the Jacobian only once every m iterations. The method may be summarized as follows:

$$\mathbf{x}^{(k,0)} = \mathbf{x}^{(k)}$$

$$\mathbf{x}^{(k,i)} = \mathbf{x}^{(k,i-1)} - \mathbf{J}_k^{-1}(\mathbf{x}^{(k,0)}) * \mathbf{r}(\mathbf{x}^{(k,i-1)}); \quad i = 1, 2, \ldots, m \tag{4.34}$$

It can be seen that $\mathbf{J}_k^{-1}$ is used m times without updating.

The following description of the *algorithm of Shamanski* uses a counter c to count these m "subiterations." At the beginning of the operation, c is set to zero and $\mathbf{J}$ factored into $\mathbf{L} * \mathbf{U}$.

(a) Compute the vector of residuals, $\Delta\mathbf{r}$.

(b) If $\max |\Delta\mathbf{r}_i| < \epsilon$, stop. Otherwise, proceed.

(c) Increment inner counter c. If $c < m + 1$, go to (d) else

(c1) set $c = 0$;

(c2) form $\mathbf{J}(\mathbf{x})$;

(c3) compute $\mathbf{J} = \mathbf{L} * \mathbf{U}$ by factorization.

(d) Solve $\mathbf{J} * \Delta\mathbf{x} = \Delta\mathbf{r}$ through $\mathbf{L} * \mathbf{z} = \Delta\mathbf{r}$ and $\mathbf{U} * \Delta\mathbf{x} = \mathbf{z}$.

(e) Compute the new $\mathbf{x}$ through $\mathbf{x} := \mathbf{x} + \Delta\mathbf{x}$.

(f) Return to (a).

This is the method proposed in [TH67] and used since then. The characteristics of it are as follows:

In the Newton–Raphson method only the upper triangle is to be retained; in Shamanski's method both $\mathbf{L}$ and $\mathbf{U}$ have to be stored, because both are needed for step (d). It is claimed that this increases the storage requirement by only 40%.

The ordering is done only once for each network configuration, by simulation, and is used repeatedly. For a new configuration another simulation run is performed. (If the change is not too large, we may prefer an updating method.)

It is further claimed that "The number of iterations required for solution is virtually independent of problem size and kind. This is strictly true only for problems with a flat voltage start and without automatic adjustments. Under these conditions an acceptable solution can be obtained in four or five iterations. The high speed of solution is due to the quadratic convergence characteristic of the Newton–Raphson method, optimally ordered elimination, and special programming techniques.

"These results may appear to contradict the statement that memory and time requirements increase approximately in direct proportion to problem size.

"The main reason the number of terms in the triangularized matrix tends to become proportional to problem size as problems become larger is that larger networks are composed of subnetworks with relatively few interconnections and the optimal ordering scheme takes advantage of this property. For example, the number of terms in the triangularized matrix of a network composed of two subnetworks with one interconnection would be equal to the sum of the terms in the triangularized matrices of the subnetworks plus one."*

---

* W. F. Tinney, C. E. Hart, "Power-Flow Solution by Newton's Method," *Trans. IEEE*, Vol. PAS-86, 1967, pp.1449-1456.

An even more efficient version of the Newton – Raphson method is described in [SA74].* It is based on the observation that in Eq. (4.30), $\mathbf{J}_{1,2} \cong \mathbf{0}$ and $\mathbf{J}_{2,1} \cong \mathbf{0}$. This means that we can write

$$\Delta\mathbf{p} = \mathbf{J}_{1,1} * \Delta\boldsymbol{\theta}; \qquad \Delta\mathbf{q} = \mathbf{J}_{2,2} * \Delta\mathbf{u} \tag{4.35}$$

This modification is termed *decoupled*, since $\Delta\mathbf{p}$ does not depend on $\Delta\mathbf{u}$ and $\Delta\mathbf{q}$ is independent of $\Delta\boldsymbol{\theta}$. From now on it will be denoted by "decoupled OOF."

The nonzero elements [Eqs. (4.27) to (4.29)] were seen to be,

$$(\mathbf{J}_{1,1})_{k,m} = (\mathbf{J}_{2,2})_{k,m} = u_k \cdot u_m \cdot [g_{k,m} \cdot \sin(\theta_{k,m}) - b_{k,m} \cdot \cos(\theta_{k,m})]$$

$$(\mathbf{J}_{1,1})_{k,k} = -b_{k,k} \cdot u_k^2 - q_k; \qquad (\mathbf{J}_{2,2})_{k,k} = -b_{k,k} \cdot u_k^2 + q_k$$

It is claimed that in practical power systems, the following assumptions are almost always valid:

$$\cos(\theta_{km}) \cong 1; \qquad \sin(\theta_{km}) \cong \theta_{km} \cong 0;$$

$$g_{km} \cdot \sin(\theta_{km}) << b_{km}; \qquad q_k << b_{kk} \cdot u_k^2$$

so that

$$\begin{aligned} (\mathbf{J}_{1,1})_{k,m} &= (\mathbf{J}_{2,2})_{k,m} \cong -b_{k,m} \cdot u_k \cdot u_m; \quad k \neq m \\ (\mathbf{J}_{1,1})_{k,k} &= (\mathbf{J}_{2,2})_{k,k} \cong -b_{k,k} \cdot u_k^2 \end{aligned} \tag{4.36}$$

and the equations can be written as

$$\Delta\mathbf{p} = (\mathbf{u}^{\mathrm{T}} * \tilde{\mathbf{B}} * \mathbf{u}) * \Delta\boldsymbol{\theta} \tag{4.37}$$

$$\Delta\mathbf{q} = (\mathbf{u}^{\mathrm{T}} * \mathbf{B}^{\#} * \mathbf{u}) * \Delta\mathbf{u} \tag{4.38}$$

Next $\tilde{\mathbf{B}} = \mathbf{B}^{\#} = -\mathbf{B}$, the negative of the susceptance matrix $\mathbf{B}$ of the network, is changed [SA74] by

(a) omitting from $\tilde{\mathbf{B}}$ "the representation of those network elements that predominantly affect MVAR flows, i.e., shunt reactances and off-nominal in-phase transformer taps."
(b) omitting from $\mathbf{B}^{\#}$ "the angle-shifting effects of phase shifters."
(c) dividing Eq. (4.37) by $\mathbf{u}$ and setting all remaining right hand $\mathbf{u}_i$ to 1 pu. Note that the $\mathbf{u}$ terms on the left-hand sides affect the behavior of the defining functions and not the coupling.
(d) "neglecting series resistances in calculating the elements of $\tilde{\mathbf{B}}$ which then becomes the DC-approximation load-flow matrix. This is of

* B. Stott, O. Alsac, "Fast Decoupled Load-Flow," *Trans. IEEE*, Vol. PAS-93, May/June 1974, pp. 859 – 69. © 1974 by IEEE. Used with permission.

minor importance, but is found experimentally to give slightly improved results."

With the preceding modifications the decoupled load-flow equations become

$$\frac{\Delta \mathbf{p}}{\mathbf{u}} = \tilde{\mathbf{B}} * \Delta \boldsymbol{\theta} \tag{4.39}$$

$$\frac{\Delta \mathbf{q}}{\mathbf{u}} = \mathbf{B}^{\#} * \Delta \mathbf{u} \tag{4.40}$$

Both $\tilde{\mathbf{B}}$ and $\mathbf{B}^{\#}$ are real and sparse. They contain only network admittances, and thus they are constant and need to be triangulated once only, at the beginning of the study. Since $\mathbf{B}^{\#}$ is symmetrical, only its upper triangular factor is stored; if phase shifters are absent or accounted for by alternative means, $\tilde{\mathbf{B}}$ is also symmetrical.

"The immediate appeal of the decoupled method is that very fast repeat solutions for $\Delta\boldsymbol{\theta}$ and $\Delta\mathbf{u}$ can be obtained using the constant triangular factors of $\tilde{\mathbf{B}}$ and $\mathbf{B}^{\#}$. These solutions may be iterated with each other in some defined manner towards the exact solution.

"[Equations (4.39) and (4.40)] are solved alternately, always using the most recent voltage values. Separate convergence tests are used for both with the criteria:

$$\max |\Delta p| \leq \epsilon_p, \quad \max |\Delta q| \leq \epsilon_q \tag{4.41}$$

and the calculation is terminated after a $\Delta\mathbf{q}$ solution (called a ½ iteration) converges."*

The advantages of this method are that it never fails to converge, that its **B** matrices are *constant* for a network configuration and symmetric, that **B** is of size n whereas **J** is of size $2n$, that it solves easily for adjustments, and that it lends itself to updating methods. *We will use it as the basic method for applying the Newton–Raphson procedure in LF calculations.*

4.2.3 The Gauss–Seidel Method

The Gauss–Seidel algorithm is needed for starting values. Our original equation for complex power was $p_k + j \cdot q_k = u_k' \cdot i_k'' = u_k' \cdot \Sigma\, u_m'' \cdot y_{km}''$, $m\Sigma = 0, \ldots, n$. Complementing it and rearranging terms yields

---

* B. Stott, O. Alsac, "Fast Decoupled Load-Flow," *Trans. IEEE,* Vol. PAS-93, May/June 1974, pp. 859-69. © 1974 by IEEE. Used with permission.

$$\frac{p_k - jq_k}{u_k''} - \Sigma\, u_m' \cdot y_{km}' = 0; \quad k = 0, 1, \ldots, m; \quad m\Sigma = 0, \ldots, n$$

The slack bus (numbered zero) has a known, constant voltage u_0, so that if we separate it from the sum, we have for $k = 1, \ldots, n$

$$\frac{p_k - jq_k}{u_k''} = \Sigma\, u_m' \cdot y_{k,m}' + u_0' \cdot y_{k0}'; \quad m\Sigma = 1, \ldots, n$$

If it were not for $(p_k - jq_k)/u_k'' \equiv z_k$, the preceding would be a linear set. We therefore may use the "trick" of assuming z_k to be constant, solving the linear set, recalculating $\mathbf{z}$, solving it again, and so on. Separating the value u_k' to be calculated from the sum yields

$$u_k' = \frac{(p_k - jq_k)/u_k'' - u_0' \cdot y_{k0}' - \Sigma\, u_j' \cdot y_{kj}' - \Sigma\, u_m' \cdot y_{km}'}{y_{kk}'}; \tag{4.42}$$

$$j\Sigma = 1, \ldots, k - 1; \quad m\Sigma = k + 1, \ldots, n$$

In Eq. (4.42) u_k' is the value to be computed and should not appear on both sides of the equation. There are two ways to deal with this problem. One is to use the "old" values on the right-hand side. The second is to multiply Eq. (4.42) by u_k'' and solve for u_k from

$$p_k - jq_k = \frac{u_k' \cdot u_k'' + u_k'' \cdot (u_0' \cdot y_{k0}' + \Sigma\, u_j' \cdot u_{kj}' + \Sigma\, u_m' \cdot y_{km}')}{y_{kk}'} \tag{4.43}$$

Since $u_k' \cdot u_k'' = u_k^2$, this is a quadratic equation in u_k'. The program could therefore proceed by *solving Eq. (4.43) for u_k in every iteration*. The question, though, is whether solving the quadratic equation (4.43) for $k = 1, .., n$ helps in reducing the number of iterations enough to offset the effort to solve a quadratic equation for every k in every iteration.

A number of load flows were run, and the conclusion was that using "old" values u_k'' on the right of Eq. (4.42) and solving Eq. (4.43) converge approximately at the same rate. Since Eq. (4.43) requires n square-root operations per iteration, it seems not to be particularly well suited for load-flow problems. It would be better to use Eq. (4.42) with "old" u_k'' on the right-hand side.

There is a vast literature concerning the convergence properties of iterative methods such as the Gauss–Seidel (GS) method. It is usually shown that under assumptions such as diagonal dominance, the methods converge (linearly). Thus Table 4.2 shows $\Sigma\, r_k^2$ where r_k = deviation of u_k from the true values of the network in [WH56].

TABLE 4.2

3	6	9	12	15	18	21
8.65E−2	2.36E−2	6.72E−3	1.86E−3	4.40E−4	6.23E−5	3.65E−5
6.85E−1	2.24E−2	8.01E−3	2.85E−3	9.41E−4	2.54E−4	3.54E−5

(The first row is the iteration number, the second is $\Sigma\, r_k^2$, and the third includes calculation with an acceleration factor.) The conclusions from this experiment (and a great many others) are that GS should be used for only a few iterations ($\leq$ 4), that convergence is in fact linear, and that acceleration factors start helping too late, so that for our purposes they should not be used.

Another conclusion which arose from numerous experiments was the fact that all iterative methods converged more slowly as system size increased. (This phenomenon prompted the advent of direct methods, which have now supplanted iterative methods in most LF applications.) This sensitivity to matrix size is not obvious, and the proof for it is shown next. (The reader not interested in the mathematical formulation may proceed to the last paragraph of this section.)

Let $G: R^n \to R^n$ be an operator with a fixed point $\tilde{\mathbf{x}}$. Then by the attraction theorem of Ostrowski [OR70], there exists a neighborhood S of $\tilde{\mathbf{x}}$ such that for any $\mathbf{x}^0 \in S$, $G^n\mathbf{x}^0 \to \tilde{\mathbf{x}}$ if (and, essentially, only if) the spectral radius of $\tilde{G}(\tilde{\mathbf{x}})$ (i.e., max λ_i, where λ_i are the eigenvalues of $\tilde{G}$) is less than 1. [If the spectral radius $\rho(\tilde{G}(\tilde{\mathbf{x}}))0 > 0$, then convergence is linear with quotient $\rho(\tilde{G}(\tilde{\mathbf{x}}))$.] Hence the deterioration of convergence with system size must mean that $\rho(\tilde{G}(\mathbf{x}))$ is close to unity when the power network becomes large. This is next proven for a nonlinear iterative method applied to a DC network, numbered $0, 1, \ldots, n$ with 0 denoting the slack bus. Direct-current equations can be derived from previous equations by setting $w_k = q_k = b_{m,n} = 0$. This in turn leads to the following DC version of the nonlinear Jacobi method (in which only $v^{(m)}$ elements appear on the right, so that all v are of the previous iteration).

$$v_k^{(m+1)} = \frac{p_k / v_k^{(m)} - \Sigma\, g_{k,j} \cdot v_j^{(m)}}{g_{k,k}};$$

$$k = 1, \ldots, n; \quad j\Sigma = 0, \ldots, n \text{ but } j \neq k$$

We may write this iteration as $\mathbf{v}^{(m+1)} = F(\mathbf{v}^{(m)})$, where F is the nonlinear Jacobi operator. Its Jacobian is

$$\begin{bmatrix} -p/g_{11}v_1^2 & -g_{12}/g_{11} & -g_{13}/g_{11} & \cdots & -g_{1n}/g_{11} \\ -g_{21}/g_{22} & -p_2/g_{22}v_2^2 & -g_{23}/g_{22} & \cdots & -g_{2n}/g_{22} \\ -g_{31}/g_{33} & -g_{32}/g_{33} & -p_3/g_{33}v_3^2 & \cdots & -g_{3n}/g_{33} \\ \cdot & \cdot & \cdot & & \cdot \\ \cdot & \cdot & \cdot & & \cdot \\ \cdot & \cdot & \cdot & & \cdot \\ -g_{n1}/g_{nn} & -g_{n2}/g_{nn} & -g_{n3}/g_{nn} & \cdots & -p_n/g_{nn}v_n^2 \end{bmatrix} = \tilde{\mathbf{F}}(\mathbf{v})$$

It is seen to be $\tilde{\mathbf{F}}(v) = \text{diag}[-p_i/(g_{ii} \cdot v_i^2)] + \tilde{\mathbf{G}} \equiv \tilde{\mathbf{D}} + \tilde{\mathbf{G}}$ where

$$\tilde{G}_{i,j} = \begin{cases} 0 & \text{if } i = j \\ \dfrac{-g_{ij}}{g_{ii}} & \text{if } i \neq j \end{cases}$$

Note that $\tilde{\mathbf{G}}$ is symmetric. Let $\mathbf{u}$ be the vector $[1, 1, \ldots, 1]^T$. Then $\mathbf{u}^T * \tilde{\mathbf{G}} * \mathbf{u} = \Sigma\Sigma\, \tilde{G}_{i,j} = \Sigma\, (-g_{i,i}^{-1} \cdot \Sigma\, g_{i,j})$, $i\Sigma = j\Sigma = 1, \ldots, n$.

Let us denote by S the set of indices of buses to which the slack bus is connected. If $i \notin S$, then $\Sigma\, g_{i,j} = -g_{i,i}$ for $i \neq j$ and hence index i contributes 1 to the outer sum. If $i \in S$, then for $j \neq i$ we have $-g_{i,i} = \Sigma\, g_{i,j} + g_{i,0}$. Hence this index contributes $1 + g_{i,0}/g_{i,i}$, and for $i\Sigma \in S$, we have

$$\mathbf{u}^T * \tilde{\mathbf{G}} * \mathbf{u} = (n - |S|) + \Sigma \left(1 + \frac{g_{i0}}{g_{ii}}\right)$$

$$= n - |S| + |S| + \Sigma \frac{g_{i0}}{g_{ii}} = n + \Sigma \frac{g_{i0}}{g_{ii}}$$

It is a basic characteristic of power system networks that the number of branches connected to any bus (including the slack bus) never exceeds a certain fixed number c (in most systems $c \leq 5$). Also since $-1 < g_{i0}/g_{ii} < 0$ and $\mathbf{u}^T * \mathbf{u} = n$, we obtain $(\mathbf{u}^T * \tilde{\mathbf{G}} * \mathbf{u})/(\mathbf{u}^T * \mathbf{u}) \geq 1 - c/n = 1 - d$.

Denote by $\lambda_{\max}(\tilde{\mathbf{G}})$ the largest eigenvalue of $\tilde{\mathbf{G}}$. By Rayleigh's theorem,

$$\lambda_{\max}(\tilde{\mathbf{G}}) = \sup \left(\frac{\mathbf{v}^T * \tilde{\mathbf{G}} * \mathbf{v}}{\mathbf{v}^T * \mathbf{v}}\right) \geq \frac{\mathbf{u}^T * \tilde{\mathbf{G}} * \mathbf{u}}{\mathbf{u}^T * \mathbf{u}}$$

where sup denotes the supremum. It follows that $\lambda_{\max}(\tilde{\mathbf{G}}) \geq 1 - d$. On the other hand, by theorem (13.5) of [No69],

$$\lambda_{\max}(\tilde{\mathbf{G}}) \leq ||\tilde{\mathbf{G}}||_\infty = \sup\,(\Sigma\, |(\tilde{\mathrm{G}})_{ij}|) = 1;$$

$$1 \leq i \leq n \quad \text{and} \quad j\Sigma = 1, \ldots, n$$

the supremum being attained for any $i \notin S$. Thus, we have

$$1 \geq \lambda_{\max}(\tilde{\mathrm{G}}) \geq 1 - d$$

Therefore, as the system size grows, λ_{max} tends to 1.

The foregoing discussion related to the eigenvalues of the *linear* part. The addition of the diagonal part cannot change matters much. By Weyl's theorem,

$$\lambda^M(\tilde{\mathbf{G}} + \tilde{\mathbf{D}}) \geq \lambda^M(\tilde{\mathbf{G}}) + \lambda^m(\tilde{\mathbf{D}}) \geq \lambda^M(\tilde{\mathbf{G}}) - \rho(\tilde{\mathbf{D}})$$

$$\geq 1 - d - \max_i \left(\frac{p_i}{v_i^2 \cdot g_{ii}} \right); \quad 1 \leq i \leq n$$

where superscripts M and m denote maximum and minimum, respectively.

For a typical power system the operating point is close to nominal voltage, $v_i = 1$, $g_{i,i} \cong 10$, and $p_i = 0.5$ (though under light loading conditions it may be much less). Taking $n = 100$ and $c = 5$, we find that

$$\rho(\tilde{\mathbf{F}}(v)) \geq 1 - 0.05 - 0.05 = 0.9$$

which indicates very slow convergence (if any at all); at least 20 iterations are required to reduce the error by one order of magnitude. If $n = 100$, $c = 5$, and each unit supplies or consumes 10% pu power, we find

$$\rho(\tilde{F}(v)) \geq 1 - \frac{5}{1000} - \frac{1}{100} = 0.985$$

and at least 150 iterations are needed to reduce the error by the same amount. It often happens in these cases that $\rho(\tilde{\mathbf{F}}(v)) > 1$ and the method diverges.

We have thus proven that *convergence of iterative methods is slowed by decreasing* d *or increasing the size of the network.*

We are now able to discuss possible applications of iterative methods. Normally they cannot compete with the Newton–Raphson methods discussed earlier, except for two cases, namely, for transient stability and contingency calculations. In these cases, LF has to be solved repeatedly, with only some powers p_k and q_k changed slightly. An iterative method can be employed so that the initial "constant" vector is chosen on the basis of the previously computed values. The iterations are therefore started from a point close to the final result (had it been exactly so, no additional iterations would be required). Since the accuracy demand is relatively low, the number of iterations will be relatively small and the method is quite efficient.

4.3 THE PROGRAMS

The program will consist of GS for 1 or 2 iterations, to provide starting values, and decoupled OOF as a main program. The Gauss–Seidel algorithm is so simple that its program will be explained now. Equation (4.42) is repeated first:

$$u_k' = \frac{(p_k - j\cdot q_k)/u_k'' - u_0'\cdot y_{k0}' - \Sigma\, u_m'\cdot y_{km}'}{y_{kk}'};$$

$$m\Sigma = 1, \ldots, n \text{ but } m \neq k$$

where we use on the right the most recent values of u_k'' and u_m'. This equation is to be computed for $k = 1, 2, \ldots, n-1, n$. Inserting complex quantities such as $u_k' = v_k' + jw_k'$, $y_{k,i}' = g_{k,i} + jb_{k,i}$, we get

$$(g_{kk} + j\cdot b_{kk})\cdot(v_k + jw_k)$$

$$= \frac{p_k - jq_k}{v_k - jw_k} - v_0\cdot(g_{k0} + jb_{k0}) - \Sigma\,(v_m + jw_m)\cdot(g_{km} + jb_{km})$$

The real and imaginary parts are

$$g_{k,k}\cdot v_k - b_{k,k}\cdot w_k$$

$$= \frac{p_k\cdot v_k + q_k\cdot w_k}{u_k^2} - v_0\cdot g_{k0} - \Sigma\,(v_m\cdot g_{k,m} - w_m\cdot b_{k,m})$$

and

$$g_{k,k}\cdot w_k + b_{k,k}\cdot v_k$$

$$= \frac{p_k\cdot w_k - q_k\cdot v_k}{u_k^2} - v_0\cdot b_{k0} - \Sigma\,(w_m\cdot g_{k,m} + v_m\cdot b_{k,m})$$

both for $m\Sigma = 1, \ldots, n$ but $m \neq k$. The simplest way is to consider the first to be an equation for v_k and solve the second for w_k in each iteration.

It was shown in Chapter 2 that a method exists which is twice as fast as GS. We will use GS, since we need only a few iterations and the data structure is more suitable.

There is a GSA program in Chapter 2. Next, we develop a *different* program, to be called GSB. The difference from the GS program of Chapter 2 is only in the terms of u_k^2. The program is as follows:

```
procedure GSB;    {This produces a single sweep. The data
                   of v, g etc., are considered global}
begin var k, m, mstrt, mstop: integer;
  vk, wk, vm, wm, gm, bm, usq, gv, gw, pk, qk, vo, go, bo, bd, gd: real;
for k := 1 to nn do {nn is the number of nodes}
begin {each indexed variable, if used at least twice, will
  be set to a similarly named scalar, e.g., vk ≡ v[k]}
vk := v[k]; wk := w[k]; usq := vk * vk + wk * wk;
vo := vsb[k]; go := gsb[k]; bo := bsb[k]; {sb stands for the slack bus}
go := gsb[k]; bd := bdiag[k]; gd := gdiag[k];
{diag stands for diagonal. These were the scalars mentioned above.
```

```
Next we prepare the sums as gv, gw}
gv := (pk * vk + qk * wk)/usq − vo * go + bd * wk;
gw := (pk * wk − gk * vk)/usq − vo * bo − bd * vk;
{For the summation in a table like 2.1 we need start and stop indices.}
mstrt := ip[k]; mstop := ip[k+1] − 1;
for m := mstrt to mstop do {accumulating the sums}
begin vm := v[m]; wm := w[m]; gm := g[m]; bm := b[m];
  gv := gv − vm * gm + wm * bm;
  gw := gw − wm * gm - vm * bm
end; {of accumulating g_kk·v_k as gv and g_kk·w_k as gw.
  We can now compute the two parts of u_k}
  v[k] := gv/gd; w[k] := gw/gd
end {of loop on k. We don't calculate here the residuals}
end {of procedure}.
```

The main program uses decoupling and is based on a program in [GL81],* which applies only to symmetric, positive-definite matrices. The advantages in restricting the type of matrices are as follows:

- Since the matrices are symmetric, $\mathbf{A} = \mathbf{L} * \mathbf{L}^{\mathrm{T}}$ can be used (Cholesky's method). This method requires half as many operations as the $\mathbf{L} * \mathbf{U}$ method.
- For a general matrix **A**, pivoting is required to reduce roundoff errors (Chapter 2). This means that we cannot exchange rows at will for optimum ordering, since we might produce a very small diagonal element and will have subsequently to exchange it for reasons of accuracy. Cholesky's method, if applied to a symmetric, positive-definite matrix, does not require interchanges (pivoting) to maintain numerical stability. Thus, according to [GL81]:

  "...we can choose to reorder **A** symmetrically
  (i) without regard to numerical stability and
  (ii) before the actual numerical factorization begins

  These options, which are normally not available to us when **A** is a general indefinite matrix have enormous practical implications. Since the ordering can be determined before the factorization begins, the location of the fill-in suffered during the factorization can also be determined. Thus, the data structure used to store **L** can be constructed *before* the actual numerical factorization, and spaces for fill-in components can be reserved. The computation then proceeds with the storage structure remaining static (unaltered). Thus the

---

* A. George, T. W. Liu, *Computer Solution of Large Sparse Positive Definite Systems*, © 1981 by Prentice-Hall, Inc. Used with permission.

three problems of (i) finding a suitable ordering (ii) setting up the appropriate storage scheme and (iii) the actual numerical computation, can be isolated as separate objects of study, as well as separate computer software modules...."

As already mentioned, in decoupled OOF, we use the susceptance matrix **B**, which is either positive-definite or at least nonnegative. We can and will therefore apply the algorithm of [GL81].

What follows is a condensed version of describing the algorithm.

There is a story about a small theater group producing Hamlet in a tiny Eastern European town and advertising it as: "Hamlet — a play by Shakespeare, improved by ...." This is how I feel explaining or "improving" on the algorithm in [GL81]. The reader is therefore strongly urged to read [GL81] where there is a much more complete description, all equations, theorems, etc., and a Fortran program.

In Section 2.4 the elimination in sparse networks was discussed both in matrix and graphical form. It was seen that elimination and fill-in can be pictured in matrix form (using × for nonzeros, a dot for fill-in, and a circle for an eliminated element) or graphically with dots indicating fill-in.

In Fig. 4.4 the 7-bus network is factored for two different numbering schemes. The first includes Fig. 4.4(a) to (g). The ×s in the matrix in Fig. 4.4(a) represent the network of Fig. 4.4(b) with $A_{i,j} = A_{j,i}$ being × if nodes i and j are connected. Additionally, the diagonal elements are also nonzero and thus represented by ×s.

The elimination in Fig. 4.4(a) proceeds by columns with an element i, j being the scalar product of row i and column j *as produced up to this point*.

Elimination of bus 1 does not enter fill-ins, but to eliminate, say, $A_{5,2}$ we have to multiply $A_{5,2}$ by $A_{2,3}$. If this is done, a fill-in in position (5, 3) and the symmetrically located (3, 5) will be generated. The best mathematical procedure to effect this is to calculate the disjunction (logical "or") of the respective rows, here 5 and 2: row 5 := row 5 $\vee$ row 2, where ×'s or dots are "true" and empty elements are "false."

As shown in Section 2.4, the elimination procedure can also be pictured by graphs. Elimination of node b in, say,

$$a \text{———} b \text{———} c$$

will introduce an additional line between nodes a and c (the "fill-in" line). Thus elimination of node 2 [equivalent to elimination of elements (3, 2), (5, 2), and (7, 2) in Fig. 4.4(a) and (c)] introduces fill-in branches (3, 5) and (3, 7) in Fig. 4.4(d).

The rest of the network elimination is as in Figs. 4.4(e) to (g), where the dots indicate fill-in lines. There are 3 dots altogether.

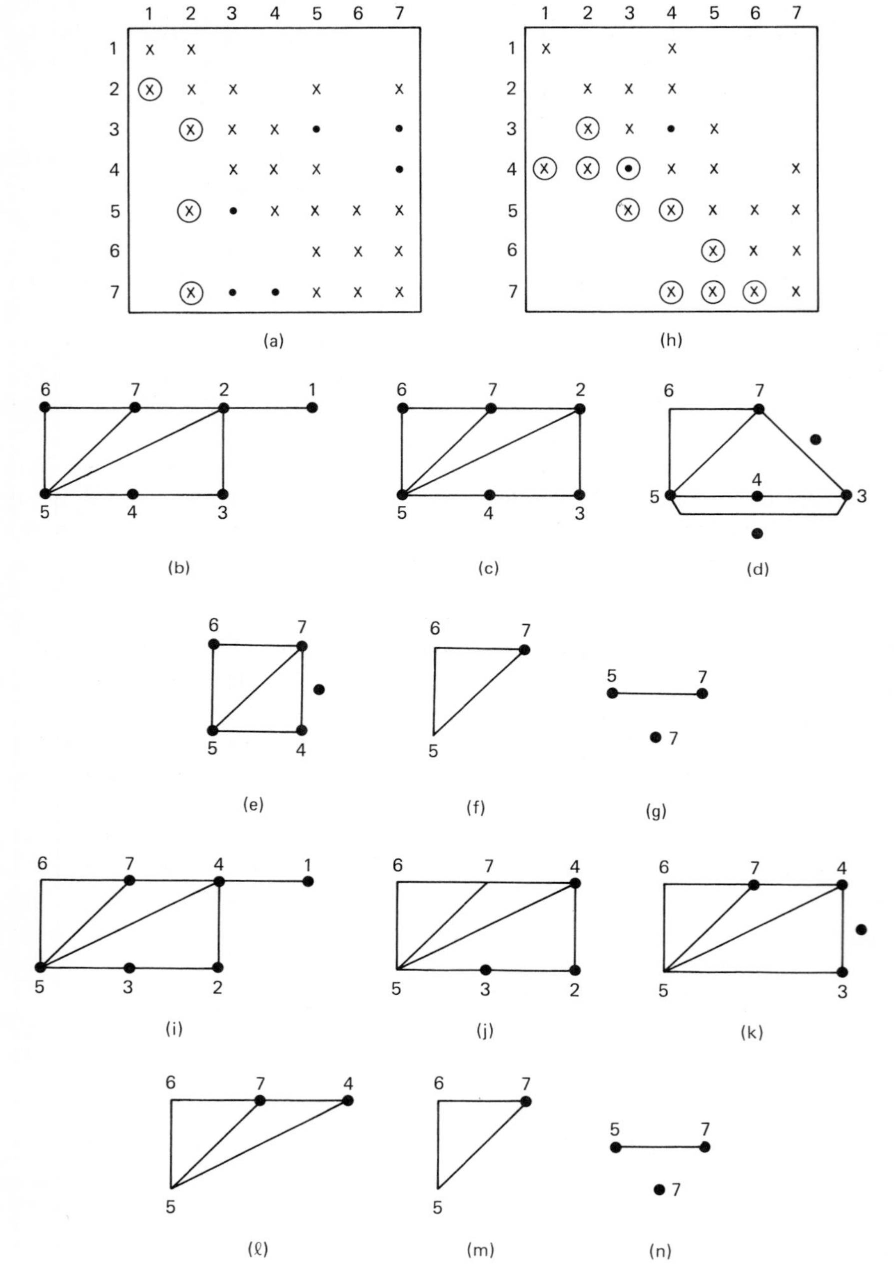

Figure 4.4 Optimally ordered factorization for two numberings.

To see whether renumbering helps, we have repeated the factorization for a renumbered network [Figs. 4.4(h) to (n)]. As seen, the number of dots was reduced to 1.

A serious problem of OOF algorithms is the storage of fill-in elements according to the sparse storage scheme of Table 2.1 or 3.5. If we store them when they are computed, then all elements of the vectors of values **g** and **b** and adjacency in Table 3.5 to the right of the new element would have to be shifted, and this requires a lot of work.

The method as advocated in [TH67] is less efficient than the method mentioned above; to see that this is so, it is enough to read the third paragraph from the top of page 1123 in this paper and count the number of **if**s. As shown in Chapter 1, **if**s require at least as much time as arithmetic operations. Fortunately, [GL81] includes a method which does not require any shifting of data. Moreover, it can be applied directly to the *original network*.

It was already mentioned that policy 2 will be used for ordering. This policy, originally developed by Markowitz in 1957 and applied first to power systems in [TH67], should be called a *minimum-degree* algorithm. By the *degree* of node i we denote the number of nodes adjacent to node i, and policy 2 specifies ordering the rows according to the minimum number of nonzeros. It can therefore be called a minimum-degree algorithm. It is called a quotient minimum degree or QMD algorithm in [GL81].

To show how it works, we reproduce from [GL81] the definition of a *reach-set*.

"The reach-set of a reachable through set E includes all nodes that are either adjacent to node a or can be reached through the set of eliminated nodes E."

Definition: The set of nodes reachable from node a is $R(a, E) \equiv$ Reach $(a, E) = \{x \notin E \mid x$ is reachable from a through $E\}$ where E is the set of nodes already eliminated.

Let us find $R(a, E)$ for Fig. 4.4(b) and apply elimination according to the sequence $x_1, x_2, \ldots, x_7$. Initially $E_0 = \varnothing$ (the empty set) and then $E_1 = \{x_1\}$, $E_2 = \{x_1, x_2\}$ etc.

$$R(x_1, E_0) = \{x_2\}; \qquad R(x_2, E_1) = \{x_3, x_5, x_7\}$$

$$R(x_3, E_2) = \{x_4, x_5, x_7\};$$

(because x_5 and x_7 can be reached from x_3 through the eliminated $x_2 \in E_2$)

$$R(x_4, E_3) = \{x_5, x_7\}; \qquad R(x_5, E_4) = \{x_6, x_7\}$$

The reach sets "predict" the fill-in elements. Thus $R(x_2, E_1)$ predicts elements (5, 3), (7, 3) and (7, 5) where the last is not a fill-in because branch (5, 7) exists in the original network. Note that since we need space for fill-in, we can see in the calculation above a preliminary step in which we find that we need in addition to spaces for **A** also spaces for $L_{5,3}$, $L_{7,3}$, and $L_{7,4}$.

What is most important is that the *original graph was not changed.* We can therefore picture the entire factorization process and *predict the place of all fill-in elements by calculating the R sets.*

Let us call attention to the fact that to reach x_4 from x_3 in $R(x_3, E_2)$ only one branch is passed, whereas to reach x_5 or x_7 two branches are passed. Sometimes the reach-set passes over 3 or more branches. This is quite inconvenient for computer implementation.

The way out of this dilemma is to produce "supernodes"; that is, whenever two adjacent nodes have been eliminated, coalesce them into one supernode numbered by the higher index (and denoted by an overbar).

The elimination would introduce supernode $\bar{x}_2$ representing x_1 and x_2, then $\bar{x}_3$ representing x_1, x_2, and x_3, and so on.

If we adopt this strategy, every path for computing R is of *length less than or equal to 2.* This advantage should be combined with the fact that to produce supernodes *we do not have to change the original graph.*

An efficient algorithm for calculating the R sets [GL81] is given in a simplified form below. It denotes the list of nodes adjacent to node x by $A[x]$ and the set of already eliminated nodes by E_i. The "and," "or," and "except for" operations on sets will be denoted by $\cdot$, $+$, and $-$ respectively.

Reach (y, E_i)

1. $R := \emptyset;$ ($\emptyset$ is the empty set)
2. **For all** $z \in A[y]$ **do**
   if $z \in E_i$ **then** $R := R + A[z]$ **else** $R := R + \{z\}$

The graph which results from the original if we coalesce connected nodes into supernodes is called a quotient graph. It can be used to represent elimination of node x_i according to the following algorithm:

Algorithm: For node x_i to be eliminated, do:

1. $T := A[x_i] \cdot E_{i-1};$ $R :=$ Reach (x_i, E_{i-1})
2. $\bar{x}_i := x_i + T;$ $E_i := E_{i-1} - T + \{\bar{x}_i\}$
3. $A[\bar{x}_i] := R.$
   For all nodes $w \in R$ **do**
   $A[w] := \{\bar{x}_i\} + A[w] - (T + \{\bar{x}_i\})$

TABLE 4.3

```
7
1 2 0
2 3 5 7 0
3 4 0
4 5 0
5 6 7 0
6 7 0
0
7
1 4 0
2 3 4 0
3 6 0
4 6 7 0
5 6 7 0
6 7 0
0
```

We next exemplify the algorithm by factoring the 7-bus network. Please follow the program OOF and its results (Tables 4.3 to 4.11), which describe the factorization of the network in Figure 4.4. We will do it painstakingly, step by step, and for each step we will describe what points 1, 2, and 3 of the *algorithm* and what the corresponding instructions of the *program* yield. Readers only interested in the results can skip this material, or at least the extracted material.

The "OOF" program is written for up to 100 nodes and uses both arrays and sets.

The data are as in Table 4.3. Each node, 1 to $n - 1$, has in its row all higher-numbered adjacent nodes and ends with a 0. Row n $(=7)$ has a single zero.

Procedure "init" cleans everything out and displays (prints) it using "dispset" for displaying various sets [Table 4.4]. The comments in the program are hopefully sufficient to clarify it.

Procedure "get_eqs" reads the data [Table 4.3] and stores the adjacency sets adj [Table 4.4]. Note that each adjacent node has 100 added to its number by the function "sac." This addition is required because coalesced supernodes will be represented by negative integers. This is also the reason that intrange was from $-$maxe to $+$maxe. Procedure "up_degree" updates the degree of all nodes.

The main program consists of calling "mindeg" until all nodes are "zapped."

According to policy 2 mentioned earlier, at each step of the elimination the node with the smallest i and degree d_i is chosen. Mindeg searches in its loop on $k1$ for the node with the smallest degree and calls "find_reach" for this node, called znode.

```
program oof(input,output);
const maxe=100; {the maximum number of equations}
      max2=201;{maximum range of sets}
type  intrange=-maxe..maxe;
      setrange=0..max2;
      narray=array[intrange] of intrange;
      sset=set of setrange;
      sarray=array[intrange] of sset;
var   degree:narray;{a vector containing the degree of every node
      ad,ip:narray; (* for second step *)
       L: array[intrange] of real;
      adj :sarray;  {a vector of adjacency sets }
      coal:sset ; {a set for coalescing nodes into supernodes}
      elim :  sset ; {the set of outstanding eliminated nodes}
      zapped :sset ;{set of original nodes already eliminated}
      reach :sset; {reach set for node currently being eliminated
     nofe :0..maxe; {number of equations}
     k,k1,k2,k3,k4,k5,k6,k7:integer; {for loop control etc}
     a,b,c,d,e,f,g,h,i,j,maxk1 :integer; {for other purposes }
function sac(eqnum:intrange):setrange;
{Converts from -100..+100 range into positive range 0..max2}
{The system doesn't like negative elements in sets}
begin (*It just adds 100 to eqnum *)
   sac:=eqnum+100
end;
procedure up_degree; {updates the degree-vector}
var k1,k2:intrange; a1 :setrange;
begin
   for k1:=-nofe to nofe do {for each node k1}
   begin a1:=0; {count in a1 its degree}
      for k2:=1 to nofe do {this is done by checking}
      if (sac(k2) in adj[k1]) and {which nodes k2 are adjacent}
      not(sac(k2) in elim) then a1:=a1+1; {to k1 but not yet }
      degree[k1]:=a1  (* eliminated *)
   end {of the for-loop}
end; {of procedure up-degree}
procedure find_reach (node:intrange);
{this procedure finds the reach-set for a particular ,given node}
var k1:intrange;     {for all nodes k1 adjacent to }
begin  reach :=[];    {"node" : if k1 has been eliminated }
    for k1:=-nofe to nofe do { but not combined, nodes }
    if sac(k1) in adj[node] then  {adjacent to k1 can be reached }
       if sac(k1) in elim then reach:=reach+adj[k1]
       else reach  :=reach+[sac(k1)];{Else k1 can be added }
       reach:=reach-[sac(node)]        {to itself}
end ;      {of procedure find-reach }
procedure dispset (dset:sset);
{Displays (prints out) the elements contained in set "dset"}
var m:integer ; first:boolean; {There is a difference, because *)
begin write('['); first :=true;(*sets of more than one element*)
   for m:=-nofe to nofe do (*need commas. Check all nodes m and }
   if sac(m) in dset then    {if m is in the set to be}
   begin                    {displayed, then :        }
      if not first then write(','); (*(1) add  commas if needed }
      write(m:3); first:=false (*(2) complete by right bracket*)
   end      {of both the if and for statement};
   writeln(']')
end ;     {of procedure display-set }
```

Program 4.1

```
procedure display; (*This procedure prints all of the information }
var a1,a2,a3,a4:integer;
begin writeln(' Display information ...');
   write (' Eliminated nodes:   '); dispset(zapped);
   write (' Outstanding nodes:  '); dispset(elim);
   writeln (' Adjacency sets:   ');
   for a1:=-nofe to nofe do
   if adj[a1]<>[] then
   begin
        write(a1:3,degree[a1]:3,'  '); dispset(adj[a1])
   end;    {of printing adjacency sets of all nodes a1 }
     write(' Reach:    '); dispset (reach) ;
     write(' Coalesced:  '); dispset (coal);
     writeln ('-------------');writeln
  end ; {of procedure displaying all the information  }
procedure init;     { Initializes by cleaning everything out }
var k1:integer;
    begin  nofe:=0 ; (*Number of eqs made 0 *)
      writeln (' Initialization');
      for k1 :=-maxe to maxe do adj[k1]:=[];
      for k1:=1 to maxe do degree[k1]:=0;
      (*All sets are initialized to the empty set *)
      reach:=[]; coal:=[]; elim:=[]; zapped:=[]
    end {of initialization };
procedure get_eqs;
{This procedure enters all nodes and their adjacency lists }
var node, adjnod:intrange;
begin readln(nofe);
   writeln(' The number of equations is ',nofe);
   repeat read(node);      {For each node between }
     if node in [1.. nofe] then  {1 and number of equations }
         repeat  read(adjnod);   {read an adjoining node }
             if adjnod in [1..nofe] then{and if one of legitimate}
             begin (*nodes appears, add it  to adjacency}
              adj[node]:=adj[node]+[sac(adjnod)];
              adj[adjnod]:=adj[adjnod]+[sac(node)]
             end                      (* something *)
             else                        (* is *)
             if adjnod<>0 then           (*wrong *)
             begin
               writeln(' Bad adjacent node-number!'); adjnod:=1
             end
         until adjnod=0
      else
      if node<>0 then
         begin node:=1;
            writeln(' bad primary node-number!')
         end
   until node=0;
   up_degree
end {of procedure get-eqs};
procedure eliminate(node:intrange);
var k1,k2:integer; suprnod:sset;
begin writeln('Eliminating node ',node:3);
    (*Find the set of coalesced nodes and the reach -set  *)
   coal:=adj[node]*elim; find_reach(node);
   writeln ('Sets coal and reach consist of :');
   dispset(coal); dispset(reach); (* Display them *)
```

Program 4.1 (cont.)

```
    if (coal=[]) then
    begin elim:=elim+[sac(node)];
      for k1:=-nofe to nofe do
      if sac(node) in adj[k1] then
      adj[k1]:=adj[k1]+reach-[sac(k1)]; adj[node]:=[]
   end
   else
   begin
      suprnod:=coal+[sac(node)];
      elim:=elim-coal+[sac(-node)];
      adj[-node]:=reach-[sac(node)];
      for k1:=1 to nofe do
      if sac(k1) in reach then
      adj[k1]:=adj[k1]-suprnod+[sac(-node)];
      for k1:=-nofe to nofe do
      if sac(k1) in suprnod then adj[k1]:=[]
   end;
   zapped:=zapped+[sac(node)];
   up_degree; display
end ;   {of procedure eliminate}
procedure mindeg; {Eliminates nodes in minimum degree order }
var   znode:intrange; {The node to be eliminated }
       supelim:sset; {Set of nodes indistiguishable with respect*)
       tempset:sset ;(*to elimination.Temporary set to compare*)
       a1:integer ;  (*reach-sets of nodes *)
       a2,k1,k2:intrange; {Temporary variables }
begin a1:=maxint; {Start degree with maximum integer}
      for k1:=1 to nofe do {If node k1 not eliminated and its degree}
      if not(sac(k1) in zapped ) and (degree[k1]<a1) then
      begin   {smaller than a1 then update znode and the }
         znode:=k1; a1:=degree[znode]
      end; {lowest numbered node of minimum degree and a1=its degree}
{ Next find the group of nodes indistinguishable from znode for*)
(* elimination purposes...and gather them into a supernode. *)
find_reach(znode); tempset:=reach;supelim:=[sac(znode)];
    for k2:=1 to nofe do
     if not(sac(k2) in zapped) then
     begin find_reach(k2);
        if tempset =reach then supelim:=supelim+[sac(k2)]
     end;
     if supelim<> [sac(znode)] then (* print a message *)
     begin write(' Nodes '); dispset(supelim);
     writeln('were indistinguishable and will be eliminated');
       writeln
     end;
    for k1:=1 to nofe do (* The nodes to be eliminated *)
    if sac(k1) in supelim then (* are in set supelim *)
    begin
    writeln('Node ',k1:3,' to be eliminated. Degree=',a1:3);
       eliminate(k1) (* This call eliminates all nodes k1 *)
    end
end  {of procedure mindeg which really is all of elimination here};
procedure elsim;       {is the simulation of elimination or }
var i,k,k1,m:integer; {part 2. It follows closely the text,}
begin                          {so NO COMMENTS ARE GIVEN }
    for k:=1 to nofe do
    for i:=1 to k-1 do
       if (sac(i) in adj[k]) then adj[k]:=adj[k]-[sac(i)];
```

Program 4.1 (cont.)

```
      for k:=1 to nofe do adj[-k]:=adj[k];
      writeln(' First pass ');
      for i:=1 to nofe do dispset(adj[i]); writeln('   ');
      for k:=1 to nofe do
      if adj[k]<>[] then
      begin m:=nofe;
         for k1:=nofe downto 1 do
         if (sac(k1) in adj[k]) and (k1<m) then m:=k1;
         adj[m]:=adj[m]+adj[k]-[sac(m)]
      end;
      writeln(' Second pass ');
      for i:=1 to nofe do dispset(adj[i]); writeln('   ');
      m:=0;
      for k:=1 to nofe do
      begin  ip[k]:=m+1;
         for i:=1 to nofe do
         if (sac(i) in adj[-k]) and (sac(i) in adj[k])
         then
            begin
            m:=m+1; read(L[m])
            end
         else
         if (sac(i) in adj[k]) and not (sac(i) in adj[-k])
         then
            begin m:=m+1; L[m]:=0.0 end;
      end;
      writeln(' Second part ');
      for i:=1 to m do write(L[i]:3:2,'   '); writeln('   ');
   end; (* of procedure which simulates elimination *)


   begin   {OF THE MAIN PROGRAM }
       init ; display; get_eqs; display;
       repeat
          mindeg
       until zapped=[sac(1)..sac(nofe)];
       (*Rewind and rename the graph in the optimum order*)
       init; display; get_eqs; display;
       (*Next we call the elimination_simulating procedure*)
       elsim;
       (*Adjacency is abandoned; arrays are restored  *)
       k1:=0; k2:=1; ip[1]:=1;
       for i:=1 to nofe do
       begin
          for j:=1 to nofe do
          if sac(j) in adj[i] then
          begin k1:=k1+1; ad[k1]:=j end;
          k2:=k2+1; ip[k2]:=k1+1
       end;
       writeln('   Final result  ad  ');
       for i:=1 to k1 do write(ad[i]:3); writeln;
       writeln('  Array ip'  );
       for i:=1 to k2 do write(ip[i]:3); writeln
   end.
```

Program 4.1 (cont.)

TABLE 4.4

```
Initialization
Display information ...
Eliminated nodes:    []
Outstanding nodes:   []
Adjacency sets:
Reach:    []
Coalesced:   []
--------------

The number of equations is                      7
Display information ...
Eliminated nodes:    []
Outstanding nodes:   []
Adjacency sets:
 1  1  [  2]
 2  4  [  1,  3,  5,  7]
 3  2  [  2,  4]
 4  2  [  3,  5]
 5  4  [  2,  4,  6,  7]
 6  2  [  5,  7]
 7  3  [  2,  5,  6]
Reach:    []
Coalesced:   []
--------------
```

Initially in the algorithm, znode = 1, so the algorithm prescribes to *Eliminate* $x_i = x_1$. [Initially $E_0 = \varnothing$; see Table 4.4.]

1. $T := A[x_i] \cdot E_0 = \varnothing$. Call Reach $(y = x_i, \varnothing)$: $z = x_2 \notin \varnothing$, so we just add node x_2 to E_0. Thus $R := \{x_2\}$.
2. $\bar{x}_1 := x_1 + T = x_1$; $E_1 := E_0 - T + \{\bar{x}_1\} = \{\bar{x}_1\}$.
3. $A[\bar{x}_1] := R = \{x_2\}$. There is only one node $w \in R$, namely, $\{x_2\}$, and therefore
$A[x_2] := \{\bar{x}_1\} + \{x_1, x_3, x_5, x_7\} - (\varnothing + \{x_1\}) = \{\bar{x}_1, x_3, x_5, x_7\}$

In the program, the temporary set "tempset" will be [2] and the set of supernodes supelim = [1]. At this point, the loop on $k2$ finds that node 1 is not yet zapped—it belongs to the supelim set. Thus, elim(1) is called.

There are no coalesced nodes at this point, since coal = node * elim = [ ] and node 2 can be reached from node 1.

Procedure "eliminate" is one big **if** statement; since coal = [ ], the part between **then** and **else** is taken with the following effect: elim := [ ] + [1] = [1]. Since node 1 is only in adj[2]:

adj[2] := [1, 3, 5, 7] + [2] − [2] = [1, 3, 5, 7].

This follows closely the elimination of x_1 above with one difference: In the program, adj[i] is made [ ], zapped := [1], and degrees are updated.

The result of eliminating x_1 is shown in Table 4.5. The node of lowest degree, denoted from now on as x_{min}, is here $x_{min} = 3$.

TABLE 4.5

```
Node    1 to be eliminated. Degree=   1
Eliminating node    1
Sets coal and reach consist of :
[]
[  2]
 Display information ...
 Eliminated nodes:     [   1]
 Outstanding nodes:    [   1]
 Adjacency sets:
  2  3  [  1,  3,  5,  7]
  3  2  [  2,  4]
  4  2  [  3,  5]
  5  4  [  2,  4,  6,  7]
  6  2  [  5,  7]
  7  3  [  2,  5,  6]
 Reach:     [  2]
 Coalesced:   []
--------------
```

Following the algorithm and Table 4.5 we have the following:

Eliminate $x_i = x_3$. ("A" sometimes replaces "adj".)

1. $T := A[x_3] \cdot E_1 = \{x_2, x_4\} \cdot \{x_1\} = \varnothing$.
Next we call Reach ($y = x_3, E_1$): $z = x_2 \notin E_1$, so $R := \{x_2\}$ and $z = x_4 \notin E_1$ as well as $R := \{x_2, x_4\}$.

2. $\bar{x}_3 := x_3 + T = x_3$; $E_2 := x_1 - T + \{\bar{x}_3\} = \{\bar{x}_1\} + \{\bar{x}_3\} = \{\bar{x}_1, \bar{x}_3\}$.

3. $A[\bar{x}_3] := R = \{x_2, x_4\}$. Nodes w are x_2 and x_4:
$A[x_2] := \{\bar{x}_3\} + \{\bar{x}_1, \bar{x}_3, x_5, x_7\} - \{x_3\} = \{\bar{x}_1, \bar{x}_3, x_5, x_7\}$
$A[x_4] := \{\bar{x}_3\} + \{x_3, x_5\} - \{x_3\} = \{\bar{x}_3, x_5\}$

The "mindeg" procedure consists now of the following steps:

- Loop on $k1$ finds znode = 3 and $a1$ = 2, i.e., the node to be eliminated is node 3 of degree 2. The reach-set of it is [2,4], so that tempset := [2,4] and supelim is [1,3].
- The loop on $k2$ scans all nodes, and since only [1] is zapped, locates the reach-sets of this node. Only the reach-set of node 3 is identical to the tempset, so that node 3 remains the only one to be eliminated.

The steps of eliminate(3) are: coal := [2, 4] * [3] = [ ]; reach := [2,4]. Since again coal is empty, the **if – then** path is taken with steps: elim := [1, 3]. For $k2$:= 2, 4 we have [3] in adj[$k1$] so that the loop produces adj[2] := [1, 3, 5, 7] + [2, 4] – [2] = [1, 3, 4, 5, 7] and adj[4] := [3, 5] + [2, 4] – [4] = [2, 3, 5]; node 2 is adjacent to node 4 and is itself always adjacent to node 2. The **if** statement ends with adj[3] := [ ] and the degrees updated.

TABLE 4.6

```
Node   3 to be eliminated. Degree=  2
Eliminating node   3
Sets coal and reach consist of :
[]
[  2,  4]
 Display information ...
 Eliminated nodes:    [  1,  3]
 Outstanding nodes:   [  1,  3]
 Adjacency sets:
  2  3  [  1,  3,  4,  5,  7]
  4  2  [  2,  3,  5]
  5  4  [  2,  4,  6,  7]
  6  2  [  5,  7]
  7  3  [  2,  5,  6]
 Reach:    [  2,  4]
 Coalesced:  []
 --------------
```

The result of eliminating x_3 is shown in Table 4.6. The next $x_{\min} = 4$ and the algorithm includes the steps:

1. $T := A[x_4] \cdot E_2 = \{x_2, \bar{x}_3, x_5\} \cdot \{\bar{x}_1, \bar{x}_3\} = \{\bar{x}_3\}$.
$z = \bar{x}_3 \in E_2$, so that $R := A[\bar{x}_3] = \{x_2, x_4\}$.
Next $z = x_5 \notin E_2$ so that $R := R + \{x_5\} = \{x_2, x_4, x_5\}$

2. $\bar{x}_4 := x_4 + T = \{\bar{x}_3, x_4\}$. Node (and row) $\bar{3}$ are not needed any more.
$E_3 := E_2 - T + \{\bar{x}_4\} = \{\bar{x}_1, x_3\} - \{\bar{x}_3\} + \{\bar{x}_4\} = \{\bar{x}_1, x_4\}$

3. $A[\bar{x}_4] = \{x_2, x_4, x_5\}$. Node w cannot be x_4. Thus, $w = x_2$:
$A[x_2] := \{x_4\} + \{\bar{x}_1, \bar{x}_3, x_5, x_7\} - \{\bar{x}_3, x_4\} = \{\bar{x}_1, \bar{x}_3, x_5, x_7\}$;
$w = x_5$: $A[5]$: $\{\bar{x}_4\} + \{x_2, x_4, x_6, x_7\} - \{\bar{x}_3, x_4\} = \{x_2, x_4, x_6, x_7\}$

In the "mindeg" procedure we now have the steps:
Loop on $k1$ locates znode $=$ [4]; $a_1 := 1$.
Reach(4) := [2, 3, 5]; tempset := [2, 3, 5]; supelim := [4].
Loop on $k2$ finds that no adj set is [2, 3, 5] and calls eliminate(4). In it coal := [2, 3, 5] * [1, 3] = [3] so that this time coal is not empty and the **else** path of the large **if** statement is taken.

We have here a supernode which includes nodes 3 and 4; it will be represented as -4. Let us repeat that there were negative nodes because every supernode is negative. Because the range extends from $-$maxe to $+$maxe, we had to use the sac function.

As a result of this step, node 4 "includes" node $\bar{3}$. We can either encircle the two separate nodes $\bar{3}$ and 4 as $\bar{4}$ or—as we will do—draw the network so that $\bar{4}$ represents both of them. Additionally, $A[\bar{x}_4]$ is now $A[\bar{x}_4] = \{x_5, x_2\}$. The results of this step are shown in Table 4.7, which corresponds to Fig. 4.4(b) after nodes 1, 3, and 4 were eliminated.

TABLE 4.7

```
Node   4 to be eliminated. Degree=  2
Eliminating node   4
Sets coal and reach consist of :
[  3]
[  2,  5]
 Display information ...
 Eliminated nodes:    [  1,  3,  4]
 Outstanding nodes:   [ -4,  1]
 Adjacency sets:
 -4  2  [  2,  5]
  2  2  [ -4,  1,  5,  7]
  5  3  [ -4,  2,  6,  7]
  6  2  [  5,  7]
  7  3  [  2,  5,  6]
 Reach:    [  2,  5]
 Coalesced:   [  3]
--------------
```

The degree of node 2 is 2, so it is eliminated next, producing a supernode which will include $\{\bar{x}_1, \bar{x}_4, x_2\}$. Note also that originally the degree of node 2 was 4 so that policy 2 should be called a changing or, better, a dynamic policy

Eliminate $x_i = x_2$:

1. $T := A[x_2]\cdot E = \{\bar{x}_1, \bar{x}_4, x_5, x_7\} \cdot \{\bar{x}_1, \bar{x}_4\} = \{\bar{x}_1, \bar{x}_4\}$ Call Reach ($y = x_2, E_3$) where $z = A[x_2] = \{\bar{x}_1, \bar{x}_4, x_5, x_7\}.z = \bar{x}_1 \in E_3$ so $R := A[\bar{x}_1] = \{x_2\}$. Next $z = \bar{x}_4 \in E_3$ so $R := R + A[\bar{x}_4] = \{x_2, x_5\}$ Next $z = x_5 \notin E_3$ so $R := R + \{x_5\} = \{x_2, x_5\}$. Finally $z = x_7 \notin E_3$ and $R := \{x_2, x_5, x_7\}$
2. $\bar{x}_2 := x_2 + \{\bar{x}_1, x_4\} = \{\bar{x}_1, x_2, \bar{x}_4\}$. Node (and row) $\bar{4}$ can represent 2 and $\bar{1}$ too. $E_4 := E_3 - T + \{\bar{x}_2\} = \{\bar{x}_1, \bar{x}_4\} - \{\bar{x}_1, \bar{x}_4\} + \{\bar{x}_2\} = \{\bar{x}_2\} \equiv \{\bar{x}_4\}$
3. $A[\bar{x}_4] := \{x_5, x_7\}$. Since x_2 was included in $\bar{x}_4$ we have $w = \{x_5, x_7\}$.

$$w = x_5 := A[x_5] := \{\bar{x}_4\} + \{\bar{x}_4, x_6, x_7\} - \{\bar{x}_4, x_2\} = \{\bar{x}_2, x_6, x_7\}$$

$$w = x_7 := A[x_7] := \{\bar{x}_4\} + \{\bar{x}_4, x_5, x_6\} - \{\bar{x}_4, x_2\} = \{\bar{x}_2, x_5, x_6\}$$

The results are as shown in Table 4.8. The network has shrunk because of supernode $\bar{x}_2$ to a triangle of nodes 5, 6, 7. All have degree 2.

We next eliminate x_6 and x_5 with the results as in Tables 4.9, 4.10, and 4.11

Eliminate $x_i = x_5$:

1. $T = A[x_5]\cdot E_4 = \{\bar{x}_4, x_6, x_7\} \cdot \{\bar{x}_4\} = \{\bar{x}_4\}$. Call reach ($y = x_5, E_4$). $z = \bar{x}_4 \in E_4$, so $R := A[\bar{x}_4] = \{x_5, x_7\}$. Next $z = x_6 \notin E_4$, so $R := R + \{x_6\} = \{x_5, x_6, x_7\} \notin E_4$ and $R := \{x_5, x_6, x_7\}$
2. $\bar{x}_5 := x_5 + T = \{\bar{x}_4, x_5\}$. Node $\bar{x}_5$ includes node $\bar{x}_4$. $E_5 := E_4 - T + \{x_5\} = \{\bar{x}_4\} - \{\bar{x}_4\} + \{\bar{x}_5\} = \{\bar{x}_5\}$

3. $A[\bar{x}_5] := R = \{x_6, x_7\} = \{\bar{x}_4\} - \{\bar{x}_4\} + \{\bar{x}_5\} = \{\bar{x}_5\}$. $w = x_6$: $A[x_6] := \{x_5\} + \{x_5, x_7\} - \{x_4, x_5\} = \{x_5, x_4\} + \{x_5, x_7\} - \{x_4, x_5\} = \{x_7\}$ $w = x_7$: $A[x_7] := \{x_4, x_5\} + \{x_4, x_5, x_6\} - \{x_4, x_5\} = \{x_4, x_5, x_6\} - \{x_4, x_5\} = \{x_6\}$

TABLE 4.8

```
 Nodes [   2,   6]
were indistinguishable and will be eliminated

Node    2 to be eliminated. Degree=   2
Eliminating node    2
Sets coal and reach consist of :
[ -4,   1]
[  5,   7]
 Display information ...
 Eliminated nodes:     [   1,   2,   3,   4]
 Outstanding nodes:    [ -2]
 Adjacency sets:
 -2   2   [   5,   7]
  5   2   [ -2,   6,   7]
  6   2   [   5,   7]
  7   2   [ -2,   5,   6]
 Reach:     [   5,   7]
 Coalesced:   [ -4,   1]
-------------
```

TABLE 4.9

```
Node    6 to be eliminated. Degree=   2
Eliminating node    6
Sets coal and reach consist of :
[]
[  5,   7]
 Display information ...
 Eliminated nodes:     [   1,   2,   3,   4,   6]
 Outstanding nodes:    [ -2,   6]
 Adjacency sets:
 -2   2   [   5,   7]
  5   1   [ -2,   6,   7]
  7   1   [ -2,   5,   6]
 Reach:     [   5,   7]
 Coalesced:   []
-------------
```

TABLE 4.10

```
Node    5 to be eliminated. Degree=   1
Eliminating node    5
Sets coal and reach consist of :
[ -2,   6]
[   7]
 Display information ...
 Eliminated nodes:    [   1,   2,   3,   4,   5,   6]
 Outstanding nodes:   [  -5]
 Adjacency sets:
 -5   1   [   7]
   7   0   [  -5]
 Reach:      [   7]
 Coalesced:    [ -2,   6]
 --------------
```

TABLE 4.11

```
Node    7 to be eliminated. Degree=   0
Eliminating node    7
Sets coal and reach consist of :
[ -5]
[]
 Display information ...
 Eliminated nodes:    [   1,   2,   3,   4,   5,   6,   7]
 Outstanding nodes:   [  -7]
 Adjacency sets:
 Reach:      []
 Coalesced:    [ -5]
 --------------
```

Eliminate $x_i = x_6$:

1. $T := A[x_6] \cdot E_5 = \{\bar{x}_5, x_7\} \cdot \{\bar{x}_5\} = \{\bar{x}_5\}$. $z = \bar{x}_5 \in E_5$ so $R := \{x_6\}$ and $z = x_7 \notin E_5$, so $R := \{x_6, x_7\}$.
2. $\bar{x}_6 := x_6 + \bar{x}_5$. This node includes all preceding nodes. $E_6 = \{\bar{x}_5\} - \{\bar{x}_5\} + \{\bar{x}_6\} = \{\bar{x}_6\}$.
3. $A[\bar{x}_6] := \{x_7\}$ and we have only $w = x_7$, so that $A[x_7] := \{\bar{x}_6\} + \{\bar{x}_6\} - \{\bar{x}_5, x_6\} = \varnothing$. We have finished.

Let us discuss the results thus far:

1. The elimination proceeds according to the sequence 1, 3, 4, 2, 6, and 5. We can therefore renumber the nodes according to Table 4.12.

TABLE 4.12

Original No.	1	2	3	4	5	6	7
New No.	1	4	2	3	6	5	7

2. Graphical elimination of the network is shown in Fig. 4.5. The number of fill-ins is only 1, namely line 3−4, instead of 3 fill-ins originally. The matrix shows the same result. As a matter of fact, the

consecutive reach-sets R and branches were: [x_2 and $\varnothing$], [$\{x_2, x_4\}$ but $2-4$ existed], [$\{x_2, x_4, x_5\}$, added branch $2-4$, which is renumbered as $3-4$], [$\{x_2, x_5, x_7\}$, nothing new], [$\{x_5, x_6, x_7\}$, nothing new], [$\{x_6, x_7\}$, nothing new]

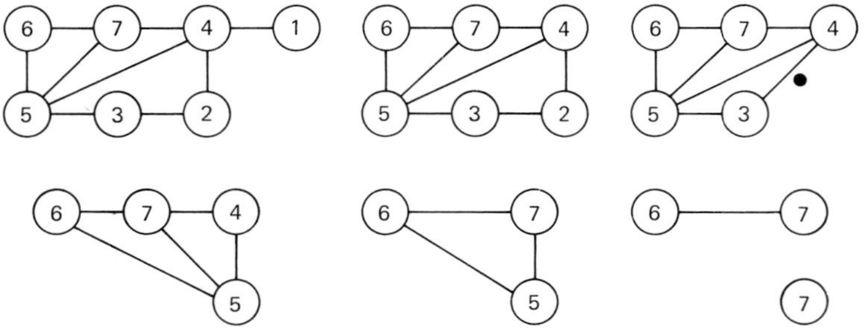

Figure 4.5 Graphical elimination.

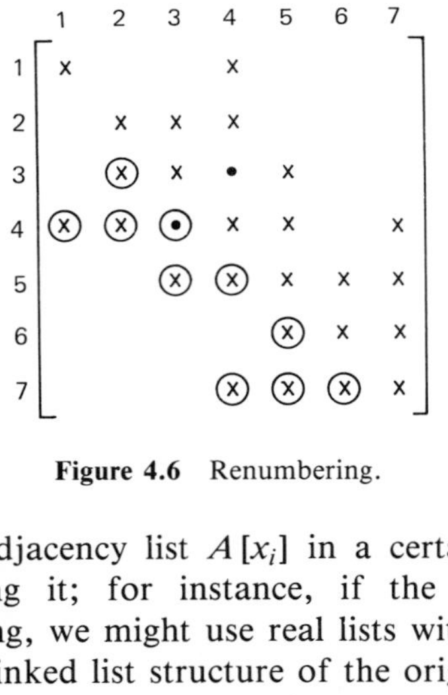

Figure 4.6 Renumbering.

3. We have used the adjacency list $A[x_i]$ in a certain way. There are other ways of doing it; for instance, if the computer language includes list processing, we might use real lists with pointers, etc. On the other hand, the linked list structure of the original network is

TABLE 4.13

1	2	3	4	5	6	7	8	9	10	11	12	13	14	15	16	17	18	19	ind
1,2	2,1	2,3	2,5	2,7	3,2	3,4	4,3	4,5	5,2	5,4	5,6	5,6	6,5	6,7	7,2	7,5	7,6		LNZ
2	1	3	5	7	2	4	3	5	2	4	6	7	5	7	2	5	6	0	adj
1	2				6		8		10				14		16			19	ip
1	2				3		4		5				6		7			8	

The adjacency lists are explicitly given here, e.g., $A[2] = [1, 3, 5, 7]$ so that this data structure could be used throughout (this is done in [GL81]).

4. There are proofs in [GL81] that the original space provided for the adjacency lists is sufficient for this entire phase—and we have seen this in the example.
5. Whenever two or more adjacent nodes were eliminated, we joined them together into a supernode. *Groups of uneliminated nodes* which behave in the same way as far as their elimination is concerned *can also be treated together as supernodes.*

A Fortran program of this part appears on pages 124–137 of [GL81].

Up to this point *we have only calculated the order in which elimination should proceed.* Next we present the algorithm for setting up data so that it includes the fill-in, without going through factorization proper.

Before doing this, let us discuss the way in which the **L** matrix will be stored. We can store it as a linked structure, which would store the nonzeros of the factored matrix. Thus, for the matrix of Table 4.13:

- LNZ could store all nonzeros in the lower triangular factor matrix.
- adj could store the second index of LNZ, i.e., j of $L_{i,j}$.
- ip could be an index for LNZ entries with

  ip(1) = position of first-column entries;
  ip(2) = position (in LNZ) of second-column entries;
  ip(i) = position (in LNZ) of ith-column entries.

The matrix in Fig. 4.6, would be stored as in Table 4.14. Rows LNZ and UNCOMPRESSED store the matrix of Fig. 4.6. Additionally, DIAG could store diagonal entries $L_{i,i}$, $i = 1$ to n (an n-by-n matrix stored as an n-vector). The amount of storage for this so-called uncompressed scheme is

$$\text{number of nonzeros in the factored matrix (for LNZ)} + [N \text{ (for DIAG)}]$$
$$+ [N \text{ (for ip)}] + [\text{number of nonzeros in } \mathbf{L} \text{ (for adj)}].$$

Next is another way to store **L**, a *compressed* scheme.

By reordering the original matrix **A** using the minimum-degree algorithm, its factored matrix **L** has entries in a certain block which fall into the same rows. This means that the vector adj can be compressed. If a row subscript for one column matches the subscript for the following entry in the subsequent column, do not make another entry in column adj. Table 4.14 shows how the A-list would be compressed. (In this case only single elements 4, 5, and 7 are compressed, but in large networks entire sets could be compressed.)

TABLE 4.14 Total storage for compressed scheme ≤ |Nonz L| + 2N*

	1	2		3		4		5		6	7
LNZ	l_{41}	l_{32}	l_{42}	l_{43}	l_{53}	l_{54}	l_{74}	l_{65}	l_{75}	l_{76}	
UNCOMPRESSED	4	3	4	4	5	5	7	6	7	7	
COMPRESSED	4	3	4	5	7	6	7				

We have a certain price to pay, for storing pointers to adj which will show where a row begins. If we consider the space for all arrays except DIAG and LNZ as overhead, then it was pointed out in [GL81] that overhead is reduced considerably in the compressed scheme. Table 4.15 reproduced from that book, shows that for some problems the overhead storage is reduced by at least 50%.

TABLE 4.15 Comparison of Uncompressed and Compressed Storage.*

Number of Equations	|Nonz(**A**)|	|Nonz(**L**)|	Overhead for Uncompressed	Overhead for Compressed
936	2664	13,870	14,806	6903
1009	2928	19,083	20,090	8085
1089	3136	18,626	19,715	8574
1440	4032	19,047	20,487	10,536
1180	3285	14,685	15,865	8436
1377	3808	16,793	18,170	9790
1138	3156	15,592	16,730	8326
1141	3162	15,696	16,837	8435
1349	3876	23,726	25,075	10,666

*From J. George and J. W. Liu, *Computer Solution of Large Sparse Positive Definite Systems*, © 1981 by Prentice-Hall, Inc. Reprinted with permission.

Symbolic factorization, which is the next step, will simulate the numerical factorization in order to obtain the structure of matrix **L**.

As was shown earlier, symbolic factorization can be regarded as determination of reachable sets (eliminated in the sequence $1, 2 \ldots, n$):

$$\text{reach}(x_i, \{x_1, \ldots, x_{i-1}\}); \quad \text{for } i = 1, \ldots, n$$

$$E_i = \{x_1, \ldots, x_i\} \quad \text{(set of eliminated nodes)}$$

where

$$\text{reach}\,(x_i, E_{i-1}) = A\,[x_i] + (\Sigma\,\{\text{reach}\,(x_r, E_{r-1}) \mid x_i \in R\,(x_r, E_{r-1})\}) - E_i.$$

The nodes reachable from x_i through an eliminated set of nodes E_{i-1} include the nodes adjacent to x_i, plus the union (sum) over all the reachable sets of which x_i is an element minus eliminated nodes E_i.

The preceding suggests an algorithm for finding the reachable sets (and structure of **L**):

Step 1 (Initialization): For $k = 1, \ldots, n$:

$$\text{reach}\,(x_{k,} E_{k-1}) := A\,[x_k] - E_{k-1}$$

Step 2 (Symbolic Factorization): For $k = 1, \ldots, n$:

$$\text{if } x_i \in \text{reach}\,(x_k,\ E_{k-1}),\ \text{then}$$

$$\text{reach}\,(x_i, E_{i-1}) := \text{reach}\,(x_i, E_{i-1}) + \text{reach}\,(x_k, E_{k-1}) - E_i$$

This scheme essentially simulates the entire factorization and would lead to the same operations count as the factorization itself. Fortunately, we can improve the efficiency of the algorithm considerably.

Consider a node x_i with nodes $x_1, \ldots, x_{i-1}$ having been eliminated. Assume that x_i is connected to two supernodes, e.g., as in Fig. 4.7. Then obviously

$$\text{reach}\,(x_i,\ E_{i-1}) = A\,[x_i] + A\,[c_1] + A\,[c_2] - E_i$$

Next choose representatives from c_1, c_2 such that x_{k1}, x_{k2} are the last nodes eliminated from sets c_1 and c_2 respectively. Then

$$\text{reach}\,(x_{i,} E_{i-1}) = A\,[x_i] + \text{reach}\,(x_{k1,} E_{k1-1}) + \text{reach}\,(x_{k2,} E_{k2-1}) - E_i$$

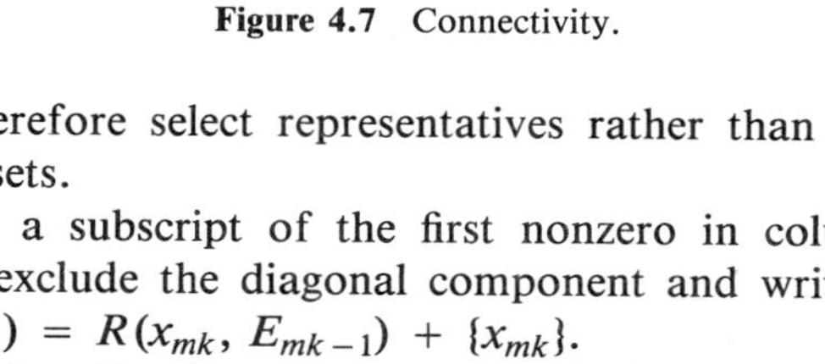

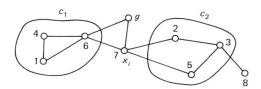

Figure 4.7 Connectivity.

We can therefore select representatives rather than having to merge many reachable sets.

Let mk be a subscript of the first nonzero in column vector **k** of matrix **L**. (We exclude the diagonal component and write R for reach.) Then $R(x_k,\ E_{k-1}) = R(x_{mk},\ E_{mk-1}) + \{x_{mk}\}$.

For $x_i \in R(x_k,\ E_{k-1})$ and $i > m_k$ it is redundant to consider $R(x_k,\ E_{k-1})$ in determining $R(x_i,\ E_{i-1})$ because all reachable nodes through x_k are included in $R(x_{mk},\ E_{mk-1})$. Thus

$$R(x_i,\ E_{i-1}) = A\,[x_i] + (\Sigma\ \{R(x_k, E_{k-1}) \mid m_k = i\}) - E_i$$

The reachable set of x_i through an eliminated set E_{i-1} includes all nodes adjacent to x_i plus the union over the reachable sets in a column k

where the minimum subscript (first entry of a nonzero in column k) $m_k = i$, minus eliminated set $E_i = \{x_1, x_2, x_i\}$. The algorithm is therefore:

Step 2 (Symbolic Factorization): Here, m is simply the minimum index in the reach list of Step 2 as computed in a previous sweep of the loop.

For $k = 1, \ldots, n$
If reach $(x_k, E_{k-1}) \neq \varnothing$ **then do**
$m = \min \{j \mid x_j \in \text{reach } (x_k, E_{k-1})\}$
reach $(x_m, E_{m-1}) :=$
reach (x_m, E_{m-1}) + reach $(x_k, E_{k-1}) - \{x_m\}$

In this case, too, an example best illustrates the algorithm. Figure 4.8 shows the original graph (with a different numbering) and the algorithm. It will be executed first with no ordering of nodes for both uncompressed and then compressed storage. Then the same will be done for the ordering we found earlier. (We thus have 4 cases.)

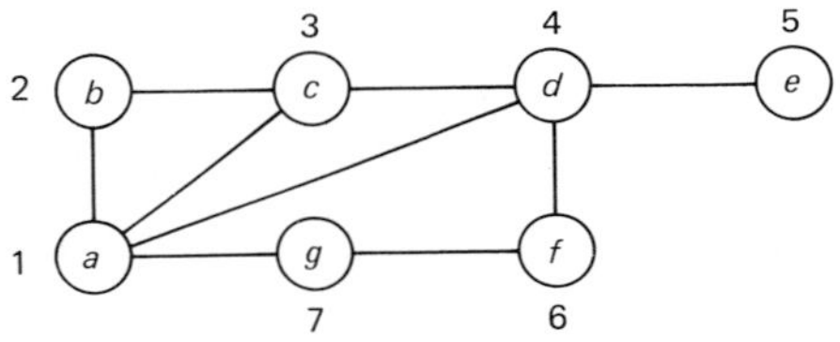

Figure 4.8 Original graph (no ordering of nodes).

Original Graph. The two steps of the algorithm are simulated next and the results are shown uncompressed in (a) and compressed in (b).

Initialization	*STEP* 2		*STEP* (Detailed calculation):
$\mathbf{R}(x_k, E_{k-1})$	$\mathbf{R}(x_k, E_{k-1})$	$k = 1, m = 2$	$R(x_2, E_1) := \{3\} + \{2, 3, 4, 7\} - \{2\} = \{3, 4, 7$
2, 3, 4, 7	2, 3, 4, 7	$k = 2, m = 3$	$R(x_3, E_2) := \{4\} + \{3, 4, 7\} - \{3\} = \{4, 7\}$
3	3, 4, 7	$k = 3, m = 4$	$R(x_4, E_3) := \{5, 6\} + \{4, 7\} - \{4\} = \{5, 6, 7\}$
4	4, 7	$k = 4, m = 5$	$R(x_5, E_4) := \{\varnothing\} + \{5, 6, 7\} - \{5\} = \{6, 7\}$
5, 6	5, 6, 7	$k = 5, m = 6$	$R(x_6, E_5) := \{7\} + \{6, 7\} - \{6\} = \{7\}$
$\varnothing$	6, 7	$k = 6, m = 7$	$R(x_7, E_6) := \{\varnothing\} + \{7\} - \{7\} = \{\varnothing\}$
7	7	Note that in Step 1, only nodes with	
$\varnothing$	$\varnothing$	$j \geq k$ are used.	

(a) Data for Uncompressed Storage:

DIAG l_{11} l_{22} l_{33} l_{44} l_{55} l_{66} l_{77} diagonal elements

adj 2 3 4 7 3 4 7 4 7 5 6 7 6 7 7

LNZ l_{21} l_{31} l_{41} l_{71} l_{32} l_{42} l_{72} l_{43} l_{73} l_{54} l_{64} l_{74} l_{65} l_{75} l_{76}

ip 1 5 8 10 13 15 16

Storage required is 7 + 15 + 15 + 7 = 44 elements.

	1	2	3	4	5	6	7
1	x			x			
2		x	x	x			
3		x	x	·			
4	x	x	·	x		x	x
5					x	x	x
6			x	x	x	x	x
7				x	x	x	x

(b) Data for Compressed Scheme:

Remove row subscripts from vector adj if they appear identical or partly identical to the subscript from the previous column. Add index iip to point to the start of row subscripts in adj for each column.

Uncompressed	A	2 3 4 7 3 4 7 4 7 5 6 7 6 7 7
compressed	A	2 3 4 7 5 6 7
	iip	1 2 3 5 6 7 8

DIAG, LNZ, and XLNZ are the same as earlier.

Storage required 7 + 15 + 7 + 7 + 7 = 43 elements.

(The second scheme removes duplications.)

(Working with small networks can hardly show the significance associated with compressing the storage vector adj.)

This graph needs yet to be reordered (Fig. 4.9); this will cut down on fill-in and thus reduce storage requirements.

The renumbered network (Fig. 4.9) is processed next and the two storage schemes (a) and (b) applied.

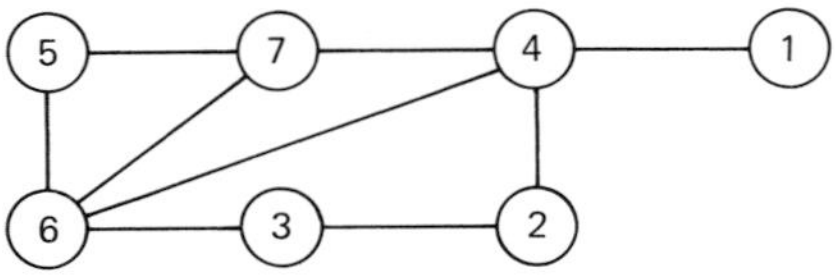

Figure 4.9 Reordered graph.

Renumbered graph.

1	2		*STEP* 2:
$\mathbf{R}(x_k, E_{k-1})$	$\mathbf{R}(x_k, E_{k-1})$	$k = 1, m = 4$	$R(x_4, E_3) = \{6,7\} + \{4\} = \{6,7\}$
4	4	$k = 2, m = 3$	$R(x_3, E_2) = \{6\} + \{3, 4\} - \{3\} = \{4, 6\}$
3, 4	3, 4	$k = 3, m = 4$	$R(x_4, E_3) = \{6,7\} + \{4, 6\} - \{4\} = \{6, 7\}$
6	4, 6	$k = 4, m = 5$	$R(x_5, E_4) = \{6, 7\} + \{5, 7\} - \{5\} = \{6, 7$
6, 7	6, 7	$k = 5, m = 6$	$R(x_6, E_6) = \{7\} + \{6, 7\} - \{6\} = \{7\}$
6, 7	6, 7	$k = 6, m = 7$	$R(x_7, E_6) = \{\varnothing\} + \{7\} - \{7\} = \{\varnothing\}$
7	7		
$\varnothing$	$\varnothing$		

a) Data for uncompressed storage:
DIAG l_{11} l_{22} l_{33} l_{44} l_{55} l_{66} l_{77}
adj 4 3 4 4 5 5 7 6 7 7
LNZ l_{41} l_{32} l_{42} l_{43} l_{53} l_{54} l_{74} l_{65} $l_{75}$$l_{76}$
ip 1 2 4 6 8 10 11
Storage $= 7+10+10+7 = 34$

b) Data for compressed scheme:

adj 4 3 4 4 5 5 7 6 7 7
ad 4 3 4 5 7 6 7
iip 1 2 3 4 6 7 8

DIAG, LNZ, ip are the same as earlier.
Storage $= 7 + 7 + 10 + 7 + 7 = 38$
Once again, this example does not show the real advantage of using the compressed storage scheme. Only in large matrices are storage savings realized. *Therefore, in our case, we will not use it.*

Let us return to program OOF (Program 4.1). Since we assume that the input was stored on a tape, we read it again, but now reordered. We could have included an array of "permutations" which would reorder them in memory, but it probably corresponds more to practice to reread the data. This is why the data in Table 4.3 include the reordered graph in its second part.

The program enters the new data and prints it out in Table 4.16, proceeds with steps 1 and 2 as evidenced by Tables 4.17 and 4.18, respectively and reads in the numerical values of **A** as those of **L**. For this, it checks if the item is a fill-in and if so, enters $L = 0.0$. The results of this, second part of "OOF" are seen in Tables 4.19 and 4.20 and correspond to the uncompressed storage scheme of the reordered graph.

The third and final part is that of actual factorization, but since we described such programs in Chapter 2, they will not be discussed again. Instead this will be a part of the project.

TABLE 4.16

```
Initialization
Display information ...
Eliminated nodes:    []
Outstanding nodes:   []
Adjacency sets:
Reach:    []
Coalesced:   []
--------------
```

TABLE 4.17

```
The number of equations is                7
Display information ...
Eliminated nodes:    []
Outstanding nodes:   []
Adjacency sets:
 1  1  [  4]
 2  2  [  3,  4]
 3  2  [  2,  6]
 4  4  [  1,  2,  6,  7]
 5  2  [  6,  7]
 6  4  [  3,  4,  5,  7]
 7  3  [  4,  5,  6]
Reach:    []
Coalesced:   []
--------------
```

TABLE 4.18

```
     First pass
    [  4]
    [  3,  4]
    [  6]
    [  6,  7]
    [  6,  7]
    [  7]
    []
```

TABLE 4.19

```
 Second pass
[  4]
[  3,  4]
[  4,  6]
[  6,  7]
[  6,  7]
[  7]
[]
```

TABLE 4.20

```
 Final result  ad
4  3  4  4  6  6  7  6  7  7
Array ip
1  2  4  6  8 10 11 11
```

4.4 NOTES AND A PROJECT

Load flow is the most basic of the programs discussed in this book. Other formulations of it can be found in literature, e.g., References [El71, SA74, SE68, TH67, WW84].

We have described an almost complete load-flow program. Such programs consist of the following packages:

1. Input of data.
2. Preprocessing of it and, in particular, calculation of the Jacobian.
3. Factorization.
4. Output of results.

Below is a program which includes parts 1, 2 and 3 (output is mostly a matter of taste). In addition to line data, bus data were entered.

In factorization, the reader is asked to complete the OOF program, but so that the sparse and compressed storage schemes are used. The project is to include it in Program 4.2, change it into decoupled OOF and run it on data prepared in Chapter 1.

```
program lf(input,output);
var n,ncap,nl : integer;

procedure loaf(var n,ncap,nl : integer);
(* n is the number of buses, ncap of capacitors, nl of lines *)
type d=1..20; t=1..40;
var b[d,d],g[d,d],J[t,t],pc[d],pe[d],pg[d],qc[d],qe[d],qg[d],
    ua[d],um[d],da[d],du[d],zl[t,1..4] : array of real;
    ind[d],line[1..40,1..2] :array of integer;
    i,ii,index,j,jj,k,kk,ll,maxit,nJ,nm1,npu,npq,typ : integer;
    angd,angi,angj,bij,bjj,bkk,bjk,bkj,conv,cs,csd,epsp,epsq,
    gij,gjj,gkk,gjk,gkj,ppq,ppc,pjk,pkj,ploss,qqg,qqc,qjk,
    qkj,qloss,r,rsq,sq,st,sn,ssd,tap,uij,uua,uum,ui,uui,uj,
    usqk,usqj,uskj,usc,ucs,x,xc,xsq : real;
conv:=3.14159/180.0; (* for converting angles *)
read(maxit,epsp,epsq);
(* maximum number of  iterations, accuracy of p and q *)
npu:=0; npq:=0; (* counts the number of pu and pq buses *)
for j:=1 to n do
begin
   readln(i,uum,uua,ppg,qqg,ppc,qqc,typ);
   (*typ is 0,1&2 for slack, generator and load-bus respectively.
   The others are voltage magnitudes and angles, generated and
   consumed powers - called sometimes load powers
   This corresponds to data as in tables 1 to 7 of chapter 1 *)

   case typ do
0:     index:=n; (*index of slack-bus is n *)
1:     npu:=npu+1; index:=n-npu;
       (*generators are 1,...,npu *)
2:     npq:=npq+1; index:=npq;
       (* consumer nodes are npu+1 to n-1 *)
   end; (*of case. Index ind was adjusted *)
   ind[i]:=index;
   pg[index]:=ppg; qg[index]:=qqg;
   pc[index]:=ppc; qc[index]:=qqc;
   um[index]:=uum; ua[index]:=uua*conv
end; (* of reading-in the data *)

(*Before reading admittances, make b and g matrices  all zero *)
for i:=1 to n do
begin
   for j:=1 to n do g[i,j]:=0.0;
   for j:=1 to n do b[i,j]:=0.0
end;
(*Dimension of the Jacobian is npq+n-1 *)
nm1:=n-1; nJ:=nm1+npq;
for i:=1 to nl do
begin (*We read tables like 1.3 and add where appropriate the tap*)
   readln(rl,ll,r,x,xc,tap); sq:=(r*r+x*x)*tap;
   line[i,1]:=ll; line[i,2]:=rl;
   j:=ind[ll]; k:=ind[rl];
   st:=sq*tap; xsq:=x/sq; rsq:=r/sq;
   zl[i,1]:=r/st; zl[i,2]:=xc-x/st;
   zl[i,3]:=rsq*tap; zl[i,4]:=xc-xsq*tap;
   b[j,k]:=b[j,k]+xsq; b[k,j]:=b[k,j]+xsq;
   b[j,j]:=b[j,j]-xsq/tap+xc; b[k,k]:=b[k,k]-xsq*tap+xc;
   g[j,k]:=g[j,k]-rsq; g[k,j]:=g[k,j]-rsq;
```

Program 4.2

(This program has been derived from a program written by Dr. Michel L. Gilles.)

```
      g[j,j]:=g[j,j]+rsq/tap; g[k,k]:=g[k,k]+rsq*tap
   end;
   for i:=1 to ncap do
   begin read(j,xc);
      k:=ind[j]; b[k,k]:=b[k,k]+xc
   end;
   (*Next, we start the Newton-Raphson routine *)
   k:=0; again:=true;(*If k>maxit or power-mismatch great, *)
   while k<maxit and again do  (* do it again sam *)
   begin (*First compute power as function of voltage *)
      for i:=1 to n do
      begin pe[i]:=0.0; qe[i]:=0.0;
         for j:=1 to n do
         begin gij:=g[i,j]; bij:=b[i,j];
            if gij<>0.0 or bij<>0.0 then
            begin angd:=ua[i]-ua[j]; uij:=um[i]*um[j];
               cs:=cos(angd); sn:=sin(angd);
               pe[i]:=pe[i]+uij*(gij*cs+bij*sn);
               qe[i]:=qe[i]+uij*(gij*sn-bij*cs)
            end;
         end
      end;
      again:=false; (*If no power difference>eps, dont do it again *)
      for i:=1 to nm1 do
      if abs(pg[i]-pc[i]-pe[i])>epsp then again:=true;
      for i:=1 to npq do
      begin j:=nm1+i;
         if abs(qg[j]-qc[j]-qe[j])>epsq then again:=true
      end;
      while again do
      begin k:=k+1;
      for i:=1 to nm1 do (*for each generator bus *)
      begin ui:=um[i]; uui:=ui*ui;
         for j:=1 to nm1 do
         begin uj:=um[j]; angd:=ua[i]-ua[j];
            gij:=g[i,j]; bij:=b[i,j];
            if i=j then J[i,j]:=-qe[i]-uui*b[i,i]
            else if ((gij=0.0) and (bij=0.0)) then J[i,j]:=0.0
            else J[i,j]:=ui*uj*(gij*sin(angd)-bij*cos(angd))
         end; (*These were according to eqs. 4-27 to 4-29 *)
         for j:=1 to npq do
         begin gij:=g[i,j]; bij:=b[i,j];
            jj:=j+nm1; uj:=um[j]; angd:=ua[i]-ua[j];
            if i=j then J[i,jj]:=pe[i]+uui*g[i,i]
            else if ((gij=0.0) and (bij=0.0)) then J[i,jj]:=0.0
            else J[i,jj]:=ui*uj*(gij*cos(angd)+bij*sin(angd))
         end (* of j *)
      end (* of i *) ;
      for i:=1 to npq do
      begin
         ii:=nm1+i; ui:=um[i]; angi:=ua[i];
         for j:=1 to nm1 do
         begin gij:=g[i,j]; bij:=b[i,j];
            uj:=um[j]; angj:=ua[j]; angd:=angi-angj;
            if i=j then J[ii,j]:=pe[i]-ui*ui*g[i,i]
            else if j=<npq then J[ii,j]:=-J[j,ii]
            else if ((gij=0.0) and (bij=0.0)) then J[ii,j]:=0.0
            else J[ii,j]:=-ui*uj*(gij*cos(angd)+bij*sin(angd))
```

Program 4.2 (cont.)

```
      end;
      for j:=1 to npq do
      begin jj:=nm1+j;
         if i<>j then J[ii,jj]:=J[i,j]
         else J[ii,ii]:=qe[i]-ui*ui*b[i,i]
      end;
   end;
(* This is the point where the matrix is first factored into
                    J  =  L  *  U
by the oof-procedure (especially if the data is changed into the
decoupled case) and then the set is solved by
         L * z = b;  U * x = z                The results are
da=angle difference; du=voltage magnitude difference-see text *)
for i:=1 to nm1 do ua[i]:=ua[i]+da[i];
for i:=1 to npq do um[i]:=um[i]+du[i+nm1]*u[i];
   end;(*of the loop solving it again *)
end;(*of the loop on k<># of iterations and mismatch=again
Having finished,we  compute and print all bus voltages & angles*)
for i:=1 to nm1 do
begin j:=ind[i];
   if j>npq then qg[i]:=qe[i]+qc[i]; da:=ua[i]*conv;
   writeln(j,um[j],da,pg[i],qg[i],pc[i],qc[i]);
end;(*Next are line-flows*)
pg[n]:=pe[n]+pc[n]; (*For the swing-bus too*)
for i:=1 to nl do
begin jj:=line[i,1]; kk:=line[i,2]; j:=ind[jj]; k:=ind[kk];
   gjj:=zl[i,1]; bjj:=zl[i,2]; gkk:=zl[i,3]; bkk:=zl[i,4];
   gjk:=g[j,k];bjk:=b[j,k];gkj:=g[k,j];bkj:=b[k,j];
   angd:=ua[j]-ua[k];
   usqj:=um[j]**2; uskj:=um[k]*um[j]; csd:=cos(angd);
   usqk:=um[k]**2; usc:=uskj*csd; ssd:=sin(angd); ucs:=uskj*ssd;
   pjk:= gjj*usqj+gjk*usc+bjk*ucs;
   pkj:= gkk*usqk+gkj*usc-bkj*ucs;
   qjk:=-bjj*usqj-bjk*usc+gjk*ucs;
   qkj:=-bkk*usqk-bkj*usc-gkj*ucs;

   (* Print out of all line-flows the way you prefer *)

end;
ploss:=0.0; qloss:=0.0;
for i:=1 to n do
begin
   ploss:=ploss+pg[i]-pc[i];
   qloss:=qloss+qg[i]-qc[i]
end;
writeln("The total losses are ",ploss,"+j* ",qloss)
end; ( O F  T H E  P R O C E D U R E LOAF=LOAD FLOW *)

begin n:=7; ncap:=4; nl:=15;
      loaf(n,ncap,nl);
end.
```

Program 4.2 (cont.)

5 State Estimation

The *objectives* of this chapter are

1. To introduce the least-squares method of state estimation.
2. To compare the algorithm of normal equations with orthogonalization.
3. To extend both algorithms and discuss bad data.
4. To supply material for state estimation (SE) programs.
5. To introduce parallel processing systems for solving state estimation problems in real time.
6. To suggest a method for running state-estimation programs off-line or on-line on a parallel or distributed processing system.

5.1 INTRODUCTION

Control and dispatch centers are equipped with supervisory (control and data-acquisition) systems. These include the measurement and transmission of critical data to the control center by *telemetry* and a monitoring, alarm, and display system for the dispatching personnel.

Supervisory systems sometimes transmit too much data (voltages, currents, frequencies, generated and consumed powers, power flows, circuit-breaker positions, etc.), and some of it might be inaccurate or even wrong.

The situation can be improved by state estimation, in which a computer produces a "clean," more accurate data base and the monitoring system displays the part of it necessary for secure operation.

The quantities that are normally measured and monitored in power system networks are either injections p_i, q_i at nodes $i = 0, \ldots, n$ or power flows $p_{k,m}$, $q_{k,m}$ over the lines. Some of the quantities of interest have to be calculated for several reasons.

1. It is very difficult or nearly impossible to measure some quantities, e.g., $\theta_i - \theta_k$ (voltage angle difference).
2. Metering and communication equipment is costly, and the number of meters should be reduced as much as possible.
3. A lost measurement can be simulated by calculating it.

Let us define $\mathbf{x}$ as the vector of all voltages $[x_0, \ldots, x_n]^T$, $\mathbf{z}$ as the telemetered line flows, injections, measured bus voltages, or pseudomeasurements, $\mathbf{W}$ as a diagonal weight matrix with W_i^2 the variance of the ith measurement, and the vectors $\mathbf{c}$ of parameters (e.g., impedances of lines) and $\mathbf{s}$ of the structure (e.g., circuit-breaker positions).

As the state vector, $\mathbf{x}$, we have chosen that set of variables which is *sufficient* to define uniquely the state of the network (e.g., v_i, w_i, or u_i, θ_i for $i = 0, 1, \ldots, n$) and, moreover, from which all other values can be explicitly calculated. Since the phase angle or w-part of the voltage of the slack bus (numbered 0) is set to zero, the dimension of the state vector is $2n + 1$ and the vector itself either of the following two:

$$\mathbf{x}^T = [v_0, v_1, \ldots, v_n, w_1, \ldots, w_n] = [x_1, x_2, \ldots, x_{2n+1}] \tag{5.1}$$

$$\mathbf{x}^T = [u_0, u_1, \ldots, u_n, \theta_1, \ldots, \theta_n] = [x_1, x_2, \ldots, x_{2n+1}] \tag{5.2}$$

If $\mathbf{x}$ and the network parameters are known, it is possible to evaluate and monitor all other quantities of the power system such as currents, injected powers, or line flows. The equations relating injections p_i and q_i to voltages were given in Eqs. (4.2) to (4.10), the power flows in Eqs. (4.11) and (4.12). These equations show that if we compute the m "measurement" values as a function of the state vector $\mathbf{x}$, we get $\mathbf{z} = \mathbf{f}(\mathbf{x}, \mathbf{c}, \mathbf{s})$, which is a set of nonlinear equations relating $\mathbf{x}$ to the m-dimensional measurement vector $\mathbf{z}$ ($\mathbf{f}$ is quadratic, since it reflects the relationship between powers and voltages).

We may assume that all measured quantities have some errors — vector $\mathbf{e}$. However, certain errors (e.g. if the meters are completely defective, if there is a break in communication between a meter and the computer, etc.) are not included in $\mathbf{e}$. Such flagrantly wrong data of, say, 40 times that of standard deviation, can be removed by a *prefiltering program*.

Below this value but above the normal deviations, the measurements will be called *bad data*. The state-estimation program (SE) has to *detect* that bad data exist, *identify* which data are bad, and, if possible, *remove* the bad measurement(s).

Using these definitions, an SE program is structured as in Fig. 5.1. Note that using the parameters **c** and **s** leads to the admittance matrix $\mathbf{Y}'$.

As already mentioned, we do not compute but measure **z**, and since measurements include errors, we have

$$\mathbf{z} = \mathbf{f}(\mathbf{x}) + \mathbf{e} \tag{5.3}$$

where **e** is an m-dimensional error vector.

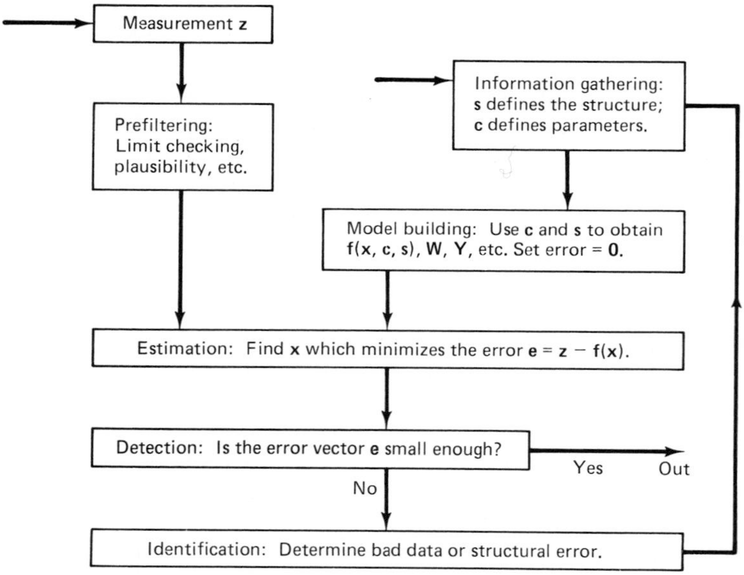

Figure 5.1 The basic algorithm of state estimation.

From Eq. (5.3) it follows that $\mathbf{e} = \mathbf{z} - \mathbf{f}(\mathbf{x})$, and it is the aim of the algorithm to calculate **x** such that the (Euclidean) norm of **e** will be minimal. The "*cost*"

$$U = ||\mathbf{e}||^2 = \mathbf{e}^T * \mathbf{e} = \Sigma\ [z_i - f_i(x)]^2; \quad i\Sigma = 1, \ldots, m \tag{5.4}$$

should be minimized. This process, known as *least-squares minimization* (see Estimation in Fig. 5.1), will be first explained using a rather trivial example.

5.1.1 A Trivial Example

Suppose we intend to estimate the value of z as a function of y. In order to get a functional relationship, a number of measurements are taken. The pairs of values (z_i, y_i) of these measurements are shown in Fig. 5.2(a). These points—mostly because of measurement errors—are not on a straight line as we hoped. However, we may draw a straight line that passes through some "center" of the measurements, i.e., so that the deviation of the measured points from the line is in some way minimal: $z = a + b \cdot y$.

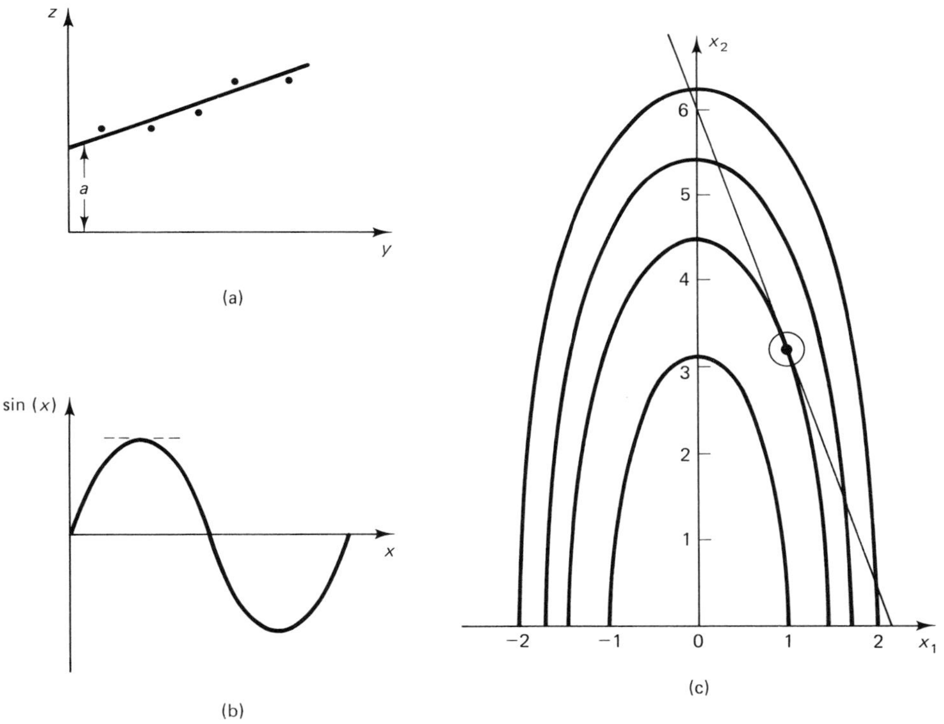

Figure 5.2 (a) Linear estimation. (b) Sine function. (c) Example.

If we have made the measurements, then the m equations $e_i = z_i - (a + b \cdot y_i)$, $i = 1, \ldots, m$, define the errors e_i, $i = 1, 2, \ldots, m$. This may also be written as

$$\begin{bmatrix} z_1 \\ \cdot \\ \cdot \\ \cdot \\ z_m \end{bmatrix} - \begin{bmatrix} 1 & y_1 \\ \cdot & \cdot \\ \cdot & \cdot \\ \cdot & \cdot \\ 1 & y_m \end{bmatrix} * \begin{bmatrix} a \\ b \end{bmatrix} = \begin{bmatrix} e_1 \\ \cdot \\ \cdot \\ \cdot \\ e_m \end{bmatrix}$$

or, in shorter notation using the m-by-2 matrix $\mathbf{M}$ of 1s and m known y_is

$$\mathbf{z} - \mathbf{M} * \mathbf{x} = \mathbf{e} \tag{5.5}$$

The "true" values should yield $\mathbf{e} = \mathbf{0}$. We seek therefore the best estimate of $\mathbf{x}$, say, $\bar{x}$, such that $\mathbf{e}$ is a minimum.

Let us define $\bar{\mathbf{x}}$ so that the sum of squares of errors should be minimal. Had we used the criterion $\Sigma\ e_i$ instead of $\Sigma\ e_i^2$, then we might have had many large deviations in the positive direction reduced to zero by many large negative deviations. Thus, despite the large deviations, the algorithm would detect nothing. It thus seems better to use the criterion *minimize* $\Sigma\ e_i^2$ *for* $i\ \Sigma = 1, \ldots, m$.

The sum to be minimized can also be written as the scalar product $\mathbf{e}^T * \mathbf{e} = [e_1, \ldots, e_m] * [e_1, \ldots, e_m]^T$.

5.1.2 The Linear Case

Equation (5.5) described a linear function, namely, $\mathbf{f}(\mathbf{x}) = \mathbf{M} * \mathbf{x}$. The scalar cost function U to be minimized is therefore $U(\mathbf{x}) = \mathbf{e}^T * \mathbf{e} = (\mathbf{z} - \mathbf{M} * \mathbf{x})^T * (\mathbf{z} - \mathbf{M} * \mathbf{x})$.

Multiplying yields $U(\mathbf{x}) = (\mathbf{z}^T - \mathbf{x}^T * \mathbf{M}^T) * (\mathbf{z} - \mathbf{M} * \mathbf{x})$.

$$U(\mathbf{x}) = \mathbf{z}^T * \mathbf{z} - \mathbf{z}^T * \mathbf{M} * \mathbf{x} - \mathbf{x}^T * \mathbf{M}^T * \mathbf{z} + \mathbf{x}^T * \mathbf{M}^T * \mathbf{M} * \mathbf{x} \tag{5.6}$$

Since $U(\mathbf{x})$ is a scalar, each of its summands is a scalar. Any scalar c equals its own transposed value $c^T = c$, (if $c = 2$, then obviously $2^T = 2$) so that the second and third products in Eq. (5.6) are equal. Thus, $\mathbf{z}^T * \mathbf{M} * \mathbf{x} = (\mathbf{z}^T * \mathbf{M} * \mathbf{x})^T = \mathbf{x}^T * \mathbf{M}^T * \mathbf{z}$. Inserting yields

$$U(\mathbf{x}) = (\mathbf{z}^T * \mathbf{z}) - 2\cdot(\mathbf{x}^T * \mathbf{M}^T * \mathbf{z}) + (\mathbf{x}^T * \mathbf{M}^T * \mathbf{M} * \mathbf{x}) \tag{5.7}$$

Before minimizing $U(\mathbf{x})$, here are some reminders concerning minimization.

In elementary calculus, if $y = f(x)$, then the maximum or minimum is that point on the curve for which the slope is horizontal, i.e., for which $dy/dx = 0$. Thus if $y = \sin(x)$ as in Fig. 5.2(b), then $dy/dx = \cos(x) = 0$ leads to an angle $x = 90°$ (for $0° < x < 180°$), and clearly this is the point where $\sin(x)$ has a maximum with a horizontal slope.

The same procedure can be followed for cases of two (or more) dimensions. Figure 5.2(c) shows a graph of $f(x) = x_1^2 + 0.1 \cdot x_2^2$ for the following values of f: 1, 2, 3, and 4.

As seen, this function describes ellipses for f_i = constant. The maximum is not bounded, but the minimum is zero. Differentiating and setting the derivative equal to zero yields $\partial f_i / \partial x_1 = 2x_1 = 0$, which implies that $x_1 = 0$; and $\partial f_i / \partial x_2 = 0.2x_2 = 0$, which implies that $x_2 = 0$.

Suppose we add as a constraint the line [see Fig. 4.2(c)]

$$x_2 = 6.19 - 2.84 \cdot x_1$$

In order to minimize or maximize f_i and at the same time satisfy the constraint, we define the Lagrangian function

$$L = f_i - \lambda \cdot (-6.19 + 2.84 \cdot x_1 + x_2)$$

Since L depends on x_1, x_2, and λ, it can be differentiated with respect to all three and the derivatives set equal to zero. The three equations are then $\partial L / \partial x_1 = 2 \cdot x_1 - 2.84 \cdot \lambda = 0$, $\partial L / \partial x_2 = 0.2 \cdot x_2 - \lambda = 0$, and $\partial L / \partial \lambda = 6.19 - 2.84 \cdot x_1 - x_2 = 0$.

Note that the last is simply the constraint equation. Solving the equations yields $\lambda = 0.69$, $x_1 = 0.97$, and $x_2 = 3.45$. This is the point at which the constraint line touches f_2. We call such a solution, a *binding* solution.

Minimization of $U(\mathbf{x})$ is an unconstrained optimization problem.

The differentiation of the second term of Eq. (5.7) yields $\partial(\mathbf{x}^T * \mathbf{M}^T * \mathbf{z})/\partial \mathbf{x} = \mathbf{M}^T * \mathbf{z}$, and since $\mathbf{z}^T * \mathbf{z}$ does not depend on $\mathbf{x}$, the condition for a minimum is

$$-2 \cdot \mathbf{M}^T * \mathbf{z} + 2 \cdot \mathbf{M}^T * \mathbf{M} * \mathbf{x} = \mathbf{0}$$

$$(\mathbf{M}^T * \mathbf{M}) * \mathbf{x} = \mathbf{M}^T * \mathbf{z} \tag{5.8}$$

In the case of Fig. 5.2(a) this linear set is with $\mathbf{M}$ as in Eq. (5.5)

$$\begin{bmatrix} m & \Sigma y_i \\ \Sigma y_i & \Sigma y_i^2 \end{bmatrix} * \begin{bmatrix} a \\ b \end{bmatrix} = \begin{bmatrix} \Sigma z_i \\ \Sigma y_i \cdot z_i \end{bmatrix}$$

The unknown vector $\mathbf{x} = [a, b]^T$ can be easily calculated from this equation.

5.1.3 Nonlinear Case

Usually the error vector includes a nonlinear vector function $\mathbf{f}(\mathbf{x})$. In that case, in order to estimate $\mathbf{x}$, an initial value $\mathbf{x}_0$ is assumed and a Taylor expansion approximates it near this point:

$$\mathbf{f}(\mathbf{x}) = \mathbf{f}(\mathbf{x}_0) + \mathbf{f}'(\mathbf{x}_0)\cdot\Delta\mathbf{x} + \mathbf{f}''(\mathbf{x}_0)\cdot\frac{\Delta\mathbf{x}^2}{2} + \cdots$$

Disregarding higher than linear terms and using vectors and matrices, we have, $\mathbf{f}(\mathbf{x}) = \mathbf{f}(\mathbf{x}_0) + \mathbf{J}(\mathbf{x}_0) * \Delta\mathbf{x} \equiv \mathbf{f}_0 + \mathbf{J}_0 * \Delta\mathbf{x}$, where the Jacobian matrix is defined through $J_{k,m} = \partial f_k / \partial x_m$ and $\mathbf{J}_i$ and $\mathbf{f}_i$ are a shorter notation for $\mathbf{J}(\mathbf{x}_i)$ and $\mathbf{f}(\mathbf{x}_i)$.

Inserting $\mathbf{f} = \mathbf{f}_0 + \mathbf{J}_0 * \Delta\mathbf{x}$ into $\mathbf{e} = \mathbf{z} - \mathbf{f}$ and letting $\Delta\mathbf{z} = \mathbf{z} - \mathbf{f}_0$ yields

$$U(\mathbf{x}) = \mathbf{e}^{\mathrm{T}} * \mathbf{e} = (\Delta\mathbf{z} - \mathbf{J}_0 * \Delta\mathbf{x})^{\mathrm{T}} * (\Delta\mathbf{z} - \mathbf{J}_0 * \Delta\mathbf{x}) \tag{5.9}$$

Comparing with $\mathbf{e} = \mathbf{z} - \mathbf{M} * \mathbf{x}$, shows that $\Delta\mathbf{z}$, $\Delta\mathbf{x}$, and $\mathbf{J}_0$ replace $\mathbf{z}$, $\mathbf{x}$, and $\mathbf{M}$, respectively, and the resulting equation can be obtained from Eq. (5.8) as

$$(\mathbf{J}_0^{\mathrm{T}} * \mathbf{J}_0) * \Delta\mathbf{x} = \mathbf{J}_0^{\mathrm{T}} * \Delta\mathbf{z}$$

It is customary not to use solely the Euclidean norm but to include the effects of measurement error distribution. Thus, U is normally $U = \mathbf{e}^{\mathrm{T}} * \mathbf{W} * \mathbf{e} = \Sigma\, e_i^2/w_i^2$ where $\mathbf{W}$ is a diagonal weighting matrix, and $W_{i,i}$ (or w_i) is the standard deviation of meter i. As a result we have

$$(\mathbf{J}_0^{\mathrm{T}} * \mathbf{W} * \mathbf{J}_0) * \Delta\mathbf{x} = \mathbf{J}_0^{\mathrm{T}} * \mathbf{W} * \Delta\mathbf{z} \tag{5.10}$$

In developing the algorithms we will assume that $\mathbf{W} = \mathbf{I}$, since it can be reintroduced in most cases by substituting $\mathbf{J}^{\mathrm{T}} * \mathbf{W}$ for $\mathbf{J}^{\mathrm{T}}$. Another possibility is to write

$$\mathbf{J}^{\mathrm{T}} * \mathbf{W} * \mathbf{J} = \mathbf{J}^{\mathrm{T}} * \mathbf{W}^{\mathrm{T}/2} * \mathbf{W}^{1/2} * \mathbf{J} = (\mathbf{W}^{1/2} * \mathbf{J})^{\mathrm{T}} * (\mathbf{W}^{1/2} * \mathbf{J})$$

and substitute $\mathbf{W}^{1/2} * \mathbf{J}$ for $\mathbf{J}$ (since $\mathbf{W}$ is a diagonal matrix, $\mathbf{W}^{\mathrm{T}} = \mathbf{W}$, and $\mathbf{W}^{1/2}$ means to extract square roots of the diagonal elements).

Defining the *normal matrix* $\mathbf{A} = \mathbf{J}_0^{\mathrm{T}} * \mathbf{J}_0$, we have the final form

$$\mathbf{A} * \Delta\mathbf{x} = \mathbf{b} \text{ where } \mathbf{A} = \mathbf{J}_0^{\mathrm{T}} * \mathbf{J}_0 \text{ and } \mathbf{b} = \mathbf{J}_0^{\mathrm{T}} * \Delta\mathbf{z} \tag{5.11}$$

This is a set of linear equations, and if higher order terms of the Taylor expansion of $\mathbf{f}(\mathbf{x})$ were really negligible, the solution would yield the correct $\mathbf{x}$. Since this is not so and additionally the Jacobian $\mathbf{J}$ is itself a function of $\mathbf{x}$, we must view Eq. (5.11) as a prescription for an iterative procedure which in a finite number of steps will compute $\mathbf{x}$ to a certain degree of accuracy. Vector $\mathbf{x}$ should therefore be changed according to

$$\mathbf{x}^{(n+1)} := \mathbf{x}^{(n)} + (\mathbf{J}_n^{\mathrm{T}} * \mathbf{J}_n)^{-1} * \mathbf{J}_n^{\mathrm{T}} * (\mathbf{z} - \mathbf{f}_n) \tag{5.12}$$

until convergence is achieved.

The above algorithm is a straightforward application of (weighted) least-squares minimization.

The equations used for developing Eq. (5.12) include those of power injections, power flows, and node voltages. Power injections were given in Eqs. (4.2) to (4.10) and the Jacobian (of load flow) in Eqs. (4.21) to (4.25). For the remaining part of the Jacobian (of state estimation) we have to differentiate Eqs. (4.11) and (4.12), with the result

$$\left.\begin{aligned}\frac{\partial p_{i,k}}{\partial v_i} &= (v_k - 2v_i)\cdot g_{i,k} - w_k\cdot b_{i,k}\\ \frac{\partial p_{i,k}}{\partial w_i} &= (w_k - 2w_i)\cdot g_{i,k} + v_k\cdot b_{i,k}\end{aligned}\right\}\quad i \neq k$$

$$\left.\begin{aligned}\frac{\partial p_{i,k}}{\partial v_i} &= v_i\cdot g_{i,k} + w_i\cdot b_{i,k}\\ \frac{\partial p_{i,k}}{\partial w_i} &= w_i\cdot g_{i,k} - v_i\cdot b_{i,k}\end{aligned}\right\}\quad i = k$$

$$\left.\begin{aligned}\frac{\partial q_{i,k}}{\partial v_i} &= (2v_i - v_k)\cdot b_{i,k} - w_i\cdot g_{i,k} - v_i\cdot y_{i,k}\\ \frac{\partial q_{i,k}}{\partial w_i} &= (2w_i - w_k)\cdot b_{i,k} + v_k\cdot g_{i,k} - w_i\cdot y_{i,k}\end{aligned}\right\}\quad i \neq k \qquad (5.13)$$

$$\left.\begin{aligned}\frac{\partial q_{i,k}}{\partial v_i} &= -v_i\cdot b_{i,k} + w_i\cdot g_{i,k}\\ \frac{\partial q_{i,k}}{\partial w_k} &= -w_i\cdot b_{i,k} - v_i\cdot g_{i,k}\end{aligned}\right\}\quad i = k$$

$$\frac{\partial u_i}{\partial v_i} = 0; \qquad \frac{\partial u_i}{\partial v_k} = 0$$

$$\frac{\partial u_i}{\partial v_i} = \frac{-v_i}{(v_i^2 + w_i^2)^{1/2}}; \qquad \frac{\partial u_i}{\partial w_i} = \frac{-w_i}{(v_i^2 + w_i^2)^{1/2}}$$

5.2 ALGORITHMS

5.2.1 Correction Matrix

We saw that solution of the state-estimation problem is equivalent to the minimization of

$$U(\mathbf{x}) = \Sigma\ [z_k - f_k(\mathbf{x})]^2; \quad k\Sigma = 1, \ldots, m \tag{5.14}$$

and for this we have to make all $\partial U / \partial x_j = 0$. From Eq. (5.14)

$$\frac{\partial U}{\partial x_j} = \Sigma\ 2 \cdot [(z_k - f_k(\mathbf{x})] \cdot \frac{\partial f_k}{\partial x_j}; \quad k\Sigma = 1, \ldots, m$$

With the usual definition of the Jacobian as an m-by-n matrix $\mathbf{J}_{r,s} = \partial f_r / \partial x_s$ we can rewrite this equation as

$$\mathbf{h}(\mathbf{x}) \equiv \mathbf{J}^{\mathrm{T}}(\mathbf{x}) * [\mathbf{z} - \mathbf{f}(\mathbf{x})] = \mathbf{0} \tag{5.15}$$

This is a system of n nonlinear, algebraic equations in the unknown $\mathbf{x}$. It may be solved by the Newton–Raphson iterative procedure through

$$\mathbf{x}^{(i+1)} = \mathbf{x}^{(i)} - \mathbf{G}_i^{-1} * \mathbf{J}_i^{\mathrm{T}} * [\mathbf{z} - \mathbf{f}_i]$$

where $\mathbf{G}$ is the Jacobian of $\mathbf{h}(\mathbf{x})$ and $\mathbf{G}_i$, $\mathbf{J}_i$, and $\mathbf{f}_i$ are the values of $\mathbf{G}$, $\mathbf{J}$, and $\mathbf{f}$, respectively, for $\mathbf{x} = \mathbf{x}^{(i)}$. The rth row of $\mathbf{G}$ is computed [Wa82] by differentiating $\mathbf{h}(\mathbf{x})$:

$$G_{rs} = \frac{\partial[\Sigma\ \{z_k - f_k(\mathbf{x})\}\ \{\partial f_k(\mathbf{x}) / \partial x_r\}]}{\partial x_s}$$

$$= \Sigma\ [z_k - f_k(\mathbf{x})] \frac{\partial^2 f_k(\mathbf{x})}{\partial x_s \cdot \partial x_r} - \Sigma \left(\frac{\partial f_k}{\partial x_s}\right) \left(\frac{\partial f_k}{\partial x_r}\right);$$

$$k\Sigma = 1, \ldots, m$$

The second sum is $(\mathbf{J}^{\mathrm{T}} * \mathbf{J})_{k,s}$. The first sum is a correction matrix $\mathbf{C}$ with elements

$$C_{s,r} = C_{r,s} = \Sigma\ (z_k - f_k(\mathbf{x})) \cdot \frac{\partial^2 f_k(\mathbf{x})}{\partial x_s \cdot \partial x_r}; \quad k\Sigma = 1, \ldots, m \tag{5.16}$$

The Newton–Raphson algorithm from Chapter 4 reduces here to a repeated application of

$$\mathbf{x}^{(i+1)} = \mathbf{x}^{(i)} + (\mathbf{J}_i^{\mathrm{T}} * \mathbf{J}_i - \mathbf{C}_i)^{-1} * \mathbf{J}_i^{\mathrm{T}} * (\mathbf{z} - \mathbf{f}_i) \tag{5.17}$$

Note that if C_i is neglected, the normal set Eq. (5.12) results. Also note that again, as in the case of load flow, *state estimation leads to a repeated solution of sets of linear equations.*

We compare next the normal set ($\mathbf{C} = \mathbf{0}$) with the modified set ($\mathbf{C} \neq \mathbf{0}$) by applying them to the 5-bus network of [SE68].

The numerical procedure is as follows. Assuming that all nodes are load nodes, the vectors $\mathbf{p}$ and $\mathbf{q}$ are read as input and a load flow calculated. This yields both the node voltages and the line flows throughout the network.

The resulting line flows $p_{k,m}$ and $q_{k,m}$ are subjected to a random variation yielding the simulated measured flows $\tilde{p}_{k,m}$ and $\tilde{q}_{k,m}$ according to $\tilde{p}_{k,m} = (1 + \epsilon_{k,m}) \cdot p_{k,m}$ and $\tilde{q}_{k,m} = (1 + \epsilon_{k,m}) \cdot q_{k,m}$ where $\epsilon_{k,m}$ is a random variable distributed uniformly between ϵ and $-\epsilon$.

Finally, state-estimation procedures are applied and the maximum change in voltage recorded for each iteration. Table 5.1 records these results for both methods and for $\epsilon = 0.01$. In a similar way, Tables 5.2 and 5.3 display results for $\epsilon = 0.1$ and $\epsilon = 0.5$, respectively. (In these tables $E(n)$ stands for 10^n.) It is seen that if the results are required with high precision, the modified method may be applied when close to the solution. Otherwise, the additional effort is wasted.

TABLE 5.1 $\epsilon = 0.01$

Iteration Number	Normal Equations	Modified Method
1	1.133E(−1)	1.156E(−1)
2	5.836E(−3)	6.550E(−3)
3	2.316E(−5)	7.070E(−5)
4	4.20E(−13)	1.25E(−16)
5	2.44E(−16)	

TABLE 5.2 $\epsilon = 0.1$

Iteration Number	Normal Equations	Modified Method
1	1.150E(−1)	1.170E(−1)
2	5.880E(−3)	6.540E(−3)
3	2.020E(−5)	6.000E(−3)
4	1.890E(−8)	8.870E(−9)
5	3.80E(−11)	1.18E(−10)
6	4.99E(−14)	

TABLE 5.3 $\epsilon = 0.5$

Iteration Number	Normal Equations	Modified Method
1	1.233E(−1)	1.240E(−1)
2	6.720E(−3)	6.400E(−3)
3	2.520E(−5)	7.310E(−5)
4	1.470E(−8)	8.080E(−9)
5	5.76E(−10)	1.07E(−10)
6	3.10E(−12)	

5.2.2 Orthogonalization

Recall that by Eq. (2.30) we had $\mathbf{Q}^T * \mathbf{A} = \mathbf{R}$ and by Eq. (2.37) we had $\mathbf{Q}^T * \mathbf{b} = \mathbf{z}$. Matrix $\mathbf{A}$ is replaced by $\mathbf{J}$, vector $\mathbf{z}$ by $\Delta\mathbf{z}$, so that these equations are replaced by:

$$\underset{m}{\begin{bmatrix} \mathbf{Q} & \overset{n}{|} & \mathbf{O} \\ & | & \end{bmatrix}}^{T} * \begin{bmatrix} \mathbf{J} \\ \ \end{bmatrix}^{n} = \begin{bmatrix} \mathbf{O} \ \diagdown \mathbf{R} \\ \hline \mathbf{O} \end{bmatrix};$$
$$\underset{m}{\begin{bmatrix} \mathbf{Q} & \overset{n}{|} & \mathbf{O} \\ & | & \end{bmatrix}}^{T} * \begin{bmatrix} \Delta\mathbf{z} \\ \ \end{bmatrix} = \begin{bmatrix} \mathbf{b} \\ \mathbf{d} \end{bmatrix} \begin{matrix} n \\ m \end{matrix} \tag{5.18}$$

$$\mathbf{Q}^T * \mathbf{J} = [\mathbf{R}, \mathbf{0}]^T; \quad \mathbf{Q}^T * \Delta\mathbf{z} = [\mathbf{b}, \mathbf{d}]^T \tag{5.19}$$

Inserting $\mathbf{J} = \mathbf{Q} * \mathbf{R}$ from Eqs. (5.18) and (5.19) into $\mathbf{J}^T * \mathbf{J} * \Delta\mathbf{x} = \mathbf{J}^T * \Delta\mathbf{z}$ yields $(\mathbf{R}^T * \mathbf{Q}^T) * (\mathbf{Q} * \mathbf{R}) * \Delta\mathbf{x} = (\mathbf{R}^T * \mathbf{Q}^T) * \Delta\mathbf{z}$ or, for the upper part,

$$\mathbf{R} * \Delta\mathbf{x} = \mathbf{b} \tag{5.20}$$

We can therefore solve the state-estimation problem, by orthogonalization $\mathbf{J} = \mathbf{Q} * \mathbf{R}$ and iterative calculation of $\Delta\mathbf{x}$ by back-substitution in Eq. (5.20).

Normal equations were the result of minimizing the cost

$$U = (\Delta\mathbf{z} - \mathbf{J} * \Delta\mathbf{x})^T * (\Delta\mathbf{z} - \mathbf{J} * \Delta\mathbf{x}) = ||\Delta\mathbf{z} - \mathbf{J} * \Delta\mathbf{x}||^2$$

where we have used the Euclidean norm. Since $||\mathbf{Q}^T|| = 1$, we can multiply each term by $\mathbf{Q}^T$ with the following result:

$$U = ||\mathbf{Q}^T * \Delta\mathbf{z} - (\mathbf{Q}^T * \mathbf{J}) * \Delta\mathbf{x}||^2$$

$$= \left|\left| \begin{bmatrix} \mathbf{b} \\ \mathbf{d} \end{bmatrix} - \begin{bmatrix} \mathbf{R} \\ \mathbf{0} \end{bmatrix} * \Delta\mathbf{x} \right|\right|^2 = \left|\left| \begin{matrix} \mathbf{b} - \mathbf{R} * \Delta\mathbf{x} \\ \mathbf{d} \end{matrix} \right|\right|^2$$

The upper part is 0 on account of Eq. (5.20) and the cost:

$$U = ||\mathbf{d}||^2 = \mathbf{d}^T * \mathbf{d} = \Sigma\, d_i^2; \quad i\Sigma = n + 1, \ldots, m \tag{5.21}$$

Orthogonalization, as described in Chapter 2, can be done by columns or by rows. In the last case, we assume $m = n + 1$, i.e. that a row m was added to an already orthogonalized n-by-n matrix. The algorithm proceeds then by rows with $\mathbf{d}$ being a scalar d.

Stated differently, orthogonalization is equivalent to solution of Eq. (5.20) or minimization of

$$U = \left(\begin{bmatrix} \mathbf{R} \\ 0 \end{bmatrix} * \Delta \mathbf{x} - \begin{bmatrix} \mathbf{b} \\ d \end{bmatrix} \right)^{\mathrm{T}} * \left(\begin{bmatrix} \mathbf{R} \\ 0 \end{bmatrix} * \Delta \mathbf{x} - \begin{bmatrix} \mathbf{b} \\ d \end{bmatrix} \right)$$

$$= (\mathbf{R} * \Delta \mathbf{x} - \mathbf{b})^{\mathrm{T}} * (\mathbf{R} * \Delta \mathbf{x} - \mathbf{b}) + d^2$$

As each new row is orthogonalized, d^2 will represent the addition to the residual sum of squares. This information is very important for bad-data detection. Also, since the measured values arrive by rows, each row should be consecutively processed (in an order which should minimize fill-in). We thus have two good reasons for choosing orthogonalization by rows.

A square-root-free method was described in Chapter 2. It will next be programmed (by rows). Basically we solve $\mathbf{A} * \mathbf{x} = \mathbf{b}$ by $\mathbf{A} = \mathbf{Q} * \mathbf{R}$; $\mathbf{Q} * \mathbf{R} * \mathbf{x} = \mathbf{b}$ and $\mathbf{R} * \mathbf{x} = \mathbf{Q}^{\mathrm{T}} * \mathbf{b} = \mathbf{z}$.

Next, substitute $\mathbf{R} = \mathbf{D}^{1/2} * \tilde{\mathbf{R}}$ and $\mathbf{z} = \mathbf{D}^{1/2} * \tilde{\mathbf{z}}$. The equation to be solved is $\mathbf{D}^{1/2} * \tilde{\mathbf{R}} * \mathbf{x} = \mathbf{D}^{1/2} * \tilde{\mathbf{z}}$, which shows that $\mathbf{D}^{1/2}$ is not needed, and the solution is obtained from

$$\tilde{\mathbf{R}} * \mathbf{x} = \tilde{\mathbf{z}} \tag{5.22}$$

At any given point, a new row $\mathbf{a}_i$ is to be orthogonalized:

$$\mathbf{a}_i = [0, \ldots, 0, A_{i,j}, A_{i,j+1}, \ldots, A_{i,n}, A_{i,n+1}]; \quad A_{i,n+1} \equiv b_i$$

Here, we have included the right-hand side $\mathbf{b}$ as the $(n + 1)$th column of $\mathbf{A}$.

Since the first nonzero term must be in column j and row j, we get as the pivot $\mathbf{a}_j = [0, \ldots, 0, A_{j,j}, A_{j,j+1}, \ldots, A_{j,n}, A_{j,n+1}]$ (it was already orthogonalized with respect to rows $k < j$).

Choose $d = A_{j,j}^2$ and a constant w and rewrite a_i and a_j as in

$$\mathbf{a}_j = [0, \ldots, 0, \sqrt{d}, \sqrt{d} \cdot \tilde{A}_{j,j+1}, \ldots, \sqrt{d} \cdot \tilde{A}_{j,n}, \sqrt{d} \cdot \tilde{A}_{j,n+1}]$$

$$\mathbf{a}_i = [0, \ldots, 0, \sqrt{w} \cdot \tilde{A}_{i,j}, \sqrt{w} \cdot \tilde{A}_{i,j+1}, \ldots, \sqrt{w} \cdot \tilde{A}_{i,n}, \sqrt{w} \cdot \tilde{A}_{i,n+1}]$$

Multiplying rows $\mathbf{a}_j$ and $\mathbf{a}_i$ by a Givens matrix

$$\begin{bmatrix} c & s \\ -s & c \end{bmatrix} * \begin{bmatrix} \mathbf{a}_j \\ \mathbf{a}_i \end{bmatrix}$$

yields $A_{i,j}^{\#} := -s \cdot \sqrt{d} + c \cdot \sqrt{w} \cdot \tilde{A}_{i,j}$, which is to be zero. With $c^2 + s^2 = 1$ and $s^2 \cdot d = c^2 \cdot w \cdot \tilde{A}_{ij}^2 = (1 - c^2) \cdot d$, we have

$$c^2 := \frac{d}{d + w \cdot \tilde{A}_{ij}^2}; \quad \tilde{d} \equiv d + w \cdot \tilde{A}_{ij}^2; \; c^2 = \frac{d}{\tilde{d}}$$

Next, the same is applied to s as follows:

$$s^2 \cdot d = (1 - s^2) \cdot w \cdot \tilde{A}_{ij}^2; \quad s^2 = \frac{w \cdot \tilde{A}_{ij}^2}{\tilde{d}}$$

The new values of $A^{\#}_{j,j}$, $A^{\#}_{j,k}$, $A^{\#}_{i,k}$, etc., are as follows:

$$A^{\#}_{j,j} := [c \cdot \sqrt{d} + s \cdot \sqrt{w} \cdot \tilde{A}_{i,j}] = \frac{\sqrt{d}}{\sqrt{\tilde{d}}} \cdot \sqrt{d} + \frac{\sqrt{w} \cdot \tilde{A}_{i,j}}{\sqrt{\tilde{d}}} \cdot \sqrt{w} \cdot \tilde{A}_{i,j}$$

$$A^{\#}_{j,j} = \frac{d + w \cdot \tilde{A}_{i,j}^2}{\sqrt{\tilde{d}}} = \frac{\tilde{d}}{\sqrt{\tilde{d}}} = \sqrt{\tilde{d}}$$

$$A^{\#}_{j,k} := [c \cdot \sqrt{d} \cdot \tilde{A}_{j,k} + s \cdot \sqrt{w} \cdot \tilde{A}_{i,k}] \cdot \frac{\sqrt{\tilde{d}}}{\sqrt{\tilde{d}}} = c^2 \cdot \sqrt{\tilde{d}} \cdot \tilde{A}_{j,k} + w \cdot \tilde{A}_{i,j} \cdot \frac{\tilde{A}_{i,k}}{\sqrt{\tilde{d}}}$$

$$A^{\#}_{j,k} := \sqrt{\tilde{d}} \cdot \left(c^2 \cdot \tilde{A}_{j,k} + w \cdot \tilde{A}_{i,j} \cdot \frac{\tilde{A}_{i,k}}{\sqrt{\tilde{d}}} \right)$$

Substituting $\tilde{c}$ and $\tilde{s}$, where $\tilde{c} \equiv c^2$ and $\tilde{s} \equiv w \cdot \tilde{A}_{i,j}/\tilde{d}$, yields

$$A^{\#}_{j,k} := \sqrt{\tilde{d}} \cdot (\tilde{c} \cdot \tilde{A}_{j,k} + \tilde{s} \cdot \tilde{A}_{i,k})$$

$$A^{\#}_{i,k} := -s \cdot \sqrt{d} \cdot \tilde{A}_{j,k} + c \cdot \sqrt{w} \cdot \tilde{A}_{i,k}$$

$$= \left(\sqrt{w} \cdot \frac{\sqrt{d}}{\sqrt{\tilde{d}}} \right) \cdot \tilde{A}_{i,k} - \left(\sqrt{w} \cdot \frac{A_{i,j}}{\sqrt{\tilde{d}}} \right) \cdot \sqrt{d} \cdot \tilde{A}_{j,k}$$

The common factor is, say, $\sqrt{w \cdot d / \tilde{d}}$ and the expression is then

$$A^{\#}_{i,k} := \sqrt{\tilde{w}} \cdot (\tilde{A}_{i,k} - \tilde{A}_{i,j} \cdot \tilde{A}_{j,k});$$

where $\tilde{w} \equiv w \cdot d / \tilde{d}$

The algorithm can be summarized by the equations

$$\begin{aligned} \tilde{d} &:= d + w \cdot \tilde{A}_{i,j}^2 \\ \tilde{c} &:= \frac{d}{\tilde{d}} \\ \tilde{w} &:= w \cdot \frac{d}{\tilde{d}} = w \cdot \tilde{c} \\ \tilde{s} &:= w \cdot \frac{\tilde{A}_{i,j}}{\tilde{d}} \\ A^{\#}_{i,k} &:= \tilde{A}_{i,k} - \tilde{A}_{i,j} \cdot \tilde{A}_{j,k}; \text{ for } k = j+1, \ldots, n+1 \\ A^{\#}_{j,k} &:= \tilde{c} \cdot \tilde{A}_{j,k} + \tilde{s} \cdot \tilde{A}_{i,k}; \text{ for } k = j+1, \ldots, n+1 \end{aligned} \tag{5.23}$$

The two rows $\mathbf{a}_j$ and $\mathbf{a}_i$ are therefore

$$\mathbf{a}_j^{\#} := [0, \ldots, 0, \sqrt{\tilde{d}}\ , \sqrt{\tilde{d}} \cdot A_{j,j+1}^{\#}, \ldots, \sqrt{\tilde{d}} \cdot A_{j,n}^{\#}, \sqrt{\tilde{d}} \cdot A_{j,n+1}^{\#}] \quad (5.24)$$
$$\mathbf{a}_i^{\#} := [0, \ldots, 0, 0, \sqrt{\tilde{w}} \cdot A_{i,j+1}^{\#}, \ldots, \sqrt{\tilde{w}} \cdot A_{i,n}^{\#}, \sqrt{\tilde{w}} \cdot A_{i,n+1}^{\#}]$$

```
program sfreegiv(input,output);
var    i,j,k,l,m,n,n1:integer;
       ajj,ajk,c,d,d1,s,xk:real;
       a:array[1..3,1..4] of real;
       w,x:array[1..3] of real;
procedure primat;
var i,j:integer;
begin    writeln;
    for i:=1 to n do
      begin
        for j:=1 to n1 do write('   ',a[i,j]:8:4);
        writeln
      end
end;

begin
   n:=3; n1:=n+1;
   for i:=1 to n do
   for j:=1 to n1 do read(a[i,j]);
   for i:=1 to n do w[i]:=1.0;
   for j:=1 to n do
   begin ajj:=a[j,j]; d:=ajj*ajj*w[j];
       for k:=j+1 to n1 do a[j,k]:=a[j,k]/ajj;
       a[j,j]:=1.0;
       for i:=j+1 to n do
       begin ajj:=a[i,j]; d1:=d+ajj*ajj*w[i];
             c:=d/d1;s:=w[i]*ajj/d1;
             for k:=j+1 to n1 do
             begin xk:=a[i,k]; ajk:=a[j,k];
                    a[i,k]:=xk-ajj*ajk;
                    a[j,k]:=c*ajk+s*xk
             end;
             w[i]:=d*w[i]/d1; d:=d1; a[i,j]:=0.0;
             primat
       end; {of i}
       w[j]:=d;
   end;   {of j }

   primat; writeln;
   for i:=n downto 1 do
   begin s:=a[i,n1];
     for j:=i+1 to n do s:=s-a[i,j]*x[j];
     x[i]:=s; write('   ',s:8:4)
   end
end.
1.0 2.0 4.0 27.0
2.0 2.0 6.0 38.0
4.0 6.0 -3.0 7.0
```

Program 5.1

```
1.0000    1.2000    3.2000   20.6000
0.0000   -2.0000   -2.0000  -16.0000
4.0000    6.0000   -3.0000    7.0000

1.0000    1.4286    0.1905    6.2381
0.0000   -2.0000   -2.0000  -16.0000
0.0000    1.2000  -15.8000  -75.4000

1.0000    1.4286    0.1905    6.2381
0.0000    1.0000   -3.2500  -13.2500
0.0000    0.0000  -17.0000  -85.0000

1.0000    1.4286    0.1905    6.2381
0.0000    1.0000   -3.2500  -13.2500
0.0000    0.0000    1.0000    5.0000

5.0000    3.0000    1.0000
```

Program 5.1 (cont.)

Program 5.1 (sfreegiv) corresponds to this algorithm and calculates also the solution by back-substitution. Applied to the set of Eq. (2.1), it yields $\mathbf{x}^T = [1, 3, 5]$ as it should have.

The advantages of this type of processing by rows are as follows:

- Measurements arrive by rows, so the method is natural.
- The scaling factors are those of **W** (the weighting matrix). Thus, the method is particularly well adapted to the weighted problem normally encountered.
- Suppose we processed a new row **x** with a resulting $\tilde{\mathbf{R}}$. If for some reason row **x** should not have been processed, we process it again, but now with the negative of the original weight. This removes row **x** and the measurement leading to it. Hence, if bad data were detected and identified, they can be removed without affecting the remaining **R**. Removing a row is thus easy and efficient. (If the normal set is solved, a bad measurement is eliminated, a new $\mathbf{A} = \mathbf{J}^T * \mathbf{W} * \mathbf{J}$ is calculated "from scratch," and the problem restarted.)
- The value of d^2 which results is very important for bad-data detection.

The algorithm would therefore start with two rows, eliminate the first element of the second row, and proceed with processing rows 3, 4, ..., m.

5.2.3 Singular-Value Decomposition

It was shown in Chapters 2 and 3 that singular-value decomposition is a form of orthogonalization. Therefore, state estimation can be solved by first decomposing the Jacobian according to

$$\mathbf{J} = \mathbf{T} * \mathbf{S} * \mathbf{V}^{\mathrm{T}} \tag{5.25}$$

Because $\mathbf{T}^{\mathrm{T}} * \mathbf{T} = \mathbf{I}$, $\mathbf{V}^{\mathrm{T}} * \mathbf{V} = \mathbf{I}$ and $\mathbf{S}^{\mathrm{T}} = \mathbf{S}$ we now have the normal matrix $\mathbf{J}^{\mathrm{T}} * \mathbf{J} = \mathbf{V} * \mathbf{S} * \mathbf{T}^{\mathrm{T}} * \mathbf{T} * \mathbf{S} * \mathbf{V}^{\mathrm{T}} = (\mathbf{V} * \mathbf{S}) *(\mathbf{S} * \mathbf{V})^{\mathrm{T}}$. With $\mathbf{J}^{\mathrm{T}} * \mathbf{z} = (\mathbf{V} * \mathbf{S}) * \mathbf{T}^{\mathrm{T}} * \mathbf{z}$, equation $\mathbf{A} * \Delta\mathbf{x} = \mathbf{b}$ to be solved is

$$(\mathbf{S} * \mathbf{V})^{\mathrm{T}} * \Delta\mathbf{x} = \mathbf{T}^{\mathrm{T}} * \mathbf{z}. \tag{5.26}$$

5.2.4 Gradient Methods

We have defined the state-estimation process as that of solving $\mathbf{r}(\mathbf{x}) \equiv \mathbf{e} = \mathbf{z} - \mathbf{f}(\mathbf{x}) = \mathbf{0}$ by minimizing the squares:

$$U(\mathbf{x}) = \Sigma\, [r_k(\mathbf{x})]^2 = \mathbf{r}^{\mathrm{T}}(\mathbf{x}) * \mathbf{r}(\mathbf{x}); \quad k\Sigma = 1, \ldots, m$$

[We will neglect the iteration index and $\mathbf{x}$ in any function $\mathbf{r}(\mathbf{x})$.] State-estimation is seen to be an unconstrained minimization problem.

To exemplify the new method, we draw a number of contours of U = constant in Fig. 5.3. Since U is quadratic, we find that with $\mathbf{z} = \mathbf{0}$, these would be circles, but since $\mathbf{z} \neq \mathbf{0}$, they are ellipses.

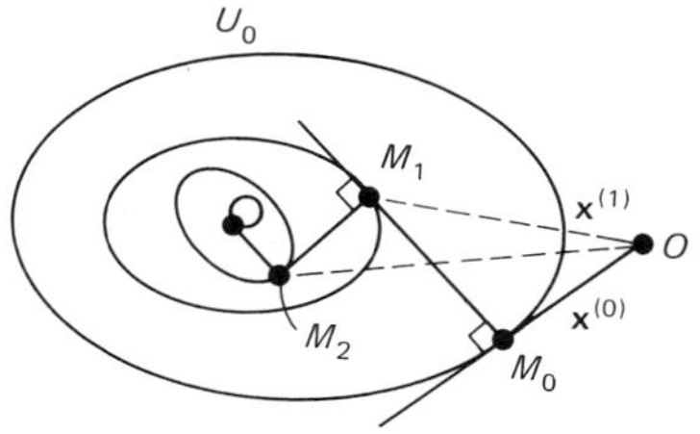

Figure 5.3 Steepest-descent method.

Suppose we start with an assumed $\mathbf{x}^{(0)}$ which corresponds to U_0. The greatest change of U will happen on the line perpendicular to U at M_0, i.e., along the negative of its gradient:

$$\mathbf{g} \equiv \mathbf{g}(U) = \left[\frac{\partial U}{\partial x_1}, \ldots, \frac{\partial U}{\partial x_m} \right]^{\mathrm{T}} \tag{5.27}$$

Therefore the approximation of $\mathbf{x}$ can be improved if the previous $\mathbf{x}$ is changed along a steepest-descent step: $\mathbf{x} := \mathbf{x} + t \cdot \mathbf{g}$. This corresponds to the triangle O, M_0, M_1 in Fig. 5.3. This figure also shows how critical is the proper choice of path length on M_0M_1. If it is chosen too small, the convergence will be too slow, but if the step size is chosen too large, the figure indicates that M_1 might lie on a U which is higher than necessary, since we have assumed

$$U_0 > U_1 > \cdots > U_r$$

If this happens, the convergence suffers again.

$U \equiv U(\mathbf{x})$ is a positive number because of the squaring, and since the smallest positive number is zero, minimization of U is equivalent to a solution of $\mathbf{r} = \mathbf{0}$.

For linear equations $\mathbf{A} * \mathbf{x} = \mathbf{b}$ we have defined the vector of residuals:

$$\mathbf{r} := \mathbf{A} * \mathbf{x} - \mathbf{b} \tag{5.28}$$

Consider the specific quadratic function of $\mathbf{x}$

$$U = 0.5\cdot(\mathbf{A} * \mathbf{x})^T * \mathbf{x} - \mathbf{b}^T * \mathbf{x} = 0.5\cdot\Sigma\, x_i\cdot\Sigma\, A_{i,k}\cdot x_k - \Sigma\, b_i\cdot x_i \tag{5.29}$$

where $k\Sigma = i\Sigma = 1, \ldots, n$. Differentiating it yields $\partial U/\partial x_i = \Sigma\, A_{i,k}\cdot x_k - b_i$, and since this is true for any i and $\partial U/\partial x_i$ are elements of the gradient of U, we have $\mathbf{g} = \mathbf{A} * \mathbf{x} - \mathbf{b} = \mathbf{r}$. It is again seen that solving $\mathbf{A} * \mathbf{x} - \mathbf{b} = \mathbf{0}$ is equivalent to minimization of U.

Insertion of $\mathbf{x} := \mathbf{x} + t\cdot\mathbf{g}$ into Eq. (5.29) yields

$$U := 0.5\cdot[\mathbf{A} * (\mathbf{x} + t\cdot\mathbf{g})]^T * (\mathbf{x} + t\cdot\mathbf{g}) - \mathbf{b}^T * (\mathbf{x} + t\cdot\mathbf{g})$$

or

$$2\cdot U := (\mathbf{A} * \mathbf{x})^T * \mathbf{x} + t\cdot[(\mathbf{A} * \mathbf{x})^T * \mathbf{g}) + (\mathbf{A} * \mathbf{g})^T * \mathbf{x}]$$
$$+ t^2\cdot(\mathbf{A} * \mathbf{g})^T * \mathbf{g} - 2\cdot\mathbf{b}^T * \mathbf{x} - 2\cdot t\cdot\mathbf{b}^T * \mathbf{g}$$

As seen earlier, the two scalars in the brackets are equal, so that

$$U := [0.5\cdot(\mathbf{A} * \mathbf{x})^T * \mathbf{x} - \mathbf{b}^T * \mathbf{x}]$$
$$+ t\cdot[(\mathbf{A} * \mathbf{x})^T * \mathbf{g} - \mathbf{b}^T * \mathbf{g}] + 0.5\cdot t^2\cdot(\mathbf{A} * \mathbf{g})^T * \mathbf{g}$$

According to Eq. (5.29), the term in the first bracket is the previous U, say, $\tilde{U}$, the second can be written as $t\cdot[(\mathbf{A} * \mathbf{x})^T - \mathbf{b}^T] * \mathbf{g} = t\cdot\mathbf{r}^T * \mathbf{g}$ [see Eq. (5.28)], so that the updated U is

$$U := 0.5t^2\cdot(\mathbf{A} * \mathbf{g})^T * \mathbf{g} + t\cdot\mathbf{r}^T * \mathbf{g} + \tilde{U}$$

This can be considered a quadratic equation in t, so that the minimum of U is obtained for the t which makes $\partial U/\partial t = 0$; $\partial U/\partial t = t\cdot(\mathbf{A} * \mathbf{g})^T * \mathbf{g} + \mathbf{r}^T * \mathbf{g} = 0$; $t := -(\mathbf{r}^T * \mathbf{g})/(\mathbf{d}^T * \mathbf{g})$ where $\mathbf{d} \equiv \mathbf{A} * \mathbf{g}$.

The steps of the *steepest-descent* method are: Start with some $\mathbf{x}_1$ and then for $i = 1, 2, \ldots$ select a direction vector $\mathbf{g}_i$ and change x_i through

$$\mathbf{x}_{i+1} := \mathbf{x}_i + t \cdot \mathbf{g}_i \tag{5.30}$$

where t and $\mathbf{d}$ are those of

$$t := \frac{-(\mathbf{r}_i^{\mathrm{T}} * \mathbf{g}_i)}{\mathbf{d}_i^{\mathrm{T}} * \mathbf{g}_i}; \quad \mathbf{d}_i := \mathbf{A} * \mathbf{g}_i \tag{5.31}$$

$\mathbf{r} = \mathbf{A} * \mathbf{x} - \mathbf{b}$ is taken in the direction of the negative gradient.

Another method is that of *conjugate gradients*. The starting points are the equations of the steepest-descent method for $i = 1$:

$$\mathbf{g}_1 = -\mathbf{r}_0 = (\mathbf{A} * \mathbf{x}_0 - \mathbf{b}); \quad \mathbf{x}_1 := \mathbf{x}_0 - t \cdot \mathbf{r}_0;$$

$$t := \frac{-(\mathbf{r}_0^{\mathrm{T}} * \mathbf{g}_1)}{\mathbf{d}_1^{\mathrm{T}} * \mathbf{g}_1}; \quad \mathbf{d}_1 := \mathbf{A} * \mathbf{g}_1$$

Note the subscripts in the vectors $\mathbf{r}_0$, $\mathbf{d}_1$, and $\mathbf{g}_1$.

For the following iterations ($i > 1$) we seek the minimum not just in any direction but on the plane spanned by $\mathbf{r}_{i-1}$ and $\mathbf{g}_i$, i.e.,

$$\mathbf{g}_i := e_{i-1} \cdot \mathbf{g}_{i-1} - \mathbf{r}_{i-1} \tag{5.32}$$

but so that $\mathbf{g}_i$ and $\mathbf{g}_{i-1}$ are conjugate on the matrix $\mathbf{A}$. For two vectors $\mathbf{g}_{i-1}$ and $\mathbf{g}_i$ to be conjugate on $\mathbf{A}$ means that $(\mathbf{A} * \mathbf{g}_i)^{\mathrm{T}} * \mathbf{g}_{i-1} = \mathbf{g}_i^{\mathrm{T}} * (\mathbf{A} * \mathbf{g}_{i-1}) = 0$. Inserting $\mathbf{g}_i$ and $\mathbf{d}_{i-1} = \mathbf{A} * \mathbf{g}_{i-1}$ shows that

$$(e_{i-1} \cdot \mathbf{g}_{i-1} - \mathbf{r}_{i-1})^{\mathrm{T}} * \mathbf{d}_{i-1} = 0$$

and the scalar e_{i-1} may be calculated from it as

$$e_{i-1} := \frac{\mathbf{r}_{i-1}^{\mathrm{T}} * \mathbf{d}_{i-1}}{\mathbf{g}_{i-1}^{\mathrm{T}} * \mathbf{d}_{i-1}}; \quad i = 2, 3, \ldots \tag{5.33}$$

For $i > 1$ we still have Eq. (5.30): $\mathbf{x}_i := \mathbf{x}_{i-1} + t_i \cdot \mathbf{g}_i$ with $t_i := -(\mathbf{r}_{i-1}^{\mathrm{T}} * \mathbf{g}_i)/(\mathbf{d}_i^{\mathrm{T}} * \mathbf{g}_i)$.

These equations can be simplified by rewriting $\mathbf{r}_i$:

$$\mathbf{r}_i = \mathbf{A} * \mathbf{x}_i - \mathbf{b} = \mathbf{A} * \mathbf{x}_{i-1} + t_i \cdot \mathbf{A} * \mathbf{g}_i - \mathbf{b} = \mathbf{r}_{i-1} + t_i \cdot \mathbf{d}_i \tag{5.34}$$

This form is more efficient, since $\mathbf{r}_{i-1}$ is known from iteration $i - 1$ and $\mathbf{d}_i$ has to be calculated anyway.

After completing step i, scalar U is a minimum point in a plane spanned by $\mathbf{r}_{i-1}$ and $\mathbf{g}_i$. Since $\mathbf{r}_i = -\mathrm{grad}(U)$ and thus is orthogonal to this plane, it follows that

$$\mathbf{r}_i^{\mathrm{T}} * \mathbf{r}_{i-1} = 0; \quad \mathbf{r}_i^{\mathrm{T}} * \mathbf{g}_i = 0 \tag{5.35}$$

Next a scalar product is computed:

$$\mathbf{r}_{i-1}^{\mathrm{T}} * \mathbf{g}_i = \mathbf{r}_{i-1}^{\mathrm{T}} * (e_{i-1}\mathbf{g}_{i-1} - \mathbf{r}_{i-1}) = e_{i-1} \cdot \mathbf{r}_{i-1}^{\mathrm{T}} * \mathbf{g}_{i-1} - \mathbf{r}_{i-1}^{\mathrm{T}} * \mathbf{r}_{i-1}$$

By Eq. (5.35): $\mathbf{r}_{i-1}^{T} * \mathbf{g}_{i-1} = 0$, so that

$$\mathbf{r}_{i-1}^{T} * \mathbf{g}_i = -\mathbf{r}_{i-1}^{T} * \mathbf{r}_{i-1} \tag{5.36}$$

and

$$t_i := (\mathbf{r}_{i-1}^{T} * \mathbf{r}_{i-1})/(\mathbf{d}_i^{T} * \mathbf{g}_i). \tag{5.37}$$

Inserting $\mathbf{d}_{i-1}$ from Eq. (5.34) into Eq. (5.33) yields $e_{i-1} = \mathbf{r}_{i-1}^{T} * (\mathbf{r}_{i-1} - \mathbf{r}_{i-2})/[\mathbf{g}_{i-1}^{T} * (\mathbf{r}_{i-1} - \mathbf{r}_{i-2})]$. From Eq. (5.35) we have that $\mathbf{r}_{i-1}^{T} * \mathbf{r}_{i-2} = 0$. Since zero is a scalar, $\mathbf{r}_{i-1}^{T} * \mathbf{g}_{i-1} = 0$ means also $\mathbf{g}_{i-1}^{T} * \mathbf{r}_{i-1} = 0$ so that

$$e_{i-1} = \frac{\mathbf{r}_{i-1}^{T} * \mathbf{r}_{i-1}}{\mathbf{g}_{i-1}^{T} * \mathbf{r}_{i-2}}$$

By transposing Eq. (5.36) we have $\mathbf{g}_{i-1}^{T} * \mathbf{r}_{i-2} = -\mathbf{r}_{i-2}^{T} * \mathbf{r}_{i-2}$ and an efficient form for e_{i-1}:

$$e_{i-1} = \frac{-(\mathbf{r}_{i-1}^{T} * \mathbf{r}_{i-1})}{\mathbf{r}_{i-2}^{T} * \mathbf{r}_{i-2}} \tag{5.38}$$

The conjugate-gradient method has an interesting history. Hestenes and Stiefel, who have developed it, also proved that it should solve $\mathbf{A} * \mathbf{x} = \mathbf{b}$ in n steps. In practice this was not true because of the inevitable roundoff errors, and its use was discontinued. Reid [Re71] then suggested using it as an iterative method and proved that its convergence is rather good for sparse systems.

Specifically for *state estimation*, we may suggest a number of modifications because $\mathbf{A} = \mathbf{J}^{T} * \mathbf{J}$, and $\mathbf{b}$ is replaced by $\mathbf{J}^{T} * \mathbf{b}$.

The normal equations were

$$\mathbf{J}^{T} * \mathbf{J} * \Delta\mathbf{x}_i + \mathbf{J}^{T} * \Delta\mathbf{z} = \mathbf{r}_i$$

We define next another residual vector:

$$\mathbf{u}_i = \mathbf{J} * \Delta\mathbf{x}_i + \Delta\mathbf{z} \tag{5.39}$$

The relationship between the two residual vectors is

$$\mathbf{r}_i = \mathbf{J}^{T} * (\mathbf{J} * \Delta\mathbf{x}_i + \Delta\mathbf{z}) = \mathbf{J}^{T} * \mathbf{u}_i \tag{5.40}$$

The denominator of t_i in Eq. (5.37) is changed through

$$\mathbf{d}_i^{T} * \mathbf{g}_i = (\mathbf{A} * \mathbf{g}_i)^{T} * \mathbf{g}_i = (\mathbf{J}^{T} * \mathbf{J} * \mathbf{g}_i)^{T} * \mathbf{g}_i = \mathbf{g}_i^{T} * \mathbf{J}^{T} * \mathbf{J} * \mathbf{g}_i$$

with $\mathbf{h} \equiv \mathbf{J} * \mathbf{g}$, this is $\mathbf{h}^{T} * \mathbf{h}$.

Since, by Eq. (5.30), $\Delta\mathbf{x}_i = \Delta\mathbf{x}_{i-1} + t_i \cdot \mathbf{g}_i$, we have $\mathbf{J} * \Delta\mathbf{x}_i + \Delta\mathbf{z} = \mathbf{J} * \Delta\mathbf{x}_{i-1} + \Delta\mathbf{z} + t_i \cdot \mathbf{J} * \mathbf{g}_i$, which with Eq. (5.39) yields

$$\mathbf{u}_i := \mathbf{u}_{i-1} + t_i \cdot (\mathbf{J} * \mathbf{g}_i) \tag{5.41}$$

The algorithm is now repeated with the original equation numbers given at left:

(5.40) $\mathbf{r}_{i-1} = \mathbf{J}^{\mathrm{T}} * \mathbf{u}_{i-1}$

(5.38) $e_{i-1} := \dfrac{-\mathbf{r}_{i-1}^{\mathrm{T}} * \mathbf{r}_{i-1}}{\mathbf{r}_{i-2}^{\mathrm{T}} * \mathbf{r}_{i-2}}$

(5.32) $\mathbf{g}_i := e_{i-1} \cdot \mathbf{g}_{i-1} - \mathbf{r}_{i-1}$

(5.37) $t_i := \dfrac{(\mathbf{r}_{i-1}^{\mathrm{T}} * \mathbf{r}_{i-1})}{(\mathbf{h}_i^{\mathrm{T}} * \mathbf{h}_i)}$ where $\mathbf{h}_i := \mathbf{J} * \mathbf{g}_i$

(5.30) $\Delta\mathbf{x}_i := \Delta\mathbf{x}_{i-1} + t_i \cdot \mathbf{g}_i$

(5.41) $\mathbf{u}_i := \mathbf{u}_{i-1} + t_i \cdot \mathbf{h}_i$

If two consecutive values of the scalar $\beta \equiv \mathbf{r}^{\mathrm{T}} * \mathbf{r}$ are stored, then after some $\mathbf{r}_{i+1}$ is calculated they are shifted by

$$\beta_{i-1} := \beta_i; \quad \beta_i := \mathbf{r}_{i+1}^{\mathrm{T}} * \mathbf{r}_{i+1}$$

This makes the calculation easier through

$$e_{i-1} := \frac{-\beta_{i-1}}{\beta_{i-2}}; \quad t_i := \frac{\beta_{i-1}}{\mathbf{h}_i^{\mathrm{T}} * \mathbf{h}_i}$$

The number of operations per iteration is only

$$\Omega \cong n^2 + n + n + (n^2 + n) + n + n = 2 \cdot n^2 + 5 \cdot n \cong 2 \cdot n^2$$

5.3 DISCUSSION

5.3.1 Computational Effort

To calculate the computational effort for the normal solution, recall that $\mathbf{J}^{\mathrm{T}} * \mathbf{J}$ for an n-by-n matrix $\mathbf{J}$ requires $\Omega_n \cong n^3$ and $\mathbf{J}^{\mathrm{T}} * \mathbf{z}$ requires another n^2. Finally, a solution requires $n^3/3$ so that altogether $\Omega_n \cong 4 \cdot n^3/3 + 3 \cdot n^2/2$.

If we assume Ω_{ort} for orthogonalization, then a method based on it will require $\Omega \cong n^2/2$ for back-substitution, n^2 for forming $\mathbf{b}$ and thus altogether $\Omega \cong \Omega_{\mathrm{ort}} + 3 \cdot n^2/2$. Orthogonalization is seen to be faster if

$$\Omega_{ort} < \frac{4 \cdot n^3}{3} \tag{5.42}$$

According to page 122 of [LH74], the Householder method—and therefore also the modified Givens method—require for orthogonalization $\Omega_{ort} = m \cdot n^2 - n^3/3$.

Usually $m > n$, but for the sake of simplicity we assume $m = n$, so that $\Omega_{ort} \cong 2 \cdot n^3/3$. This means that *orthogonalization for dense matrices can be done with less effort than solving the normal equations.* As a matter of fact, $m < 2n$ assures this result.

The main part of Ω_n was n^3 required for multiplying $\mathbf{J}^T$ by $\mathbf{J}$. It was shown in Chapter 4 that this number can be reduced very substantially for sparse matrices. Moreover, the solution of the *normal set* can be done very efficiently using the OOF algorithm of Chapter 4. The static policy, as developed in Chapter 2 for orthogonalization, does not seem to be as efficient.

Fortunately, a recent paper [GH81] shows that orthogonalization can also be done efficiently in the sparse cases.

Recall that the normal set is

$$\mathbf{A} * \Delta\mathbf{x} = \mathbf{b}; \quad \mathbf{A} = \mathbf{J}^T * \mathbf{J}; \quad \mathbf{b} = \mathbf{J}^T * \Delta\mathbf{z}$$

with $\mathbf{J}$ an m-by-n matrix, $\mathbf{A}$ an n-by-n matrix, and $\Delta\mathbf{x}$, $\mathbf{b}$, and $\Delta\mathbf{z}$ being n-by-1, n-by-1, and m-by-1 vectors, respectively. Orthogonalization, with $\mathbf{Q}$ an m-by-n and $\mathbf{R}$ an n-by-n triangular matrix, is

$$\mathbf{Q}^T * \mathbf{J} = [\mathbf{R}, \mathbf{0}]^T$$

Since $\mathbf{A} = \mathbf{J}^T * \mathbf{J} = \mathbf{J}^T * \mathbf{Q} * \mathbf{Q}^T * \mathbf{J} = (\mathbf{Q}^T * \mathbf{J})^T * (\mathbf{Q}^T * \mathbf{J}) = [\mathbf{R}, \mathbf{0}] * [\mathbf{R}, \mathbf{0}]^T = \mathbf{R} * \mathbf{R}^T$ and the factorization of $\mathbf{A}$ can be written as $\mathbf{A} = \mathbf{L} * \mathbf{L}^T$ we have

$$\mathbf{R} * \mathbf{R}^T = \mathbf{L} * \mathbf{L}^T \tag{5.43}$$

The fill-in of $\mathbf{R}$ is that of $\mathbf{L}$, and the proposed algorithm of orthogonalization can be extended to sparse cases as follows:

1. Determine the structure of $\mathbf{A} = \mathbf{J}^T * \mathbf{J}$ (but *not* its numerical values).
2. Order the normal matrix according to the OOF algorithm of Chapter 4.
3. Apply a symbolic factorization to the reordered matrix $\mathbf{A}^{\#}$, generating a row-oriented structure for storing $\mathbf{R}^{\#}$.
4. Compute $\mathbf{R}^{\#}$ by processing the rows of $\mathbf{J}^{\#}$ one by one (Eqs. 5.23). Apply the rotations also to $\Delta\mathbf{z}$ (see $\mathbf{b}$, $\mathbf{d}$ of Eq. 5.19).
5. Solve $\mathbf{R}^{\#} * \Delta\mathbf{x} = \mathbf{b}$.

Note that steps 1, 2, and 3 are exactly those we would do in the case of solving the normal set and that $\mathbf{R}^{\#}$ is $\mathbf{R}$ with reordered *columns*. This supplies one more reason for row processing. Additionally, a full row of **J** would introduce much fill-in, and one way to avoid it is to use updating.

If SVD [Eq. (5.26)] is used, then the steps require the following numbers of operations: Multiplication of $\mathbf{T}^{\mathrm{T}} * \mathbf{z}$ requires n^2, division by $S_{i,i}$ requires n, and multiplication by $\mathbf{V}$ another n^2 operations. Thus only $(2n^2 + n)$ operations are required, but since according to [LH74] the direct part of Eq. (5.25) will need $2n^3$ and the iterative $4n^3$, we get for the overall count $\Omega = 6n^3 + 2n^2 + n \cong 6n^3$.

This is much higher than the number of operations in the normal and orthogonalization methods. In section 5.6, the proposed program will nevertheless be based on SVD.

5.3.2 Errors

The main reason to suggest orthogonalization* for the solution of the state-estimation problem is that it has lower errors.

To be able to discuss errors, the network of [SE68] was again used and a load flow was run which supplied the true voltages $\mathbf{x}_t$. The power flows were computed and, with a random error superimposed, were viewed as measurements.

Two programs are compared in [WH82]. Program P1 is based on the normal equations method (but computes also eigenvalues λ_k of **A** and singular values s_i of both **A** and **J**); program P2 solves the state estimation by way of orthogonalization. Both programs start from a flat voltage profile $v_k + j \cdot w_k = 1 + j \cdot 0$ for $k = 2, \ldots, 5$, and in both Shamanski's method is used with c varied from 1 to 4 (the Jacobian being recomputed every time or every fourth time). Convergence is checked by three different residuals:

$$
\begin{aligned}
\rho_m &= \max\,[x_k^{(i+1)} - x_k^{(i)}] \\
\rho &= \Sigma\,[x_k^{(i+1)} - x_k^{(i)}]^2 \\
\rho_T &= \Sigma\,[x_{tk} - x_k^{(i)}]^2; \qquad k\Sigma = 1, \ldots, m
\end{aligned} \tag{5.44}
$$

with the maximum and summations applied to all nodes k. Normally, only ρ (and sometimes ρ_m) are computed for iterations $i = 2, 3, \ldots$, but since in this particular case the true values of the voltages $\mathbf{x}_t$ are known, ρ_T can be computed. It will yield a true indication of how far from the correct solution the state vector $\mathbf{x}^{(i)}$ is at the end of iteration i.

Table 5.4 shows these residuals for $c = 4$ and Table 5.5 for $c = 1$, i.e., for recomputing **L**, **D** or **Q**, **R** every fourth or every single iteration.

---

* Y. Wallach, E. Handschin, "State Estimation by Orthogonalization and Splitting." First published in the *International Journal of Electrical Power Energy Systems*, Butterworths & Co. Ltd. U.K., Vol. 4, No. 3 (July 1982) pp. 177-84. Used with permission.

It can be seen that, for the normal set (program P1), ρ_T increases (instead of decreasing), but for orthogonalization, it decreases—as it should. This means that the true error, as used in this program, increases for the normal method but decreases for orthogonalization.

TABLE 5.4 Development of residuals for $c = 4$ during $i = 1, \ldots, 12$ iterations.

i	1	2	3	4	5	6	7	8	9	10	11	12
P1												
ρ_m	598	426	251	145	34	21	14	11	11	10	10	10
ρ	104	42	15	5	0	0	0	0	0	0	0	0
ρ_T	357	474	587	670	692	705	715	722	728	733	738	744
P2												
ρ_m	438	96	56	33	21	17	15	13	12	11	10	10
ρ	22	3	1	0	0	0	0	0	0	0	0	0
ρ_T	331	325	322	320	318	315	312	306	306	303	300	297

TABLE 5.5 Development of residuals for $c = 1$ during $i = 1, \ldots, 12$ iterations.

i	1	2	3	4	5	6	7	8	9	10	11	12
P1												
ρ_m	598	407	221	117	60	30	15	11	11	10	10	10
ρ	104	38	12	3	1	0	0	0	0	0	0	0
ρ_T	357	469	567	613	669	692	707	716	724	730	736	742
P2												
ρ_m	438	98	58	34	20	17	15	14	12	12	11	10
ρ	22	3	1	0	0	0	0	0	0	0	0	0
ρ_T	331	326	324	322	320	317	314	311	308	304	301	298

TABLE 5.6 True, initial, and final voltages.

	v_2	w_2	v_3	w_3	v_4	w_4	v_5	w_5
x_t	462	−513	204	−892	192	−950	121	−1090
$x_{p2}^{(2)}$, $c = 1$	438	103	5	50	−6	−6	90	−50
$x_{p1}^{(2)}$, $c = 1$	598	134	527	56	523	1	325	−52
$x_{p2}^{(12)}$, $c = 4$	473	234	−235	38	228	−21	187	−251
$x_{p1}^{(12)}$, $c = 4$	813	473	1379	156	1387	103	712	−128

The comparison of the two programs may also be based on the voltage computation instead of the residuals. Table 5.6 shows the complex voltages in the five network buses, comparing the true values $\mathbf{x}_t$ with the values after 2 and 12 iterations and keeping the matrices constant for $c =$

4 and $c = 1$ iterations. To save space, $(v_k - 1)\cdot 10^4$ and $w_k \cdot 10^4$ are shown. Note that the x_{p1} voltages are further from the true values in iteration $i = 12$ than they were in iteration $i = 2$.

The reason why the poor accuracy of normal solutions was not detected hitherto is also indicated in Tables 5.4 and 5.5. Normally, values of $\mathbf{x}_t$ are not available and convergence is tested by ρ or ρ_m, both of which decrease in P1 for both $c = 1$ or $c = 4$. As shown by ρ_T, it would be better to stop after a single iteration of P1, since further work increases the difference of $\mathbf{x}$ from $\mathbf{x}_t$ (Table 5.6) and as mentioned above, without any warning from ρ or ρ_m. It is comforting to note that in the orthogonalization program P2 all three residuals including ρ_T decrease, so that $\mathbf{x}^{(12)}$ is in fact closer to $\mathbf{x}_t$, than was $\mathbf{x}^{(1)}$.

It should be stressed again that *the most important feature of any state-estimation program is the accuracy of the results.* Weighted least-squares, "normal" solutions suffer from having lower accuracy.

Accuracy is normally determined by the condition number cond(**A**) of matrix **A**, so that although it is always greater than or equal to 1, the larger it is the less accurate is the solution.

The condition number of **A** may be calculated in various ways: one is to use singular values, another is to compute all eigenvalues λ_i and then substitute $\text{cond}(\mathbf{A}) \cong |\lambda_{max}|/|\lambda_{min}|$.

TABLE 5.7 Singular values and eigenvalues for matrices A and B.

$s_J^{(1)}$	66.46	46.63	42.14	30.97	25.73	14.29	12.70	9.8
$s_A^{(1)}$	4417.00	2174.00	1776.00	959.00	662.00	204.00	161.00	98.00
$\lambda_A^{(1)}$	−3098.00	−1220.00	−66.10	7.07	10.53	774.60	1989.00	3386.00
$s_J^{(12)}$	75.45	52.88	47.60	32.08	27.32	15.59	13.70	10.60
$s_A^{(12)}$	5694.00	2796.00	2266.00	1029.00	746.00	243.00	188.00	112.00
$\lambda_A^{(12)}$	−4054.00	−1599.00	−72.07	5.11	20.19	855.00	2385.00	4364.00

Table 5.7 lists the eigenvalues of **A**, and cond(**A**) can be computed as 479 at $i = 1$, the first iteration. Not only is this value too high, but for $i = 12$ it even increases (to 854), so that the accuracy decreases instead of increasing with consecutive iterations. This can also be seen in Table 5.6, which shows that $\mathbf{x}^{(1)}$ is closer to $\mathbf{x}_t$ than is $\mathbf{x}^{(12)}$; the difference between $\mathbf{x}^{(i)}$ and $\mathbf{x}_t$ increases more by roundoff than it is decreased by further iterations of $\mathbf{A} * \Delta\mathbf{x} = -\mathbf{b}$.

In order to compare methods P1 and P2, use a better definition of cond(**A**): $\text{cond}(\mathbf{A}) = |s_{max}|/|s_{min}|$, with s_i a singular value of matrix **A**.

The condition numbers of both **A** and **J** computed in this way are 6.73 and 45.29 for **J** and **A** at iteration 1 and 7.12 and 50.84 at iteration 12. Since cond(**A**) > cond(**J**), the accuracy of the normal least-squares solution is lower than that of orthogonalization. As a matter of fact, since $\mathbf{A} = \mathbf{J}^T * \mathbf{J}$ and $\mathbf{S}$ is a diagonal matrix $\mathbf{S} = \text{diag}[s_i]$, we have

$$\text{cond}(\mathbf{A}) = [\text{cond}\,(\mathbf{J})]^2 \tag{5.45}$$

Hence, using $\mathbf{A}$ instead of $\mathbf{J}$ will increase quadratically the sensitivity of the method to roundoff error! This result is not affected by further iterations: the condition number at $i = 12$ is even higher than at $i = 1$.

As a matter of fact, it is well known that the information matrix $\mathbf{A} = \mathbf{J}^T * \mathbf{J}$ may even be singular with no accuracy at all.

A matrix is singular if a column exists that is a linear combination of other columns (call it *trouble*). The measurements could be changed if we had an indication of trouble, but neither the Newton–Raphson nor the orthogonalization method yields such an indication.

Suppose a 4-by-2 matrix $\mathbf{J}$ has all elements 1 except $\mathbf{J}_{4,2} = 1 - \epsilon$ where ϵ is such that it can be stored in a computer word but that $\epsilon^2 \cong 0$. Then

$$\mathbf{A} = \mathbf{J}^T * \mathbf{J} = \begin{bmatrix} 4 & 4 - \epsilon \\ 4 - \epsilon & 4 - 2\epsilon + \epsilon^2 \end{bmatrix} \cong \begin{bmatrix} 4 & 4 - \epsilon \\ 4 - \epsilon & 4 - 2\epsilon \end{bmatrix}$$

Using Cholesky decomposition in the form $\mathbf{A} = \mathbf{U}^T * \mathbf{U}$ with $\mathbf{U}$ an upper-triangular matrix yields $u_{11}^2 = 4$, $u_{11} = 2$, $u_{12} \cdot u_{11} = 4 - \epsilon$, $u_{12} = 2 - \epsilon/2$, $u_{12}^2 + u_{22}^2 = 4 - 2\epsilon$ and $u_{22}^2 = -\epsilon^2/4 \cong 0$.

Since row 2 of $\mathbf{U}$ consists of two zeros, the matrix is singular. This is not the fault of the factorization $\mathbf{A} = \mathbf{U}^T * \mathbf{U}$ but of the fact that $\mathbf{A}$ is nearly singular (two nearly identical columns). Had we made also $\epsilon = 0$, it would be singular.

There are two ways to detect singularity or near-singularity. One is to compute the singular values; another is to compute the *covariance matrix*,

$$\mathbf{C} = (\mathbf{J}^T * \mathbf{J})^{-1} \tag{5.46}$$

If the normal solution and $\mathbf{J}^T * \mathbf{J} = \mathbf{A}$ is used, an inversion of $\mathbf{A}$ is required. The reason for computing the covariance matrix is to determine *whether* an inversion is safe. Thus in this case no attempt should be made to compute the covariance matrix.

In orthogonalization, $\mathbf{J} = \mathbf{Q} * \mathbf{R}$, we have $\mathbf{J}^T * \mathbf{J} = \mathbf{R}^T * \mathbf{Q}^T * \mathbf{Q} * \mathbf{R}$; but since $\mathbf{Q}$ is orthonormal, $\mathbf{Q}^T * \mathbf{Q} = \mathbf{I}$ and $\mathbf{C} = (\mathbf{R}^T * \mathbf{R})^{-1} = \mathbf{R}^{-1} * (\mathbf{R}^{-1})^T$.

To compute it, we have to invert a right upper-triangular matrix, which requires $\Omega \cong n^3/6$, and multiply it by a lower-triangular matrix for another $n^3/6$. Altogether $\Omega \cong n^3/3$ is the "price" for computing $\mathbf{C}$.

If SVD is used, the elements of $\mathbf{C}$ are

$$\mathbf{C} = (\mathbf{V} * \mathbf{S} * \mathbf{T}^{\mathrm{T}} * \mathbf{T} * \mathbf{S} * \mathbf{V}^{\mathrm{T}})^{-1}$$
$$= (\mathbf{V} * \mathbf{S}^2 * \mathbf{V}^{\mathrm{T}})^{-1} = \mathbf{V} * \mathbf{S}^{-2} * \mathbf{V}^{\mathrm{T}}$$
$$C_{ij} = \frac{\Sigma\, V_{i,k} * V_{j,k}}{s_k^2}; \qquad k\Sigma = 1, \ldots, n$$

In this case, computing **C** requires only $\Omega \cong O(n^2)$.

Instead of computing **C**, recall that if some singular value, say s_j of **J** is small relative to the the largest s_1, then **J** is nearly singular.

In on-line execution there is no time to perform a singular or eigenvalue analysis. To supply the dispatcher with information on the condition number, in P1 it could be approximated by [SRS73]

$$\text{cond}(\mathbf{A}) \cong \frac{|\max\,(A_{k,k})|}{|\min\,(A_{k,k})|} \tag{5.47}$$

and the normal matrix would have to be computed. If orthogonalization is used, **A** is not computed. Its diagonal elements will be recomputed only once, since **Q** does not change significantly. In the cases discussed here, cond(**A**) would increase from 13.87 to 15.51 as P1 progresses, indicating that, at least, the weighted least-squares solution would lead to large errors.

Orthogonalization, $\mathbf{J} = \mathbf{Q} * \mathbf{R}$, is mathematically equivalent to $\mathbf{A} = \mathbf{L}^{\mathrm{T}} * \mathbf{L}$ because $\mathbf{J}^{\mathrm{T}} * \mathbf{J} = \mathbf{R}^{\mathrm{T}} * \mathbf{Q}^{\mathrm{T}} * \mathbf{Q} * \mathbf{R} = \mathbf{R}^{\mathrm{T}} * \mathbf{R}$. Still, orthogonalization shows higher accuracy for the following reason. In elimination $A_{k,k}$ of Eq. (5.47) represents the square of the length of $\mathbf{h} = \mathbf{J}^{\mathrm{T}} * \Delta\mathbf{z}$, whereas in orthogonalization $r_{k,k}$ represents the square of the length of **h**, but only after it was orthonormalized to $h_1, \ldots, h_{k-1}$. Thus, in elimination the loss of significant figures occurs as the square of length but in orthogonalization as the length of h_k.

5.3.3 Remarks on Bad Data

We have mentioned that bad data have to be *detected*, which data are bad have to be *identified*, and finally the bad (data) measurement has to be *removed*.

For detection we need a function of residuals that is easily computed and has quite different values with and without bad data. Such a function is the cost

$$U = [\mathbf{z} - \mathbf{f}(\mathbf{x})]^{\mathrm{T}} * \mathbf{W} * [\mathbf{z} - \mathbf{f}(\mathbf{x})]$$

We can therefore process each (row) measurement z_m as it arrives and compute U by Eq. (5.21). If U shows a large jump, bad data have been detected. Note that d is an indication of whether U increases considerably or not.

For the calculation of U and for identification we resort to statistical considerations. They are outside the scope of this book but lead to the following *detection* procedure based on the jump in U as evidenced by the value of d:

Define $\zeta_1 = (d - k)/\sqrt{2k}$, where $k = m - n$ and, if $k > 30$, then calculate $\zeta_2 := \sqrt{2d} - \sqrt{2k}$. If $\zeta_1 < \gamma$ ($\gamma \cong 1.65$) or if $k > 30$ and $\zeta_2 < \gamma$, then there are no bad data.

We can also define normalized residuals, $\tilde{r}_w = \sqrt{\mathbf{W}} \cdot r$ and $\tilde{r}_N = \sqrt{\text{diag}(\mathbf{A})^{-1}} \cdot r$, and use $\tilde{r}_W < \gamma$ or $\tilde{r}_N < \gamma$ as tests.

For a single bad data item, the $\tilde{r}_N$ test is usually the best, but since it requires the off-line calculation of diag($\mathbf{A}^{-1}$), it is advisable to use the pairs $\zeta < \gamma$ and $\tilde{r}_W < \gamma$.

The $\tilde{r}_W$ values are needed anyway for *identification*, which we do as follows: Put all $\tilde{r}_W$ in descending order of magnitude and remove measurement z_i, which corresponds to the maximum $\tilde{r}_W$. Go through the detection process again, and if $\zeta \geq \gamma$ or $\tilde{r}_W \geq \gamma$, then remove the second measurement, and so on.

In *orthogonalization* we have seen that d^2 is added automatically to U. Thus, ζ_1 and/or ζ_2 can be computed and the test performed after *each* row is processed. If U is too large, then we first update k and ζ_1 and perform the test.

5.3.4 Decoupling

The algorithm we used for load flow was based on decoupling; the same can be done in state estimation. The Jacobian can be written with some blocks being zero submatrices:

$$\mathbf{J}^{\mathrm{T}} * \mathbf{J} = \begin{bmatrix} \mathbf{0} & \mathbf{A}^{\mathrm{T}} & \mathbf{0} & \mathbf{B}^{\mathrm{T}} & \mathbf{0} \\ \mathbf{C}^{T} & \mathbf{0} & \mathbf{D}^{\mathrm{T}} & \mathbf{0} & \mathbf{E}^{\mathrm{T}} \end{bmatrix} * \begin{bmatrix} \mathbf{0} & \mathbf{C} \\ \mathbf{A} & \mathbf{0} \\ \mathbf{0} & \mathbf{D} \\ \mathbf{B} & \mathbf{0} \\ \mathbf{0} & \mathbf{E} \end{bmatrix} = \begin{bmatrix} \mathbf{F} & \mathbf{0} \\ \mathbf{0} & \mathbf{G} \end{bmatrix}$$

Multiplying $\mathbf{J}^{\mathrm{T}} * \mathbf{J}$, we get

$$\mathbf{F} = \mathbf{A}^{\mathrm{T}} * \mathbf{A} + \mathbf{B}^{\mathrm{T}} * \mathbf{B}; \qquad \mathbf{G} = \mathbf{C}^{\mathrm{T}} * \mathbf{C} + \mathbf{D}^{\mathrm{T}} * \mathbf{D} + \mathbf{E}^{\mathrm{T}} * \mathbf{E}$$

If vector $\mathbf{b}$ is also split into $\mathbf{b}_1$ and $\mathbf{b}_2$, we are to solve two independent sets:

$$\mathbf{F} * \Delta\mathbf{x}_1 = \mathbf{b}_1 \quad \text{and} \quad \mathbf{G} * \Delta\mathbf{x}_2 = \mathbf{b}_2 \tag{5.48}$$

If we orthogonalize $\mathbf{A} = \mathbf{Q}_A * \mathbf{R}_A$ and $\mathbf{B} = \mathbf{Q}_B * \mathbf{R}_B$, then $\mathbf{F}$ can be rewritten as $\mathbf{F} = \mathbf{R}_A^{\mathrm{T}} * \mathbf{Q}_A^{\mathrm{T}} * \mathbf{Q}_A * \mathbf{R}_A + \mathbf{R}_B^{\mathrm{T}} * \mathbf{Q}_B^{\mathrm{T}} * \mathbf{Q}_B * \mathbf{R}_B = \mathbf{R}_A^{\mathrm{T}} * \mathbf{R}_A + \mathbf{R}_B^{\mathrm{T}} * \mathbf{R}_B = \mathbf{R}_A^{\mathrm{T}} * [\mathbf{R}_A + (\mathbf{R}_A^{\mathrm{T}})^{-1} * \mathbf{R}_B^{\mathrm{T}} * \mathbf{R}_B]$, and on the right-hand side we have

$$\mathbf{R}_A * \mathbf{Q}_A * \mathbf{b}_1 + \mathbf{R}_B * \mathbf{Q}_B * \mathbf{b}_2$$

$$= \mathbf{R}_A * [\mathbf{Q}_A * \mathbf{b}_1 + (\mathbf{R}_A)^{-1} * \mathbf{R}_B * \mathbf{Q}_B * \mathbf{b}_2]$$

We thus have as the solution

$$\mathbf{P} = (\mathbf{R}_A^{\mathrm{T}})^{-1} * \mathbf{R}_B; \quad [\mathbf{R}_A + \mathbf{P} * \mathbf{R}_B] * \Delta\mathbf{x} = \mathbf{c}_1 + \mathbf{P} * \mathbf{c}_2 \tag{5.49}$$

Therefore $\mathbf{c}_1$ and $\mathbf{c}_2$ are the result of including the right-hand side in the orthogonalization process.

It is left as an exercise to see if it would be more efficient actually to calculate **F** and **G** and apply the orthogonalization separately to Eq. (5.48).

5.3.5 Constrained SE

Next we discuss the constrained state-estimation problem.

In the general case the cost $U = \mathbf{e}^{\mathrm{T}} * \mathbf{e} = (\mathbf{x} - \mathbf{z})^{\mathrm{T}} * (\mathbf{x} - \mathbf{z})$ is to be minimized, subject to some linear constraints:

$$\mathbf{C} * \mathbf{x} + \mathbf{c} = \mathbf{0} \tag{5.50}$$

As in other minimization problems, we include the constraints in a Lagrangian function

$$L = (\mathbf{x} - \mathbf{z})^{\mathrm{T}} * (\mathbf{x} - \mathbf{z}) - 2\cdot\boldsymbol{\lambda}^{\mathrm{T}} * (\mathbf{C} * \mathbf{x} + \mathbf{c}) \tag{5.51}$$

and differentiate it. Then $\partial L/\partial \mathbf{x}$ is compared to zero:

$$\frac{\partial L}{\partial \mathbf{x}} = 2\cdot\mathbf{x} - 2\cdot\mathbf{z} - 2\cdot\boldsymbol{\lambda}^{\mathrm{T}} * \mathbf{C} = \mathbf{0}$$

Thus $\mathbf{x} = \mathbf{C}^{\mathrm{T}} * \boldsymbol{\lambda} + \mathbf{z}$. Since $\mathbf{e} = \mathbf{x} - \mathbf{z}$, the error vector is

$$\mathbf{e} = \mathbf{C}^{\mathrm{T}} * \boldsymbol{\lambda} \tag{5.52}$$

Substitution of $\mathbf{x}$ into Eq. (5.50) yields $\mathbf{C} * \mathbf{C}^{\mathrm{T}} * \boldsymbol{\lambda} + (\mathbf{C} * \mathbf{z} + \mathbf{c}) = \mathbf{0}$. Then $\mathbf{c}$ can be included in the vector of $\mathbf{C} * \mathbf{z}$, so that this equation is rewritten as

$$\mathbf{C} * \mathbf{C}^{\mathrm{T}} * \boldsymbol{\lambda} + \mathbf{C} * \mathbf{z} = \mathbf{0} \tag{5.53}$$

These represent a normal set for the Lagrange coefficients $\boldsymbol{\lambda}$. Instead of solving them, we orthogonalize: $\mathbf{C}^{\mathrm{T}} = \mathbf{Q} * \mathbf{R}$; then we insert $\mathbf{C}^{\mathrm{T}}$ into Eq. (5.53). This yields $\mathbf{R}^{\mathrm{T}} * \mathbf{Q}^{\mathrm{T}} * \mathbf{Q} * \mathbf{R} * \boldsymbol{\lambda} + \mathbf{R}^{\mathrm{T}} * \mathbf{Q}^{\mathrm{T}} * \mathbf{z} = \mathbf{0}$ or a triangular set

$$\mathbf{R} * \boldsymbol{\lambda} + \mathbf{Q}^{\mathrm{T}} * \mathbf{z} = \mathbf{0} \tag{5.54}$$

in which $\mathbf{Q}^{\mathrm{T}} * \mathbf{z}$ is the orthogonalized right-hand vector $\mathbf{z}$.

Next insert $\boldsymbol{\lambda}$ from Eq. (5.54) into Eq. (5.52):

$$\mathbf{e} = -\mathbf{C}^{\mathrm{T}} * \mathbf{R}^{-1} * \mathbf{Q}^{\mathrm{T}} * \mathbf{z} = -\mathbf{Q} * \mathbf{R} * \mathbf{R}^{-1} * \mathbf{Q}^{\mathrm{T}} * \mathbf{z}$$
$$= -\mathbf{Q} * (\mathbf{Q}^{\mathrm{T}} * \mathbf{z}) = \mathbf{x} - \mathbf{z}$$

The algorithm therefore adds to orthogonalization [steps (a) and (b) below] only a matrix–vector multiplication in step (c):

(a) $\mathbf{C}^T = \mathbf{Q} * \mathbf{R}$
(b) $\mathbf{h} = \mathbf{Q}^T * \mathbf{z}$
(c) $\mathbf{x} = \mathbf{z} - \mathbf{Q} * \mathbf{h}$

Note that the computational effort required here is low because matrix **C** is smaller than matrix **J**.

In the case of electric power systems [APA77] we may use the fact that some nodes have zero injected power.* This is true at switching and multilevel stations. The fact that a node has no power injected into it (or out of it) is a property of the node (and not of the load), is known with absolute certainty, and is available at no cost at all.

With **x** as the voltage vector, constraints can also be expressed as $\mathbf{g(x)} = \mathbf{0}$, in which the nonlinear function **g** relates all the voltages to (nodes of) zero powers. Using a Taylor series around $\bar{\mathbf{x}}$, we rewrite it as $\mathbf{g}(\bar{\mathbf{x}}) + \mathbf{G} * \Delta\mathbf{x} = \mathbf{0}$ where the additional Jacobian matrix **G** is a p-by-n matrix ($p < n$): $G_{i,j} = \partial g_i / \partial x_j$.

The Lagrange function L is in this case [with $\Delta\mathbf{h} = -\mathbf{g(x)}$]:

$$L = (\Delta\mathbf{z} - \mathbf{J} * \Delta\mathbf{x})^T * \mathbf{W} * (\Delta\mathbf{z} - \mathbf{J} * \Delta\mathbf{x}) \\ - 2\cdot\boldsymbol{\lambda}^T * (\Delta\mathbf{h} - \mathbf{G} * \Delta\mathbf{x}) \tag{5.55}$$

Differentiations with respect to $\Delta\mathbf{x}$ and $\boldsymbol{\lambda}$ yield

$$\partial L / \partial(\Delta\mathbf{x}) = 2\cdot\mathbf{J}^T * \mathbf{W} * \mathbf{J} * \Delta\mathbf{x} - 2\cdot\mathbf{J}^T * \mathbf{W} * \Delta\mathbf{z} + 2\cdot\mathbf{G}^T * \boldsymbol{\lambda} = \mathbf{0}$$

$$\partial L / \partial\boldsymbol{\lambda} = -2\cdot(\Delta\mathbf{h} - \mathbf{G} * \Delta\mathbf{x}) = \mathbf{0}$$

Vector $\boldsymbol{\lambda}$ or $\boldsymbol{\lambda}_{k+1}$ is that of iteration $k + 1$, whereas all other matrices and vectors are of iteration k.

The last two equations can be summarized as

$$\begin{bmatrix} \mathbf{J}^T * \mathbf{W} * \mathbf{J} & \mathbf{G}^T \\ \mathbf{G} & \mathbf{0} \end{bmatrix} * \begin{bmatrix} \Delta\mathbf{x} \\ \boldsymbol{\lambda}_{k+1} \end{bmatrix} = \begin{bmatrix} \mathbf{J}^T * \mathbf{W} * \Delta\mathbf{z} \\ \Delta\mathbf{h} \end{bmatrix}$$

Insertion of $\boldsymbol{\lambda}_{k+1} = \boldsymbol{\lambda}_k + \Delta\boldsymbol{\lambda}$ with any iteration index yields

$$\begin{bmatrix} \mathbf{J}^T * \mathbf{W} * \mathbf{J} & \mathbf{G}^T \\ \mathbf{G} & \mathbf{0} \end{bmatrix} * \begin{bmatrix} \Delta\mathbf{x} \\ \Delta\boldsymbol{\lambda} \end{bmatrix} = \begin{bmatrix} \mathbf{J}^T * \mathbf{W} * \Delta\mathbf{z} - \mathbf{G}^T * \boldsymbol{\lambda} \\ \Delta\mathbf{h} \end{bmatrix} \tag{5.56}$$

Suppose we differentiate the basic Lagrangian of Eq. (5.51) with respect to $\boldsymbol{\lambda}$: $\partial L / \partial\boldsymbol{\lambda} = -2\cdot(\mathbf{C} * \mathbf{x} + \mathbf{c}) = \mathbf{0}$. In sum, we have

---

* F. C. Aschmoneit, N. M. Peterson, E. C. Adrian, "State Estimation with Equality Constraints", PICA-Conference, 1977. © 1977 by IEEE. Used with permission.

$$\begin{bmatrix} \mathbf{I} & -\mathbf{C}^T \\ -\mathbf{C} & \mathbf{0} \end{bmatrix} * \begin{bmatrix} \mathbf{x} \\ \boldsymbol{\lambda} \end{bmatrix} = \begin{bmatrix} \mathbf{z} \\ \mathbf{c} \end{bmatrix} \tag{5.57}$$

Comparing this with Eq. (5.56) and Eq. (5.55) with (5.51) shows that algorithm (a), (b), (c) can be used provided we substitute $\mathbf{J} * \Delta\mathbf{x}$ for $\mathbf{x}$, $\Delta\mathbf{z}$ for $\mathbf{z}$ and $\mathbf{G}$ for $\mathbf{C} * \mathbf{J}$.

It might be asked whether it would not be better to include the zero powers as pseudomeasurements with a very high weight (at least 10 times that of the best measurement). As noted in [APA77] this decreases the rate of convergence and increases the fill-in. On the other hand, as we have seen, making it into a constrained state estimation will not change these characteristics.

The main advantage of including the zero-injection nodes is in increasing the *redundancy*. The redundancy is measured in $\eta = (m - n)/n = m/n - 1$. Thus if $m = 200$ and $n = 150$, we have $\eta = 4/3 - 1 = 1/3$; but if 100 zero-injection nodes are included as measurements, $m = 300$ and $\eta = 1$, so that redundancy has increased threefold.

Since it is known that higher redundancy leads to more accurate state estimation, the suggestion is made to include zero-injection nodes.

5.4 PARALLEL SYSTEMS FOR REAL-TIME EXECUTION

Power system calculations are done either off-line or on-line. In the first case, as exemplified by load flow, the results are needed for planning and it is unimportant whether the program runs 3 or 2 minutes—even whether it runs in the morning or in the evening. Not so with SE; it is an on-line problem which must be solved as fast as possible and just when the dispatcher wants the results.

Let us see why.

The dispatcher bases all decisions on the state of the network and therefore has to know it all the time. There was a time when the dispatchers used the supervisory control and data-acquisition system exclusively, but, as already explained, the information is now processed by an SE program. We can thus visualize the dispatcher as either looking at the display of results provided by SE all the time or activating it whenever needed. In both cases the dispatcher cannot wait long for data because they change constantly, and so the results are correct if and only if they are given for the data currently measured; it must be an on-line job done more or less instantaneously, i.e., in real time.

As already mentioned, if such an on-line SE program exists, we could base the economic dispatch program on it, instead of on the load-flow program with a possible greater cost reduction. Even more important, if we had an on-line SE then we could ensure the "security" of the network, by possibly running contingency studies in real time. At present they are based on load-flow programs, and we conclude that if possible we should run SE programs on-line.

The first impulse of an electrical engineer will be to say: "So what if SE has to be run in real time? We will use a faster computer to squeeze a lot of computations into the 5 to 15 seconds we consider instantaneous."

Unfortunately, the problem is not that simple.*

An average power system might have at present about 1000 buses and therefore 1000 complex equations which form the basis of all programs. Even if we assume that the network is extremely sparse, say, 8 nonzeros in a row (3 lines connected to each bus), we have to solve an extremely large system (by eliminating $\cong 4 \cdot 2000 = 8000$ nonzero elements). Since a solution of a set is required for every iteration, we arrive at solution times of minutes (not seconds). Still, couldn't we make a computer fast enough to do it in seconds?

The *speed* of computers has increased enormously since their introduction in the 1940s. To exemplify, compare addition of two numbers. This operation required about 300 milliseconds in 1944 (on a relay computer), 300 microseconds in 1954 (on a tube computer), and 300 nanoseconds in 1964 (on the CDC-6600). Assume that today an addition should be completed in 300 picoseconds. An electrical signal would travel only 9 cm (about 3.5 in.) during this time — a very difficult assignment, since the distance between the memory and the CPU may be larger than that, making access time longer. Extremely small computers are envisaged now, but these computers will have to be cooled cryogenically and will hardly be used by utilities. We conclude therefore that *we need a different solution.*

Such a solution may use a parallel processing system in which p processors are connected in parallel. If all of them always worked simultaneously, the speed would also increase p-fold (solving our speed problem). They would also add other advantages:

The *cost effectiveness* of parallel systems of p mini- or microcomputers is good because large and very large integration technologies favor the small processor. Large units which rely on specialized logic are less able to exploit these technologies. Additionally, large production lines lower overhead and software costs.

Expandability is another advantage of parallel processing systems. If single computers are used, then whenever a larger unit is required, the old one is abandoned and a new one bought or leased. It seems better to use a parallel processing system and add processing power if and when needed.

---

* The material on parallel processing systems is based on Y. Wallach, *Alternating Sequential Parallel Processing*, Springer-Verlag, New York, 1982. © 1982 by Springer-Verlag, Berlin, Heidelberg, New York, Tokyo. Used with permission.

The *main advantage* which would accrue from the use of parallel processing systems is related to *reliability and availability*. A single computer is as reliable as the weakest of its parts, so that every failure is catastrophic. In parallel processing systems the idea is that the $p - 1$ remaining processors can and will go on working and thus provide (slightly degraded) service.

The next question is which of the existing parallel processing systems should be used. A number of them have recently been developed. They are usually classified SIMD for single-instruction-multiple-data and MIMD for multiple-instruction-multiple-data-stream systems. In SIMD systems, exemplified by Illiac, a controller issues the instructions with the processing elements either executing them in *lock-step* synchronism or idling (for a particular instruction). MIMD systems can be viewed as composed of p separate computers working asynchronously on p related or unrelated jobs. MIMD systems could also be subdivided into tightly coupled systems, e.g., "C.mmp" with a common memory, or loosely coupled systems, where messages are exchanged through handshaking, e.g., "Cm*." (for more information on these systems, see [Wa82]).

The difficulties in applying existing systems to power network problems are as follows:

1. SIMD systems have a rather low efficiency in general and for power systems in particular, primarily because data must be stored so that they are available without much shifting. In many cases power system problems lead to sparse and irregular matrices, so that the processing elements are idle most of the time. This also leads to difficult programming. Because of the asymmetry of SIMD systems (a single controller, instruction processor, slaves, etc., all different), reliability and availability are practically nonexistent. As a matter of fact, the failure of a single processing element leads to a system "down."
2. MIMD systems also show low speedups. The reason is that they work with a common memory, so that *contention* problems exist, i.e., more than one processor approaches memory at the same time. Memory, especially in the operating system areas, must be protected by locks or semaphores, jobs have to be queued, and the resulting cumbersome operating system may be counterproductive. Because of this, in at least one case it was found that adding processors decreased instead of increasing the speed.

We have seen why existing parallel processing systems are not really applicable to the particular problems we have in mind. The reasons for low acceptance on a more general level were given in [BS76] as follows:

1. "The basic nature of engineering is to be conservative. This is a classical deadlock situation: we cannot learn how to program multiprocessors until such systems exist; a system cannot be built before programs are ready."
2. "The market doesn't demand them. Another deadlock: how can the market demand them if the market doesn't even know that such a structure can exist? IBM has not yet blessed the concept." (This was said in 1976.)

It was mentioned once that we might be trying to protect our programming jobs and thus reject solutions which would shift employment patterns. Since the computer industry is more programmer bound than hardware limited, the reason is valid, but the correct conclusion should be that any parallel system to be introduced must be such that the amount of additional software for it is minimal or easily produced and understood: *Reprogramming must be easy.* Unfortunately, in all better-known systems reprogramming requires a major effort.

There exists a much more fundamental reason for the low acceptance of existing parallel processing systems: Our computational procedures are really sequential, as evidenced by any book on numerical analysis. Lately some completely parallel algorithms have been developed — mostly for problems which are inherently parallel, e.g., Ballistic Missile Defense. For others, even with ingenuity, the algorithms are hardly completely parallel (or purely sequential). There will always be parts which can be done concurrently but also parts which must proceed sequentially, at least for jobs which are not inherently parallel. In the SIMD systems mentioned previously all the elements except one would be idle during sequential parts; this is the case of *sequentialization*.

Hence, we conclude that instead of trying to bend natural algorithms in order to avoid sequentialization, we should build a hardware which adapts itself as easily as possible to the mixed nature of algorithms and then develop programs for those algorithms. Such systems have been built and are explained next.

Basic Model. The idea behind an alternating-sequential-parallel (ASP) system is to alternate the sequential and parallel steps of a job, and to try to minimize, instead of eliminate completely, the sequential steps of a program. It is clear that such combined programs will show higher speedups if the changeover between sequential and parallel steps can be done rapidly. We will describe hardware which does just that.

The hardware for an ASP system was built recently [Te82]. A simplified model of its structure is shown in Fig. 5.4(a) and its mode of operation in Fig. 5.4(b).

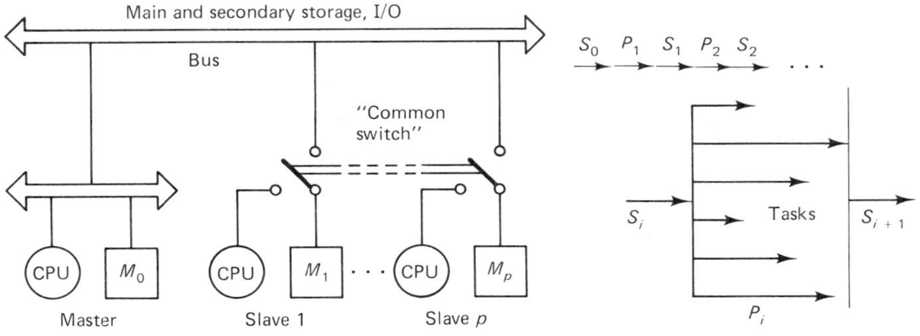

Figure 5.4 (a) Block diagram of ASP. (b) ASP processing.

Initially the "common switch" in Fig 5.4(a) is "up"; all p private memories $M_1, \ldots, M_p$ are part of the master's address space so that it can assign and deposit programs and data there [step S_0 in Fig. 5.4(b)]. With the common switch "down" each slave works on its own local memory; this is a parallel step [P in Fig. 5.4(b)]. When all slaves have finished, the common switch changes into its vertical position and the master takes over, transfers data between or into the slaves, and starts another P step. The sequential and parallel steps alternate [Fig. 5.4(b)] until the job is finished and a new one initiated by the master.

At the end of every sequential step, the master broadcasts the starting address of the first instruction to the program counters of all slaves and WAITs (this instruction exists in most microprocessors and effectively removes the master). When all slaves complete their tasks, a signal is sent to the master, activating it (from the next point in the control program, as stored in its program counter). The slaves WAIT. Since in both cases a bit write changes the WAIT into a GO command, *no interrupt handling is necessary and the time of switchover is extremely short* (this is termed read/write bit-handshaking).

The ASP structure has many novel features as compared to other parallel systems. SIMD systems, such as Illiac, have a single control unit which produces the (single) instruction microsequence and broadcasts it to all (64) processing elements. ASP has (p + 1) control units, so that at any time p possibly different microsequences may be observed. The processing elements of Illiac are nonstandard and thus costly units, while the slaves of ASP are off-the-shelf microprocessors. The units of Illiac can route (exchange) data among themselves; the slaves of ASP can exchange data during sequential steps, that is, by the master. Illiac is slowed down by sequentialization; ASP is built for it. For Illiac, special languages such as "Glypnir" had to be developed; ADA is the language for ASP. The data outlay for Illiac is complicated because it must be such that routing is minimized; data are stored in ASP simply as "slices."

Tightly coupled MIMD systems (e.g., C.mmp) have a common memory, to which the processing elements have access through a (crossbar) switch. The slaves of an ASP do not have access to the memory of the master, and there is no crossbar switch. Since the scheduling of ASP by the master is part of the control program, no task synchronization is needed, no deadlocks can occur, and special operating-system primitives (semaphores, etc.) are not needed.

In loosely coupled MIMD systems (e.g., Cm*) each address is mapped to a common address space. Each slave has access to all of the memory. In ASP only the master may access all of the memory; the slaves cannot. Most importantly, in loosely coupled MIMD systems messages are exchanged between the slaves using interrupts and handshaking. In ASP, only some messages can be exchanged between the slaves; the changeover between parallel and sequential steps is done extremely fast—not as in MIMD.

Both MIMD types have really independent computers; ASP does not.

Since at any one time the slaves may execute different instructions, there are no single-instruction streams (in lock-step). They work on a single program instead of many, and there is no common access to memory and no real sharing of resources — the system is not MIMD either. *The system represents a completely new concept* (although a tightly coupled MIMD system could be made to work in an ASP mode).

It has been shown that ASP is neither SIMD nor MIMD. In West Germany an ASP system was actually built [KK79] by the Siemens Company and called SMS 201. We will discuss it next.

SMS 201 consists of a Data-General Eclipse as master and 128 Intel-8080's as slaves, connected by a common bus. On the basis of the experience gained by running programs on SMS 201, the following problems were identified and the following changes were made in the system assembled [Te82] at Wayne State University in Detroit:

1. SMS 201 is not symmetric, i.e., the master is a different computer, much larger than the slaves. Since availability and reliability are of great concern, the system should be symmetric.
2. The common switch of SMS 201 is rather complicated; in ASP it can be constructed from direct-memory-access units. Using them ensures that each slave is represented by a small number of addresses thus allowing a very large memory space. They also facilitate broadcast and block transfer of data over the bus.
3. SMS 201 has an off-line operating system. For on-line processing a real-time operating system is needed.

4. Each of the "parallel instructions" of SMS 201 translates into a multiprogramming-type interrupt with resulting large overhead times. ADA uses tasks which correspond to the manner in which ASP works.

Advantages over Other Systems. The following are advantages of ASP over SIMD and MIMD systems.

1. ASP is completely symmetric, and even the master may be replaced. Thus, *the reliability (availability) is much higher.*
2. There are no shared resources. The bus is used only by the master. The local memories are used by the master during the S steps, by the slaves during the P steps. Thus, *no deadlock is possible, no locks and semaphores are needed, and the operating system will not be too complicated.*
3. *Programming ASP is very simple.* As a matter of fact, it can be programmed in ADA the new language [DoD83] developed by the U.S. Department of Defense. Compilers for ADA only started appearing recently, but since there are similarities between ADA and Pascal, the latter is used in this book; the reader should find it relatively easy to translate them at a later time.
4. The *speedup* was computed, and at least for the cases of linear algebra that were checked in [Wa82], it was reasonably high, sometimes approaching the optimal value.
5. Present technology (LSI and VLSI) favors microprocessors because they require no special logic and are mass produced. ASP is built from such standard units and *is thus rather cost effective.*

The main reason that parallel systems have not been accepted lies in the need for extensive reprogramming, in rather unusual languages. Next, we will show how to program ASP.

To see how humans calculate, let us visualize the process of walking around a block. The mind probably instructs the legs to walk in a straight line to the next corner, and while the legs obey (and move simultaneously, concurrently and thus in parallel), the mind (the "master") can be dealing with other problems.

Arriving at the corner, the mind takes over and on the basis of information provided by the eyes, directs the legs on the next part of the walk. If we stop, the master is working and planning, but the legs ("slaves") are at rest. The decision having been made, the roles will be reversed again, with the legs working and the master either working or not. If this goes on for some time, we have a model of ASP processing. Another example is eating: Both hands can be used simultaneously to put the food into the mouth, but swallowing is sequential.

Quite generally calculations also consist of parts which may proceed independently and parts which are interdependent and thus inherently sequential. We should adapt the hardware to this mixed nature of algorithms and not force it to be done either completely sequential or completely parallel. This was not done in parallel-processing systems, and since a complete parallelization was attempted, the results were rather disappointing. (This observation holds also for computers which were specifically proposed for power system problems [EPRI77].)

Examples. For describing ASP programs we will use a notation which closely follows Fig. 5.4. Thus, the ith parallel step will be named Pi, the jth sequential step Sj. The operations themselves will be explained in words or the usual mathematical notation.

We will discuss two examples: first a very simple one to introduce the notation and later the diakoptics method.

In the first example, suppose we have to compute $y = \Sigma\, c_i \cdot \exp(x_i)$; $i = 1, \ldots, 80$ on an ASP with $p = 8$ slaves. Rewrite y as:

$$y = \Sigma\, \Sigma\, c_i \cdot \exp(x_i); \quad i = j \cdot q \tag{5.58}$$

where the double sum is for $q = 1, \ldots, 8$ (q is the number of the slave) in the outer sum and $j = 1, \ldots, 10$ in the inner sum. The program for computing it would be as follows:

S0: Transfer c_i and x_i, for $i = (q - 1) \cdot 10 + 1$ to $10 \cdot q$, to slave q ($q = 1, \ldots, 8$). Thus, c_i and x_i, for $i = 1$ to 10, would be transferred to slave 1, for $i = 11$ to 20 to slave 2, etc. A "program" to compute the sum of the corresponding ten products would also be transferred to all slaves (by broadcasting it).

P1: Each of the eight slaves computes its partial sum, say, $y^{(q)}$, for slave q.

S1: The master gathers these partial sums and computes

$$y = \Sigma\, y^{(q)}; \qquad q\Sigma = 1, \ldots, 8$$

in its (main) store. (In this case the program is so simple that two sequential steps and a single parallel step will suffice.)

The measure of success of any algorithm is the achieved speedup. It was found that it is much simpler to calculate its inverse, which we will call the *time-reduction ratio*, defined for any algorithm through

$$\rho = \frac{t_p}{t_s} \tag{5.59}$$

where t_p is the time to solve the problem on ASP, t_s the time on a sequential computer. Optimally, ρ should be $1/p$, i.e., the use of p slaves should reduce the time p-fold; practice shows that $\rho > 1/p$. The time on ASP includes time t_s required for all sequential steps (done now on p slaves) and in addition the time $\tilde{t}$ [see Fig. 5.4(b)] for equalization of tasks and transfer of w words of information. Thus

$$\rho = \frac{t_s/p + \tilde{t}}{t_s} = 1/p + \tilde{t}/t_s$$

This shows why we prefer to compute ρ instead of the speedup; the calculation is simpler. The lower the additional term $\tilde{t}/t_s$, the better.

The times are estimated by counting the number of operations, Ω.

A valid criticism of results from the complexity theory is that it does not include data transfer. To be more practical, we may include τ as the time needed to transfer a word over the bus and π as the synchronization time. The latter includes waiting for the longest task [Fig. 5.4(b)] and starting an S step following completion of a P step.

Let us denote by ω the time required to perform a single addition and a single multiplication. For a widely used minicomputer ω, τ, and π are 6.8, 0.08, and 13.6 μs, respectively. We also use per-unit values: $\tilde{\tau} = \tau/\omega$ and $\tilde{\pi} = \pi/\omega$, which for the minicomputer mentioned are $\tilde{\pi} = 2$ and $\tilde{\tau} = 1/85$, respectively. Since in general π is by far the longest time, we postulate a *parallelization principle*:

The algorithm should be scheduled so as to minimize the number of required synchronizations.

In the preceding program, each time we start a sequential step, we need one synchronization π. We transfer 80 c_is and 80 x_is in S0 and 8 y^qs in S1. Since the y^qs must be summed, altogether $168\tau + 4\omega$ are needed for S0 and S1. If we assume that we need 10 terms (9ω) for each $\exp(x_i)$, then 100ω are required for P1 in each slave. The ratio is $\rho = (104\omega + 168\tau + \pi)/(800\omega) \cong 1/8 + (168\tilde{\tau} + \tilde{\pi})/800 \cong 1/8 + 4/800 \cong 1/8$. The speedup is thus approaching the ideal value of $1/\rho \cong 8$.

The second example is that of diakoptics, as discussed in Chapter 3. To be more specific, suppose we "cut" the 14-bus network in Fig. 3.8 so that nodes (a to g), (h to k) and (l to n) are in each section. Two cuts are done: one through lines 9, 10, and 14, another through 12, 16, and 20. The equations to be solved are (3.24) to (3.28). They can use a matrix as shown in Fig. 5.5, where x, $-$, and $+$ replace the nonzero admittance values, -1, and $+1$, respectively.

The six zero blocks were not shown, since they will not be stored at all. Only the diagonal of $-\mathbf{Z}_t$ will be stored, and some form of sparse

	1 *a*	2 *b*	3 *c*	4 *d*	5 *e*	6 *f*	7 *g*	8 *h*	9 *i*	10 *j*	11 *k*	12 *l*	13 *m*	14 *n*	15 1	16 2	17 3	18 4	19 5	20 6				
1 *a*	x	x	0	x	0	0	0								0	0	0	0	0	0		v_a		i_1^g
2 *b*	x	x	x	x	x	0	0								0	0	0	0	0	0		v_b		0
3 *c*	0	x	x	x	0	0	0								0	0	0	0	0	0		v_c		0
4 *d*	0	x	x	x	x	0	0								−	0	0	0	0	0		v_d		0
5 *e*	x	x	0	x	x	0	0								0	−	0	0	0	0		v_e		0
6 *f*	0	0	0	0	0	x	x								0	0	0	0	0	0		v_f		0
7 *g*	0	0	0	x	0	x	x								0	0	0	0	0	0		v_g		0
8 *h*								x	0	0	x				+	0	+	−	0	0		v_h		0
9 *i*								0	x	x	0				0	+	0	0	−	−		v_i		0
10 *j*								0	x	x	x				0	0	0	0	0	0	*	v_j	=	0
11 *k*								x	0	x	x				0	0	0	0	0	0		v_k		0
12 *l*												x	x	0	0	0	0	+	0	0		v_l		0
13 *m*												x	x	x	0	0	0	0	+	0		v_m		0
14 *n*												0	x	x	0	0	0	0	0	+		v_n		i_2^g
15 1	0	0	0	−	0	0	0	+	0	0	0	0	0	0	x	0	0	0	0	0		i_1		0
16 2	0	0	0	0	−	0	0	0	+	0	0	0	0	0	0	x	0	0	0	0		i_2		0
17 3	0	0	0	0	0	0	−	+	0	0	0	0	0	0	0	0	x	0	0	0		i_3		0
18 4	0	0	0	0	0	0	0	−	0	0	0	+	0	0	0	0	0	x	0	0		i_4		0
19 5	0	0	0	0	0	0	0	0	−	0	0	0	+	0	0	0	0	0	x	0		i_5		0
20 6	0	0	0	0	0	0	0	0	−	0	0	0	0	+	0	0	0	0	0	x		i_6		0

Figure 5.5

storage scheme will be used to store the incidence matrix $\mathbf{A}_t$. For instance, we could use the fact that each column of $\mathbf{A}_t$ has exactly one +1 and one −1, storing it as

1	2	3	4	5	6
−d	−e	−g	−h	−i	−i
h	i	h	l	m	n

where letters will be substituted by numbers.

We will not use sparsity and assume that each of the $(p + 1)$ blocks has the same size n-by-n [see Eq. (3.24) and Fig. 3.11]. The program is:

S0: Transfer $\mathbf{Y}_1, \mathbf{Y}_2, \ldots, \mathbf{Y}_p$ of $\mathbf{Y}_r$ to the slaves and broadcast $\mathbf{A}_t$ to all p slaves.

P1: Each slave $q = 1, \ldots, p$ factors its matrix $\mathbf{Y}_q$ according to $\mathbf{Y}_q = \mathbf{L}_q * \mathbf{U}_q$ and solves Eq. (3.27) for $\mathbf{F}_q$ by $\mathbf{L}_q * \mathbf{H}_q = \mathbf{A}_q$ followed by $\mathbf{U}_q * \mathbf{F}_q = \mathbf{H}_q$.

Matrices $\mathbf{E}_q$ are computed by Eq. (3.28): $\mathbf{E}_q = \mathbf{A}_q^{\mathrm{T}} * \mathbf{F}_q$

S1: The p matrices $\mathbf{E}_q$ are transferred to the master, subtracted there from $\mathbf{Y}_{p+1}$ which is then broadcast to all slaves. Vector $\mathbf{x}_{p+1}$ computed from $\mathbf{L}_{p+1} * \mathbf{U}_{p+1} * \mathbf{x}_{p+1} = \mathbf{b}_{p+1}$ is also broadcast.

P2: Each of the p slaves solves $\mathbf{L}_q * \mathbf{U}_q * \mathbf{x}_q = \mathbf{b}_q - \mathbf{A}_q * \mathbf{x}_{p+1}$.

S2: The resulting subvectors $\mathbf{x}_q$ are transferred to the master.

Counting only the more time-consuming operation-counts leads to: $\Omega \cong [p \cdot n^3 \cdot \tau] + [\omega \cdot n^3/3 + \omega \cdot n^3] + [(p+1) \cdot n^2 \cdot \tau + p \cdot n^2 \cdot \omega + \omega \cdot n^3/3 + 2 \cdot n^2 \cdot \omega] + [p \cdot n^2 \cdot \omega] + [p \cdot n \cdot \tau]$ and since sequentially $\Omega \cong (p \cdot n)^3/3$ also to $\rho \cong \dfrac{5+p}{p^3} + \dfrac{6}{n \cdot p^2} + \dfrac{3 \cdot \tilde{\tau}}{p^2} + \dfrac{6 \cdot \tilde{\pi}}{p^3 \cdot n^3}$

For $p = 10$ and $n = 1000$, we have $\rho \cong 0.015$ and a speedup of 66.6... This is higher than expected and will be explained later.

The better-known algorithm explained in the 5 points at end of section 3.2 was also programmed. The results of running both programs on the 14-bus network and other runs lead to the following comparison:

- Algorithm 1 is better for an ASP system, since it operates on smaller (sub)-matrices during a parallel step whereas algorithm 2 operates on the large $\mathbf{Y}_r$ matrix in the master, i.e., *serially.*
- Algorithm 2 is better for a single sequential computer, since the number of steps is smaller. All parallel tasks of algorithm 1 (and there are many of them) are done in parallel and would have to be sequentialized if a single computer is available.
- The overall conclusion is that algorithm 1 is better for an ASP, whereas algorithm 2 is better for a single computer.
- Another conclusion is that *ASP is an idea whose time has come.*

Some recent technical developments indicate that ASP or some other type of multiprocessor will most likely replace the process-control computers presently used in power-dispatch control centers.

I refer here primarily to a new "microframe" computer (the iAPX432) and real-time languages such as ADA or Modula. Reference [Or83] describes this computer and some features of ADA. The point I want to make is that a utility with a good engineering staff could assemble a multiprocessing system from a number of such computers and program it in a real-time language. The systems would then be faster, more reliable, more available, and expandable at a lower cost; however, this means that utility companies would have to abandon their natural conservatism.

In this section some of the programs to be run on such systems will be discussed. This should allay the fears concerning software, programming, etc.*

An ASP system if installed for electric power control would have at its center the programs in Fig. 5.6. Let us review them.

The main purpose of the computer is to form a data base for operational control, load-sharing between neighboring companies, optimizing energy generation and distribution (costs), issuance of strategies in the event of disturbances (e.g., blackouts), analysis of network history, logging, pricing, etc. The data base must be consistent, accurate, and reliable. It cannot rely solely on measured values, since these contain errors and may even be downright wrong. Therefore, an SE program provides for filtering and correcting the measured values. At the completion of the SE program, the dispatcher has a good approximation to the state of the network, prefiltered, relevant, and checked. Since these data form the basis of the other programs, SE is central to electric power control (Fig. 5.6).

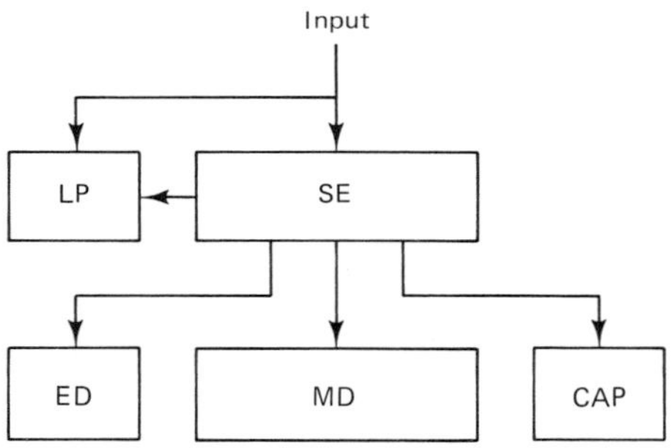

Figure 5.6 Control programs.

It is first used for checking input data against low and high boundaries. This is the limit-checking program, LP. It is also used by the economic dispatch (ED) program, the contingency analysis program (CAP) and the monitoring, alarm, and display (MD) programs.

The aim of ED programs is to adjust generation so that all loads are supplied and the cost of generation is minimal; in short, it is an optimization program. The (security) constraints may modify considerably the minimum operating cost. It may also be required to compute by CAP the effects of losing one or more lines of the network or even to find that branch (or branches) which, if removed, would cause other parts of the

* L. Richter, Y. Wallach, "Remarks on Real-Time Operating Systems," *Microprogramming and Microprocessing*, Vol. 7, 1981, pp. 304-11. © 1981 by North-Holland Publ. Co. Used with permission.

network to be overloaded. The ED program suggests the best generation of energy. CAP recommends corrective actions in case of contingencies: generation rescheduling, line switching, load shedding, etc.

MD will monitor line diagrams, lists of de-energized systems, circuit breakers and relays, etc. It will include an alarm system for any voltage, current, or power outside its limits and a display program. It will also include supporting activities such as interchange billing, energy accounting and tariffication, printing of reports and logs, scheduling of work orders and maintenance, and accounting. It relies heavily on sorting.

Two observations are important to make:

1. The programs are simple, but the data size enormous. Consider the ED program. As will be shown in Chapter 6, the steady-state of the network is adjusted iteratively until an optimum is achieved. The load-flow program to be used was shown to be a set of nonlinear, complex, algebraic equations of size 2000-by-2000 (on the average).

   CAP has either to compute short-circuit currents or run load flows for every contingency. The size of the problem is thus readily appreciated.
2. The network changes dynamically (circuits in/out, generation up/down, etc.). The programs mentioned will therefore normally proceed according to some *cycle*, say, LP, SE, ED, CAP, and MD, but should a real contingency appear, the entire data base is worthless (because it changes continually). Hence in cases of emergencies, network data should not be stored.

Efficient ASP versions of the above problems are as follows: CAP and LF will use an algorithm described in Chapter 8; SE will use a special decomposition technique and orthogonalization; short-circuit calculations (Chapter 3) may be based on diakoptics; LP and MD are simple and will be done by the master.

It was found [RW81] that a cycle for networks of $n = 1000$ would require a time of

$$t_1 \cong 9.75 \cdot 10^{-6} \cdot \frac{n^2}{p} \text{ minutes} \tag{5.60}$$

For 1000 buses, this would be about $10/p$ minutes. On the other hand, for small and/or dense systems the time is higher than that indicated by Eq. (5.60).

Let us now compute the time required by the remaining programs, if done by the (single) master. The number of measurements is $8n$ (for all lines) and $2n$ (for all nodes). Assuming 1.65 μsec for a single comparison and that LP checks each value against a minimum and maximum point, it needs $\tilde{t}_2 = 10n \cdot 3.3 = 33n$ μsec.

The output will use "smart" terminals which normally include 64 kbytes of memory, work at about 9600 baud, have raster scan and good color quality. They will not use more time than LP. Additionally, MD would have to sort the data to be displayed, but this time is known to be inversely proportional to p. Thus if p displays are assumed, another $\tilde{t}_2$ will be needed for output. The total time is $t_2 \cong 66n$ μsec.

Comparing t_1 and t_2, we conclude that if we consider only the workload cycle, the master will need much less time for completing limit checking and displays than the slaves need for SE, ED, and CAP. The master may thus be used for processing interrupts.

Let us assume $n = 1000$. Then $t_1 = 10/p$ minutes. If a cycle is to be completed once every minute (this was once required in the United Kingdom), then $p =$ *10 slaves would be sufficient.*

The model of computation on ASP is also to some degree that of "distributed" processing. In this case we envisage each of the p slaves to service a geographical area and the master to be the control-center computer. We obviously cannot work here in the ASP mode, because the distances are large and require different times of transfer. Instead, we might let the master initiate the same calculation in every slave and let them interrupt the master *whenever they have completed their task*. Such interrupts will be transferred over dedicated or common telephone lines, and problems such as how to ensure the shortest route have to be solved. Still, the ideas of how to solve problems in parallel are the same or similar to those of ASP and will be treated together in the rest of the book.

5.5 A DECOMPOSITION METHOD*

This section follows essentially [WHB81].

Let us start with a preliminary but basic remark. Least-squares estimation is defined so that under certain conditions (to be discussed), the network may be divided into p subnetworks. Each slave may then be assigned a single subnetwork which it estimates by applying any of the algorithms described earlier. The results obtained by the p slaves are then transferred to the master, which coordinates them.
The conditions mentioned are:

1. The "subnetworks" result from a fictitious cutting of lines. *Only* lines on whose two ends both active and reactive powers are measured may be cut.

---

* This section essentially follows Y. Wallach, E. Handschin, C. Bongers, "An Efficient Parallel-Processing Method for Power-System State Estimation," *Trans. IEEE*, Vol. PAS-100, 1981, pp. 4402-4406. © 1981 by IEEE. Used with permission.

2. Every partial network must obey the *observability principle*, which in a simplified form may be stated as follows: In order to estimate a network, its Jacobian matrix **J** must not have linearly dependent columns.

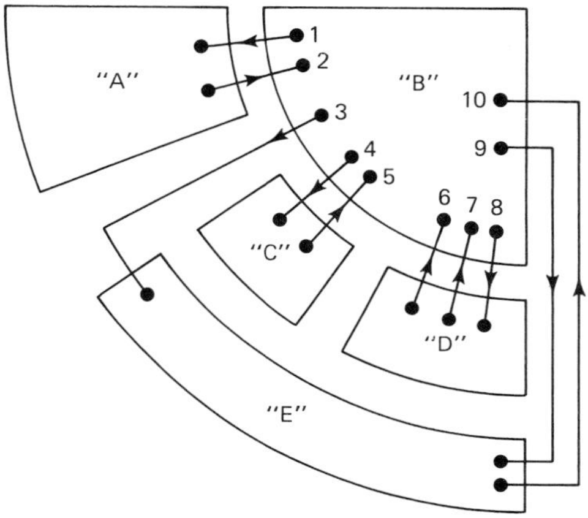

(a)

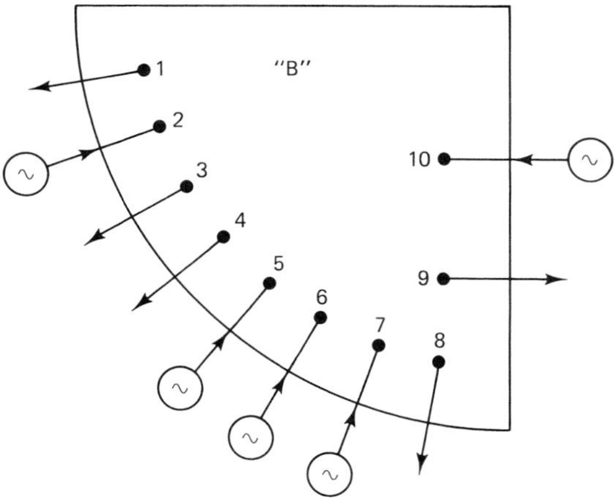

(b)

Figure 5.7 A network and a partial network.

The justification for subdividing the network (see Fig. 5.7) is as follows.

The solution for subnetwork B in Fig. 5.7(b) is completely equivalent to that in Fig. 5.7(a). We have treated each line through which power flows out of subnetwork B as a load node and each node through which power flows into B as a generator node. Because of condition 1, we may do this in every line which was cut; because of condition 2, we may be assured that enough measurements were taken so that all subnetworks can be estimated.

Basically, a subnetwork such as B in Fig. 5.7 *does not "know"* that it is part of a larger network. The measured values for the additional fictitious load and generator nodes are in no way different from its internal nodes. All show errors to be leveled out by the state-estimation algorithm.

Obviously we can solve the partial state-estimation problems on different computers—either geographically distributed or as a local ASP system.

The algorithm consists of the S1 and S2 steps done by the master and the P1 step done by all p slaves.

S1: The master "divides" the network data among the p slaves, checking first that both conditions are obeyed. Other data, such as those needed to compute $\mathbf{f}(\mathbf{x})$ for

$$(\mathbf{J}^{\mathrm{T}} * \mathbf{J}) * \Delta\mathbf{x} = \mathbf{J}^{\mathrm{T}} * [\mathbf{z} - \mathbf{f}(\mathbf{x})]$$

are also transferred. If the number of values to be transferred through the bus is m, we need the "time" $m\tau$ for it. (We assume that SE programs are stored in the local memories, prior to the activation of step S1.)

P1: Each slave estimates its subnetwork. As we will see, it needs $i \cong 3$ iterations for it; assuming an even distribution of $h = m/p$ data per slave, i.e., matrices of order h-by-h, we need altogether

$$\Omega_1 = \frac{3h^3}{3} = \frac{m^3}{p^3}$$

operations for factorization. Since back-substitution is proportional to m^2, computing $\mathbf{f}(\mathbf{x})$ to m (m is assumed large even for the subnetworks), the times for these two operations may be neglected in comparison to Ω_1.

S2: The master collects the data, for which it needs the time $t_2 = m \cdot \tau$.

Next we calculate the time needed by a single computer. We will assume that in this case all data movement may be neglected, so that the time for estimating the (uncut) network is $\Omega_s \cong (3m^3/3) = m^3$.

The time reduction ratio is therefore

$$\rho \cong \frac{(m^3/p^3)\omega + 2m\tau + \pi}{m^3\omega} = \frac{1}{p^3} + \frac{2\tilde{\tau}}{m^2} + \frac{\tilde{\pi}}{m^3} \qquad (5.61)$$

Since we consider only large networks, we may neglect the terms with $\tilde{\tau}$ and $\tilde{\pi}$, and for execution on an ASP, we get

$$\rho \cong \frac{1}{p^3} \tag{5.62}$$

This exceptionally good ratio is obtained because

1. Each slave works most of the time independently of and concurrently with other slaves. It inverts the matrix $\mathbf{A} = \mathbf{J}^T * \mathbf{J}$ and computes i times $\mathbf{A} * \Delta\mathbf{x} = \mathbf{b}$. During this entire time, it works completely autonomously; it has no connection with other computers and needs none.
2. The data to be transferred initially by the master and gathered by it at the end of computation are transferred by blocks, hence rather fast.
3. Only one synchronization is needed. We thus obey the parallelization principle.
4. We will show later that convergence is the same as for the uncut network. If this network is divided evenly, no reduction of speedup is due to asymmetry of tasks.
5. We assumed that $1/p$ is the optimum ratio. It stands to reason that with, say, $p = 10$ slaves we cannot compute faster than 10 times on a single computer. In our case, though, the speedup would be about 1000. The explanation is that in our case practically all the time is taken by elimination, which is proportional to n^3 of the matrix. Thus a network of size n/p needs only n^3/p^3 operations—a very low ρ indeed.

In actual practice, the ratio will not be so good, because of the following factors:

1. The matrices are very sparse, so that their factorization is proportional to n or n^2 rather than n^3. The ratio is thus between $1/p$ and $1/p^2$.
2. It might be argued that since we have $p + 1$ computers (p slaves and a master), the optimum ratio should be $1/(p + 1)$ instead of $1/p$.

The time required for completion is directly proportional to convergence. Should we need more iterations for any of the subnetworks, this would decrease speedup. The examples below show that this is not the case.

Let us add here that this algorithm can also be used on single, stand-alone process-control computers. In fact, the division principle and the algorithm based on it are independent of the number of processors and can be used by a single processor as well. Suppose the network is fictitiously torn into k approximately equal parts, and let a single computer estimate each subnetwork sequentially in turn. It will require about $(n/k)^3$ operations for each of the subnetworks and approximately $k(n/k)^3 = n^3/k^2$ for all k subnetworks. For practical networks, k can be at least 10, thus reducing the solution time 100-fold. This is certainly a considerable speedup but actually will be reduced by the following factors:

1. The sparsity: If we assume that for extremely sparse matrices, $\Omega \cong n^c$ with $1 < c < 3$, then

$$\rho \cong \frac{(m^c/p^c)\cdot\omega + 2m\cdot\tau + \pi}{m^c\cdot\omega} = \frac{1}{p^c} + \frac{2\tilde{\tau}}{m^{c-1}} + \frac{\tilde{\pi}}{m^c}$$

2. The value k cannot be made arbitrarily large, since this would violate the two conditions mentioned above.
3. Tearing introduces "additional nodes"; for example, the subnetwork a of the 14-bus IEEE network (Fig. 5.8) has for case 0 nodes 2, 4, 10, 14 in addition to 1, 5, 6, 11, 12, 13 and subnetwork b has nodes 1, 5, 11, 13 in addition to nodes 2, 3, 4, 7, 8, 9, 10, 14. For the original network n was 14. For subnetwork a, $n = 10$; and for subnetwork b, $n = 12$. Thus, the "time" would be $10^3 + 12^3 = 2728$ instead of 2744, i.e., there is practically no computational gain. It should be noted that this resulted from the network chosen being very small and highly interconnected. However, for practical large networks the theoretical gain of k^2 will be only insubstantially reduced by the inclusion of the additional nodes.

It has thus been shown that *the proposed method leads to high gain in all state-estimation procedures as currently used, without any modification of existing hardware or software.*

In order to prove the merits of the method, the IEEE 14- and 30-bus networks were simulated. The 14-bus system [Fig. 5.8(a)] was cut into two subnetworks in a number of ways denoted as cases 0, 1, 2, and 3. In each case the solution began from a "flat start" and *needed three iterations of the Newton–Raphson procedure in order to converge.* The results obtained for the uncut as well as for the two subnetworks in each of the four cases are shown in Tables 5.8, 5.9, and 5.10. Compared to the uncut networks, these show a remarkable closeness of estimated values.

It was shown that the measure of closeness of solution is the sum of the squares of errors $U(\mathbf{x})$ mostly normalized in order for the results to be independent of the number of measurements and unknowns. For our four cases, $U(\mathbf{x})$ is shown in Table 5.11. All values are so small that we reach

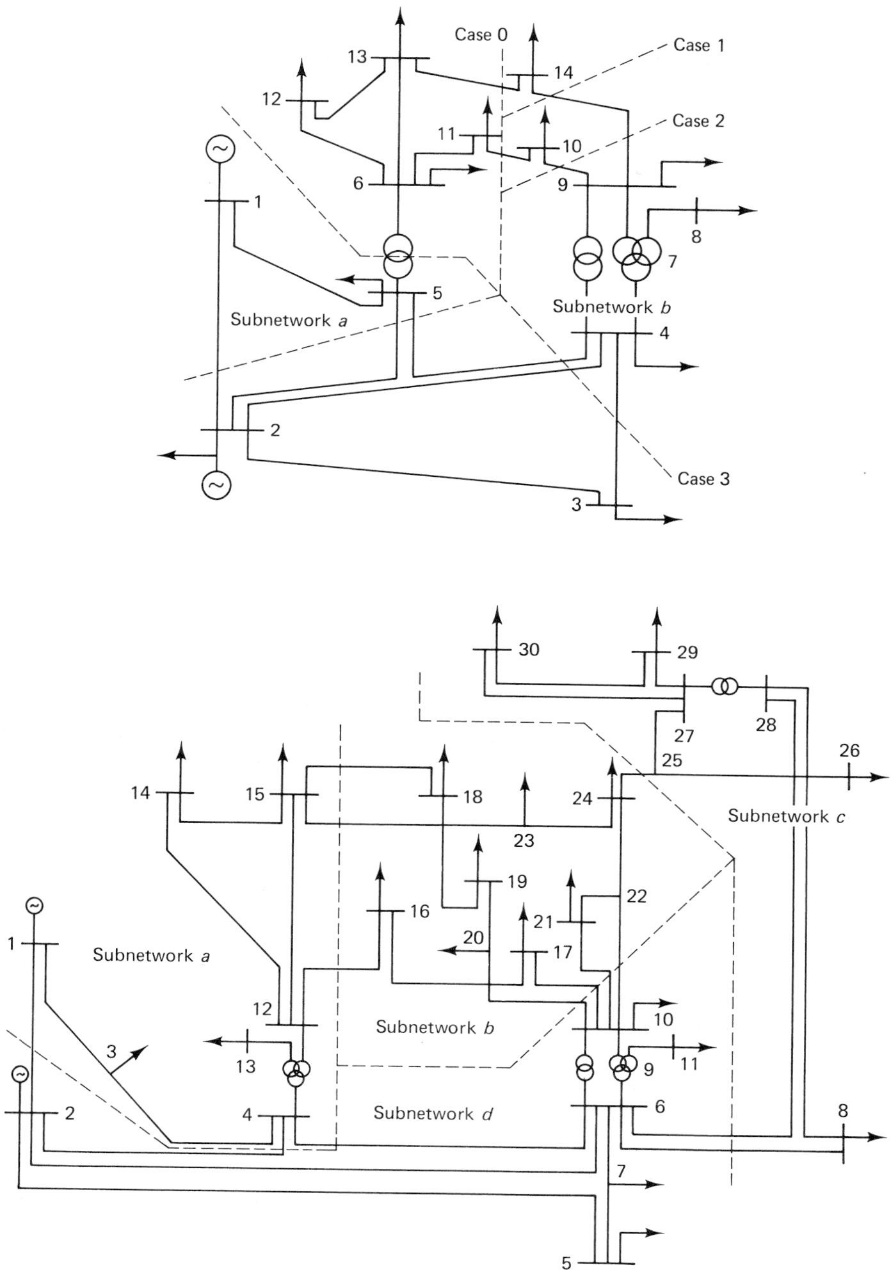

Figure 5.8 Cutting the 14-bus and 30-bus networks.

TABLE 5.8 Comparison of estimated voltages v_a, v_b, in subnetworks a and b to v_0 of the uncut network (voltages v_0, v_a, v_b, in pu values).

Bus		Case 0		Case 1		Case 2		Case 3	
	v_0	v_a	v_b	v_a	v_b	v_a	v_b	v_a	v_b
1	1.061	1.065	1.061	1.061	1.059	1.059	1.059	1.060	—
2	1.046	1.050	1.046	1.046	1.045	1.044	1.046	1.045	1.049
3	1.011	—	1.010	—	1.011	—	1.012	1.010	1.014
4	1.019	1.020	1.017	1.018	1.019	1.021	1.020	1.017	1.020
5	1.020	1.023	1.019	1.020	1.021	1.021	1.022	1.020	1.022
6	1.070	1.070	—	1.070	—	1.071	—	1.069	1.070
7	1.059	—	1.062	—	1.064	—	1.065	—	1.061
8	1.091	—	1.092	—	1.088	—	1.091	—	1.090
9	1.055	—	1.056	1.053	1.057	1.058	1.060	—	1.055
10	1.050	1.052	1.052	1.048	1.053	1.052	1.056	—	1.051
11	1.056	1.056	1.058	1.057	1.061	1.058	—	—	1.056
12	1.055	1.055	—	1.056	—	1.056	—	—	1.056
13	1.048	1.050	1.050	1.051	—	1.049	—	—	1.052
14	1.035	1.038	1.038	1.035	1.035	1.036	1.044	—	1.035

the following conclusion: *We may cut the networks in any way we deem best provided all subnetworks obey the decomposition conditions.*

The next question is whether a network can be split into more than two networks. To this effect, the 30-bus network [Fig. 5.8(b)] was divided into four subnetworks and the partial solutions compared to the overall (convergence was again obtained in three iterations, in all cases). The values of $U(\mathbf{x})$ as they appear in Table 5.11 are so small that we may draw the following conclusion: *The network may be cut into $p > 2$ subnetworks*, thus providing work for all p slaves.

In case 0 in Fig. 5.8(b) we have reversed the power flow of line $1-2$ (made it -156.7). The result was that

1. Subnetwork A had a very large cost, U.
2. The normalized residual flow in line $1-2$ was unusually large.

This shows that both detection and identification of bad data are feasible in this scheme.

Whether bad data can be detected by the measurement system of a subnetwork depends mainly on the local redundancy, defined for each bus j through $\eta_j = m_j/n_j$, where m_j comprises the number of measurements

TABLE 5.9 The estimated real-power flows in the uncut (p_0) and divided networks (p_a, p_b), always per MW.

Line from – to		Case 0		Case 1		Case 2		Case 3	
	p_0 (uncut net)	p_a	p_b	p_a	p_b	p_a	p_b	p_a	p_b
1 – 2	156.5	156.7	156.3	157.1	156.3	159.7	155.2	155.1	—
1 – 5	75.8	75.9	—	74.8	—	74.4	—	75.1	—
2 – 3	72.9	—	72.3	—	72.2	—	71.7	72.9	—
2 – 4	56.4	—	56.4	—	55.9	—	55.5	56.5	54.9
2 – 5	42.0	42.3	41.9	40.5	41.5	39.0	41.3	41.7	—
3 – 4	−22.7	—	−22.1	—	−22.5	—	−22.4	−22.5	−23.6
4 – 5	−60.5	−66.6	−60.7	−62.9	−60.3	−61.8	−59.6	−62.2	−59.8
4 – 7	29.4	—	29.3	—	29.4	—	28.6	—	26.1
4 – 9	16.6	—	16.2	—	16.0	—	16.0	—	15.6
5 – 6	44.9	42.6	—	43.7	—	43.6	—	44.2	43.4
6 – 11	8.6	7.3	—	9.0	—	7.6	—	—	6.6
6 – 12	8.4	7.7	—	7.6	—	7.3	—	—	8.4
6 – 13	20.4	17.4	—	17.5	—	18.4	—	—	19.4
7 – 8	−1.5	—	−2.9	—	−1.8	—	−0.7	—	−0.4
7 – 9	28.1	—	26.6	—	25.0	—	26.6	—	29.2
9 – 10	5.8	—	4.6	—	4.8	3.6	1.7	—	5.3
9 – 14	10.2	—	9.0	8.6	8.5	9.3	13.3	—	10.9
10 – 11	−3.3	−5.5	−3.1	−7.4	−3.7	−3.6	—	—	−4.0
12 – 13	2.6	1.6	—	1.7	—	2.5	—	—	1.8
13 – 14	5.5	7.0	4.7	6.6	—	5.7	—	—	5.8

at bus j and at *all* its direct neighbors; n_j is the corresponding number of unknown state variables. A local redundancy of 2 is considered optimal for a sufficient detection probability of bad data.

In state estimation, error control is even more important than speedup. The program is run in the first place in order to remove the measurement errors. Because of this, we might prefer to use orthogonalization instead of factorization in estimating the subnetworks. As shown in earlier sections, this will reduce the errors, but because orthogonalization requires a higher Ω, the speedup may fall even below $1/p$.

State estimation is an on-line program, and we would expect an indication that the matrix is close to being singular. As shown in Section 5.3, singular values could then be used for state-estimation of such partial networks and the covariance matrix $\mathbf{C}$ of Eq. (5.46) would provide an indication of trouble.

TABLE 5.10 The estimated reactive-power flows in the uncut (q_0) and divided networks (q_1, q_b), always per MVAR.

Line from-to	q_0	Case 0		Case 1		Case 2		Case 3	
	uncut network	q_a	q_b	q_a	q_b	q_a	q_b	q_a	q_b
1−2	−20.1	−21.1	−19.8	−19.9	−22.3	−21.1	−23.6	−20.6	—
1−5	3.9	4.7	—	4.0	—	2.7	—	4.1	—
2−3	3.4	—	4.2	—	3.3	—	3.2	3.6	—
2−4	−2.1	—	−1.2	—	−2.5	—	−2.8	−1.2	−0.4
2−5	1.1	2.4	1.8	1.4	−0.1	0.2	0.5	1.6	—
3−4	3.0	—	2.8	—	2.6	—	2.3	3.7	3.9
4−5	16.2	14.6	15.0	15.9	13.2	19.5	16.3	14.7	14.7
4−7	−7.9	—	−10.3	—	−10.1	—	−10.3	—	−8.1
4−9	0.1	—	−0.5	—	−0.5	—	−0.6	—	0.2
5−6	13.0	14.0	—	12.8	—	12.8	—	12.8	13.5
6−11	3.6	3.8	—	2.8	—	3.2	—	—	4.4
6−12	2.3	2.3	—	2.2	—	2.7	—	—	2.0
6−13	8.4	7.1	—	6.7	—	8.7	—	—	5.8
7−8	−18.9	—	−17.6	—	−14.8	—	−15.7	—	−17.7
7−9	4.6	—	6.5	—	6.6	—	5.9	—	5.6
9−10	4.7	—	3.8	—	3.8	5.4	4.3	—	4.2
9−14	3.1	—	2.7	3.1	4.9	4.2	0.2	—	3.2
10−11	−2.0	0.1	−2.3	−1.7	−2.9	−1.7	—	—	−1.6
12−13	1.2	0.9	—	0.8	—	0.9	—	—	0.4
13−14	1.0	0.5	1.4	1.7	—	1.2	--	—	2.3

TABLE 5.11 Normalized cost U^*.

	Normalized $U(\mathbf{x})$ Net a	Net b		Normalized $U(\mathbf{x})$
Uncut net	−1.17		Uncut net	−0.03
Case 0	−0.099	−0.18	Net a	−0.73
Case 1	0.16	0.08	Net b	−1.03
Case 2	−1.03	−0.76	Net c	0.66
Case 3	0.50	−0.25	Net d	0.36

* Y. Wallach, E. Handschin, C. Bongers, "An Efficient Parallel-Processing Method for Power-System State-Estimation," *Trans. IEEE*, Vol. PAS-100, 1981, pp. 4402−6 © 1981 by IEEE. Used with permission.

5.6 NOTES AND PROJECTS

State estimation is a relatively new subject in power system practice, and the material is found in papers rather than in books. A good early exposition can be found in [Ha72]. The book by Lawson and Hansen [LH73] is recommended for further reading and can also be used for the following projects.

We have discussed the normal, orthogonalization and SVD algorithms for solving the state-estimation problem. The four projects below apply to all three:

1. The use of SVD for state estimation is summarized in Eqs. (5.25) and (5.26). As seen there, first the Jacobian is factored as $\mathbf{J} = \mathbf{T} * \mathbf{S} * \mathbf{V}^{\mathrm{T}}$ and then the problem solved by repeatedly calculating

$$\mathbf{S} * \mathbf{V}^{\mathrm{T}} * \Delta\mathbf{x} = \mathbf{T}^{\mathrm{T}} * \mathbf{z} \tag{5.63}$$

Since $\mathbf{T}^{\mathrm{T}} * \mathbf{z}$ is a vector, say, $\mathbf{c}$, $\mathbf{S}^{-1} * (\mathbf{T}^{\mathrm{T}} * \mathbf{z})$ can be obtained simply by dividing every c_i by the corresponding s_i. Thus we have to solve repeatedly

$$\mathbf{V}^{\mathrm{T}} * \Delta\mathbf{x} = \mathbf{b} \quad \text{where} \quad b_i = \frac{c_i}{s_i} \tag{5.64}$$

Additionally, $\mathbf{V}$ is orthonormal ($\mathbf{V} * \mathbf{V}^{\mathrm{T}} = \mathbf{I}$) so that the solution is simply

$$\Delta\mathbf{x} = \mathbf{V} * \mathbf{b} \tag{5.65}$$

The project is then to combine SVD with decomposition so that each partial network is solved by SVD. We would then have the best of all worlds: a fast, efficient program with low error accumulation and swift indication of trouble. Moreover, it could be applied on a single processor, on a parallel or even a distributed system.

The SVD procedure was discussed and listed in Chapter 3. Any reader who is not satisfied with the simple-minded "cutting" of Section 5.5 may find more sophisticated decomposition methods in literature. Reference [VR83] mentions most of them (and has a good general list of references). The project then is to combine the SVD program with any of the decomposition techniques.

2. Another project would be to substitute the square-root-free method of Givens (procedure "sfreegiv") either instead of SVD or in a program which does not decompose the network.

3. Another project would be to write a straightforward least-squares, normal-equations procedure. The only part that is really missing is that of the enlarged Jacobian.
4. Finally, let me remind the reader that bad data have hardly been treated at all and the reader can add them to any of the programs mentioned above.

6 Optimal Power Dispatch

The *objectives* of this chapter are

1. To describe the problem as that of minimizing the cost or losses.
2. To define the Newtonian, **B**-matrix, and gradient algorithms.
3. To provide material for developing programs for the first two of these methods.
4. To suggest using a gradient algorithm for optimum power dispatch on a parallel-system for use in real time.

6.1 INTRODUCTION

The amount of power to be supplied to the network at a given time depends on the consumption. According to the law of conservation of power (and energy), the total generated power equals the total consumed power and losses:

$$\Sigma\, p_i^g = \Sigma\, p_k^c + p_L; \quad i\Sigma = 1, \ldots, n^g; \quad k\Sigma = 1, \ldots, n^c; \tag{6.1}$$

where superscripts g and c denote generation and consumption, respectively, and p_L is the total (active) loss in the network.

Simply stated, if some Δp is added to, say, p_j^g and subtracted from p_m^g, with $j \neq m$, then the sum $\Sigma\, p_i^g$ is not changed. The same applies to the consumed powers. Since p_j^g may have cost more (or less) than p_m^g and only the sums are important, the problem of the optimum or economic dispatch (ED) arises.

When power stations are built, space is normally reserved for adding generators. Thus, we find generators installed at various times and consequently with different efficiencies. Numerically, we are given a different input/output curve for every generator. A typical curve is shown in Fig. 6.1. It has the fuel input (f in, say, Btu/h) as a function of the power output p (in, say, MW), but if the ordinates are multiplied by the cost of one Btu ($/Btu), the result is the fuel cost per hour as a function of power output p. Normally, f can be approximated by (see Table 1.2b) constants c, d, and e where

$$f_i = 0.5 \cdot c_i \cdot p_i^2 + d_i \cdot p_i + e_i \tag{6.2}$$

For different generators these constants are different with $0.04 \leq c \leq 0.07$ and $1.5 \leq d \leq 3$, and all curves of f are mildly quadratic as in Eq. (6.2). The constant e was not mentioned since we will use the *incremental cost* df/dp instead of the fuel cost and in the differentiation of the f curve c disappears: $df/dp = c \cdot p + d$.

Figure 6.1 (a) Fuel cost f. (b) Incremental fuel cost df/dp.

A quadratic equation is a good approximation, but utilities actually use a piecewise quadratic function and df/dp is therefore *piecewise linear*. Function f will consist of five to nine segments, and df/dp may have discontinuities. Note also that generation presents constraints in the form of a minimum and maximum power output, $p_{\min} \equiv p^{\mathrm{m}}$ and $p_{\max} \equiv p^{\mathrm{M}}$.

The consumed powers are forecast. There are long- and short-term forecasts; here only short-term forecasts will be mentioned. These may be calculated every hour and depend on the season (more heat needed in winter than in fall), the time of day (industrial load), as well as the temperature and other factors. All of these factors are only approximations, and the problem is that p^c depends on them to a rather high degree. So it was estimated that a temperature error of 3°F will change the consumed power by 1% and that is about all we are prepared for, since a 2% forecast error might lead either to the use of inefficient, small "peaking" generators (if we need more than was predicted) or to too large a reserve (if we need less than predicted). Whether utilities in fact use predictions or aim for reducing the total generation is another question.

The total cost f_t and power (disregarding losses) are

$$f_t = \Sigma f_i; \ \Sigma p_i^g = \Sigma p_k^c; \ i\Sigma = 0, \ldots, n^g; \ k\Sigma = n^g + 1, \ldots, n \quad (6.3)$$

The minimum would be calculated from $df_t/dp_i = 0$. The sums introduce a constraint and this means that instead of f_t, the function to be differentiated is

$$L = f_t - \lambda \cdot (\Sigma p_i^g - \Sigma p_k^c); \ i\Sigma = 0, \ldots, n^g; \ k\Sigma = n^g + 1, \ldots, n$$

where λ is the Lagrange multiplier (here \$/MWh). Setting the derivative of L with respect to any p_m equal to zero yields

$$\frac{df_m}{dp_m} = \lambda; \ m = 0, \ldots, n^g \quad (6.4)$$

Since an incremental cost curve is a measure of how costly it will be to produce the next increment of power dp, criterion Eq. (6.4) means that it should cost the same λ from every generator.

Returning to the two-generator example of Chapter 1 and Fig. 6.2 and assuming that there are no losses p_L in the network lines, then if we shift some generation from a less to a more efficient plant, the price increase (or df/dp) in the more efficient plant *is lower* than the savings in the less efficient plant. Thus altogether we have saved some money but obviously can do it only until $df_1/dp_1 = df_2/dp_2$. Mathematically this criterion of equal incremental costs is formulated by Eq. (6.4).

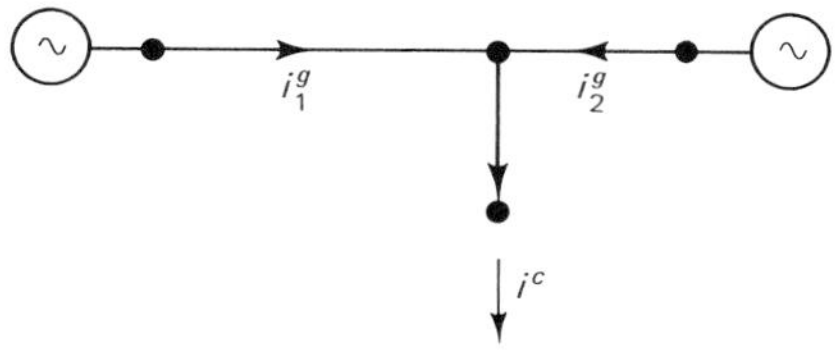

Figure 6.2 A three-bus network.

If we assume that all consumer loads were predicted, we will be able to define the problem as follows:

The law of conservation of energy and the Lagrangian are

$$\Sigma p_i^g - \Sigma p_j^c - p_L = 0; \ i\Sigma = 0, 1, \ldots, n^g; \ j\Sigma = n^g + 1, \ldots, n \quad (6.5)$$

$$L = \Sigma f_i - \lambda \cdot (\Sigma p_i^g - \Sigma p_j^c - p_L) \quad (6.6)$$

Differentiating with respect to the unknown p_i^g yields

$$\frac{\partial f_i}{\partial p_i^g} - \lambda \cdot \left(1 - \frac{\partial p_L}{\partial p_i^g}\right) = 0; \quad i = 0, \ldots, n^g \tag{6.7}$$

These are $n^g + 1$ equations which, together with Eq. (6.5), are sufficient for the calculation of $n^g + 1$ values p_i^g and the Lagrange multiplier λ. The number of equations thus equals that of the unknowns, and the problem can be solved.

If it is also assumed that p_L is independent of all p^gs, then instead of Eq. (6.7) $\partial f_i / \partial p_i^g = \lambda$ are to be solved together with Eq. (6.5).

The simplest way is to use the incremental cost curves (Fig. 6.3) of $\partial f / \partial p_i^g$ (M\$/MW) in the following way:

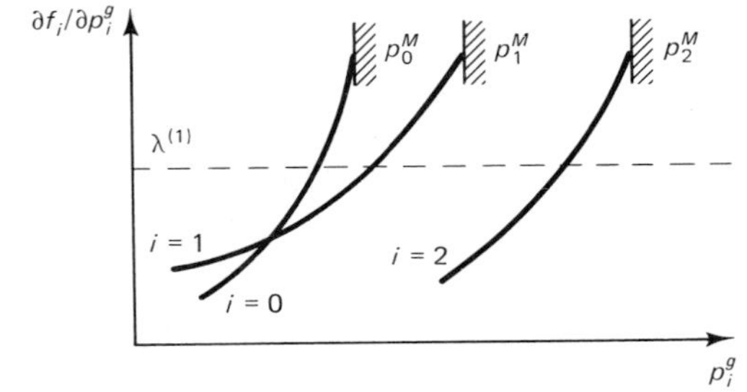

Figure 6.3 Incremental costs.

Assume a $\lambda^{(1)}$ and find the corresponding p_i^g from Fig. 6.3. Inserting these into Eq. (6.5) yields a p_L, so the cost function can be computed. Next, shift λ to $\lambda^{(2)}$ and repeat the construction. If any $p_i^g \geq p_i^{\mathrm{M}}$, or $p_i^g \leq p_i^{\mathrm{m}}$, set the generation momentarily (i.e, not permanently) at the limit. Proceed, as long as either $f(p^g)$ or p_L is decreased; whenever this is not possible anymore, the algorithm has found the best incremental cost λ for all generators (all p_j^c are constant).

This method has the advantage of extreme simplicity and uses correct incremental cost curves, which usually have jumps (discontinuities) and are thus only partially differentiable. Its disadvantages include the fact that constraints were only partially accounted for, a restricted set of variables was used and, most important, that p_L was assumed, quite incorrectly, to be independent of the generated powers. Approximation methods for computing $\partial p_L / \partial p_i^g$ will be given next.

First of all, the total losses (p_L) of the network to be included are:

$$\Sigma\, p_i^g = \Sigma\, p_k^c + p_L \tag{6.8}$$

Therefore, we have to calculate how these losses depend on the generated or consumed powers. Second, there is another way to view the "cost" to be minimized, namely, make it p_L instead of f (fuel cost). We may say that we have two definitions: that of minimum fuel cost and that of minimum losses.

The solution of load flow sets aside one plant, the slack-bus generator, for which the voltage ($u \cdot \epsilon^{j\theta}$) is prescribed but the power ($p + j \cdot q$) is left open. Therefore the slack generator could supply all of the (active) losses in the network, and the minimum loss problem is seen to be equivalent to the minimization of power p_S supplied by the slack generator.

The network imposes certain constraints on the problem in that the variables must satisfy Kirchhoff's network equations. In power system parlance this means that the load-flow equations must be satisfied:

$$\mathbf{r}(\mathbf{a}, \mathbf{e}, \mathbf{x}) = \mathbf{0} \tag{6.9}$$

Here, **a** is the vector of a priori known quantities (e.g., the admittances or loads), **e** is the vector of quantities to be controlled (e.g., p^g or u), and **x** is the vector of state variables (i.e., the voltages $u = v + jw$ of all nodes).

Load flow is not the only constraint to be satisfied. The generated powers and the computed voltages must stay within certain limits, a fact expressed through

$$\mathbf{h}(\mathbf{a}, \mathbf{e}, \mathbf{x}) \geq \mathbf{0} \tag{6.10}$$

The *economic dispatch problem* is seen to be defined as follows: *Given*

- a power system governed by Eq. (6.9),
- a set of inequality constraints [Eq. (6.10)],
- a set of a priori known values **a**,

calculate the control vector **e** which will minimize either the cost or the losses (equivalently, p_S).

The economic dispatch (ED) problem is seen to be a *nonlinear constrained optimization problem* (nonlinear because load flow is nonlinear). It is solved usually in one of the following three ways:

1. Using the Kuhn–Tucker theorem, a *Lagrangian function*

   $$L = c + \boldsymbol{\lambda}^{\mathrm{T}} * \mathbf{r} + \mathbf{k}^{\mathrm{T}} * \mathbf{h}$$

   is minimized. Here all λ are arbitrary and

   $$\mathbf{k} \geq \mathbf{0}, \quad \mathbf{k}^{\mathrm{T}} * \mathbf{h} = 0$$

   It is assumed that **r** and **h** are convex. The variables $\boldsymbol{\lambda}$ and **k** are known as dual variables associated with the equality and inequality constraints. For $\mathbf{k}^{\mathrm{T}} * \mathbf{h} = 0$, either $k_i = 0$ or $h_i = 0$ or both are zeros for all i. If $k_i = 0$, h_i may be any function—not necessarily on the boundary given by $\mathbf{h} = \mathbf{0}$. If $\mathbf{k}$ is positive throughout, $\mathbf{h} = \mathbf{0}$, so that the optimization result is on the boundary. Therefore, the condition for $\mathbf{k}$ shows where the solution lies.

The Lagrangian function L may be extremely complicated, so that it is not surprising that one of the best-known methods disregards the inequality constraint entirely and solves first $\partial L / \partial \mathbf{x} = \mathbf{0}$; $L = c + \boldsymbol{\lambda}^{\mathrm{T}} * \mathbf{r}$.

The inequality constraints are then treated separately following the solution of the preceding. Since the solution will use the Newton–Raphson method, we will call it the Newtonian method. It is essentially that of Eqs. (6.5) and (6.7) and Fig. 6.3.

2. Another approach to solve either one of the optimization problems is by a *direct method*. Here Eq. (6.9) is first solved for an assumed control vector $\mathbf{e}_0$. The resultant state vector $\mathbf{x}_0$ is used to check the inequality constraints and to evaluate the cost. The algorithm relies for its progress on the ability to choose a better $\mathbf{e}_1$ and so on—the simplest choice being to proceed in the direction of the *steepest descent*, i.e., in the direction in which the cost drops most steeply. Most of these *gradient* techniques are summarized in [SM74].

   In both methods the dimensionality is extremely high, $n = 1000$ being the average. Thus, the Jacobian matrix needed while solving load flow with the Newton–Raphson method would be 2000-by-2000 (the equations are complex) and their sparsity is only a partial relief.

3. The third and oldest approach is to use a reduced set [Ki58], i.e., to model the effects of the network by mathematical functions which involve only the controlled variables. In this method the problem may be defined as follows: Minimize cost

$$c = \Sigma\, c(p_i^g); \quad i\Sigma = 0, \ldots, n^g$$

subject to

$$\Sigma\, p_i^g = p_L + \Sigma\, p_j^c; \qquad i\Sigma = 0, \ldots., n^g; \quad j\Sigma = n^g + 1, \ldots, n$$

and

$$(p_i^g)^{\mathrm{m}} \le p_i^g \le (p_i^g)^{\mathrm{M}} \text{ for } i = 1, 2, \ldots, n^g$$

where

$$p_L = (\mathbf{p}^g)^{\mathrm{T}} * \mathbf{B} * \mathbf{p}^g + \mathbf{b}_0^{\mathrm{T}} * \mathbf{p}^g + b_{00}$$

The dimension has been reduced from n to $n^g + 1$ (n = number of nodes, $n^g + 1$ = number of generator nodes). Normally, this will be a reduction of about 90%, but the problem is how to compute matrix $\mathbf{B}$, vector $\mathbf{b}_0$, and scalar b_{00}. As evidenced by [Ki58], books could be and have been written on this subject.

We will next take the two-generator example of Fig. 6.2 in order to get a feeling for what is involved in the calculation of matrix **B**.

The loss in the simple network of Fig. 6.2 is

$$p_L = 3 \cdot i_1^2 r_1 + 3 \cdot i_2^2 \cdot r_2 + 3 \cdot (i^c)^2 \cdot r_3$$

If we assume that i_1 and i_2 are in phase, then $i^c = i_1 + i_2$ and

$$p_L = 3 \cdot i_1^2 \cdot (r_1 + r_3) + 3 \cdot 2 \cdot i_1 \cdot i_2 \cdot r_3 + 3 \cdot i_2^2 \cdot (r_2 + r_3)$$

The two generator currents can be calculated from

$$\sqrt{3} \cdot v_1 \cdot i_1 \cdot \cos(\psi_1) = p_1; \quad \sqrt{3} \cdot v_2 \cdot i_2 \cdot \cos(\psi_2) = p_2$$

so that we get, with $\gamma_1 = v_1 \cdot \cos(\psi_1)$ and $\gamma_2 = v_2 \cdot \cos(\psi_2)$,

$$p_L = \frac{p_1^2 \cdot (r_1 + r_3)}{\gamma_1^2} + \frac{2 \cdot p_1 \cdot p_2 \cdot r_3}{\gamma_1 \cdot \gamma_2} + \frac{p_2^2 \cdot (r_2 + r_3)}{\gamma_2^2}$$

This can be written as

$$p_L = B_{11} \cdot p_1^2 + 2 \cdot B_{12} \cdot p_1 \cdot p_2 + B_{22} \cdot p_2^2 = \mathbf{p}^{\mathrm{T}} * \mathbf{B} * \mathbf{p}$$

$$p_L = [p_1, p_2] * \begin{bmatrix} B_{11} & B_{12} \\ B_{12} & B_{22} \end{bmatrix} * \begin{bmatrix} p_1 \\ p_2 \end{bmatrix}$$

where $B_{11} = (r_1 + r_3)/\gamma_1^2$, $B_{22} = (r_2 + r_3)/\gamma_2^2$, and $B_{12} = r_3/(\gamma_1 \cdot \gamma_2)$.

From these expressions we can conclude the following:

- The factors (B_{ij}) are dependent on the voltages and power factors, but these are not known unless we have first run a load flow. We will hardly want to run a load flow for *every* situation and thus have to take an average value of sorts.
- Normally, utilities use a single set of **B**, that is, a single average per day. This is clearly not accurate enough, so that this method should be used only in a way which will average much more often. We will in fact propose using it so that the averaging is done every few minutes.
- Resistance appeared in the numerators. We have assumed that the currents are in phase, and if we drop this assumption, impedances instead of resistances will appear. In any case, since normally admittances are known, it is required to invert **Y** to get the **Z**-bus matrix or to factor matrix **Y** according to **Y** = **L** * **U**.
- The constraints **h (a, e, x)** ≥ **0** were not included at all. If they should be included, we had better use a mathematical programming method, capable of handling functional equality constraints, e.g., a gradient method.

In the following sections we are going to discuss the Newtonian, **B**-matrix, and gradient methods in more detail.

6.2 NEWTONIAN METHODS

The first method [DT68] to be discussed consists of the solution of a load flow by the Newton–Raphson method and an optimum adjustment by the steepest-descent method. The problem is first restated as follows:*

The state vector $\mathbf{x}$ is

$$\mathbf{x} \equiv [\theta_1, \ldots, \theta_{n-1}, u_1, \ldots, u_c \mid p_s, q_k, \ldots, q_s]^{\mathrm{T}} = [\mathbf{x}_a, \mathbf{x}_b]^{\mathrm{T}} \qquad (6.11)$$

The load or consumer buses are renumbered 1 to c, the generators $k = c + 1$ to n with the slack bus numbered either s or n. The two subvectors:

- $\mathbf{x}_a$ includes all voltage angles except the given $\theta_s = 0$ of the slack bus and all voltage magnitudes for the load buses.
- $\mathbf{x}_b$ includes the slack-bus power p_n (or p_s) and q of all generator buses.

The control vector $\mathbf{z}$ includes all real powers of generators except for the slack bus:

$$\mathbf{z} \equiv [p_k, \ldots, p_{n-1}]^{\mathrm{T}} \qquad (6.12)$$

The remaining values of consumed powers p^c and generated voltages are known and are treated as a parameter (vector): $\mathbf{a} \equiv [u_k, \ldots, u_s \mid p_1^c, \ldots, p_s^c]$. The load-flow equation is

$$\mathbf{r}(\mathbf{x}, \mathbf{z}) = \mathbf{0} \qquad (6.13)$$

and the objective function to be minimized is the cost of generation $f = \Sigma\, c_i(p_i^g)$; $i\Sigma = k, \ldots, s$, of all generators (including the slack generator). If we denote by m all generators except the slack bus and collect the known values of coefficients c_i, d_i, and e_i of Eq. (6.2) into an m-by-m diagonal matrix $\mathbf{C}$, m-vector $\mathbf{d}$, and the scalar $e = \Sigma\, e_i$, $i\Sigma = k, \ldots, n \equiv 1, \ldots, m - 1$ then the cost function can be expressed as

$$f = (0.5 \cdot \mathbf{z}^{\mathrm{T}} * \mathbf{C} * \mathbf{z} + \mathbf{z}^{\mathrm{T}} * \mathbf{d} + \mathrm{e}) + (0.5 \cdot c_s \cdot p_s^2 + d_s \cdot p_s + e_s) \qquad (6.14)$$

where the second summand derives from the slack bus.

If we view Eq. (6.13) as equality constraints and disregard inequalities, the Lagrangian is

* H. W. Dommel, W. F. Tinney, "Optimal Power Flow Solutions," *Trans. IEEE*, Vol. PAS-87, No. 10, pp.1866-76, October 1968. © 1968 by IEEE. Used with permission.

$$L \equiv f\,(\mathbf{x}, \mathbf{z}) + \boldsymbol{\lambda}^{\mathrm{T}} * \mathbf{r}\,(\mathbf{x}, \mathbf{z}) \tag{6.15}$$

Differentiating L yields the three sets

$$\partial L / \partial \mathbf{x} = \partial f / \partial \mathbf{x} + [\partial \mathbf{r}/\partial \mathbf{x}]^{\mathrm{T}} * \boldsymbol{\lambda} = 0 \tag{6.16}$$

$$\partial L / \partial \mathbf{z} = \partial f / \partial \mathbf{z} + [\partial \mathbf{r}/\partial \mathbf{z}]^{\mathrm{T}} * \boldsymbol{\lambda} = 0 \tag{6.17}$$

$$\partial L / \partial \boldsymbol{\lambda} = \mathbf{r} = 0 \tag{6.18}$$

Note that the last is the load-flow equation and that $\partial \mathbf{r}/\partial \mathbf{x} = \mathbf{J}$ is the Jacobian as used for solving LF by the Newton–Raphson method. The algorithm is therefore as follows:

(a) Assume a set of forcing parameters (usually p and q for load and p and u for generator buses).

(b) Find a feasible solution by solving load flow [Eq. (6.18)]. Store the factored Jacobian $\mathbf{J} \equiv [\partial \mathbf{r}/\partial \mathbf{x}] = \mathbf{L} * \mathbf{U}$.

(c) Find vector $\boldsymbol{\lambda}$ by back-substitution in Eq. (6.16), i.e., by solving $\mathbf{J}^{\mathrm{T}} * \boldsymbol{\lambda} = -\partial \mathbf{f}/\partial \mathbf{x}$.

(d) For the optimal $\mathbf{f}$, $dL/d\mathbf{z}$ should be zero. Here, the gradient $\mathbf{g} = \partial f / \partial \mathbf{z} + [\partial \mathbf{r}/\partial \mathbf{z}]^{\mathrm{T}} * \boldsymbol{\lambda}$ of Eq. (6.17) is not zero. It is computed and its norm $||\mathbf{g}||$ used in (e) as follows.

(e) If $||\mathbf{g}|| < \epsilon$, then the present $\mathbf{f}$ is optimal. Otherwise, adjust $\mathbf{f}$ through $\mathbf{f} := \mathbf{f} - \gamma \cdot \mathbf{g}$ and return to (b).

Note that solving load flow is an integral part of the algorithm and that $\mathbf{g}$ is the gradient of the objective function $\mathbf{f}$. As an example, Fig. 5.3 indicates a few moves from an initial point 0 according to this algorithm and a choice of γ yet to be described. As mentioned in Chapter 5, choosing γ too small would assure convergence but require too many iterations, whereas γ too large might lead to oscillations around the minimum point.

Load-flow equations were of the type $p_k - \cdots = 0$, and $q_k - \cdots = 0$. For the development of the algorithm we will rename the first rp and last rq. We can then define [Gi84] two (column) vectors $\mathbf{r}_a$ and $\mathbf{r}_b$ and the vector of residuals $\mathbf{r}$ as

$$\mathbf{r}_a \equiv [rp_1, \ldots, rp_{n-1}, rq_1, \ldots, rq_c]^{\mathrm{T}}$$

$$\mathbf{r}_b \equiv [rp_s, rq_k, \ldots, rq_s]^{\mathrm{T}} \tag{6.19}$$

$$\mathbf{r} = \begin{bmatrix} \mathbf{r}_a \\ \mathbf{r}_b \end{bmatrix}$$

In the same way, the Lagrangian consists of two vectors:

$$\boldsymbol{\lambda}_a = [\lambda p_1, \ldots, \lambda p_{n-1}, \lambda q_1, \ldots, \lambda q_c]^{\mathrm{T}}$$

$$\boldsymbol{\lambda}_b = [\lambda p_s, \lambda q_k, \ldots, \lambda q_s]^{\mathrm{T}} \tag{6.20}$$

$$\boldsymbol{\lambda} = \begin{bmatrix} \boldsymbol{\lambda}_a \\ \boldsymbol{\lambda}_b \end{bmatrix}$$

The Jacobian of load flow was $J_{i,k} = [(\partial \mathbf{r}_a)_i/(\partial \mathbf{x})_k]$. The matrix of $[\partial \mathbf{r}_b/\partial \mathbf{x}]$ will here be called $\mathbf{R}$. With this notation, $-[\partial \mathbf{r}/\partial \mathbf{x}]$ required in Eq. (6.16) is

$$-[\partial \mathbf{r}/\partial \mathbf{x}] = \begin{bmatrix} \mathbf{J} & \mathbf{0} \\ \mathbf{R} & -\mathbf{I} \end{bmatrix}; \qquad -[\partial \mathbf{r}/\partial \mathbf{x}]^{\mathrm{T}} = \begin{bmatrix} \mathbf{J}^{\mathrm{T}} & \mathbf{R}^{\mathrm{T}} \\ \mathbf{0} & -\mathbf{I} \end{bmatrix}$$

All $\partial \mathbf{f}/\partial \mathbf{x}$ are 0, except for $\partial \mathbf{f}/\partial p_s$. Equation (6.16), namely, $\boldsymbol{\lambda} = -[\partial \mathbf{r}/\partial \mathbf{x}]^{-\mathrm{T}} * [\partial \mathbf{f}/\partial \mathbf{x}]$, therefore yields

$$\boldsymbol{\lambda} = \begin{bmatrix} \mathbf{J}^{-\mathrm{T}} & \mathbf{J}^{-\mathrm{T}} * \mathbf{R}^{\mathrm{T}} \\ \mathbf{0} & -\mathbf{I} \end{bmatrix} * \begin{bmatrix} 0 \\ \cdot \\ \cdot \\ \cdot \\ 0 \\ \partial \mathbf{f}/\partial p_s \\ 0 \\ \cdot \\ \cdot \\ 0 \end{bmatrix} \tag{6.21}$$

The first "row" of this equation is $\boldsymbol{\lambda}_a = \mathbf{J}^{-\mathrm{T}} * \mathbf{R}^{\mathrm{T}} * [\partial f/\partial p_s, 0, \ldots, 0]^{\mathrm{T}}$ Premultiply by $\mathbf{J}^{\mathrm{T}}$ to get $\mathbf{J}^{\mathrm{T}} * \boldsymbol{\lambda}_a = \mathbf{R}^{\mathrm{T}} * [\partial f/\partial p_s, 0, \ldots, 0]^{\mathrm{T}}$.

Multiplication of $\mathbf{R}^{\mathrm{T}}$ by the single nonzero value $\partial f/\partial p_s$ is identical to multiplying $\partial f/\partial p_s$ by the first column of $\mathbf{R}^{\mathrm{T}}$ or by

$$\mathbf{y} \equiv [-\partial rp_s/\partial \theta_1, \ldots, -\partial rp_s/\partial \theta_{n-1}, -\partial rp_s/\partial u_1, \ldots, -\partial rp_s/\partial u_k]^{\mathrm{T}}$$

Equation (6.16) therefore becomes (with $\mathbf{J}^{\mathrm{T}} = \mathbf{U}^{\mathrm{T}} * \mathbf{L}^{\mathrm{T}}$)

$$\mathbf{U}^{\mathrm{T}} * \mathbf{L}^{\mathrm{T}} * \boldsymbol{\lambda}_a = [\partial f/\partial p_s] * \mathbf{y} \tag{6.22}$$

This equation will be used calculate λ_a.

The second "row" of Eq. (6.21) has a single nonzero element $\lambda p_s = -\partial f/\partial p_s$ and $[\lambda q_k, \ldots, \lambda q_s]^{\mathrm{T}} = \mathbf{0}^{\mathrm{T}}$.

Next we evaluate Eq. (6.17) as follows. From Eq. (6.14), $[\partial f/\partial \mathbf{z}] = \mathbf{C} * \mathbf{z} + \mathbf{d}$.

Multiplication of $[\partial \mathbf{r}/\partial \mathbf{z}]^{\mathrm{T}}$ by $\boldsymbol{\lambda}$ yields

$$\begin{array}{c} 1 \\ \\ m \end{array}\left[\begin{array}{c|c|c|c|c} \mathbf{O} & \mathbf{I} & \mathbf{O} & 0 & \mathbf{O} \end{array}\right]_{\;1\;\; c\;\, k\;\; n-1\;\; c\;\, s\;\; k\;\; s} * \begin{bmatrix} \boldsymbol{\lambda}_a \\ \boldsymbol{\lambda}_b \end{bmatrix} = [\lambda p_k, \ldots, \lambda p_{n-1}]^{\mathrm{T}}$$

The zero submatrices and vectors are the result of the respective r_i not being functions of $\mathbf{z}$.

Equation (6.17) is therefore rewritten as

$$\mathbf{C} * \mathbf{z} + \mathbf{d} + [\lambda p_k, \ldots, \lambda p_n]^{\mathrm{T}} = \mathbf{0} \tag{6.23}$$

This completes the calculation of $\boldsymbol{\lambda}$, with $\boldsymbol{\lambda}_a$ calculated from Eq. (6.22) and $\boldsymbol{\lambda}_b$ from Eq. (6.23).

Next, the choice of γ is discussed with a view not so much to getting very accurate results (not to be achieved in the gradient method anyway) but to getting a good value for γ. For this, assume that f is a quadratic function of γ or that, in order to calculate γ, the Taylor expansion of L is

$$L = L_0 + \gamma\cdot(\partial L_0/\partial\gamma) + 0.5\cdot\gamma^2\cdot(\partial^2 L_0/\partial\gamma^2)$$

Its derivative is $\partial L/\partial\gamma = (\partial L_0/\partial\gamma) + \gamma\cdot(\partial^2 L_0/\partial\gamma^2)$. If set to zero, it yields

$$\gamma = -\frac{\partial L_0/\partial\gamma}{\partial^2 L_0/\partial\gamma^2} \tag{6.24}$$

Since $\mathbf{z} := \mathbf{z} - \gamma\cdot[\partial L/\partial\mathbf{z}]$ we have $\partial\mathbf{z}/\partial\gamma = -\partial L/\partial\mathbf{z}$. The numerator of γ is

$$\partial L/\partial\gamma = [\partial L/\partial\mathbf{z}]^{\mathrm{T}} * [\partial\mathbf{z}/\partial\gamma] = -\,[\partial L/\partial\mathbf{z}]^{\mathrm{T}} * [\partial L/\partial\mathbf{z}] \tag{6.25}$$

Note that the elements of this scalar product are $\Sigma\,(\partial L/\partial z_i)^2$. If differentiated, they yield

$$2\cdot\Sigma\,\frac{\partial L}{\partial z_i}\cdot\frac{\partial^2 L}{\partial z_i\cdot\partial z_i}$$

and since this last is matrix $\mathbf{C}$, also $2\cdot[\partial L/\partial\mathbf{z}]^{\mathrm{T}} * \mathbf{C}$.

Next, we calculate the denominator of Eq. (6.24):

$$\frac{\partial^2 L}{\partial\gamma^2} = \frac{\partial}{\partial\gamma}\left[\frac{\partial L}{\partial\gamma}\right] = -\,\frac{\partial}{\partial\gamma}\left\{\left[\frac{\partial L}{\partial\mathbf{z}}\right]^{\mathrm{T}} * \left[\frac{\partial L}{\partial\mathbf{z}}\right]\right\}$$

$$= - \left\{ \frac{\partial}{\partial \mathbf{z}} \left[\frac{\partial L}{\partial \mathbf{z}} \right]^{\mathrm{T}} * \left[\frac{\partial L}{\partial \mathbf{z}} \right] \right\}^{\mathrm{T}} * \frac{\partial \mathbf{z}}{\partial \gamma}$$

$$= -2 \cdot \left[\frac{\partial L}{\partial \mathbf{z}} \right]^{\mathrm{T}} * \mathbf{C} * \left[\frac{\partial L}{\partial \mathbf{z}} \right]$$

Using this shows that

$$\gamma = 0.5 \cdot \frac{[\partial L / \partial \mathbf{z}]^{\mathrm{T}} * [\partial L / \partial \mathbf{z}]}{[\partial L / \partial \mathbf{z}]^{\mathrm{T}} * \mathbf{C} * [\partial L / \partial \mathbf{z}]} \tag{6.26}$$

We have now all equations for the algorithm, and Program 6.1, developed by Dr. M. Gilles [Gi84] of Wayne State University, presents the part of the program which used them.

Inequality constraints have not been included in the program. This could be done as follows. First, two types of inequality constraints should be distinguished. Those on the control variables are of the form

$$z^{\mathrm{m}} \leq \mathbf{z} \leq z^{\mathrm{M}} \tag{6.27}$$

e.g., $u^{\mathrm{m}} \leq u \leq u^{\mathrm{M}}$ on a generator node. They can be accounted for by making $z_i = z^{\mathrm{m}}$ or $z_i = z^{\mathrm{M}}$ whenever z arrives at a minimum (m) or maximum (M) point. When this happens, z_i remains constant but its part in the gradient vector $\mathbf{g}$ has to be computed, since in the following iteration z_i might be different from the limit. Equation (6.27) is also used for the slack bus ($i = s$), which therefore only takes up the balance of power but no longer determines the voltage level throughout the system.

If the control variables do not obey Eq. (6.27) but the x parameters ($x^{\mathrm{m}} \leq \mathbf{x} \leq x^{\mathrm{M}}$) do, then they must be considered "functional" inequalities, since $\mathbf{x}$ is a function of $\mathbf{a}$ and $\mathbf{z}$. Normally, $u^{\mathrm{m}} \leq u \leq u^{\mathrm{M}}$ on a load bus is a constraint of this type and the voltage u is obviously the *result* of the calculation. Figure 6.4(a) shows the curves typical for a 3-bus system like that in Fig. 6.2 and $u_3 \leq 1.0$. Breaking off the calculation at point A would be wrong, since the minimum may be another point on the constraint line, say, B.

As mentioned in [DT78]: "Functional constraints can be accounted for by a penalty method in which the objective function is augmented by penalties for functional constraint violations. This forces the solution back sufficiently close to the constraint. This method was chosen for three reasons:

1. Functional constraints are seldom rigid limits in the strict mathematical sense but are rather soft limits. (For instance $u \leq 1.0$ on a load node really means that u should not exceed 1 by too much, and $u = 1.01$ may still be permissible. The penalty method produces just such soft limits.)

```
(* In this program ng, npu and npq are the
 number of generators (n+1), of pu and
of pq buses. Additionally nm1 = n - 1 *)
aux:=alpha[ng]*pg[0]+beta[ng];
(* The del-vector computed in the next 20 lines includes
   -dr/dangle from 1 to mm1 and dr/du from 1 to npq.
   Together it constitutes vector df/dpg(0).  *)
for j:=1 to nm1 do
if (g[0,j]=0.0) and (b[o,j]=0.0)
(*i.e., the two buses are not connected*)
then
   del[j]:=0.0
else
   del[j]:=aux*u[0]*u[j]*
   (g[0,j]*sin(angle[0]-angle[j])-
   b[0,j]*cos(angle[0]-angle[j]);
if npq<>0
then
for j:=1 to npq do
begin jj:=mm1+1;
   if (g[0,j]=0.0) and (b[0,j]=0.0)
   then
      del[jj]:=0.0
   else
      del[jj]:=aux*u[0]*(g[0,j]*cos(angle[0]-
      angle[j])+b[0,j]*sin(angle[0]-angle[j]);
end;
(* The next 16 lines  make a forward-backward substitution
   to solve Eq. (6.16) for lambda**T using J=L*U *)
del[1]:=del[1]/J[1,1];
if n>=2
then
begin
   for i:=2 to n do
   begin ii:=i-1;
      for j:=1 to ii do
      del[i]:=del[i]-J[j,i]*del[j];
      del[i]:=del[i]/J[i,i]
   end;
   for i:=nm1 downto 1 do
   begin ii:=i+1;
      for jj:=ii to n do
      del[i]:=del[i]-J[j,i]*del[j]
   end
end; (* of the big if_loop *)
    (* The next two lines  compute dlambda/du *)
for i:=1 to npv do
lambda:=del[i+npq]+alpha[i]*pg[i+npq]+beta[i];
aux1:=0.0; aux2:=0.0; (* These are the numerator and *)
for i:=1 to npu do            (* denominator of gamma *)
begin
   aux:=lambda[i]*lambda[i];
   aux1:=aux+aux1; aux2:=aux2+alpha[i]*aux
end;
(* Next z:=z-mu*dlambda/dz is computed *)
for i:=1 to npv do
begin in:=i+npq;
   lambda[i]:=0.5*aux1*lambda[i]/aux2;
```

Program 6.1

```
        pg[in]:=pg[in]+lambda[i];
        if pg[in]>pmax[i] then pg[in]:=pmax[i];
        if pg[in]<pmin[i] then pg[in]:=pmin
    end;
    for i:=1 to npv do
    if abs(lambda[i])>eps then
    (* return to the load-flow program *)
```

Program 6.1 (cont.)

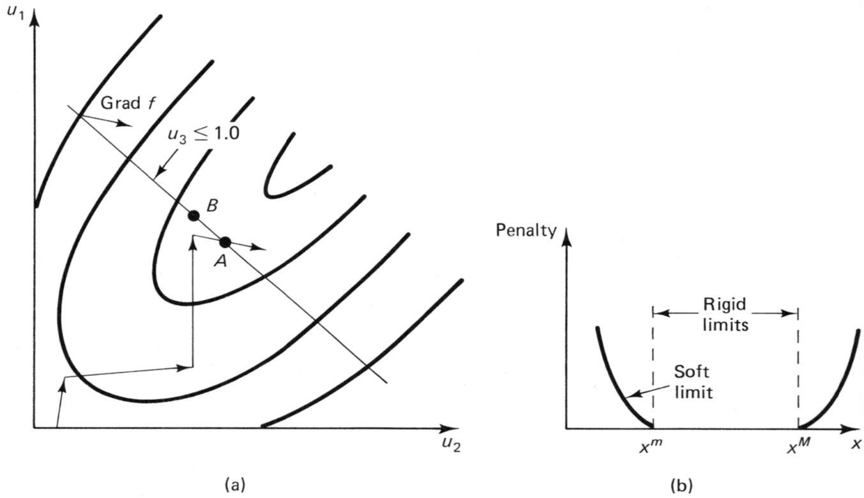

Figure 6.4 (a) Minimization. (b) Penalty function.

2. The penalty method adds very little to the algorithm, as it simply amounts to adding terms to $\partial\mathbf{f}/\partial\mathbf{x}$ (and also to $\partial\mathbf{f}/\partial\mathbf{e}$ if the functional constraint is also a function of **e**.)
3. It produces feasible power flow solutions, with the penalties signaling the trouble spots, where poorly chosen rigid limits would exclude solutions."

Suppose that a penalty w_j accounts for each constraint. The objective function f should be replaced by $f^{\#} := f + \Sigma\, w_j$.

For constraints like those of Fig. 6.4(b) the penalty functions used were $w_j = s_j \cdot (x_j - x_j^{\mathrm{M}})^2$, whenever $x_j > x_j^{\mathrm{M}}$ and $w_j = s_j \cdot (x_j - x_j^{\mathrm{m}})$, whenever $x_j < x_j^{\mathrm{m}}$.

The LF set is written as

$$\begin{bmatrix} \mathbf{J}_{11} & \mathbf{J}_{12} \\ \mathbf{J}_{21} & \mathbf{J}_{22} \end{bmatrix} * \begin{bmatrix} \Delta\boldsymbol{\theta} \\ \Delta\mathbf{u}/\mathbf{u} \end{bmatrix} = \begin{bmatrix} \Delta\mathbf{p} \\ \Delta\mathbf{q} \end{bmatrix}$$

and solved. Then $\boldsymbol{\lambda}^p$ and $\boldsymbol{\lambda}^q$ follow from

$$\begin{bmatrix} \mathbf{J}_{11} & \mathbf{J}_{12} \\ \mathbf{J}_{21} & \mathbf{J}_{22} \end{bmatrix}^{\mathrm{T}} * \begin{bmatrix} \boldsymbol{\lambda}^p \\ \boldsymbol{\lambda}^q \end{bmatrix} = -a\cdot \begin{bmatrix} \mathbf{b} & \Sigma\, \partial w_j/\partial\theta \\ \mathbf{d} & -\Sigma\,(\partial w_j/\partial u)\cdot u \end{bmatrix} \tag{6.28}$$

In Eq. (6.28), penalty factors w_j enter only if they are functions of the particular θ or u, $\boldsymbol{\lambda}^p$ and $\boldsymbol{\lambda}^q$ are subvectors associated with real and reactive power equality constraints, $a = 1$ for loss and $a = \partial c_s/\partial p_s^g$ for cost minimization, and for vectors we have $b_k = \partial p_s/\partial\theta_k$ and $d_k = (\partial p_s/\partial u_k)\cdot u_k$.

Note that if the $\mathbf{J}$ matrix was factored into $\mathbf{L} * \mathbf{U}$ for solving LF, then $\mathbf{J}^{\mathrm{T}} = \mathbf{U}^{\mathrm{T}} * \mathbf{L}^{\mathrm{T}}$ so that solution of Eq. (6.28) is just a forward and backward-substitution.

We adapt next a very simple decoupled algorithm developed in [JW78] for load-flow to the loss-minimization problem. The losses in a line $i-k$ are

$$\begin{aligned}\Delta s_{i,k} &= u_{i,k}'\cdot i_{i,k}'' = u_{i,k}'\cdot y_{i,k}''\cdot u_{i,k}'' \\ &= y_{i,k}''\cdot[(u_i\cdot\epsilon^{j\psi_i} - u_k\cdot\epsilon^{j\psi_k})\cdot(u_i\cdot\epsilon^{-j\psi_i} - u_k\cdot\epsilon^{-j\psi_k})] \\ &= y_{i,k}''\cdot[u_i^2 - u_i\cdot u_k\cdot\epsilon^{j(\psi_i-\psi_k)} - u_i\cdot u_k\cdot\epsilon^{j(\psi_k-\psi_i)} + u_k^2]\end{aligned}$$

Since $\epsilon^{j\alpha} = \cos(\alpha) + j\cdot\sin(\alpha)$, the inner part of the brackets is with

$$\alpha = \psi_i - \psi_k$$

$$\cos(\alpha) + j\cdot\sin(\alpha) + \cos(\alpha) - j\cdot\sin(\alpha) \quad\text{or}\quad 2\cdot\cos(\alpha) = 2\cos(\psi_i - \psi_k)$$

Thus,

$$\Delta s_{ik} = y_{ik}''\cdot[u_i^2 + u_k^2 - 2\cdot\mathrm{Re}\,(u_i'\cdot u_k'')]$$

For the imaginary part,

$$\mathrm{Im}\,(u_i'\cdot u_k'') = \mathrm{Im}\,(u_i\cdot\epsilon^{j\psi_i}\cdot u_k\cdot\epsilon^{-j\psi_k})$$

$$= u_i\cdot u_k\cdot\mathrm{Im}\,[(\cos(\psi_i) + j\cdot\sin(\psi_i))\cdot(\cos(\psi_k) - j\cdot\sin(\psi_k))] = u_i\cdot u_k\cdot\gamma$$

Since the angles ψ are small, $\sin(\psi) \cong \psi$, $\cos(\psi) \cong 1$, and thus

$$\gamma = \psi_i - \psi_k + \epsilon_{ik}$$

where ϵ is a correction term accounting for $\psi \neq 0$. The power injected at bus i is the sum

$$s_i = \Sigma\,(u_i'\cdot y_{ik}''\cdot u_k'') = \Sigma\, y_{ik}''\cdot u_i'\cdot u_k'' + y_{ii}''\cdot u_i^2; \qquad (6.29)$$

$$k\Sigma = 1, \ldots, n, \text{ but } k \neq i$$

Substituting $u_i'\cdot u_k'' = \text{Re}\,(u_i'\cdot u_k'') + j\cdot\text{Im}\,(u_i'\cdot u_k'')$ as calculated earlier into Eq. (6.29) yields

$$s_i = y_{ii}''\cdot u_i^2 + \Sigma\, y_{ik}''\cdot\left[\frac{u_i^2 + u_k^2 - \Delta s_{ik}/y_{ik}''}{2} + j\cdot(\psi_i - \psi_k + \epsilon_{ik})\right]$$

$$s_i - \Sigma\,\frac{\Delta s_{ik}}{2} - j\,\Sigma\, y_{ik}''\cdot\epsilon_{ik}$$

$$= \Sigma\, y_{ik}''\cdot\left(\frac{u_k^2}{2} - j\cdot\psi_k\right) + u_i^2\cdot\left(y_{ii}'' + \frac{\Sigma y_{ik}''}{2}\right) + j\cdot\Sigma\, y_{ik}''\cdot\psi_i$$

As usual, the definitions of self and mutual admittances are $Y_{ii} \equiv \Sigma\, y_{ik}$ for $k\Sigma = 1, 2, \ldots, n$ and $Y_{ik} = -y_{ik}$, so that the basic equation is

$$s_i + 0.5\cdot\Sigma\,\Delta s_{ik} - j\cdot\Sigma y_{ik}''\cdot\epsilon_{ik}$$

$$= \Sigma\, y_{ik}''\cdot\left(\frac{u_k^2}{2} - j\psi_k\right) + (y_i'' + Y_{ii}'')\cdot\frac{u_i^2}{2} - j\cdot(y_{ii}'' - Y_{ii}'')\cdot\psi_i$$

For the complex power mismatch Δs_i and incremental changes Δu^2 and $\Delta\psi$, the preceding should be differentiated. The second and third terms have increments of zero, so that

$$\Delta s_i = \Sigma\, y_{ik}''\cdot(0.5\cdot\Delta u_k^2 - j\cdot\Delta\psi_k) + 0.5\cdot(y_{ii}'' + Y_{ii}'')\cdot\Delta u_i^2 - j\cdot(y_{ii}'' - Y_{ii}'')\cdot\Delta\psi_i$$

Separating the real and imaginary parts yields:

$$\Delta p_i = \Sigma\left(G_{ik}\cdot\frac{\Delta u_k^2}{2} - B_{ik}\cdot\Delta\psi_k\right) + (g_{ii} + G_{ii})\cdot\frac{\Delta u_i^2}{2} - (b_{ii} - B_{ii})\cdot\Delta\psi_i$$

$$\Delta q_i = -\Sigma\left(B_{ik}\cdot\frac{\Delta u_k^2}{2} - G_{ik}\cdot\Delta\psi_k\right) - (b_{ii} + B_{ii})\cdot\frac{\Delta u_i^2}{2} - (g_{ii} - G_{ii})\cdot\Delta\psi_i \qquad (6.30)$$

Note that Y_{ii}, G_{ii}, and B_{ii} include summations but y_{ii}, g_{ii}, and b_{ii} do not.

Equation (6.30) may be generalized for all i and written as

$$\begin{bmatrix}\Delta\mathbf{p}\\ \Delta\mathbf{q}\end{bmatrix} = \begin{bmatrix}-\tilde{\mathbf{B}} & -\tilde{\mathbf{G}}\\ -\mathbf{G}^{\#} & -\mathbf{B}^{\#}\end{bmatrix} * \begin{bmatrix}\Delta\boldsymbol{\psi}\\ \dfrac{\Delta\mathbf{u}^2}{2}\end{bmatrix} \qquad (6.31)$$

The terms of the **B** submatrices are

$$\tilde{B}_{ij} = B_{ij} - b_{ii} + B_{ii}; \quad B^{\#}_{ij} = B_{ij} - b_{ii} - B_{ii} \tag{6.32}$$

and the **G** submatrices may be neglected because they are quite small. Thus *the decoupled equations* from Eq. (6.31) are

$$\Delta \mathbf{p} \cong -\tilde{\mathbf{B}} * \Delta \boldsymbol{\psi} \tag{6.33}$$

$$\Delta \mathbf{q} \cong -\mathbf{B}^{\#} * \frac{\Delta \mathbf{u}^2}{2} \tag{6.34}$$

with Eq. (6.33) applied to all load and nonslack generation buses, while Eq. (6.34) is applied to load buses only.

These equations were used in [JW78] for LF, but there is no reason why they could not be used for economic dispatch.

6.3 THE B-MATRIX METHOD

The quadratic form of the loss formula can be written as

$$p_L = (\mathbf{p}^g)^{\mathrm{T}} * \mathbf{B} * \mathbf{p}^g + (\mathbf{p}^g)^{\mathrm{T}} \cdot \mathbf{b} + c \tag{6.35}$$

where

p_L is the real power loss

$\mathbf{p}^g$ is the vector of generated real powers

B and **b** are n-by-n and n-by-1 arrays of loss coefficients

c is a constant loss coefficient scalar

The calculation of **B**, **b** and c follows [SGH79]:*

If we sum up all generated currents i_j^g and all load or consumer currents i_j^c of all n buses, then we get the (complex) current vector

$$\mathbf{i}' = \mathbf{i}^g + \mathbf{i}^c \tag{6.36}$$

With $\mathbf{Z}'$ as the complex bus impedance matrix and a voltage vector $\mathbf{u}' = \mathbf{Z}' * \mathbf{i}'$ we have for the complex power loss

$$p_L + jq_L = \mathbf{u}^{\mathrm{T}} * \mathbf{i}'' = (\mathbf{i}')^{\mathrm{T}} * \mathbf{Z}^{\mathrm{T}} * \mathbf{i}'' \tag{6.37}$$

Note that $\mathbf{Z}^{\mathrm{T}} * \mathbf{i}''$ is an n-vector and therefore $p_L + jq_L$ is a (complex) scalar. Note also that $\mathbf{Z}^{\mathrm{T}}$ was written instead of $(\mathbf{Z}')^{\mathrm{T}}$. In order not to have such double superscripts the primes will be dropped wherever the meaning is clear.

---

* R. R. Shoults, W. Mack Grady, S. Helmick, "An Efficient Method for Computing Loss Coefficients Based upon the Method of Least Squares," *Trans. IEEE*, Vol. PAS-98, November/December 1979, © 1979 by IEEE. pp. 2144-52. Used with permission.

Comparing Eq. (6.37) with (6.35) shows that we need **i** as a function of $\mathbf{p}^g$ in order to be able to calculate **B**, **b**, and c. In order to achieve this, we will apply two transformations:

- Express load currents $\mathbf{i}^c$ as a function of $\mathbf{i}^g$ alone.
- Express $\mathbf{i}^g$ in terms of $\mathbf{p}^g$ as required.

1. To achieve the first objective, we compute the total load current $i^t = \Sigma\, i_k^c;\ k\Sigma = 1, 2, \ldots, n$
   Next, we make the assumption that the load current i_i^c of any bus i is linearly related to the total load current i^t, i.e., $i_i^c = k_i \cdot i^t + i_i^0$, where k_i is a complex constant of proportionality and i_i^0 is a complex constant intercept on the i^c axis (see Fig. 6.5)

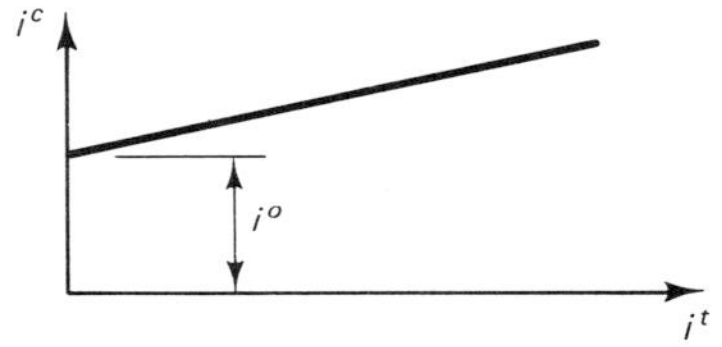

Figure 6.5 Consumed current.

By Kirchhoff's current law, the sum of all bus currents is zero:

$$\Sigma\,(i_k^g + i_k^c) = 0;\quad k\Sigma = 1, 2, \ldots, n$$

Substituting $\Sigma\, i_k^c = -\,\Sigma\, i_k^g = i^t$ yields

$$i_i^c = -k_i \cdot \Sigma\, i_j^g + i_i^{0;}\quad j\Sigma = 1, 2, \ldots, n$$

Since this equation holds for all $i = 1, \ldots, n$, it can be written as

$$\mathbf{i}^c = -\mathbf{k} \cdot i^G + \mathbf{i}^0;\quad i^G = \Sigma\, i_j^g;\quad j\Sigma = 1, 2, \ldots, n$$

Finally this $\mathbf{i}^c$ is inserted into Eq. (6.36) to yield

$$\mathbf{i} = \mathbf{i}^g - \mathbf{k} \cdot i^G + \mathbf{i}^0 \qquad (6.38)$$

We can form $\mathbf{k} \cdot i^G$ by multiplying every k_i by the scalar i^G, but we can also write it so that we need not form i^G at all, e.g., as $\mathbf{K} * \mathbf{i}^g$. If we assume that there are three generators and four buses, we get for instance:

$$\begin{bmatrix} k_1 & k_1 & k_1 \\ k_2 & k_2 & k_2 \\ k_3 & k_3 & k_3 \\ k_4 & k_4 & k_4 \end{bmatrix} * \begin{bmatrix} i_1^g \\ i_2^g \\ i_3^g \end{bmatrix} = \begin{bmatrix} k_1 \cdot i^G \\ k_2 \cdot i^G \\ k_3 \cdot i^G \\ k_4 \cdot i^G \end{bmatrix} = \mathbf{k} \cdot i^G = \mathbf{K} * \mathbf{i}^g \tag{6.39}$$

Equation (6.38) may be rewritten as

$$\mathbf{i} = (\mathbf{I} - \mathbf{K}) * \mathbf{i}^g + \mathbf{i}^0 \tag{6.40}$$

where $\mathbf{I}$ is the identity matrix. This is the required form of $\mathbf{i} = \mathbf{f}(\mathbf{i}^g)$ with $\mathbf{K}$ and $\mathbf{i}^0$ yet to be determined.

2. In order to achieve the second transformation, we assume that the reactive power q_i^g supplied by a generator i is linearly related to the active power p_i^g it supplies:

$$q_i^g = s_i \cdot p_i^g + q_i^0$$

where s_i is a factor of proportionality and q_i^0 the intercept. If this is inserted into $i_i^g = (p_i^g - j \cdot q_i^g)/u_i''$ of generated currents, we get

$$i_i^g = \frac{p_i^g - j \cdot (s_i \cdot p_i^g + q_i^0)}{u_i''} = \frac{(1 - j \cdot s_i) \cdot p_i^g}{u_i''} - \frac{j \cdot q_i^0}{u_i''}$$

Let us define $s_i^g = (1 - j \cdot s_i)/u_i''$, $s_i^0 = -j \cdot q_i^0/u_i''$. The current can be rewritten as

$$i_i^g = s_i^g \cdot p_i^g + s_i^0; \quad i = 1, 2, \ldots, n \tag{6.41}$$

As an example,

$$\begin{bmatrix} i_1^g \\ i_2^g \\ i_3^g \end{bmatrix} = \begin{bmatrix} s_1^g \cdot p_1^g \\ s_2^g \cdot p_2^g \\ s_3^g \cdot p_3^g \end{bmatrix} + \begin{bmatrix} s_1^0 \\ s_2^0 \\ s_3^0 \end{bmatrix} \tag{6.42}$$

$$= \begin{bmatrix} s_1^g & 0 & 0 \\ 0 & s_2^g & 0 \\ 0 & 0 & s_3^g \end{bmatrix} * \begin{bmatrix} p_1^g \\ p_2^g \\ p_3^g \end{bmatrix} + \begin{bmatrix} s_1^0 \\ s_2^0 \\ s_3^0 \end{bmatrix}$$

$$= \mathbf{S}^G * \mathbf{p}^g + \mathbf{s}^0$$

Therefore, if $\mathbf{S}^G$ is a diagonal matrix formed by s_i^g, Eq. (6.41) can be rewritten as

$$\mathbf{i}^g = \mathbf{S}^G * \mathbf{p}^g + \mathbf{s}^0 \tag{6.43}$$

which is the required $\mathbf{i}^g = \mathbf{f}(\mathbf{p}^g)$ with $\mathbf{S}^G$ yet to be determined.

In order to produce an equation in the form of Eq. (6.35), we first substitute Eq. (6.43) into (6.40). This yields

$$\mathbf{i} = (\mathbf{I} - \mathbf{K}) * (\mathbf{S}^G * \mathbf{p}^g + \mathbf{s}^0) + \mathbf{i}^0 = \mathbf{C}' * \mathbf{p}^g + \mathbf{i}^k$$

where we combined the constant terms:

$$\mathbf{i}^k = (\mathbf{I} - \mathbf{K}) * \mathbf{s}^0 + \mathbf{i}^0 \tag{6.44}$$

and defined $\mathbf{C}' \equiv \mathbf{S}^G * (\mathbf{I} - \mathbf{K})$. Next insert this into Eq. (6.37) to yield with $\mathbf{d} \equiv (\mathbf{i}^k)''$

$$\begin{aligned} p_L + j \cdot q_L &= [\mathbf{C}' * \mathbf{p}^g + \mathbf{i}^k]^{\mathrm{T}} * \mathbf{Z}^{\mathrm{T}} * [\mathbf{C}' * \mathbf{p}^g + \mathbf{i}^k]'' \\ &= [(\mathbf{p}^g)^{\mathrm{T}} * \mathbf{C}' + (\mathbf{i}^k)^{\mathrm{T}}] * \mathbf{Z}^{\mathrm{T}} * [\mathbf{C}'' * (\mathbf{p}^g)'' + (\mathbf{i}^k)''] \\ &= (\mathbf{p}^g)^{\mathrm{T}} * \mathbf{C}' * \mathbf{Z}^{\mathrm{T}} * \mathbf{C}'' * (\mathbf{p}^g)'' + (\mathbf{p}^g)^{\mathrm{T}} * \mathbf{C}' * \mathbf{Z}^{\mathrm{T}} * \mathbf{d} \\ &\quad + (\mathbf{i}^k)^{\mathrm{T}} * \mathbf{Z}^{\mathrm{T}} * \mathbf{C}'' * (\mathbf{p}^g)'' + (\mathbf{i}^k)^{\mathrm{T}} * \mathbf{Z}^{\mathrm{T}} * \mathbf{d} \end{aligned} \tag{6.45}$$

This is in the form of $p_L + j \cdot q_L \equiv (\mathbf{p}^g)^{\mathrm{T}} * \mathbf{B} * \mathbf{p}^g + \mathbf{b}^{\mathrm{T}} * \mathbf{p}^g + c$ provided we define

$$(\mathbf{p}^g)^{\mathrm{T}} * (\mathbf{C}')^{\mathrm{T}} * \mathbf{Z}^{\mathrm{T}} * \mathbf{C}'' * (\mathbf{p}^g)'' \equiv (\mathbf{p}^g)^{\mathrm{T}} * \mathbf{B} * (\mathbf{p}^g)''$$

$$(\mathbf{p}^g)^{\mathrm{T}} * (\mathbf{C}')^{\mathrm{T}} * \mathbf{Z}^{\mathrm{T}} * \mathbf{d} + [(\mathbf{i}^k)^{\mathrm{T}} * \mathbf{Z}^{\mathrm{T}} * \mathbf{C}'' * (\mathbf{p}^g)''] \equiv \mathbf{b}^{\mathrm{T}} * \mathbf{p}^g$$

and

$$(\mathbf{i}^k)^{\mathrm{T}} * \mathbf{Z}^{\mathrm{T}} * \mathbf{d} \equiv c$$

We have thus computed

$$\mathbf{B} = \mathrm{Re}\,\{\mathbf{S}^G * (\mathbf{I} - \mathbf{K})^{\mathrm{T}} * \mathbf{Z}^{\mathrm{T}} * (\mathbf{I} - \mathbf{K})'' * (\mathbf{S}^G)''\} \tag{6.46}$$

$$\begin{aligned} \mathbf{b} &= \mathrm{Re}\,\{[\mathbf{S}^G * (\mathbf{I} - \mathbf{K})^{\mathrm{T}} * \mathbf{Z}^{\mathrm{T}} * (\mathbf{i}^k)''] \\ &\quad + [(\mathbf{i}^k)^{\mathrm{T}} * \mathbf{Z}^{\mathrm{T}} * (\mathbf{I} - \mathbf{K})'' * (\mathbf{S}^G)'']^{\mathrm{T}}\} \end{aligned} \tag{6.47}$$

$$c = \mathrm{Re}\,\{(\mathbf{i}^k)^{\mathrm{T}} * \mathbf{Z}^{\mathrm{T}} * (\mathbf{i}^k)''\} \tag{6.48}$$

As seen, the quantities required in order to calculate **B**, **b** and c in Eqs. (6.46) to (6.48) are $\mathbf{S}^G$, **K**, and $\mathbf{i}^k$ [or, because of Eq. (6.44), also $\mathbf{s}^0$ and $\mathbf{i}^0$). By either running two or more load flows or inserting values calculated on-line by a state estimator, all four can be found: **K** and $\mathbf{i}^0$ from Eqs. (6.40) and (6.39), $\mathbf{S}^G$ and $\mathbf{s}^0$ from Eqs. (6.41) and (6.42). We need at least two runs, since we will use the least-squares procedure as defined in Chapter 5. This calculation proceeds as follows:

(a) The current was

$$i_j^c = k_j \cdot i^t + i_j^0 \tag{6.49}$$

From each "experiment" (load flow or state estimation) the values i_j^c and i^t are known ($i = 1, \ldots, n$).

Suppose we have made $j = 1, \ldots, m$ experiments. Then for every j,

$$(i_m^c)_j = k_m \cdot i_j^t + i_m^0 \tag{6.50}$$

If j is a parameter, then for every j we get one point (i_j^c, i^t) on the graph in Fig. 6.5. We can, therefore, drop index m, since one graph will exist for every bus i.

$$i_j^c = k \cdot i_j^t + i^0 \tag{6.51}$$

The errors e are

$$e_j = i_j^c - (i^0 + k \cdot i_j^t); \quad j = 1, 2, \ldots, m \tag{6.52}$$

$$\begin{bmatrix} e_1 \\ e_2 \\ \cdot \\ \cdot \\ \cdot \\ e_m \end{bmatrix} = \begin{bmatrix} i_1^c \\ i_2^c \\ \cdot \\ \cdot \\ \cdot \\ i_m^c \end{bmatrix} - \begin{bmatrix} 1 & i_1^t \\ 1 & i_2^t \\ \cdot & \cdot \\ \cdot & \cdot \\ \cdot & \cdot \\ 1 & i_m^t \end{bmatrix} * \begin{bmatrix} i^0 \\ k \end{bmatrix}$$

or $\mathbf{e} = \mathbf{i}^c - \mathbf{M} \cdot \mathbf{x}$ for every bus i.

This is exactly our starting equation in Chapter 5. It leads to

$$\mathbf{M}^T * \mathbf{M} * \mathbf{x} = \mathbf{M}^T * \mathbf{i}^c \tag{6.53}$$

which is to be solved repeatedly. In this particular case

$$\mathbf{M}^T * \mathbf{M} = \begin{bmatrix} m & \sigma \\ \sigma & \mu \end{bmatrix} \tag{6.54}$$

where $\sigma = \Sigma\, i_j^t$, $j\Sigma = 1, \ldots, m$, and $\mu = \Sigma\, (i^t)_j^2$, $j\Sigma = 1, \ldots, m$, and

$$\mathbf{b} \equiv \mathbf{M}^T * \mathbf{i}^c = \begin{bmatrix} \Sigma\, i_j^c \\ \Sigma\, (i_j^t \cdot i_j^c) \end{bmatrix}; \quad j\Sigma = 1, 2, \ldots, m \tag{6.55}$$

(b) In every experiment,

$$i_i^g = s_i^g \cdot p_i^g + s_i^0; \quad i = 1, \ldots, n \tag{6.56}$$

with (i_i^g, p_i^g) measured, (s_i^0, s_i^g) to be calculated. In the same way as in (a) we get

$$\mathbf{M}^{\mathrm{T}} * \mathbf{M} = \begin{bmatrix} m & \Sigma\, p_i^g \\ \Sigma\, p_i^g & \Sigma\, (p_i^g)^2 \end{bmatrix}; \quad \mathbf{M}^{\mathrm{T}} * \mathbf{i}^g = \begin{bmatrix} \Sigma\, i_i^g \\ \Sigma\, (i_i^g \cdot p_i^g) \end{bmatrix} \tag{6.57}$$

Actually writing

$$m \cdot i^0 + \sigma \cdot k = b_1 \tag{6.58}$$

$$\sigma \cdot i^0 + \mu \cdot k = b_2 \tag{6.59}$$

for every bus shows that we can calculate (i^0, k) by elimination.

This might be slightly confusing, so it will be exemplified by a small program for the 5-bus network of [SE68].

The program inputs the **Y** matrix and inverts it. The slack bus and line-charging were removed. **Y** and $\mathbf{Z} = \mathbf{Y}^{-1}$ are, respectively:

TABLE 6.1

10.8333 - j32.5000	-1.66667 + j5.000	-1.66667 + j5.000	-2.5000 + j7.500
-1.6678 + j5.00000	12.91667 - j38.75	-10.0000 + j30.00	0.0000 + j0.000
-1.6667 + j5.00000	-10.0000 + j30.00	12.9167 - j38.75	-1.2500 + j37.500
-2.5000 + j7.50000	0.0000 + j0.000	-1.2500 + j37.50	3.7500 - j11.250

0.016875+j0.050571	0.012571+j0.037714	0.013429+j0.040286	0.015714+j0.047143
0.012571+j0.037714	0.029714+j0.089143	0.026286+j0.078857	0.017143+j0.051429
0.013429+j0.040286	0.026286+j0.078857	0.031713+j0.095143	0.019524+j0.058571
0.015714+j0.047143	0.017143+j0.051429	0.019524+j0.058571	0.043651+j0.130952

The results of two load flows are shown in Table 6.2. The currents injected into a bus k can be calculated form $i_k := (p_k - j \cdot q_k)/u_k''$. For instance, the current injected into bus 2 in the first case (LF 1) is

$$i_2 := \frac{0.2 - j \cdot 0.2}{1.047438 \cdot \exp(j \cdot 2.806358)} = 0.186039 - j0.104705$$

where $p_2 = 0.4 - 0.2 = 0.2$ and $q_2 = 0.3 - 0.1 = 0.2$. (The voltages and powers can be looked up in [SE68] and Table 6.2(c)).

The resulting currents are summarized below. Included is also $i^t = \Sigma\, i_k^c,\ k\Sigma = 1, \ldots, n$.

Finally note that column i^c shows the sum of the load *and* charging currents for every bus.

Matrix $\mathbf{M}'$ is defined as

$$\mathbf{M}' = \begin{bmatrix} i_1^t & 1 \\ i_2^t & 1 \end{bmatrix} = \begin{bmatrix} (1.589920 - j0.234757) & 1 \\ (2.275624 - j0.559361) & 1 \end{bmatrix}$$

TABLE 6.2(a) Currents for load flow Number 1

FOR LOAD FLOW NUMBER 1

Bus	Load current	Charging current	Injected current
1	0.00000+j0.000000	0.000000+j0.0583000	0.000000+j0.058300
2	0.18604-j0.010470	0.004359+j0.0088925	0.190398-j0.015780
3	0.42459-j0.184174	0.004906+j0.0561160	0.429857-j0.128058
4	0.38456-j0.084933	0.005229+j0.0560530	0.389793-j0.028880
5	0.57551-j0.160822	0.004362+j0.0404830	0.579872-j.0120339
The	total current is therefore	:=	1.589920-j.0234757

FOR LOAD FLOW NUMBER 2

Bus	Load current	Charging current	Injected current
1	0.000000+j0.000000	0.000000+j0.058300	0.000000+j0.058300
2	0.266577-j0.153541	0.006379+j0.088803	0.272956-j0.064351
3	0.603547-j0.286336	0.006965+j0.055018	0.610512-j0.231318
4	0.551287-j0.144671	0.007428+j0.054918	0.558715-j0.089753
5	0.827220-j0.271780	0.006221+j0.039541	0.833441-j0.232239
The	total current is therefore	:=	2.275624-j0.559361

TABLE 6.2(b) Results for load flow Number 2

First load flow

bus	u	teta	pg	pc	qg	qd
1	1.060000	0.000000	1.295868	0.074217	0.000000	0.000000
2	1.047438	-2.806358	0.400000	0.300006	0.200000	0.100000
3	1.024176	-4.996976	0.000000	0.000000	0.450000	0.150000
4	1.023567	-5.329145	0.000000	0.000000	0.400000	0.050000
5	1.017937	-6.160273	0.000000	0.000000	0.600000	0.100000

Second load flow

bus	u	teta	pg	pc	qg	qd
1	1.060000	0.000000	1.856598	-0.147590	0.000000	0.000000
2	1.047438	-4.108901	0.600000	0.690520	0.290000	0.140000
3	1.008304	-7.214741	0.000000	0.000000	0.640000	0.210000
4	1.007594	-7.702934	0.000000	0.000000	0.570000	0.070000
5	1.000688	-8.941617	0.000000	0.000000	0.860000	0.140000

TABLE 6.2(c)

Line	Pline	Qline
1_2	1.274164	1.244837
1_3	0.582434	0.557938
2_3	0.357012	0.349287
2_4	0.403811	0.394246
2_5	0.794014	0.769919
3_4	0.267226	0.266484
4_5	0.090730	0.090081

Line	Pline	Qline
1_2	0.888638	0.874534
1_3	0.407230	0.395311
2_3	0.246943	0.243428
2_4	0.279361	0.274948
2_5	0.548229	0.536977
3_4	0.188739	0.188382
4_5	0.063330	0.063023

Next, we calculate $(\mathbf{M}')^{\mathrm{T}} * \mathbf{M}'$:

$$\begin{bmatrix} 8.074306 & (3.865544 + j0.794118) \\ (3.865544 - j0.794118) & 2.0 \end{bmatrix}$$

By Eq. (6.53) we have $\mathbf{x} = (\mathbf{M}^{\mathrm{T}} * \mathbf{M})^{-1} * \mathbf{M}^{\mathrm{T}} * \mathbf{i}^c$ and this leads to

$$\begin{bmatrix} k \\ i^0 \end{bmatrix} = \begin{bmatrix} (-1.191372 - j0.563981) & (1.191373 + j0.563982) \\ (3.026584 + j0.617001) & (-2.026585 - j0.617003) \end{bmatrix} * \begin{bmatrix} i_1^c \\ i_2^c \end{bmatrix}$$

This equation is true for $i = 1, 2, \ldots, 5$, and by insertion of currents from Tables 6.2 and 6.3 we get the corresponding k and i^0 values.

Bus 1: $k_1 = 0.0$; $i_1^0 = 0.0 + j0.058300$
Bus 2: $k_2 = 0.125751 - j0.011305$; $i_2^0 = -0.006881 + j0.031714$
Bus 3: $k_3 = 0.273465 - j0.021135$; $i_3^0 = 0.000032 - j0.030258$
Bus 4: $k_4 = 0.235581 + j0.022747$; $i_4^0 = 0.009899 - j0.009742$
Bus 5: $k_5 = 0.365206 + j0.009694$; $i_5^0 = -0.003051 - j0.050018$

Note that in this particular case it is not required to go through the least-squares method. Indeed, two load flows give two equations with two unknowns.

Next we deal with *generators* and, in particular, generator currents.

Since $i^g = (p^g - j \cdot q^g)/u''$, we get for the slack bus $p_1^g = 1.295868$ and 0.4 for the second generator.

Bus 1: $i_1^g = 1.222517 + j0.070016$
Bus 2: $i_2^g = 0.367403 - j0.304773$

Total generated power for load flow 1 is $1.589920 - j0.234757$.

In the second load flow, these powers are 1.856598 and 0.6, so that

Bus 1: $i_1^g = 1.751508 + j0.139236$
Bus 2: $i_2^g = 0.524117 - j0.698597$

Total generated power for load flow 2 is $2.275625 - j0.559361$.

From the two load flows, the generated powers lead to

$$\mathbf{M}_1 = \begin{bmatrix} 1.295868 & 1 \\ 1.856598 & 1 \end{bmatrix}$$

We have $\mathbf{M}_1$, since we took the values for bus 1. Again, we calculate $\mathbf{A} = \mathbf{M}_1^T * \mathbf{M}_1$, $\mathbf{A}^{-1}$, and then $\mathbf{A}^{-1} * \mathbf{M}_1^T$. Then we do the same for bus 2.

$$\mathbf{A} = \begin{bmatrix} 5.126230 & 3.152466 \\ 3.152466 & 2 \end{bmatrix} : \quad \mathbf{A}^{-1} = \begin{bmatrix} 6.360957 & -10.02635 \\ -10.02635 & 16.303863 \end{bmatrix}$$

$$\mathbf{A}^{-1} * \mathbf{M}_1 = \begin{bmatrix} -1.783389 & 1.783390 \\ 3.311037 & -2.311038 \end{bmatrix}$$

$$\mathbf{M}_2 = \begin{bmatrix} 0.4 & 1 \\ 0.6 & 1 \end{bmatrix}; \quad \mathbf{A}_2 = \begin{bmatrix} 0.52 & 1 \\ 1 & 2 \end{bmatrix}$$

$$\mathbf{A}_2^{-1} = \begin{bmatrix} 50 & -25 \\ -25 & 13 \end{bmatrix}; \quad \begin{bmatrix} -5 & 5 \\ 3 & -2 \end{bmatrix} = \mathbf{A}_2 * \mathbf{M}_2$$

Equations (6.39) and (6.42) can be written, respectively, as

$$\begin{bmatrix} i_2 \\ i_3 \\ i_4 \\ i_5 \end{bmatrix} = \begin{bmatrix} -k_2 & 1-k_2 \\ -k_3 & -k_3 \\ -k_4 & -k_4 \\ -k_5 & -k_5 \end{bmatrix} * \begin{bmatrix} i_1^g \\ i_2^g \end{bmatrix} + \begin{bmatrix} i_2^0 \\ i_3^0 \\ i_4^0 \\ i_5^0 \end{bmatrix}$$

$$\begin{bmatrix} i_1^g \\ i_2^g \end{bmatrix} = \begin{bmatrix} s_1^g & 0 \\ 0 & s_2^g \end{bmatrix} * \begin{bmatrix} p_1^g \\ p_2^g \end{bmatrix} + \begin{bmatrix} s_1^0 \\ s_2^0 \end{bmatrix}$$

If the second is inserted into the first, it will yield

$$\begin{bmatrix} i_2 \\ i_3 \\ i_4 \\ i_5 \end{bmatrix} = \begin{bmatrix} -k_2 \cdot s_1^g & (1-k_2) \cdot s_2^g \\ -k_3 \cdot s_1^g & -k_3 \cdot s_2^g \\ -k_4 \cdot s_1^g & -k_4 \cdot s_2^g \\ -k_5 \cdot s_1^g & -k_5 \cdot s_2^g \end{bmatrix} * \begin{bmatrix} p_1^g \\ p_2^g \end{bmatrix} + \begin{bmatrix} -k_2 \cdot s_1^0 + (1-k_2) \cdot s_2^0 & -i_2^0 \\ -k_3 \cdot s_1^0 - k_3 \cdot s_2^0 & -i_3^0 \\ -k_4 \cdot s_1^0 - k_4 \cdot s_2^0 & -i_4^0 \\ -k_5 \cdot s_1^0 - k_5 \cdot s_2^0 & -i_5^0 \end{bmatrix}$$

$$= \mathbf{C} * \begin{bmatrix} p_1^g \\ p_2^g \end{bmatrix} + \mathbf{d}$$

All we need here are the power values:

Bus 1: $s_1^g = 0.943398 + j0.123446$; $s_1^0 = 0.0 - j0.089954$
Bus 2: $s_2^g = 0.783570 - j1.969120$; $s_2^0 = 0.053975 + j0.482875$

Next, matrix $\mathbf{C}' \equiv \mathbf{S}^G * (\mathbf{I} - \mathbf{K})$, and vector $\mathbf{d} \equiv (\mathbf{i}^k)''$ are calculated:

$$\mathbf{C}' = \begin{bmatrix} -0.120029 - j0.004858 & 0.707296 - j1.712643 \\ -0.260595 - j0.013819 & -0.172662 - j0.555046 \\ -0.219439 - j0.050541 & -0.229386 + j0.446063 \\ -0.343338 - j0.542290 & -0.305253 + j0.711539 \end{bmatrix}$$

$$\mathbf{d} = \begin{bmatrix} 0.035865 + j\cdot 0.465789 \\ -0.023033 - j\cdot 0.136567 \\ 0.006121 - j\cdot 0.103534 \\ -0.018954 - j\cdot 0.194038 \end{bmatrix}$$

All items are now ready for

$$\begin{aligned} \mathbf{B} &= \mathrm{Re}\{\mathbf{C}^{\mathrm{T}} * \mathbf{Z}^{\mathrm{T}} * \mathbf{C}''\} \\ \mathbf{b} &= \mathrm{Re}\{\mathbf{C}^{\mathrm{T}} * \mathbf{Z}^{\mathrm{T}} * \mathbf{d}'' + (\mathbf{C}'')^{\mathrm{T}} * \mathbf{Z} * \mathbf{d}'\} \\ c &= \mathrm{Re}\{\mathbf{d}^{\mathrm{T}} * \mathbf{Z}^{\mathrm{T}} * \mathbf{d}''\} \end{aligned} \tag{6.60}$$

The program (bedip) used here is Program 6.2. It results in

$$P_{\mathrm{opt}} = [p_1^g p_2^g] * \begin{bmatrix} 0.021140 & -0.047721 \\ 0.056552 & 0.050707 \end{bmatrix} * \begin{bmatrix} p_1^g \\ p_2^g \end{bmatrix}$$

$$+ [p_1^g p_2^g] * \begin{bmatrix} 0.001829 \\ -0.021558 \end{bmatrix} + 0.002917$$

If we insert p_1^g and p_2^g and compare the total generated power in the two load flows, we get

First LF: $p_{\mathrm{opt}} = 0.044854$, but from LF, 0.045868
Second LF: $p_{\mathrm{opt}} = 0.094338$, but from LF, 0.096598

As seen, there is a reduction of p_{opt}, as we have hoped.

Note: The treatment of LF current introduces an error. It is obvious that charging currents and load currents *do not* vary in the same way, and lumping them together in the load currents leads to an error in the assumption of a linear rule. On the other hand, accuracy is not the prime concern in ED problems — speed is (see Section 6.4).

The **B** coefficients were computed above. How do we use them? First note that the Lagrangian for the case of $p_L \neq 0$ is $L = f_T - \lambda \cdot (\Sigma\, p_i^g - \Sigma\, p_k^c - p_L)$. Differentiation and setting to zero yields

```
program bedip(input,output);
type lar=array[1..4,1..4] of real;
     mar=array[1..4,1..2] of real;
     sar=array[1..2,1..2] of real;
     lvec=array[1..4] of real;
     svec=array[1..2] of real;
var h,i,j,k:integer;
    bore,boim,bnnre,bnnim,iim,im,pi,pr,re,rre,zi,zr:real;
    zre,zim:lar;  pre,pim:mar;  bnr,bni:sar;
    opre,opim:lvec;  bnore,bnoim:svec;
begin
read(n,m);
for i:=1 to n do
for j:=1 to n do read(zre[i,j],zim[i,j]);
for i:=1 to n do
for j:=1 to m do read(pre[i,j],pim[i,j]);
for i:=1 to n do read(opre[i],opim[i]);
for i:=1 to n do
begin writeln; writeln(' Matrix Z ');
   for j:=1 to n do write(zre[i,j]:7:4);
   for j:=1 to n do write(zim[i,j]:7:4)
end; writeln;
for i:=1 to n do
begin writeln; writeln(' Powers ');
   for j:=1 to m do write(pre[i,j]:7:4);
   for j:=1 to m do write(pim[i,j]:7:4)
end; writeln(' Vector Opre ');
for i:=1 to n do write(opre[i],opim[i]);
writeln; {The loop below computes BN = C' * C"}
for i:=1 to m do
for j:=1 to m do
begin  bnnre:=0.0; bnnim:=0.0;
   for k:=1 to n do
   for h:=1 to n do
   begin pr:=pre[k,i]; zr:=zre[k,h]; pi:=pim[k,i]; zi:=zim[k,h];
      re:=pr*zr-pi*zi;
      im:=pr*zi+pi*zr;
      pr:=pre[h,j]; pi:=pim[h,j];
      bnnre:=bnnre+re*pr+im*pi;
      bnnim:=bnnim+im*pr-re*pi;
   end;
   bnr[i,j]:=bnnre; bni[i,j]:=bnnim
end; {The loop below computes vector b}
for i:=1 to m do
begin bore:=0.0; boim:=0.0;
   for k:=1 to n do
   for j:=1 to n do
   begin pr:=pre[k,i]; zr:=zre[k,j];
      pi:=pim[k,i];  zi:=zim[k,j];
      re:=pr*zr-pi*zi; im:=pr*zi+pi*zr;
      rre:=pr*zr+pi*zi; iim:=pr*zi-pi*zr;
      or:=opre[i]; oi:=opim[i];
      bore:=bore+re*or-im*oi+rre*or-iim*oi;
      boim:=boim+im*or-re*oi+rre*or-iim*oi
   end;
   bnore[i]:=bore; bnoim[i]:=boim
end;
```

Program 6.2

```
bore:=0.0;  boim:=0.0; {Two parts of scalar c}
for i:=1 to n do
for j:=1 to n do
begin
   re:=zre[i,j]*opre[j]+zim[i,j]*opim[j];
   im:=zim[i,j]*opre[j]-zre[i,j]*opim[j];
   bore:=bore+re*opre[i]-im*opim[i];
   boim:=boim+re*opim[i]+im*opre[i]
end;
writeln; writeln('   BNN   ');
for i:=1 to m do
for j:=1 to m do
begin
   write(bnr[i,j]:7:3,'+j*',bni[i,j]:7:3);
   writeln
end;
writeln; writeln('    BNO    '); writeln;
for i:=1 to m do
   write(bnore[i]:7:3,'+j*',bnoim:7:3);
writeln; writeln('   BOO   '); writeln;
writeln(bore:7:3,'+j*',boim:7:3)
end.
```

Program 6.2 (cont.)

$$\frac{df_T}{dp_i^g} - \lambda + \lambda\cdot\frac{dp_L}{dp_i^g} = 0$$

$$\frac{df_T}{dp_i^g} = \lambda\cdot\left(1 - \frac{dp_L}{dp_i^g}\right)$$

so that the rule of optimum dispatch is

$$k_i\cdot\frac{df_T}{dp_i^g} = \lambda \tag{6.61}$$

instead of

$$\frac{df_T}{dp_i^g} = \lambda \tag{6.62}$$

with

$$k_i = \frac{1}{1 - dp_L/dp_i^g} \tag{6.63}$$

as the so-called penalty factor for bus i. Since $\partial p_L/\partial p_i^g$ is always less than one, if losses p_L increase, $1 - \partial p_L/\partial p_i^g$ will decrease and k_i will be above 1. This explains the name "penalty factor."

In theory one cannot put a limit on $\partial p_L/\partial p_i$, i.e., we have $-\infty \le \partial p_L/\partial p_i \le +\infty$. This can be seen from Fig. 6.6.

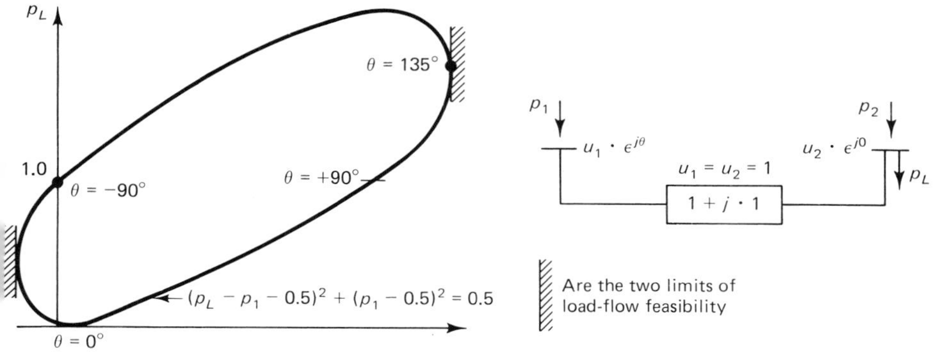

Figure 6.6 A network which proves limits of feasibility.

As is seen from this example, theoretically we can have negative penalty factors. In practice (normal operating conditions), however, $\partial p_L / \partial p_i$ is close to zero, so that penalty factors are close to one.

In most cases $\partial p_L / \partial p_i$ is less than 1 and the method can be applied to this case too. Moreover, since

$$\mathbf{p}_L = (\mathbf{p}^g)^{\mathrm{T}} * \mathbf{B} * \mathbf{p}^g + \mathbf{b}^{\mathrm{T}} * \mathbf{p}^g + c$$

differentiation yields

$$\frac{\partial p_L}{\partial p_i^g} = 2 \cdot \Sigma\, B_{im} \cdot p_m + b_i; \quad m\Sigma = 1, \ldots, n^g$$

The final prescription for a minimum is therefore

$$\frac{\partial f_T / \partial p_i^g}{1 - 2 \cdot \Sigma\, B_{im} \cdot p_m - b_i} = \lambda \tag{6.64}$$

6.4 PARALLEL CONJUGATE-GRADIENT METHODS

First note that the **B**-matrix method can be applied in real time and be programmed for an ASP system. All that is necessary is to adapt the calculation of the **B** coefficients and evaluation of Eq. (6.60) to such systems.

Assuming that **Z** is given and two load flows have been run, Eq. (6.40) will supply the current vector **i**; since the values are independent, the n buses are divided among the p slaves with each calculating its share of currents. The master then sums the currents for calculation of $\mathbf{i}^t$.

To calculate vectors **k** and $\mathbf{i}^0$, Givens' method is applied to matrix **M** and vector $\mathbf{i}^c$. Since $\mathbf{i}^g$ by Eq. (6.41) again constitutes a set of independent equations, it is calculated the same way **i** was. For **K**, **S**, and **C**, another application of Givens' method is required. The results [Eq. (6.45)] require a matrix-by-matrix parallel multiplication and was shown in [Wa82] to have a very high speedup.

A matrix-by-vector multiplication is also required in Eq. (6.60). Actually, since $\Sigma B_{im} \cdot p_m$ is required for all $i = 1, \ldots, n^g$, each slave could multiply a "slice" of rows of **B** with vector **p**. This necessitates only the transfer of **p** to all slaves. If the master transfers a given value for $\lambda^{(i)}$, each slave could be viewed as being responsible for its share of generators and the master just compares the total power generation of an iteration (i) with that of $(i - 1)$.

The development of such a program is left as an exercise. Next, yet another method is discussed.

First, it will be shown [Wa68]* that the load-flow problem is an *unconstrained minimization* problem. If we redefine u' as $v - j \cdot w$ instead of $v + jw$ (for the slack bus $u_0' = 1 - j \cdot 0$), then the LF equations are for $k = 1, \ldots, n$:

$$\Sigma\,(g_i \cdot v_i + b_{ki} \cdot w_i) + g_{k0} + \frac{q_k \cdot w_k - p_k \cdot v_k}{v_k^2 + w_k^2} = 0$$

$$\Sigma\,(b_{ki} \cdot v_i - g_{ki} \cdot w_i) + b_{k0} + \frac{q_k \cdot v_k + p_k \cdot w_k}{v_k^2 + w_k^2} = 0$$

for $i\Sigma = 1, \ldots, n$.

Using **r** as the column vector of residuals and defining

$$\mathbf{e} \equiv [v_1, v_2, \ldots, v_n, w_1, \ldots, w_n]^{\mathrm{T}}$$

$$\mathbf{Y} = \begin{bmatrix} \mathbf{G} & \mathbf{B} \\ \mathbf{B} & -\mathbf{G} \end{bmatrix}$$

$$\mathbf{y}_0 \equiv [g_{10}, \ldots, g_{n0}, b_{10}, \ldots, b_{n0}]$$

$$\mathbf{a} = \left[\frac{q_1 \cdot w_1 - p_1 \cdot v_1}{v_1^2 + w_1^2}, \ldots, \frac{q_n \cdot v_n + p_n \cdot w_n}{v_n^2 + w_n^2} \right]^{\mathrm{T}}$$

we have $\mathbf{r} = \mathbf{Y} * \mathbf{e} + \mathbf{y}_0 + \mathbf{a}$.

The solution will obviously minimize (set to zero):

$$f = \Sigma\, r_i^2; \quad i\Sigma = 1, \ldots, 2 \cdot n \tag{6.65}$$

Let me digress for a moment. In [Wa68] a new method is proposed as follows: Use as a gradient vector

---

* Y. Wallach, "Gradient Methods for Load-Flow Problems," *Trans. IEEE*, Vol. PAS-87, No. 5, May 1968, pp. 1314–18. © 1968 by IEEE. Used with permission.

$$\tilde{z}_i = \frac{-(\partial f / \partial e_i)}{\partial^2 f / \partial e_i^2} \tag{6.66}$$

instead of

$$z_i = \left[\frac{\partial f}{\partial e_1}, \ldots, \frac{\partial f}{\partial e_{2n}} \right]^{\mathrm{T}} \tag{6.67}$$

The method should then be invariant to a shift of axes and consequently should converge faster. The second derivatives of Eq. (6.66) are the Hessian matrix $\mathbf{H} = \partial^2 r_i / \partial e_j^2$, which consists here of two diagonal submatrices.

This leads to a gradient vector with $\tilde{z}_i = z_i / \rho_i$ where

$$\rho_i = (\alpha_i + \beta_i) + 2(\gamma_i + \delta_i); \quad i = 1, \ldots, n$$

$$\rho_i = (\alpha_i + \beta_i) - 2(\gamma_i + \delta_i); \quad i = n + 1, \ldots, 2n$$

$$\alpha_i = \Sigma\ (g_{ki}^2 + b_{ki}^2); \quad k\Sigma = 1, \ldots, n$$

$$\beta_i = d_i^2 + t_i^2; \qquad \gamma_i = g_{ii} \cdot d_i - b_{ii} \cdot t_i$$

$$d_i = \frac{p_i \cdot (v_i^2 - w_i^2) - 2 q_i v_i w_i}{(v_i^2 + w_i^2)^2}$$

$$t_i = \frac{q_i \cdot (v_i^2 - w_i^2) + 2 p_i v_i w_i}{(v_i^2 + w_i^2)^2}$$

$$\delta_i = \frac{r_i \cdot (p_i v_i \phi_i + q_i w_i \psi_i) + r_{n+i} \cdot (p_i w_i \psi_i - q_i v_i \phi_i)}{(v_i^2 w_i^2)^3}$$

$$\phi_1 = 3 \cdot w_i^2 + v_i^2; \qquad \psi_i = 3 \cdot v_i^2 - w_i^2$$

The equations are simple — the Hessian even more so. Unfortunately, the method showed slow convergence.

Returning to the main subject, minimization of f in Eq. (6.65) shows that LF is really a minimization problem and in this particular case could be solved by the conjugate-gradient method of Chapter 5.

In the present context, the question is whether the conjugate-gradient method can be implemented on ASP.

A number of methods to do just that were proposed in [HW84]† and two of them follow next. First, recall from Section 5.2.4 that a set of vectors $\{\mathbf{d}_i, i = 1, \ldots., n\}$ is conjugate with respect to a Hessian matrix **H**, if and only if

† E. C. Housos, O. Wing, "Parallel Gradient Optimization Methods," *Journal of Optimization Theory & Applications*, February 1984. Used with permission.

$$\mathbf{d}_i^{\mathrm{T}} * (\mathbf{H} * \mathbf{d}_j) = \begin{cases} 0 & \text{for } i \neq j \\ 1 & \text{for } i = j \end{cases}$$

Conjugate vectors with respect to the Hessian matrix of the objective function can be used in minimizing Eq. (6.65). If the problem is quadratic, then the Hessian is constant and the minimum of a quadratic function

$$f(\mathbf{x}) = \mathbf{x}^{\mathrm{T}} * (\mathbf{H} * \mathbf{x}) + \mathbf{b}^{\mathrm{T}} * \mathbf{x} + c,$$

"can be found by performing linear searches along a set $\{\mathbf{d}_i,\ i = 1, \ldots, n\}$ of conjugate directions with respect to **H** once and only once in any order.

"For parallel computation this implies that if a set of p conjugate directions with respect to **H** and p processors are available, then the solution of the quadratic optimization problem can be found in *one* major parallel step and an additional step that involves the addition of the local minima. In algorithmic form, assuming that p processors are available, this can be formulated as follows:

Step 1. Use the kth processor to calculate μ_k such that

$$f(\mathbf{x}^0 + \mu_k \cdot \mathbf{d}_k) = \min_\mu f(\mathbf{x}^0 + \mu \cdot \mathbf{d}_k) \tag{6.68}$$

Step 2.

$$\tilde{\mathbf{x}} = \mathbf{x}^0 + [\Sigma\ \mu_k \cdot \mathbf{d}_k];\ \ k\Sigma = 1 \cdots \tag{6.69}$$

where $\mathbf{x}^0$ is the initial point and $\tilde{\mathbf{x}}$ is the minimum point for quadratic f. For nonquadratic cases the process must be iterated. In order for such algorithms to be useful, there must exist an efficient procedure for calculating a set of conjugate directions with respect to the Hessian at the current point in the iterating procedure.

"In order to assess the convergence characteristics of the conjugate direction method when applied to power system problems, several computational experiments were performed... The results obtained are illustrated by Fig. 6.7. It can be seen that for the load-flow problem, the algorithm converged in a fixed number of parallel iterations independently of the size of the problem. The load-flow problem is not highly nonlinear, and thus the previous assumptions seem to hold well."

The second algorithm suggested in [HW84] starts by choosing n *orthogonal* search vectors $\mathbf{d}_i$, $i = 1, \ldots, n$ where n is the dimension of the problem and an initial point $\mathbf{x}^0$, calculating $f(\mathbf{x}^0)$ and setting the iteration count to 1 (IT = 1). Choose a number b as the initial step of the line search procedure. Set $k = 1$.

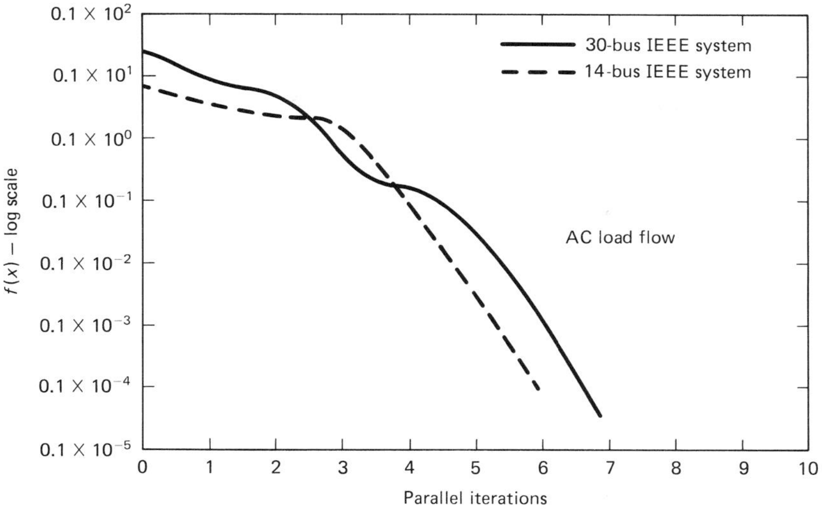

Figure 6.7 Results of applying the algorithm.

Step 1. Find the n one-dimensional minima along the n search vectors. That is,

$$\min_{\mu} f(\mathbf{x}^0 + \mu \cdot \mathbf{d}_i) = f(\mathbf{x}^0 + \mu_i \cdot \mathbf{d}_i); \; i = 1, \ldots, n$$

Stop if the solution has been found.

Normalize each of the search directions. That is, estimate $\mathbf{d}_i^{\mathrm{T}} * (\mathbf{H} * \mathbf{d}_i)$ for $i = 1, \ldots, n$, and set

$$\tilde{\mathbf{d}}_i := \frac{\mathbf{d}_i}{[\mathbf{d}_i^{\mathrm{T}} * (\mathbf{H} * \mathbf{d}_i)]^{1/2}}$$

This step can be implemented in *parallel* using up to n processors.

Step 2. Set $\mathbf{x}_{n+1} = \mathbf{x}^0 + (\Sigma \, \mu_i \cdot \mathbf{d}_i)$, $i\Sigma = 1, \ldots, n$. Set $\mathbf{x} = \mathbf{x}_i$ such that $f(\mathbf{x}_i) = \min_k f(\mathbf{x}_k)$; $k = 1, \ldots, n+1$ where $\mathbf{x}_j = \mathbf{x}^{(0)} + \mu_j \cdot \mathbf{d}_j$, $j = 1, \ldots, n$.

Also calculate

$$C_{ik} = f(\mathbf{x}^0 + \beta \cdot \mathbf{d}_i + \beta \cdot \mathbf{d}_k)/\beta^2 + f(\mathbf{x}^0) - f(\mathbf{x}^0 + \beta \cdot \mathbf{d}_i) - f(\mathbf{x}^0 + \beta \cdot \mathbf{d}_k)$$

for all $i = 1, \ldots, n$, $i \neq k$, and set

$$\mathbf{d}_i := \frac{\tilde{d}_i - C_{ik} \cdot \tilde{\mathbf{d}}_k}{(1 - C_{ik}^2)^{1/2}}$$

for all $i \neq k$ for which $0 < |C_{ik}| < 1$.

Step 3. Set IT = IT + 1 and k = MOD (IT, n). Go to Step 1.

This algorithm reduced the number of parallel iterations needed for the solution of typical power system problems considerably and will next be programmed in a way similar to the algorithm in [HW82]*:

In the initial, sequential step the master would:

S1:

$k := 1$; $it := 1$, {it is an iteration count}
$s := 0.01$; {initial step of the line search procedure}
{The master should choose initial $\mathbf{x}$ and a set of orthogonal vectors $\mathbf{d}_i$, $i = 1, \ldots, n$, where n = dimension of the problem.}
calculate $f(\mathbf{x})$;
{Call a function to calculate initial cost. The master transfers the program, $\mathbf{x}$, step-size k to all slaves and $\mathbf{d}_i$ as well as starting address adrs$_i$ to all slaves i_1, $i = 1, \ldots, p$.}

P1:

{Slave i calculates μ_i such that $f(\mathbf{x}^{(it-1)} + \mu_i \cdot \mathbf{d}_i)$ is minimal and estimates}
$C_{ii}^2 := \mathbf{d}_i^{\mathrm{T}} * (\mathbf{H} * \mathbf{d}_i)$; $\tilde{\mathbf{d}}_i := \mathbf{d}_i / C_{ii}$

S2:

{Transfer all $\tilde{\mathbf{d}}_i$, μ_i, $f(\mathbf{x}^{(it-1)} + \mu_i \mathbf{d}_i)$ and C_{ii} to the master, which then redistribute them to all the slaves}

P2:

{Slave i, $i = 1, \ldots, n$ but $k \neq i$, calculates}
$C_{ik} := [f(\mathbf{x}^{(it-1)} + s \cdot \mathbf{d}_i) + s \cdot C_{kk} \cdot \tilde{\mathbf{d}}_k + f(\mathbf{x}^{(it-1)}) -$
$\quad f(\mathbf{x}^{(it-1)} + s \cdot \mathbf{d}_i) - f(\mathbf{x}^{(it-1)} + s \cdot \mathbf{d}_k)] \,/\, s^2$
if abs $(C_{ik}) > 0$ **and** abs $(C_{ik}) < 1$ **then**
$\quad \mathbf{d}_i := (\tilde{\mathbf{d}}_i - C_{ik} \cdot \tilde{\mathbf{d}}_k)/(1 - C_i^2)^{1/2}$
{Simultaneously, slave k calculates}
$\mathbf{x}_{n+1} := \mathbf{x}^{(it-1)} + \Sigma\, \mu_i \cdot \mathbf{d}_i$; $i \Sigma\ 1, \ldots, n$
for $j := 1$ **to** n **do** $\mathbf{x}_j := \mathbf{x}^{(it-1)} + \mu_j \cdot \mathbf{d}_j$;
calculate $f(\mathbf{x}_k)$.
{such that f is minimum for $k := 1, \ldots, n$} $\mathbf{x}^{(it)} := \mathbf{x}_i$

S3:

{Stop the process if converged. Otherwise}
{Get all $x_i^{(it)}$ and distribute them}
$it := it + 1$; $k :=$ it **mod** n;
{Transfer ks};
goto P1;

---

* E. C. Housos, O. Wing, "Parallel Optimization with Applications to Power Systems," *Trans. IEEE*, Vol. PAS-101, No. 1, 1982, pp. 244-48. Used with permission.

For the calculation of speedup, it is assumed that four function evaluations ϕ are required for every linear search. Thus, the time required on a single computer, namely, all parallel steps, is

$$t_s = 4\cdot\phi\cdot n + 4\cdot\omega\cdot n^2 + n^2\cdot\omega + (n-1)\cdot\phi + 3\cdot n^2\cdot\omega + \phi + 2n^2\cdot\omega$$

The terms are: function evaluations for the n linear searches, the calculation of 4 different points for each of them where two n-dimensional vectors have to be added, n normalizations with n multiplications each, $n-1$ function evaluations, for each of which the evaluation point is calculated, another function evaluation, and, finally, the n^2 multiplications by μ. For large n, only terms with n^2 require time comparable to that of function evaluations. Thus, the time is approximately $t_s \cong 5\cdot\phi\cdot n + 10\cdot\omega\cdot n^2$

In the same way, for parallel execution:

$$t_p \cong 5\cdot\phi + (2\cdot\omega + 4\cdot\tau)\cdot n^2$$

The ratio is therefore

$$\rho \cong \frac{5\cdot\phi + (2\cdot\omega + 4\cdot\tau)\cdot n^2}{5\cdot\phi\cdot n + 10\cdot\omega\cdot n^2}$$

If $10\cdot\omega\cdot n^2$ is partially disregarded,

$$\rho \cong \frac{1}{n} + (2\cdot\omega + 4\cdot\tau)\left[5\cdot\frac{\phi}{n} + 10\cdot\omega\right] \cong \frac{1}{n} + \frac{n\cdot(2\omega + 4\tau)}{5\cdot\phi}$$

As seen, if $5\cdot\phi >> n\cdot(2\cdot\omega + 4\cdot\tau)$, then $\rho \cong 1/n$ and the optimal speedup of n (assumed to be p) is achieved.

6.5 NOTES AND PROJECTS

Newtonian methods are based on [DT68], the **B**-matrix formulation is that of [SGH79], and the gradient method is that of [HW82]. Most textbooks discuss this problem at length. In particular, [WW84] is recommended.

The material for writing an off-line program using the Newtonian approach was given and consists of:

- The load-flow program of Chapter 4.
- The equations for all terms of the Jacobian.
- The optimization program in Section 6.2.

The reader may therefore combine them into a working program for off-line application.

Economic dispatch programs are normally used off-line, but we suggested a real-time use and will therefore propose two additional projects.

At the beginning of section 6.4, we discussed the use of the **B**-matrix method for real-time execution. For that, the state estimation has to be solved as discussed in Chapter 5. Such a project would combine them and run dispatch optimization based on state estimation. It is intriguing to see if more energy can be saved if state estimation replaces load flow.

Finally, the second algorithm of 6.4 could be simulated for real-time, parallel execution.

7 The Stability Problem

The *objectives* of this chapter are

1. To define the problem mathematically starting from simplifying assumptions and models (of generators).
2. To solve the problem by the simplest method, that of equal area and then by solving the differential equations numerically.
3. Calculate the *equivalents*.
4. Describe a fast Gauss–Seidel program.

7.1 INTRODUCTION

One scenario for the stability problem could be as follows: A fault (short circuit) occurs at some point of the network. The currents throughout the network rise almost instantaneously; the closer to the fault location, the higher they are because the network attenuates the increase. Let us then look at some generator close to the fault location. Its (mechanical) power input (p_m) can only change slowly, since the turbines change their speed only sluggishly. Consequently, the voltage of the generator, being proportional to the magnetic flux and speed, remains essentially constant. The current of the generator increases, and thus the electrical output p_e of this generator increases very substantially. An imbalance of powers

$$p_a = p_m - p_e \tag{7.1}$$

results and slows down the generator. This in turn not only reduces the voltage but shifts its angle relative to other voltages of the network. Since a voltage difference (and this can be brought about both by magnitudes and by angles) leads to higher currents, we seem to have a snowballing effect: The current increases, the speed decreases, the angle difference increases, the current increases, and so on.

Relays installed throughout the network are supposed to prevent such calamities and at some point disconnect parts of the network (but not yet the generator). The question, though, is whether this will suffice. If it does, that is, if the disconnecting of some load or the faulted part of the network will reduce the current and the transients will die out, the network was stable; otherwise it was unstable.

The scenario could be different, but the result is the same, namely an increase in the angle difference.

The highest currents result from a three-phase balanced fault and we will concentrate on this case. This simplifies the analysis, since we are allowed to use the positive sequence network and do not need to concern ourselves with the negative and zero-sequence networks. Another simplifying assumption is that the time constants involved are such that phasors can be used. The reader interested in the behavior of the network at the very start of the disturbance is referred to [BMR76].

Since we are already at the assumptions, let us add the following:

- All generators of a particular power station may be combined (under certain conditions still to be discussed), but the power stations have to be dealt with on an individual basis. As already mentioned, stations nearer the fault location are affected more than those remote from it. The speeds, angles, etc., of their representative lumped generators may therefore be quite different.
- Because of this, it is best to base the calculation on the angles δ_i of the rotors, but this immediately poses the question as to how to measure them. If n^g generators are present, then there are $n^g + (n^g - 1) + \cdots + 2 + 1$ different angles; altogether $n^g \cdot (n^g + 1)/2$, and this number is too large.

  Fortunately, we know that the mechanical speed with which the rotor rotates ω_m is *changing* very slowly compared to the electrical speed of $\omega_e = 377$ rad/sec, since the network was assumed to go on working with a frequency of about 60 cps. We will therefore measure all angles *relative* to this synchronous speed ω_e. Figure 7.1 shows the rotor rotating at the mechanical speed ω_m, the field produced in the stator rotating with the synchronous speed ω_e, and the angle δ changing because of changes in ω_m.
- We have already assumed that we can use phasors for voltages and currents throughout the network. The connection between them and

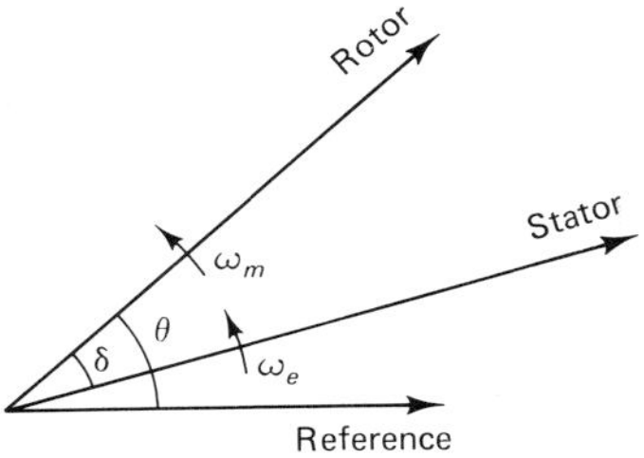

Figure 7.1 Rotating axes.

the powers was seen to result in load flow and thus nonlinear, algebraic equations. On the other hand, Newton's law of motion leads to differential equations for every generator (and actually every motor of the network). We thus have to combine differential with algebraic equations. How this is done will be discussed after the differential equations are derived, and for this we need some models to be discussed next.

We will start from the mechanical motion. Newton's law for linear motion is probably remembered from high school as $F = m \cdot a$ where F is the force, m the mass, and a the acceleration. Generators *rotate*, and we therefore have to change the law.

The angle of the stator field (Fig. 7.1) at any given time t is $\omega_e \cdot t$, and since the mechanical field differs from it by δ, we have $\theta = \omega_e \cdot t + \delta$. The velocity for linear motion is $v = ds/dt$ or for rotation $\omega = d\theta/dt = \omega_e + d\delta/dt$. The angular acceleration is $\alpha = d\omega/dt = d^2\theta/dt^2 = d^2\delta/dt^2$, since ω_e = constant and therefore $d\omega_e/dt = 0$. In sum, we have

$$T = J \cdot \frac{d^2\theta}{dt^2} \equiv J \cdot \alpha \tag{7.2}$$

where T is the torque, J is the moment of inertia, and α is the angular acceleration.

Equation (7.1) could have been written for torques as $T_a = T_m - T_e$ with the understanding that whenever the mechanical torque exceeds the electrical, an acceleration (T_a positive) results and, for the opposite case, a speed reduction will occur.

Power is force times velocity, which with the correspondence introduced earlier is $P = T \cdot \omega$ for rotation. Multiplying the torques by ω and denoting $J \cdot \omega$ by M yields

$$p_a = M \cdot \frac{d^2\delta}{dt^2} = p_m - p_e \tag{7.3}$$

Let us next discuss the electrical power produced by a synchronous generator. The generated voltage is proportional to the flux and speed and will be denoted by e' (the electromotive force). The voltage at the terminals is less than e' because of the voltage drop in the generator. Here we introduce another, but still reasonable assumption, namely that $R_{\text{gen}} << X_{\text{gen}}$, so that only the reactance of the generator $X \equiv X_{\text{gen}}$ is to be accounted for. On the other hand, for a generator with salient poles, we have to use two axes: the direct axis (same as that of a pole) and the quadrature axis (90° to the pole). Since we will then split the stator current i' into these directions, we have Fig. 7.2, from which

$$e' - i_d \cdot x_d = v \cdot \cos(\beta); \qquad i_q \cdot x_q = v \cdot \sin(\beta) \tag{7.4}$$

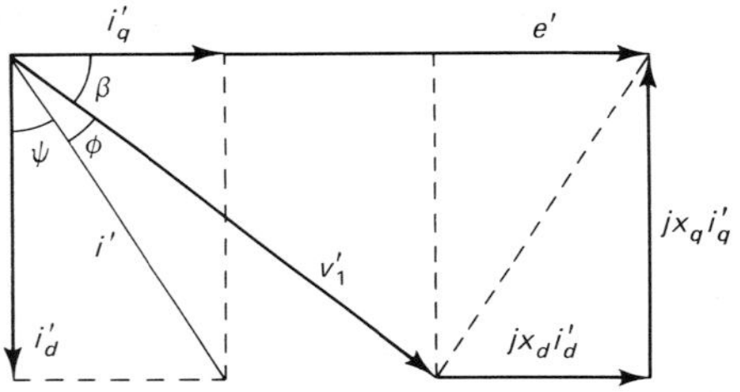

Figure 7.2 Phasor diagram.

We used the direct and quadrature directions as well as angles β, ψ, and ϕ — the last as that between the voltage and current phasors v' and i'. The generated power is $p^g + j \cdot q^g = v \cdot i \cdot \cos(\phi) + j \cdot v \cdot i \cdot \sin(\phi)$.

From Fig. 7.2, $\psi + \phi + \beta = 90°$ or $\phi = 90 - (\beta + \psi)$, so that

$$i' \cdot \cos(\phi) = i' \cdot \sin(\beta + \psi) = i' \cdot \sin(\beta) \cdot \cos(\psi) + i' \cdot \cos(\beta) \cdot \sin(\psi)$$

$$= i' \cdot \cos(\psi) \cdot \sin(\beta) + i' \cdot \sin(\psi) \cdot \cos(\beta) = i_d \cdot \sin(\beta) + i_q \cdot \cos(\beta)$$

and similarly for $i' \cdot \sin(\phi)$. The real power is $p^g = v \cdot i \cdot \cos(\phi) = v \cdot i_q \cdot \cos(\beta) + v \cdot i_d \cdot \sin(\beta)$

Insertion of Eq. (7.4) into the last expression yields $p^g = i_q \cdot (e - i_d \cdot x_d) + i_d \cdot (i_q \cdot x_q)$.

For round rotors, there is no difference between x_d and x_q, so that $x = x_d = x_q$ and we have

$$p^g = e \cdot i_q = (v \cdot \frac{e}{x}) \cdot \sin(\beta) \tag{7.5}$$

If we define the maximum power as $p^{\mathrm{M}} = v \cdot e / x$, then the generated power can be expressed as a sinusoidal function $p^{g} = p^{\mathrm{M}} \cdot \sin(\beta)$ with $\sin(\beta) = 1$ for maximum.

Since the mechanical power is approximately constant, we have all parts of Eq. (7.3), the *swing equation*:

$$p_m - p^{\mathrm{M}} \cdot \sin(\beta) = M \cdot \frac{d^2\delta}{dt^2} \tag{7.6}$$

We make three additional remarks:

- A damping component of $D \cdot \omega = D \cdot d\delta / dt$ should be subtracted from the right-hand side, but since it is normally small, we will neglect it.
- If English units are used then $M = (R \cdot H)/(180 \cdot f)$ where R is the rating of the machine in MVA, f is the frequency (60 cps) and H is $[2.31 \cdot (WR^2) \cdot n^2 \cdot 10^{-10}]/(\text{MVA rating})$. In the latter equation WR^2 is the weight times the radius squared and n the speed (in rpm). We will use M as previously and the swing equation according to Eq. (7.6).
- In this Chapter we deal only occasionally with phasors and reserve the prime for differentiation, that is $y' = dy/dx$.

Equation 7.6 uses $\sin(\beta)$, but since we assumed that the voltage v rotates at the reference speed ω_e we may use $\sin(\delta)$ instead. The angular speed is $\omega = d\delta/dt$, so that Eq. (7.6) may be replaced by two first-order equations:

$$p_m - p^M \cdot \sin(\delta) = M \cdot \frac{d\omega}{dt}; \qquad \omega = \frac{d\delta}{dt} \tag{7.7}$$

This is the set of two first-order, nonlinear (because of the sine) *differential equations to be solved.* Before we review how to solve it, we discuss first a simple criterion of stability.

Let us assume that we deal with a single generator connected to an "infinite bus" through a reactance x. The infinite bus represents the rest of the network, and its voltage and frequency are assumed to be constant and not affected by the fault. The fault or other disturbances (e.g., sudden opening of a line) have the effect of changing x.

To see what is meant by stability, we use Eq. (7.6) and graph $p^M \cdot \sin(\delta)$ and $p_m = $ constant in Fig. 7.3. An equilibrium exists at an angle δ_1 where $p_m = p_e$, $d^2\delta/dt^2 = 0$, and therefore $\omega = d\delta/dt$ is constant. Next, suppose that for some reason the angle increased to δ_2. At this point $p_e > p_m$, $d\delta^2/dt^2 < 0$, and the angle will be reduced.

Because of inertia this reduction is not instantaneous; the generator moves to an angle $\delta > \delta_2$, but because $d^2\delta/dt^2 < 0$, it slows down,

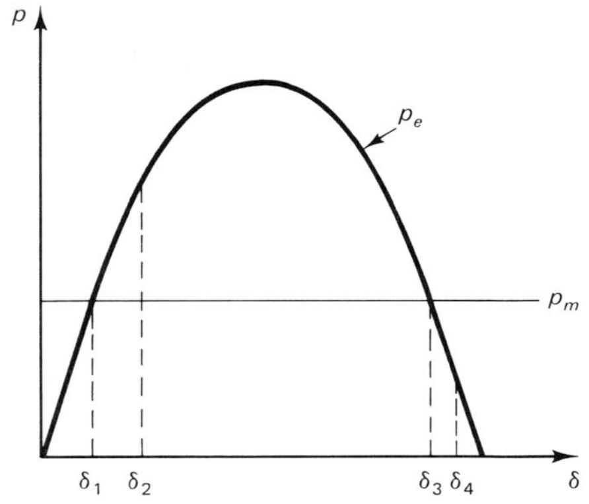

Figure 7.3 Power/angle relationship.

reversing the trend. It will not remain at δ_1 either but overshoot to an angle $\delta < \delta_1$, etc., oscillating around δ_1 until, because of friction, damping, etc., it settles back to $\delta = \delta_1$.

In Fig. 7.3, δ_3 is also an equilibrium point where $p_m = p_e$, $d^2\delta/dt^2 = 0$, and consequently $\omega \equiv d\delta/dt$ is constant. The difference is that if for some reason δ increases to δ_4, $p_m > p_e$ and the generator is accelerating further and further (until the situation becomes extreme or the generator is disconnected from the network). Angle δ_3 is therefore an unstable equilibrium point.

A generator should not operate at an unstable equilibrium. The question is: If the generator swings past δ_2, can it arrive at δ_3? If so, the situation is unstable; if not, the situation is stable.

Recall that $d(d\delta/dt)^2/dt = 2\cdot(d\delta/dt)\cdot(d^2\delta/dt^2)$ and insert $d^2\delta/dt^2$ into the swing equation. This yields

$$2\cdot(d\delta/dt)\cdot(p_m - p_e) = M\cdot d(d\delta/dt)^2/dt$$

$$(d\delta/dt)^2 = (2/M)\cdot\int_0^\delta (p_m - p_e)\cdot d\delta \tag{7.8}$$

This equation shows the integral to be proportional to power (or energy). It is used to compute δ for which $d\delta/dt$ (and therefore also its square) is zero, since for $d\delta/dt = 0$, δ is constant and the rotor has "stopped" oscillating (relative to the synchronously rotating frame).

Suppose a fault occurs and the network reactance x increases, at least until a relay clears the fault. The situation is then as in Fig. 7.4, where p_{e1} shows the power before the fault occurred, p_{e2} during the fault, and p_{e3} after the fault was cleared.

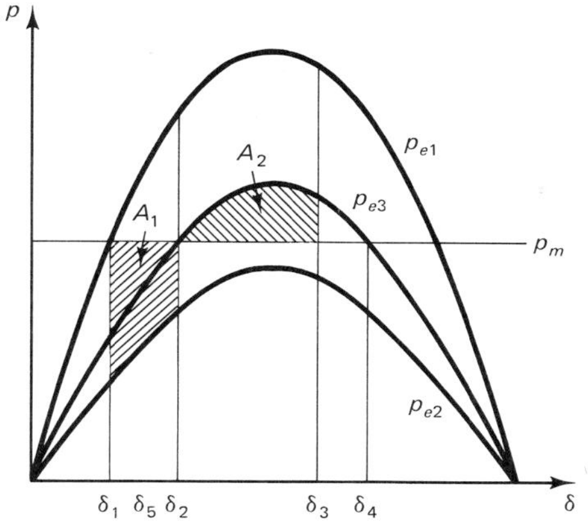

Figure 7.4 A scenario.

Originally $p_m = p_{e1}$ at angle δ_1. If the fault is cleared at angle δ_2, the p_e curve changes to pe_3 at this point. The area A_1 in Fig. 7.4 is proportional to $\Delta p \cdot (\delta_2 - \delta_1)$, i.e., power times distance or accumulated energy [Eq. (7.8)].

After the fault has been cleared, $p_{e3} > p_m$, and the rotor decelerates, loosing kinetic energy. If the angle δ_3 for which $A_1 = A_2$ is $\delta_3 < \delta_4$, then the situation will be restored to an equilibrium at δ_2, but if δ_3 happens to be δ_4, then the rotor arrived at the unstable point. Actually, the question should be posed differently: What is the latest clearing angle δ_2 for which the system is still stable?

To answer this question, we rewrite Eq. (7.8) as

$$\int_{\delta_1}^{\delta_2} [p_m - p_{e2}^{\mathrm{M}} \cdot \sin(\delta)] \cdot d\delta = \int_{\delta_2}^{\delta_4} [-p_m + p_{e3}^{\mathrm{M}} \cdot \sin(\delta)] \cdot d\delta \tag{7.9}$$

Integration yields $p_m(\delta_2 - \delta_1) + p_{e2}^{\mathrm{M}}[\cos(\delta_2) - \cos(\delta_1)] = p_{e3}^{\mathrm{M}}[\cos(\delta_4) - \cos(\delta_2)] - p_m(\delta_4 - \delta_2)$ and the only unknown in this transcendental equation is δ_2. We could solve it numerically (see [DB74]), but it seems better to employ a cut-and-try routine based on repeatedly calculating the areas A_1 and A_2. This is so because areas can be computed very efficiently in computers.

Suppose $y = f(x)$ is given and the area beneath it bounded by $x = a$ and $x = b$ is to be calculated (Fig. 7.5). We can divide the distance $(b - a)$ into n strips each of width $h = (b - a)/n$ and approximate each strip by a trapezoid whose area (Fig. 7.5) is $A_i \cong 0.5 \cdot h \cdot (y_{i+1} + y_i)$. Summing all n trapezoids yields $A \cong 0.5 \cdot h \cdot [(y_0 + y_1) + (y_1 + y_2) + \cdots + (y_{n-2} + y_{n-1}) + (y_{n-1} + y_n)]$

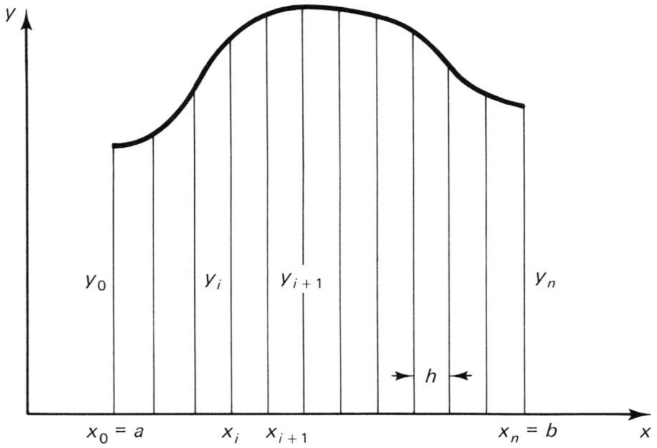

Figure 7.5 Trapezoidal integration.

Note that each y_i except y_0 and y_n appears twice, so that

$$A \equiv h\cdot[(\Sigma\, y_i) + 0.5\cdot(y_0 + y_n)]; \quad i\Sigma = 1, 2, \ldots, n-1 \tag{7.10}$$

This is an exceptionally simple formula and could be applied, were it not for the fact that errors are obviously large, because we have approximated the curve $y = f(x)$ by a series of straight lines.

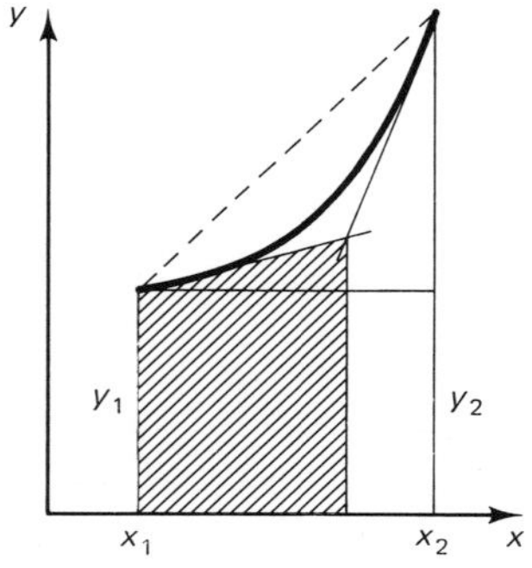

Figure 7.6 Two trapezes.

To have an idea of how large the errors are, consider Fig. 7.6. We have approximated the area of the strip by a trapezoid or through

$$I = \int_{x_1}^{x_2} f(x)\cdot dx \cong 0.5\cdot h\cdot(y_1 + y_2) \tag{7.11}$$

Suppose we replace this area by the two trapezoids, bounded upwards by the slopes $(df/dx)_{x=x1} \equiv y_1'$; and $(df/dx)_{x=x2} \equiv y_2'$. Since the area is the sum of the two trapezoids, we have

$$\tilde{I} \cong \int f(x)\cdot dx \tag{7.12}$$

$$\cong \frac{h[y_1 + (y_1 + h\cdot y_1'/2) + y_2 + (y_2 - h\cdot y_2'/2)]}{4}$$

$$\tilde{I} \equiv \frac{h\cdot y_1 + y_2}{2} + \frac{h^2\cdot(y_1' - y_2')}{8} = I + \frac{h^2(y_1' - y_2')}{8}$$

The error is therefore of the order of $h^2/8$ (if the function does not change its derivatives too abruptly).

As seen, the error can be reduced if h is made smaller, but then more strips have to be added and we might find that the accumulated roundoff error increases. Therefore, normally Simpson's formula is used instead of the trapezoidal. It uses three points for every strip:

$$I \cong \frac{h\cdot(y_1 + 4\cdot y_2 + y_3)}{6} \tag{7.13}$$

and has a truncation error proportional to h^4.

In practice, Simpson's formula would be used in conjunction with Eq. (7.9), trying various δ_2 until the two sides match. This yields the critical clearing angle δ_2.

7.2 THE ALGORITHMIC STEPS

7.2.1 Simplified Procedure

Let us start by describing in principle the solution for a small network (Fig. 7.7). Each of the steps will then be generalized. The generators will be represented as voltages or electromotive forces e_i' and reactances jx_i^g. Because the voltages have to be known throughout the network, a load flow must be run before stability is analyzed.

As a result of the load-flow study, we compute generator currents, voltages, and load admittances as follows:

$$\begin{aligned} i_1^g &:= (s_i^g/u_1)''; & i_3^g &:= (s_3^g/u_3)'' \\ e_1' &:= u_1' + i_1^g\cdot jx_1^g; & e_3' &:= u_3' + i_3^g\cdot jx_3^g \\ y_2' &:= s_2''/u_2^2; & y_4' &:= s_4''/u_2^2 \end{aligned} \tag{7.14}$$

Note that in Eq. (7.14) loads were represented as admittances and that the admittances of the generators are $y_i^g = -j/x_i^g$ for $i = 1$ and 3. Using them, the network of Fig. 7.7(b) can be represented by a 4-by-4 matrix **Y**,

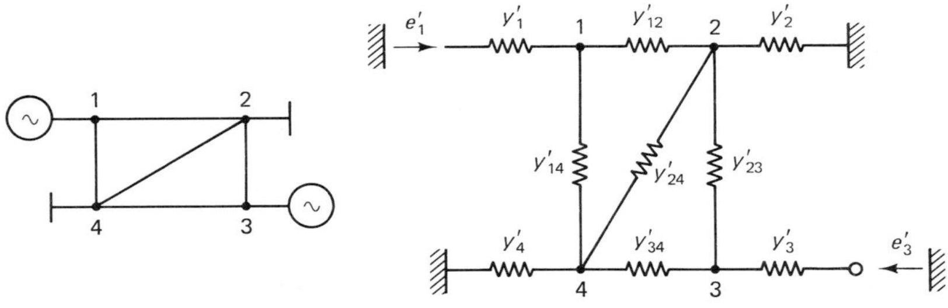

Figure 7.7 A small network and its model circuit.

with $Y_{i,i}' := \Sigma y_{i,j}'$, for all buses j connected to bus i (including y_1', y_2', y_3' and y_4') and $Y_{i,j}' := -y_{i,j}'$.

Because of a fault, generator 1 is disconnected at $t = 0$. Obviously it will start running faster, since it dropped the entire load. The assumption is made that the voltages remain constant. Since generator 1 is disconnected, it does not supply any current and the equations of the network are

$$\begin{bmatrix} Y_{11}' & Y_{12}' & Y_{13}' & Y_{14}' \\ Y_{21}' & Y_{22}' & Y_{23}' & Y_{24}' \\ Y_{31}' & Y_{32}' & Y_{33}' & Y_{34}' \\ Y_{41}' & Y_{42}' & Y_{43}' & Y_{44}' \end{bmatrix} * \begin{bmatrix} u_1' \\ u_2' \\ u_3' \\ u_4' \end{bmatrix} = \begin{bmatrix} 0 \\ 0 \\ (i_3^g) \\ 0 \end{bmatrix} \tag{7.15}$$

From Eq. (7.14) we have that $(i_3^g)' = (e_3' - u_3')/(jx_3^g)$.

Equation (7.15) is thus a set of linear algebraic equations and could be solved *except* that e_3' is not known for times after $t = 0$. To calculate it, the differential equations must be solved.

Let us rewrite Eq. (7.7) with x_1 and x_2 substituting for δ_1 and ω_1 of generator 1. Since there are now two generators, x_3 and x_4 substitute for δ_3 and ω_3. This defines a (column) vector $\mathbf{x}$ through:

$$\mathbf{x} = [\delta_1, \omega_1, \delta_3, \omega_3]^{\mathrm{T}}; \qquad \omega_i = d\delta_i/dt \tag{7.16}$$

The set of differential equations is therefore

$$x_2 = \frac{dx_1}{dt}; \qquad x_4 = \frac{dx_3}{dt} \tag{7.17}$$

$$M_1 \cdot \frac{dx_2}{dt} = p_{m1} - p_1^{\mathrm{M}} \cdot \sin(x_1); \qquad M_3 \cdot \frac{dx_4}{dt} = p_{m3} - p_3^{\mathrm{M}} \cdot \sin(x_3) \tag{7.18}$$

The mechanical powers p_{m1} and p_{m3} are those developed by the turbines before the fault occurred ($t \leq 0$). They could have been computed as input powers from the LF results. Since generator 1 is disconnected, $p_1^M = 0$ but $p_3^M = u_3' \cdot e_3' / (x_3^g)'$.

Equations (7.18), the "swing" equations for $t > 0$, are

$$M_1 \cdot \left(\frac{dx_2}{dt} \right) = p_{m1} \tag{7.19}$$

$$M_3 \frac{dx_4}{dt} = p_{m3} - \frac{u_3' \cdot e_3'}{(x_3^g)'} \cdot \sin(x_3)$$

Altogether, there are 4 nonlinear differential equations for the 4 unknown variables x_i, $i = 1, \ldots, 4$ defined in Eq. (7.16). They can be solved for $t > 0$ because their initial value is known as $\mathbf{x}^{(0)} = [\delta_1^{(0)}, 0, \delta_3^{(0)}, 0]^T$.

In the next section, the methods of solving ordinary, initial-value, nonlinear differential equations will be reviewed. At this point note that solving Eqs. (7.17) and (7.19), will provide values of $\mathbf{x}$ at $t + \Delta t$ (Δt should not be too large). At the end of $t + \Delta t = 0 + \Delta t = \Delta t$, the new angles δ_i and therefore voltages e_i' are known.

The situation repeats itself. Each time e_i' are known, a load flow or Eq. (7.15) is solved for the bus voltages, currents, etc. Having computed these, view them as initial values and integrate the differential equations for another Δt.

Suppose that at some time T_1, generator 1 is connected to the network. At this point, its angle δ_1 may be quite large (in respect to the synchronously rotating reference or to generator 2) and will produce large currents in the network. The procedure to calculate them is the same as before and consists of alternately solving algebraic and differential equations. This could also be explained as follows: Because of high generator inertias, changes of δ_i are small compared to $\omega = 377$ rad/sec for the synchronously rotating frame. The lines and transformers can therefore be considered in a 60-Hz steady state. Thus, all powers, voltages, and currents are related by *algebraic* equations [load flow and Eq. (7.15)] whereas the generators respond according to differential equations (7.17) and (7.19).

This short review leads to the following questions to be answered in this chapter.

1. Loads were represented as constant impedances. Other representations are possible, and the best should be chosen. This and the influence of damping will be discussed in Section 7.2.2.
2. Numerical solution of ordinary, initial-value, nonlinear differential equations will be reviewed in Section 7.3.

3. For small deviations, normal modes will be reviewed in Section 7.3.
4. The number of algebraic and differential equations may be prohibitively large, and reduction is called for. If passive parts of the network outside the area of main concern are represented as an "equivalent," the number of algebraic equations will be reduced. Generators can be lumped together only if they are "coherent." Both equivalency and coherency will be discussed in Section 7.4.
5. In all previous cases, algebraic equations were solved by the Newton–Raphson method and factorization. Iterative solution using the fast Gauss–Seidel (FGS) algorithm may be more suitable and will be discussed in Section 7.5.

Even after all this is reviewed, only a small part of a possible program will be covered. Since there is no scarcity of packages for solving differential equations, the reader can use them. On the other hand, the literature on the fast Gauss–Seidel method is scarce, and its program will be discussed.

7.2.2 Load Representation and Damping

Loads are mostly nonlinear functions of voltages. The common form of this relationship is

$$p_k = a_{s,k} + a_{i,k} \cdot u_k + a_{z,k} \cdot u_k^2; \qquad q_k = b_{s,k} + b_{i,k} \cdot u_k + b_{z,k} \cdot u_k^2$$

where subscripts k, s, i, and z denote a load bus, power, current, and impedance, respectively. The as and bs are assumed to be constants.

Normally, only one of the three factors is left, and the following cases can be distinguished.

For $a_{s,k} = a_{i,k} = b_{s,k} = b_{i,k} = 0$, it follows that $a_{z,k} = p_k/u_k^2 = g_k$; $b_{z,k} = q_k/u_k^2$; $y_k' = g_k + j \cdot b_k$. This is the *constant-admittance* case and represents the load current as $i_k' = (g_k + j \cdot b_k) \cdot (v_k + j \cdot w_k)$.

Next is the case of only $a_{i,k} \cdot u_k'$, and $b_{i,k} \cdot u_k'$ nonzero. Since power divided by voltage is current, this case corresponds to $p_k + j \cdot q_k = (a_{i,k} + j \cdot b_{i,k}) \cdot u_k'$. The load current for this *constant-current* case is

$$i_k' = \frac{s_k''}{u_k''} = \frac{p_k - j \cdot q_k}{v_k - j \cdot w_k} = (a_{ik} - j \cdot b_{ik}) \cdot \epsilon^{j\delta_k}$$

where δ_k is the angle of voltage at bus k.

Finally, the *constant-power* case is represented by

$$i_k' = \frac{a_{sk} - j \cdot b_{sk}}{v_k - j \cdot w_k}$$

We will represent loads as constant admittances:

$$y_k' = \frac{i_k'}{u_k'} = \frac{i_k' \cdot u_k''}{u_k^2} = \frac{p_k - j \cdot q_k}{u_k^2}$$

The choice was dictated by simplicity and by the fact that in most cases a constant y is as accurate as other choices.

As the speed of the rotor deviates from the synchronous, additional currents are induced, and they tend to slow down the motion on account of the dissipated power. It was found that the damping power is approximately

$$p_d \cong d_k \cdot \frac{d\delta_i}{dt}$$

For times of less than a second after a change, damping can be disregarded. In mid-term or long-term stability studies, it should not.

7.3 SOLVING THE DIFFERENTIAL EQUATIONS

The differential equations (7.16) to (7.19) are of the form

$$y' = f(x, y) \tag{7.20}$$

where y_i' is the slope dy/dx at a point (x_i, y_i) and y is a function of x. From Eq. (7.20) and Fig. 7.8 we can conclude that

$$y_2 \cong y_1 + \int_{x_1}^{x_2} f(x, y) \cdot dx$$

and the integral calculated by the trapezoidal formula is

$$y_2 \cong y_1 + \frac{h \cdot (y_1' + y_2')}{2} = y_1 + \frac{h \cdot [f(x_1, y_1) + f(x_2, y_2)]}{2} \tag{7.21}$$

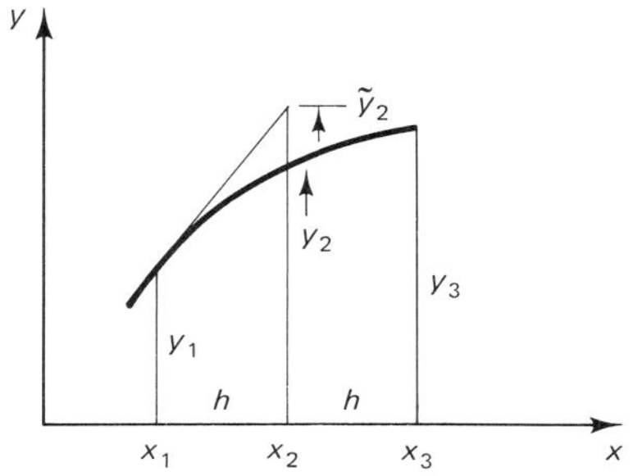

Figure 7.8 Integration.

The unknown y_2 also appears in the function $f(x_2, y_2)$, and therefore Eq. (7.21) is a nonlinear algebraic equation for y_2. It could be solved iteratively as follows: Substitute some approximated $y_2^{(0)}$ on the right; this yields a new $y_2^{(1)}$. Substitute $y_2^{(1)}$ into $f(x_2, y_2)$ and get $y_2^{(2)}$, etc. The process might converge to a correct solution y_2 of Eq. (7.21) but may involve too much work, and we are usually satisfied with one or two iterative steps. If a single step is applied, we *predict* $\tilde{y}_2$ by using the slope at (x_1, y_1), i.e.,

$$\tilde{y}_2 = y_1 + h \cdot y_1' = y_1 + h \cdot f(x_1, y_1) \tag{7.22}$$

If we are satisfied with this $\tilde{y}_2$ as the computed value of y_2, we have a simple procedure called *Euler's method.*

In order to reduce its error, we correct y_2 once, that is, compute the *corrector*

$$y_2 = y_1 + \frac{h \cdot [f(x_1, y_1) + f(x_2, \tilde{y}_2)]}{2} \tag{7.23}$$

This can be viewed either as the application of Eq. (7.21) or as using the second time around an average value for the slope $[f(x_1, y_1) + f(x_2, \tilde{y}_2)]/2$. Use of both Eqs. (7.22) and (7.23) is called *Heun's method.*

We still have large errors because we used the inaccurate trapezoidal rule for integration and because we interrupted the iterations after two steps. We increase accuracy by using Simpson's formula [Eq. (7.13)] instead of the trapezoidal rule. For this we need three points, and if we assume such to be known (Fig. 7.8), then

$$\int f(x, y) \cdot dx \cong \frac{h \cdot [f(x_1, y_1) + 4 \cdot f(x_2, y_2) + f(x_3, y(x_3))]}{3}$$

Factor $h/3$ comes about as a result of inserting $2h$ into Eq. (7.13). We do not know the value $y(x_3)$, which is what we want to calculate, but can predict that it will not be far from some $f(x_2, y_3)$ such that the nonlinear equation

$$y_3 = y_1 + \frac{h \cdot [y_1' + 4 \cdot y_2' + f(x_3, y_3)]}{3}; \quad y' \equiv \frac{dy}{dx} \tag{7.24}$$

is obeyed. Again, as in Heun's method, we will predict y_3 by interpolation. We know x_1, y_1', x_2, y_2' and so can assume a third-degree polynomial (we know 4 values) passing through (x_1, y_1) and (x_2, y_2) with slopes of y_1' and y_2', respectively. From it we get the following value of y at $x = x_3$:

$$y_3^{\#} \cong 5y_1 - 4y_2 + 2hy_1' + 4hy_2' \tag{7.25}$$

Substitution of this $y_3^\#$ into $f(x_3, y_3)$ in Eq. (7.24) yields a value for the corrector. We still have a problem, though, because in Eq. (7.25) we used y_2 and we do not know it. If we use for it Heun's value of Eq. (7.23), we get the following procedure for advancing one step at a time:

$$y_2^\# := y_1 + h \cdot y_1'; \quad y_2 := y_1 + h \cdot [y_2' + f(x_2, y_2^\#)] \tag{7.26}$$

$$y_3^\# := y_1 - 2h \cdot f(x_2, y_2^\#) + 4h \cdot y_2' \tag{7.27}$$

$$y_3 := y_1 + \frac{y_1' + 4 \cdot y_2' + f(x_3, y_3^\#)}{6}$$

Insertion of Heun's values is seen to have simplified the expressions for $y_3^\#$ and y_3. This method is called the *First Runge–Kutta* method. It uses quantities k defined by

$$k_1 \equiv 2h \cdot y_1' = 2h \cdot f(x_1, y_1)$$

$$k_2 \equiv 2h \cdot f(x_1 + h,\ y_1 + k_1/2)$$

$$k_3 \equiv 2h \cdot f(x_1 + h,\ y_1 + k_1/4 + k_2/4)$$

$$k_4 \equiv 2h \cdot f(x_1 + 2h,\ y_1 - k_2 + 2k_3)$$

Finally, we reduce the step to h, as it should be, i.e., replace $2h$ by h and y_3 by y_2 and get

$$k_1 := h \cdot f(x_1, y_1)$$

$$k_2 := h \cdot f(x_1 + \frac{h}{2},\ y_1 + \frac{k_1}{2})$$

$$k_3 := h \cdot f(x_1 + \frac{h}{2},\ y_1 + \frac{k_1}{4} + \frac{k_2}{4})$$

$$k_4 := h \cdot f(x_1 + h,\ y_1 - k_2 + 2k_3)$$

With known x_1 and y_1, the next y is then

$$y_2 := y_1 + \frac{k_1 + 4 \cdot k_3 + k_4}{6} \tag{7.28}$$

A second Runge–Kutta method, quite similar to the first, equates $k_1 = k_2$ when computing k_3 and $k_2 = k_3$ when computing k_4. This method (normally associated with Runge and Kutta) is represented by the equation

$$y_2 := y_1 + \frac{k_1 + 2 \cdot k_2 + 2 \cdot k_3 + k_4}{6} \tag{7.29}$$

where

$$k_1 := h \cdot f(x_1, y_1); \quad k_2 := h \cdot f(x_1 + \frac{h}{2}, y_1 + \frac{k_1}{2})$$

$$k_3 := h \cdot f(x_1 + \frac{h}{2}, y_1 + \frac{k_2}{2}); \quad k_4 := h \cdot f(x_1 + h, y_1 + k_3)$$

It is seen to use an "average" slope and has the advantage of being self-starting. This means that if (x_1, y_1) are known and $f(x, y)$ is given, the method can proceed to $x_1 + m \cdot h$ where $m = 1, 2, \ldots$.

There exist a number of so-called multistep methods, but they require a number of values $y_1, y_2, \ldots, y_i$ in order to calculate y_{i+1}; these methods are not self-starting. Both at the start of the study and whenever a relay clears a fault or changes the network in some other way, we cannot use them.

Before we compare errors, let us reflect why they are important in the present context. We solve the stability problem so that a "snapshot" is taken of the network, then the differential equations are solved for $(t + \Delta t)$, another snapshot taken, etc. These snapshots are the algebraic equations we discussed earlier.

We have spent considerable time to introduce and use methods which solve algebraic equations with lower errors. It seems then a waste to use "expensive" methods for algebraic equations and sacrifice the accuracy obtained with so much effort, by using an inaccurate integration formula.

To get an idea of how errors influence the solution, we repeat the development of Euler's method. Given the function f and initial value y_0 in $dy/dx = f(x, y)$, the slope line $f(x, y_0)$ is drawn. The assumption is made here that this slope is constant from $x = 0$ to $x = h$, i.e., for the *step size h*. In this way, the solution curve is approximated by the polygon in Fig. 7.9, which joins the points $(0, y_0)$, (h, y_1), $(2h, y_2)$, etc., through repeated application of

$$y_{i+1} := y_i + h \cdot f(i \cdot h, y_i) \tag{7.30}$$

Both Fig. 7.9 and Eq. (7.30) show that the error is proportional to step size h, which leads to a dilemma. To reduce the error, h should be made as small as possible, but this means that more steps will be required, making the calculations more laborious and leading to error accumulation.

Suppose we use Taylor's expansion:

$$y_{n+1} = y_n + h \cdot y_n' + h^2 \cdot y_n''/2 + h^3 \cdot y_n'''/3! + \cdots + h^p \cdot y_n^{(p)}/p!$$

Eulers' method results if this series is truncated and only the first two terms are left. To find its error, it may be noted [CL75] that if the last term of the Taylor series used is $h^p \cdot y^{(p)}/p!$ where $y^{(p)}$ is the pth derivative at point x_0, then the truncation error is bounded by

$$\epsilon_n \leq K_p \cdot h^p \tag{7.31}$$

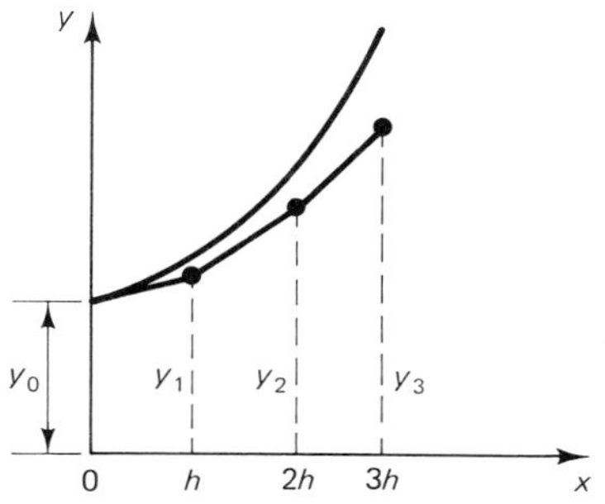

Figure 7.9 Error accumulation.

This is the error, denoted up to now by $O(h^p)$, since K_p is constant. To appreciate its significance, assume $h = 0.01 = 10^{-2}$. Then for increasing p values, $\epsilon_1 \leq 0.01 \cdot K_1$, $\epsilon_2 \leq 0.0001 \cdot K_2$, $\epsilon_3 \leq 0.000001 \cdot K_3$, and $\epsilon_m \leq 10^{-2m} \cdot K_m$. Since the K_i are constants, these errors are of order $O(0.01)$, $O(0.0001)$, $O(0.000001)$, ..., $O(h^{-2m})$ and the dramatic decrease of h^{-p} shows that the higher p is chosen, the smaller is the error — but then for a given integration interval, more integration steps are needed. Stated differently: given a maximum truncation error, a much larger step size could be chosen if a higher order series is chosen. This will decrease the number of steps but require more derivatives to be computed. In Euler's method:

$$y_{n+1} = y_n + h \cdot y_n' + O(h^2) \tag{7.32}$$

the local error is $O(h^2)$ because all powers h^p for $p \geq 2$ were neglected.

Let us add the *modified Euler's method*, based on an average slope and on $y_{n+1} = y_n + 0.5 \cdot h \cdot (y_n' + y_{n+1}')$. The error bound of this modified method can be calculated by comparing this y_{n+1} with the Taylor series $y_{n+1} = y_n + h \cdot y_n' + h^2 \cdot y_n''/2 + h^3 \cdot y_n'''/6$. If the second derivative is approximated by $y_n'' \cong (y_{n+1}' - y_n')/h$, then

$$y_{n+1} = y_n + h \cdot \frac{y_n' + 0.5 \cdot h \cdot (y_{n+1}' - y_n')}{h} + O(h^3) \qquad \text{and}$$

$$y_{n+1} = y_n + 0.5 \cdot h \cdot [y_n' + 0.5 \cdot y_{n+1}'] + O(h^3) \tag{7.33}$$

This shows the local error for the modified Euler method to be $O(h^3)$.

To summarize and include time as in the swing equation we rewrite Heun's method, the modified Euler's method, and the Runge-Kutta method

$$x_{n+1} = x_n + 0.5 \cdot h \cdot [f(t_n) + f(t_n + h)] \tag{7.34}$$

$$x_{n+1} = x_n + 0.5 \cdot h \cdot [f(t_n) + 0.5 \cdot f(t_{n+1})] \tag{7.35}$$

$$x_{n+1} = x_n + (k_1 + 2k_2 + 2k_3 + k_4)/6 \tag{7.36}$$

where

$$k_1 = h \cdot f(t_n); \quad k_2 = h \cdot f(t_n + k_1/2)$$

$$k_3 = h \cdot f(t_n + k_2/2); \quad k_4 = h \cdot f(t_n + k_3)$$

As seen in Fig. 7.9, there is an accumulation of errors from step to step; since the number of steps is proportional to $1/h$, the global error is $O(h^n/h) = O(h^{n-1})$. For the two methods of Euler, the global error is $O(h)$, and $O(h^2)$ respectively, and for the Runge–Kutta method it is $O(h^4)$.

The efficiency of the methods depends on the number of function evaluations. In Euler's method, there is a single function evaluation, in the modified method there are two, and in the Runge–Kutta method four are required. The ratio of "work" is thus 1:2:4, but the ratio of global errors is h, h^2, h^4 and since $h << 1$, the Runge–Kutta method is considered the most efficient.

The Runge–Kutta method can be used so that the step size is automatically adjusted. This is done at certain points of computation, say, at t_n. First an approximate solution x_{n+1} is computed as usual. Then the same is calculated by using two steps, i.e., $x_{n+1/2}$ and $x_{(n+1/2)+1/2}$. Comparing the last with x_{n+1} gives an indication of the size of the error. If the two quantities are not sufficiently close, the step size is decreased.

To exemplify the error growth, solve the following two equations numerically and compare with the known result for two different values of h. These equations and solutions are

$$y' = 0.5 \cdot x \cdot y; \quad \text{Solution: } y = \epsilon^{0.25 \cdot x^2}$$

$$y' = y - 0.5 \cdot x/y; \quad \text{Solution: } y = \sqrt{2x+1}$$

Normal Modes. For small deviations, there exists an approach to the problem which [BSM75]* does not necessitate solving the swing equations. The rotor angles are given by

$$\theta_i = \theta_i^s + \delta_i \tag{7.37}$$

where θ_i^s is the steady-state value and δ_i is an incremental angle. Since θ_i^s are constant, their derivatives are zero and the swing equations can be rewritten as

---

* R. T. Byerly, D. E. Sherman, D. K. McLain, "Normal Modes and Mode Shapes Applied to Dynamic Stability Analysis," *Trans. IEEE*, Vol. PAS-94, No. 2, March/April, 1975, pp. 224-29. © 1975 by IEEE. Used with permission.

$$M_i \cdot \frac{d^2\theta_i}{dt^2} = p_{mi} - p_{ei} \tag{7.38}$$

If the loads are converted to impedances and the generators represented by electromotive forces and constant x values, then the **Y** matrix can be simplified until *only* the internal buses of the generators remain. In that case by Eqs. (4.9) and (4.26) the electrically generated power is

$$p_{ei} = -e_i^2 \cdot G_{i,i} - \Sigma\ e_i \cdot e_j \cdot G_{i,j} \cdot \cos(\theta_i - \theta_j) - \Sigma\ e_i \cdot e_j \cdot B_{i,j} \cdot \sin(\theta_i - \theta_j) \tag{7.39}$$

$G_{i,j}$ and $B_{i,j}$ are the "real and imaginary components of the off-diagonal terms [BSM75] of the reduced admittance matrix, and $G_{i,i}$ is the real component of the diagonal term. The minus signs appear because the original nodal equations were written in the form of current into the bus. This means that the original off-diagonal terms are the actual branch admittances, and, in general, the imaginary components of the off-diagonal terms in the reduced matrix will have the same algebraic signs as normal susceptance terms; that is, $B_{ij} < 0$."

Equation (7.39) must be linearized. From Eq. (7.37),

$$\theta_i - \theta_j = (\theta_{i0}^s - \theta_{j0}^s) + (\delta_i - \delta_j)$$

With $\cos(\delta_i - \delta_j) \cong 1$ and $\sin(\delta_i - \delta_j) \cong \delta_i - \delta_j$, the following are valid:

$$\cos(\theta_i - \theta_j) \cong \cos(\theta_{i0} - \theta_{j0}) - (\delta_i - \delta_j) \cdot \sin(\theta_{i0} - \theta_{j0})$$

and

$$\sin(\theta_i - \theta_j) \cong \sin(\theta_{i0} - \theta_{j0}) + (\delta_i - \delta_j) \cdot \cos(\theta_{i0} - \theta_{j0})$$

Using these approximations in Eq. (7.39), and replacing p_{ei} yields the linearized swing equation:

$$M_i \cdot d^2\delta/dt^2 = p_{mi} + e_i^2 \cdot G_{ii} + \Sigma\ e_i e_j G_{ij}[\cos(\theta_{i0} - \theta_{j0}) - (\delta_i - \delta_j) \cdot \sin(\theta_{i0} - \theta_{j0})] + \Sigma\ e_i e_j B_{ij}[\sin(\theta_{i0} - \theta_{j0}) + (\delta_i - \delta_j) \cdot \cos(\theta_{i0} - \theta_{j0})]$$

In the steady state there will be no acceleration, so that

$$\delta_i = \delta_j; \quad d^2\delta/dt^2 = 0$$

$$p_{mi} + e_i^2 \cdot G_{ii} + \Sigma\ e_i e_j G_{ij} \cdot \cos(\theta_{i0} - \theta_{j0}) + \Sigma\ e_i e_j B_{ij} \cdot \sin(\theta_{i0} - \theta_{j0}) = 0$$

Consequently, the swing equation simplifies to

$$M_i \cdot d^2\delta/dt^2 = \Sigma\ e_i e_j G_{ij}(\delta_i - \delta_j) \sin(\theta_{i0} - \theta_{j0}) + \Sigma\ e_i e_j B_{ij}(\delta_i - \delta_j) \cos(\theta_{i0} - \theta_{j0}) \tag{7.40}$$

It is convenient to separate the δ_i terms and rewrite this as

$$\begin{aligned} M_i \cdot d^2\delta/dt^2 &= [-\Sigma\ e_j G_{ij} \sin(\theta_{i0} - \theta_{j0})] \cdot \delta_i \\ &+ [\Sigma\ e_i e_j G_{ij} \sin(\theta_{i0} - \theta_{j0})] \cdot \delta_j \\ &+ [\Sigma\ e_i e_j B_{ij} \cos(\theta_{i0} - \theta_{j0})] \cdot \delta_i \\ &- [\Sigma\ e_i e_j B_{ij} \cos(\theta_{i0} - \theta_{j0})] \cdot \delta_j \end{aligned} \tag{7.41}$$

By using Eq. (7.41) for each generator, the following system of differential equations can be written:

$$(\mathbf{A} + \mathbf{D}) * \boldsymbol{\delta} = M_i \cdot d^2\delta/dt^2 \quad \text{(for any } i\text{)} \tag{7.42}$$

where

$$A_{i,j} = -e_i \cdot e_j \cdot G_{i,j} \cdot \sin(\theta_{i0} - \theta_{j0}) \tag{7.43}$$

$$A_{i,i} = \Sigma\ e_i \cdot e_j \cdot G_{i,j} \cdot \sin(\theta_{i0} - \theta_{j0}) = -\Sigma\ A_{i,j} \tag{7.44}$$

$$D_{i,j} = -e_i \cdot e_j \cdot B_{i,j} \cdot \cos(\theta_{i0} - \theta_{j0}) \tag{7.45}$$

$$D_{i,i} = \Sigma\ e_i \cdot e_j \cdot B_{i,j} \cdot \cos(\theta_{i0} - \theta_{j0}) = -\Sigma\ D_{i,j} \tag{7.46}$$

Unless there are phase shifters in the system, $G_{i,j} = G_{j,i}$ and $B_{i,j} = B_{j,i}$. Also, since $\sin(x) = -\sin(-x)$ and $\cos(x) = \cos(-x)$, it follows that the matrix **A** is skew symmetric and the matrix **D** is symmetric.

As in the decoupled load flow, it is assumed that the dominant part of Eq. (7.42) is the **D** matrix, and the problem can be reduced to a symmetric system of equations $\mathbf{D} * \boldsymbol{\delta} = M_i \cdot d^2\delta_i/dt$. Dividing each individual equation by the corresponding M_i yields

$$\mathbf{C} * \boldsymbol{\delta} = d^2\delta_i/dt; \qquad \text{where } C_{i,j} = \frac{D_{i,j}}{M_i} \tag{7.47}$$

Let us assume that the rotor oscillates according to $\boldsymbol{\delta} = \mathbf{h} \cdot \sin(\omega t)$ where $\boldsymbol{\delta}$ and $\mathbf{h}$ are vectors of dimension n. Then $d\delta/dt = \mathbf{h}\omega \cos(\omega t)$ and $d^2\delta/dt^2 = -\mathbf{h}\omega^2 \sin(\omega t)$. Substituting δ and $d^2\delta/dt^2$ into Eq. (7.47) yields

$$\mathbf{C} * \mathbf{h} \cdot \sin(\omega t) = -\mathbf{h}\omega^2 \sin(\omega t)$$

If this is to be valid for all values of time, then

$$(\mathbf{C} + \omega^2 \cdot \mathbf{I})\ \mathbf{h} = \mathbf{0}$$

must also be satisfied. This equation defines an eigenvalue problem. The eigenvalues λ_j and eigenvectors $\mathbf{h}^j$ are determined so that

$$(\mathbf{C} - \lambda_j \mathbf{I}) * \mathbf{h}^j = \mathbf{0} \tag{7.48}$$

and the natural frequencies are given by

$$\omega_j = \sqrt{-\lambda_j}$$

As can be seen from δ, the corresponding eigenvectors $\mathbf{h}^j$ indicate the relative amplitude of the generator rotor oscillations at a given frequency, and also indicate the relative velocity deviations, as shown by $\partial\delta/\partial t$.

Equation (7.48) can be solved by the method of Givens, which has already been discussed. For this the matrix $\mathbf{C}$ was made symmetric.

7.4 EQUIVALENTS

The case for equivalencing was made convincingly 15 years ago [BSCN69] as follows:*

> The trend in digital analysis of power-system studies is to include more of the adjacent power systems in greater detail. Theoretically this should produce more accurate results. Actually the study cost is greatly increased, and with doubtful gain in accuracy. The increased cost is due to longer computer running time and the increased work of assembling the data. Frequently data preparation is such a chore that many items are assigned assumed values. Such procedure can degrade the study rather than improve it and may nullify the advantages of the more detailed representation. Further, the printed results become so voluminous that they obscure the part of the study that is of value. From a practical engineering point-of-view it would be ridiculous to attempt to determine the exact effect of every disturbance on every piece of equipment throughout the interconnected system. Actually, such an analysis, even if it were possible, would be useless because the probability of encountering the studied condition is extremely small.
>
> Generally, for stability studies it is necessary to study only the areas affected severely enough.... If a sufficiently accurate and easily calculated stability equivalent could be developed, it would greatly reduce these difficulties and more useful information could be obtained for a given analysis cost.

To develop equivalents, start from Gaussian elimination of the first k variables in $\mathbf{i} = \mathbf{Y} * \mathbf{u}$.† An admittance $Y_{m,q}$ is changed according to

$$Y_{m,q} := Y_{m,q} - Y_{p,q} \cdot (\frac{Y_{m,p}}{Y_{p,p}}); \qquad 1 < m \leq k; \; p = 1, \ldots, k$$

---

* H. E. Brown, R. B. Shipley, D. Coleman, R. E. Nied, "A Study of Stability Equivalents," *Trans. IEEE*, Vol. PAS-88, No. 3, March 1969, pp. 200-7. © 1969 by IEEE. Used with permission.

† The following section is adapted from [EP77]. Copyright © 1977, Electric Power Research Institute. EPRI EL-456 (Volume 1), *Development of Dynamic Equivalents for Transient Stability Studies.* Reprinted with permission.

where p is the pivot row. After $k-1$ steps, set $i = \mathbf{Y} * u$ is reduced to

$$\begin{matrix} \uparrow \\ \text{rem} \\ \downarrow \\ \uparrow \\ \text{ret} \\ \downarrow \end{matrix} \begin{bmatrix} i_1 \\ \\ - \\ i_k \\ \\ i_n \end{bmatrix} = \left[\begin{array}{ccc|cc} Y_{11} & Y_{12} & \cdots & Y_{1k} & Y_{1n} \\ & \mathbf{0} & & & \\ - & - & - & - & - \\ & & & Y_{kk} & Y_{kn} \\ & & \mathbf{0} & \cdot & \cdot \\ & & & Y_{nk} & Y_{nn} \end{array}\right] * \begin{bmatrix} u_1 \\ \\ - \\ u_k \\ \\ u_n \end{bmatrix} \tag{7.49}$$

Index rem stands for "removed" and ret for "retained." The currents i_k to i_n can therefore be written as:

$$\mathbf{i}_{\text{ret}} = \mathbf{0} * \mathbf{u}_{\text{rem}} + \mathbf{Y}_{\text{ret}} * \mathbf{u}_{\text{ret}}; \quad \mathbf{i}_{\text{ret}} = \mathbf{Y}_{\text{ret}} * \mathbf{u}_{\text{ret}} \tag{7.50}$$

This equation can be considered to represent an equivalent network which includes only the retained nodes $k, k+1, \ldots, n$. The branches in this network correspond to the nonzero admittances in matrix $\mathbf{Y}_{\text{ret}}$.

As shown by Eq. (7.50), Gaussian elimination effectively reduces the number of buses. There is though no guarantee that the number of lines will also decrease, and this is significant, since the overall computation time mainly depends upon the number of lines and not the number of buses. For instance elimination of column k in Eq. (7.49), may also be pictured as in Fig. 7.10 with the branches connected to node i replaced by an equivalent network. The number of lines has not decreased.

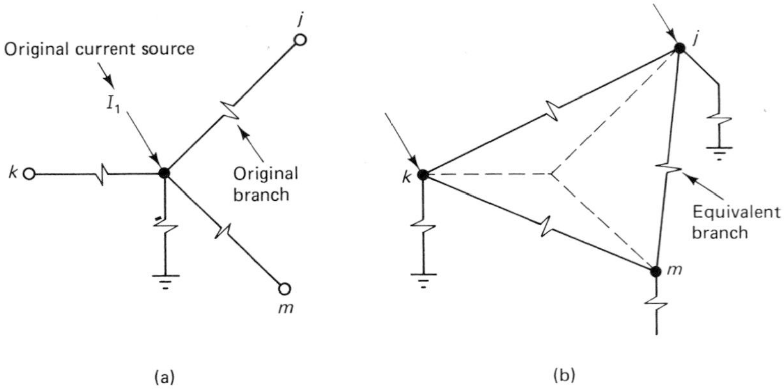

Figure 7.10 Elimination of node i from the equivalent **Y** matrix. (a) Before elimination. (b) After elimination.

As already mentioned, power system networks are very sparse; typically the number of lines is only 1.5 to 2.0 times the number of buses. As shown by Fig. 7.10 a network reduction eliminates buses but adds equivalent lines (fill-in). "In the worst case, when complete fill-in of the bus admittance matrix occurs, the number of branches will equal $n \cdot (n - 1)/2$ (n is the number of retained buses). Since n may easily exceed several hundred it is obvious that elimination of nodes should be applied judiciously otherwise, the equivalent network may have many more branches than the original one."[EP77]

Sparsity techniques (OOF) have been applied successfully earlier in the book in order to minimize fill-in. The application of an optimum ordering scheme tends to delay the fill-in as long as possible by first selecting nodes which cause the least fill-in and leaving the nodes which cause the most fill-in until last. Consequently, the subset of nodes which remains when the number of Y-matrix elements is a minimum can be retained to preserve sparsity.

Figure 7.11 shows the performance of the sparsity-oriented reduction algorithm on a network when OOF is used. "Point A represents the start, point B is where the number of Y matrix elements is a minimum and point C is the result of eliminating all nonessential nodes. An OOF program can detect the point at which the number of Y-matrix elements is a minimum. It is therefore suggested to order the bus elimination using a sparsity oriented scheme and to terminate the bus elimination when the number of terms in the equivalent admittance matrix starts increasing instead of decreasing."[EP77] Elimination itself is done later but terminated at the indicated point.

"As the bus eliminations are performed it is possible for the number of Y-matrix terms to alternately increase and decrease. The approach above ensures that the minimum number of Y-matrix elements is obtained." [EP77]

As seen earlier Kron's method is equivalent to elimination. We can therefore use it for calculating an equivalent.

The use of Kron's method for producing an equivalent is exemplified by the network of Fig. 7.12 and follows [BSCN69]. The admittances of the lines are:

TABLE 7.1 Admittances of the lines.

Line	5−6	5−3	6−4	3−4	3−1	4−2
Admittance	3.0	1.0	0.25	0.8125	3.0	1.25

If we start with node 5 and add lines 5−6 and 5−3, we get by Kron's method Fig. 7.13(a). This matrix is inverted with $Y_{5,5}$, being the pivot. For example, we get:

$$Y_{6,3} := Y_{6,3} - Y_{5,3} \cdot Y_{6,5} / Y_{5,5} = 0 - 1.0 \cdot 3.0/4.0 = -0.75$$

$$Y_{5,3} := Y_{5,3} / Y_{5,5} = -1.0/4.0 = -0.25.$$

Having used pivot 5, we erase column 5 and row 5. The result is Fig. 7.14(b).

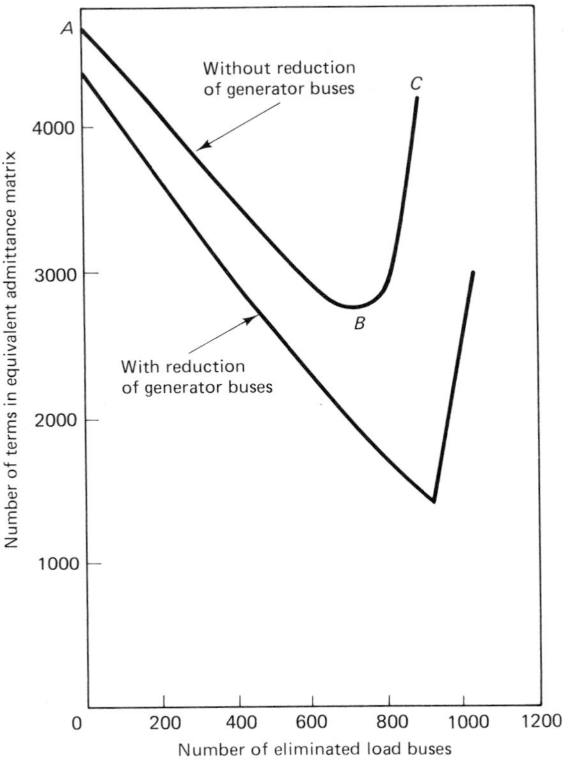

Figure 7.11 Sparsity-oriented reduction of load buses in systems with and without prior reduction of generator buses.

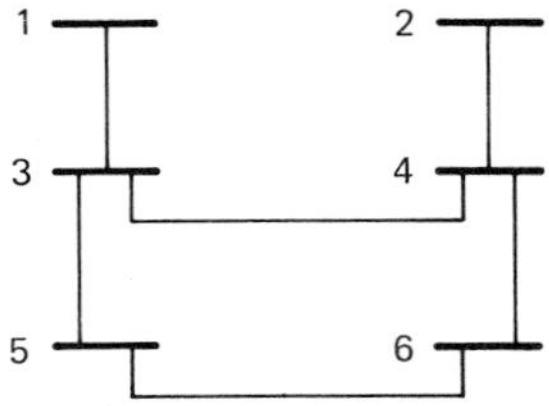

Figure 7.12 A six-bus system.

Next we add line 6–4 with $Y_{6,4} = 0.25$. The matrix is shown in Fig. 7.13(c). We use again Kron's method, pivoting on $Y_{6,6}$, modifying all elements not in row 6 or column 6 as for example in:

$$Y_{5,4} := Y_{5,4} - Y_{6,4} \cdot Y_{6,6}^{-1} \cdot Y_{3,6} = 0 - (-0.25) \cdot (1/1.0) \cdot (-0.75) = -0.1875$$

The resulting Fig. 7.13(d) has now all nodes except 1 and 2 to which we want to reduce the entire network. Line 3 − 1 is added [Fig. 7.14(e)], reduced by pivoting on $Y_{3,3}$ so that with column 3 erased, we get Fig. 7.13(f). Finally we add line 4 − 2 and reduce the matrix, removing column 4 and row 4. The result [Fig. 7.13(g)] shows the matrix of the equivalent network connecting nodes 1 and 2.

$$\begin{array}{c|ccc} & 5 & 6 & 3 \\ \hline 5 & 4 & -3 & -1 \\ 6 & -3 & 3 & 0 \\ 3 & -1 & 0 & 1 \end{array}$$

(a)

$$\begin{array}{c|cc} & 6 & 3 \\ \hline 6 & 0.75 & -0.75 \\ 3 & -0.75 & 0.75 \end{array}$$

(b)

$$\begin{array}{c|ccc} & 6 & 3 & 4 \\ \hline 6 & 1.00 & -0.75 & -0.25 \\ 3 & -0.75 & 0.75 & 0 \\ 4 & -0.25 & 0 & 0.25 \end{array}$$

(c)

$$\begin{array}{c|cc} & 3 & 4 \\ \hline 3 & 0.1875 & -0.1875 \\ 4 & -0.1875 & 0.1875 \end{array}$$

(d)

$$\begin{array}{c|ccc} & 3 & 4 & 1 \\ \hline 3 & 4.0 & -1.0 & -3.0 \\ 4 & -1.0 & 1.0 & 0 \\ 1 & -3.0 & 0 & 3.0 \end{array}$$

(e)

$$\begin{array}{c|cc} & 4 & 1 \\ \hline 4 & 0.75 & -0.75 \\ 1 & -0.75 & 0.75 \end{array}$$

(f)

$$\begin{array}{c|cc} & 1 & 2 \\ \hline 1 & 0.46875 & -0.46875 \\ 2 & -0.46875 & 0.46875 \end{array}$$

(g)

Figure 7.13 A six-bus system.

Up to now, only passive elements of the network have been reduced. The need to retain generator buses in elimination has been a limiting factor in network reduction because their retention does not enhance sparsity and inhibits the process of deriving a smaller equivalent. For example, if only the generator buses are retained, then the equivalent admittance matrix will be completely full for almost all practical networks. Reduction of the generator buses reduces the number of buses which have to be retained, and thus makes it possible to compute an equivalent which has fewer admittances then would otherwise be possible. To illustrate this, Fig. 7.11 compared the reduction of load buses in a network with and without prior reduction of generator buses. As shown, a much smaller network is obtained when the generator buses are eliminated first.

Next the equations for eliminating generator buses from the network admittance matrix on the basis of coherency are developed. For the purpose of this derivation, we consider that *two terminal generator buses are coherent if the ratio of their complex voltages is constant.*

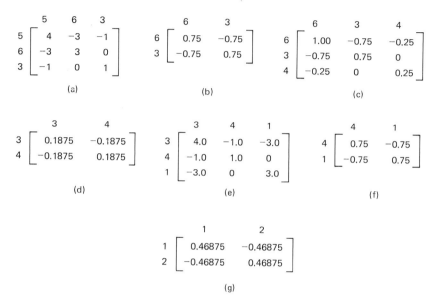

For the equivalencing procedure, the network is divided into three parts.

1. A group of generator buses that have been determined to be coherent and are to be reduced. It will be called C (for coherent).
2. The buses at the boundary of this coherent group, to be called B.
3. The rest of the network, i.e., the study area to be called A.

The third part of the network is not modified by the algorithm and will not be included in its description. The network is described with the bus admittance matrix as $\mathbf{i} = \mathbf{Y} * \mathbf{u}$, or

$$\begin{bmatrix} \mathbf{i}_A \\ \mathbf{i}_B \\ \mathbf{i}_C \end{bmatrix} = \begin{bmatrix} \mathbf{Y}_{AA} & \mathbf{Y}_{AB} & \mathbf{0} \\ \mathbf{Y}_{BA} & \mathbf{Y}_{BB} & \mathbf{Y}_{BC} \\ \mathbf{0} & \mathbf{Y}_{CB} & \mathbf{Y}_{CC} \end{bmatrix} * \begin{bmatrix} \mathbf{u}_A \\ \mathbf{u}_B \\ \mathbf{u}_C \end{bmatrix} \tag{7.51}$$

For ease of notation, the group of buses designated by A will be included with B from now on. Since $\mathbf{Y}_{CA} = \mathbf{Y}_{AC} = \mathbf{0}$, no generality is lost by reducing the notation in this manner.

Suppose that group B (including A) contains m buses and group C contains $n - m$ buses. Equation (7.51) can be expanded again to yield Eq. (7.52)

$$\left[\begin{array}{c} i_1 \\ \cdot \\ \cdot \\ \cdot \\ i_m \\ \hline i_{m+1} \\ \cdot \\ \cdot \\ \cdot \\ i_n \end{array}\right] = \left[\begin{array}{ccc|ccc} Y_{1,1} & \cdots & Y_{1,m} & Y_{1,m+1} & \cdots & Y_{1,n} \\ \cdot & \cdot & \cdot & \cdot & \cdot & \cdot \\ \cdot & \cdot & \cdot & \cdot & \cdot & \cdot \\ \cdot & \cdot & \cdot & \cdot & \cdot & \cdot \\ Y_{m,1} & \cdots & Y_{m,m} & Y_{m,m+1} & \cdots & Y_{m,n} \\ \hline Y_{m+1,1} & \cdots & Y_{m+1,m} & & \cdots & Y_{m+1,n} \\ \cdot & \cdot & & \cdot & \cdot & \cdot \\ \cdot & & & \cdot & \cdot & \cdot \\ \cdot & \cdot & & \cdot & \cdot & \cdot \\ Y_{n,1} & \cdots & Y_{n,m} & Y_{n,m+1} & \cdots & Y_{n,n} \end{array}\right] * \left[\begin{array}{c} u_1 \\ \cdot \\ \cdot \\ \cdot \\ u_m \\ \hline u_{m+1} \\ \cdot \\ \cdot \\ \cdot \\ u_n \end{array}\right] \tag{7.52}$$

Rewriting Eq. (7.52) for each bus $i = 1, \ldots, n$, we have

$$i_i = \Sigma\, Y_{ij} \cdot u_j + \Sigma\, Y_{ik} \cdot u_k \tag{7.53}$$

$$j\Sigma = 1, \ldots, m; \quad k\Sigma = m + 1, \ldots, n$$

where the first summation is over group B and the second summation is over group C.

Description of the Equivalent. The equivalent will be formed by replacing group C with a single equivalent bus t, that is reducing Eq. (7.52) to

$$\begin{bmatrix} i_1 \\ \cdot \\ \cdot \\ \cdot \\ i_m \\ \text{—} \\ i_t \end{bmatrix} = \left[\begin{array}{ccc|c} Y_{11} & \cdots & Y_{1m} & Y_{1t} \\ \cdot & & \cdot & \cdot \\ \cdot & & \cdot & \cdot \\ \cdot & & \cdot & \cdot \\ Y_{m1} & \cdots & Y_{mm} & Y_{mt} \\ \text{—} & \text{—} & \text{—} & \text{—} \\ Y_{t1} & \cdots & Y_{tm} & Y_{tt} \end{array}\right] * \begin{bmatrix} u_1 \\ \cdot \\ \cdot \\ \cdot \\ u_m \\ \text{—} \\ u_t \end{bmatrix}$$

Derivation of the Equivalent. The basis of the algorithm is that the power flow at each of the boundary buses of the coherent group is conserved. Similarly, power production of the coherent group is conserved.

Equation (7.53) is first rewritten with $i = b$, a bus on the boundary. Then $i_b = \Sigma\ Y_{bj} \cdot u_j + \Sigma\ Y_{bk} \cdot u_k$ for $j\Sigma \in B,\ k\Sigma \in C$.

The power injection at bus b, is $s_b' = i_b'' \cdot u_b'$ or $s_b' = (\Sigma\ u_j'' \cdot Y_{bj}'' + \Sigma\ u_k'' \cdot Y_{bk}'') \cdot u_b'$ where the first summation is the contribution to the power at b by other buses in the boundary and the second summation is the contribution from the entire coherent group.

In the reduced network the entire coherent group will be replaced by a single bus t with the voltage u_t' and Y_{bt}' term bt of the reduced bus-admittance matrix. The power at b will then become

$$s_b' = u_t'' \cdot Y_{b,t}' \cdot u_b' + \Sigma\, u_k'' \cdot Y_{b,k}'' \cdot u_b'; \quad k\Sigma = 1, \ldots, m$$

Equating the two forms of s_b' results in

$$\Sigma\, u_j'' \cdot Y_{bj}'' \cdot u_b' + \Sigma\, u_k'' \cdot Y_{bk}'' \cdot u_b' = u_t'' \cdot Y_{bt}'' \cdot u_b' + \Sigma\, u_k'' \cdot Y_{bk}'' \cdot u_b'$$

The sums over k can be deleted: $\Sigma\ u_j'' \cdot Y_{bj}'' = u_t'' \cdot Y_{bt}''$, $j\Sigma = m + 1, \ldots, n$. Taking a conjugate and dividing by u_t' yields

$$Y_{bt}' = \frac{\Sigma\ u_j' \cdot Y_{bj}'}{u_t'} = \Sigma\ Y_{bj}' \cdot \frac{u_j'}{u_t'} \tag{7.54}$$

This equation implies that term bt of the bus-admittance matrix is determined as soon as a voltage u_t' is chosen for the equivalent.

The selection of the voltage u_t' is arbitrary and is defined as the average of the voltage magnitudes of the buses eliminated; the angle is chosen as the average angle.

$$u_t = \frac{\Sigma\, \tilde{u}_j}{n - m}; \qquad \theta_t = \frac{\Sigma\, \tilde{\theta}_j}{n - m} \tag{7.55}$$

The second step in the derivation of the equivalent is the conservation of power in the group of buses to be eliminated. If c denotes a bus in the coherent group, the total power of the group is $s_c' = \Sigma\, i_c''\cdot u_c'$, $c\Sigma = m + 1, \ldots, n$.

Current i_c' can be calculated using Eq. (7.53) as $i_c' = \Sigma\, Y_{cj}'\cdot u_j' + \Sigma\, Y_{ck}'\cdot u_k'$. Substitution yields

$$s_c' = \Sigma_c (\Sigma_j\, u_j''\cdot Y_{cj}''\cdot u_c' + \Sigma_k u_k''\cdot Y_{ck}''\cdot u_c')$$

where $c\Sigma = k\Sigma = m + 1, \ldots, n$ and $j\Sigma = 1, \ldots, m$. The order of summations can therefore be exchanged, so that

$$s_c' = \Sigma_j \Sigma_c u_j''\cdot Y_{cj}''\cdot u_c' + \Sigma_k\, \Sigma_c\, u_k''\cdot Y_{ck}''\cdot u_c' \tag{7.56}$$

The same expression for the reduced network is

$$s_c' = (\Sigma_k u_k''\cdot Y_{tk}''\cdot u_t') + u_t''\cdot Y_{tt}''\cdot u_t' \tag{7.57}$$

The first term in Eqs. (7.56) and (7.57) represents power flow to the boundary. The remaining terms deal with power internal to the coherent group and equivalent. Since each group should have its power conserved, they are equated:

$$u_t''\cdot Y_{tt}''\cdot u_t' = \Sigma_k \Sigma_c u_k''\cdot Y_{ck}''\cdot u_c' \tag{7.58}$$

$$\Sigma_j \Sigma_c u_j''\cdot Y_{cj}'' u_c' = \Sigma_j u_j''\cdot Y_{tj}''\cdot u_t'$$

where we have used the fact that indices k and j run over boundary buses. Thus for $j = b$, the last equation yields

$$u_b''\cdot Y_{t,b}''\cdot u_t' = \Sigma_c\, u_b''\cdot Y_{c,b}''\cdot u_c'$$

Since u_b'' is independent of summation on $c\Sigma = m + 1, \ldots, n$, it can be factored out and eliminated. Dividing by u_t' and taking the conjugate yields then

$$Y_{t,b}' = \Sigma\, Y_{c,b}'\cdot \frac{u_c''}{u_t''} \tag{7.59}$$

Division of Eq. (7.58) by $u_t''\cdot u_t'$ yields the self-admittance:

$$Y_{t,t}' = \Sigma_k\, \Sigma_c \left(\frac{u_k'}{u_t'} \right) \cdot Y_{c,k}' \cdot \left(\frac{u_c''}{u_t''} \right) \tag{7.60}$$

Comparing Eq. (7.59) with Eq. (7.54) shows that $Y_{t,b}' \neq Y_{b,t}'$. The magnitude is the same, however, indicating that a phase-shifting transformer has been introduced in the line from the equivalent bus t to each boundary bus b. The phase shift is half the angular difference of $Y'_{b,t}$ and $Y'_{t,b}$.

Concluding, we have for buses $m + 1, \ldots, n$ to be reduced:

- Voltage of the equivalent from Eq. (7.55).
- $Y'_{b,t}$ of the reduced matrix, with b as a boundary node, from Eq. (7.54).
- $Y'_{t,b}$ from Eq. (7.59).
- The self-admittance $Y'_{t,t}$ of the equivalent from Eq. (7.60).
- The generation at the equivalent bus is the sum of the generation at each bus eliminated.
- The load at the equivalent bus is the sum of the load at each bus eliminated.

We have thus reduced the number of lines and generators. Next, nonlinear loads are included. First the real and reactive loads are expressed differently than in Section 7.2.2, namely, as

$$p_j = (f_{sj} + f_{ij} \cdot \frac{u_j}{u_{j0}} + f_{zj} \cdot \frac{u_j^2}{u_{j0}^2}) \cdot p_{j0}$$

$$q_j = (g_{sj} + g_{ij} \cdot \frac{u_j}{u_{j0}} + g_{zj} \cdot \frac{u_j^2}{u_{j0}^2}) \cdot q_{j0}$$

where the f_{si}, f_{ij}, f_{zi} and g_{si}, g_{ij}, g_{zi} are the fractional coefficients and describe the relative proportion of constant power, current, and impedance terms at base voltage u_0 and base power p_{j0}, q_{j0}. Note that

$$f_{sj} + f_{ij} + f_{zj} = 1$$

and

$$g_{sj} + g_{ij} + g_{zj} = 1$$

The method described below extends the Gaussian elimination procedure to handle nonlinear loads by approximating them as constant current sinks. This is done (for bus j) as follows:

- The constant-impedance part of the load is included within the admittance matrix.
- The constant-current part of the load on a bus to be eliminated (bus j) is converted to a current sink, i_{ij}. Note that this is an approximation when the voltage of the bus deviates from the base condition. The load current now maintains a constant phase with respect to the reference angle rather than the voltage angle, as shown in Figure 7.14(a).
- The constant-power part of the load is converted to a current sink, i_{sj}.

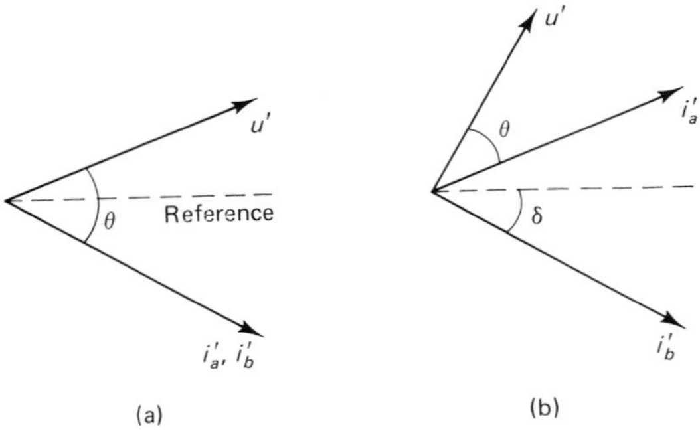

Figure 7.14 (a) Original base condition $i_a = i_b$. Effect of voltage rotation on nonlinear load modeled as constant-power factor current (i_a) and constant-current sink (i_b). (b) Condition with rotation of bus voltage.

The nodal admittance equation can therefore be written as

$$\begin{bmatrix} \mathbf{i}_1 \\ \mathbf{0} \end{bmatrix} = \begin{bmatrix} \mathbf{Y}_{11} & \mathbf{Y}_{12} \\ \mathbf{Y}_{21} & \mathbf{Y}_{22} \end{bmatrix} * \begin{bmatrix} \mathbf{u}_1 \\ \mathbf{u}_2 \end{bmatrix} + \begin{bmatrix} \mathbf{0} \\ \mathbf{i}_I \end{bmatrix} + \begin{bmatrix} \mathbf{0} \\ \mathbf{i}_s \end{bmatrix}$$

where $\mathbf{i}_I$ and $\mathbf{i}_s$ correspond to constant current and power, respectively, and subscripts 1 and 2 denote buses to be retained and to be eliminated.

The second and first rows yield

$$\mathbf{0} = \mathbf{Y}_{21} * \mathbf{u}_1 + \mathbf{Y}_{22} * \mathbf{u}_2 + \mathbf{i}_I + \mathbf{i}_s$$

or

$$\mathbf{u}_2 = -\mathbf{Y}_{22}^{-1} * (\mathbf{Y}_{21} * \mathbf{u}_1 + \mathbf{i}_I + \mathbf{i}_s)$$

$$\mathbf{i}_1 = \mathbf{Y}_{11} * \mathbf{u}_1 + \mathbf{Y}_{12} * \mathbf{u}_2$$

$$= \mathbf{Y}_{11} * \mathbf{u}_1 - \mathbf{Y}_{12} * \mathbf{Y}_{22}^{-1} * (\mathbf{Y}_{21} * \mathbf{u}_1 + \mathbf{i}_I + \mathbf{i}_s)$$

We define an equivalent admittance $\tilde{\mathbf{Y}}_{11}$ and two *current sinks* $\tilde{\imath}_I$ and $\tilde{\imath}_s$:

$$\tilde{\mathbf{Y}}_{11} \equiv \mathbf{Y}_{11} - \mathbf{Y}_{12} * \mathbf{Y}_{22}^{-1} * \mathbf{Y}_{21}$$

$$\tilde{\imath}_I \equiv -\mathbf{Y}_{12} * \mathbf{Y}_{22}^{-1} * \mathbf{i}_I; \qquad \tilde{\imath}_s = -\mathbf{Y}_{12} * \mathbf{Y}_{22}^{-1} * \mathbf{i}_s$$

Then we get for the currents $\mathbf{i}_1 := \tilde{\mathbf{Y}}_1 * \mathbf{u}_1 + \tilde{\mathbf{i}}_I + \tilde{\mathbf{i}}_s$.

The currents $\mathbf{i}_I$ and $\mathbf{i}_S$ are the equivalent-current sinks on the retained buses. These current sinks are reconverted to constant-current and constant-power type load, respectively, using

$$s_{Ij}' = u_j' \cdot (\tilde{\imath}_{Ij})''; \qquad s_{sj}' = u_j' \cdot (\tilde{\imath}_{sj})'$$

The constant-impedance portion of the equivalent load is obtained by calculating the shunt admittance $\tilde{y}_j$ from the ith row of the equivalent admittance matrix $\tilde{\mathbf{Y}}$. The constant-impedance type component of complex power is then given by

$$s_{zj}' = u_j^2 \cdot \tilde{y}_j'$$

The various load coefficients f_{ij}, f_{sj}, f_{zj}, and g_{ij}, g_{sj}, g_{zj} are obtained by summing and rotating the complex components s_{ij}, s_{sj} and s_{zj}.

The dynamic equivalencing program is seen to include the capability for reducing nonlinear loads which consist of constant-impedance, constant-current (at fixed power factor) and constant-power components.

The Gaussian elimination procedure approximates the latter two as ideal current sinks. "A pair of current sinks is introduced to replace the constant-current and constant-power components of load at each bus. The base case load-flow voltages are used to perform this conversion. The current sinks are reduced by the standard Gaussian elimination formula. Each pair of equivalent current sources on each retained bus is then reconverted to an equivalent constant-current component and an equivalent constant-power component.

"In order to maintain accuracy with the current sink reduction method, the network is divided into subareas which are roughly coherent. The subareas are defined by grouping one or more control areas." [EP77]

The equivalents developed thus far have all been applicable to off-line planning studies. In such applications [CD78],* "one is given the luxury of knowing everything about the entire system.... For on-line security assessment applications, information about external systems is lacking in many respects. As one departs from the study system boundaries into neighboring systems, network topology information becomes harder to come by, let alone voltage conditions, schedules, and actual loads. Even if some reasonable knowledge of all these is attained at some hour of the day, a few hours later this knowledge is rendered useless because of switching operations, changing load and generation conditions, and so on."

Assuming that only the state estimator provides information about the study system, Reference [CD78] came up with a method of calculating the equivalent. In it the "equivalencing problem is formulated as an optimization problem. Switching operations, together with on-line state estimation, are the main sources of information to obtain the equivalent model. This equivalent model consists of fictitious network branches. These fictitious branches may be complex admittance elements between the boundary buses or between these buses and ground (shunt elements). The conductances and susceptances of these elements are the unknown variables. The vector of the unknown variables is denoted by **u**."

---

* G. Contaxis, A. S. Debs, "Identification of External System Equivalents for Steady-State Security Assessment," *Trans. IEEE*, Vol. PAS-97, No. 2, March/April, 1978, pp. 409–414.

We denote by $\mathbf{x}$ the vector of the complex bus voltages of the internal system, calculated by a state estimator. Let the vectors $\mathbf{x}_a$ and $\mathbf{x}_b$ denote the pre- and post-outage vectors of the complex bus voltages, respectively. Also let the vectors $\mathbf{s}$ denote the vectors of the real and reactive injections at the boundary buses before and after the kth outage. Then

$$\mathbf{s}_b = \mathbf{A}_b * \mathbf{u} + \mathbf{t}_b; \quad \mathbf{s}_a = \mathbf{A}_a * \mathbf{u} + \mathbf{t}_a$$

where $\mathbf{A}_a \equiv \mathbf{A}(\mathbf{x}_a)$; $\mathbf{A}_b \equiv \mathbf{A}(\mathbf{x}_b)$ and $\mathbf{t}_b$, $\mathbf{t}_a$ are vectors of pre- and post-outage power flows from the boundary buses to the internal system. These are known quantities. $\mathbf{A}_b$ and $\mathbf{A}_a$ are matrices which are strictly dependent on $\mathbf{x}_b$, $\mathbf{x}_a$.

The difference between the pre- and post-outage injections at the boundary buses becomes

$$\mathbf{d}_k = \mathbf{s}_b - \mathbf{s}_a = (\mathbf{A}_b - \mathbf{A}_a) * \mathbf{u} + \mathbf{t}_b - \mathbf{t}_a = \mathbf{H}_k * \mathbf{u} + \mathbf{m}_k$$
$$k = 1, \ldots, N$$

where N is the number of switching operations considered in the internal system. Matrix $\mathbf{H}_k$ and vector $\mathbf{m}_k$ of the internal system are known quantities.

If the equivalent representation was exact, then

$$\mathbf{d}_k = \mathbf{0}; \quad k = 1, \ldots, N$$

In practice this is not feasible, since the last equation represents an overdetermined set of equations. Hence we seek a solution which will minimize the following defined error:

$$c = \Sigma\, (\mathbf{H}_k * \mathbf{u} + \mathbf{m}_k)^{\mathrm{T}} * (\mathbf{H}_k * \mathbf{u} + \mathbf{m}_k); \quad k\Sigma = 1, \ldots, N \qquad (7.61)$$

If b is the number of boundary buses, then with $e = c/(N \cdot b)$ and e_p a predetermined value, the equivalent is considered satisfactory if $e < e_p$.

This is obviously equivalent to minimization of Eq. (7.61) (a least-squares objective) constrained by $e < e_p$."

The details can be found in [CD78]. An important point made and then verified by tests is that in many cases the unconstrained solution is sufficient and so the problem can be solved as a least-squares optimization problem.

7.5 PROGRAMS

Having dealt with parts of the program, let us combine them. It is assumed that some parts of the network are represented by equivalents so that the program should deal with the "entire" network. In the spirit of top-down design, the following modules (subroutines) are to be used:

LF: A load-flow program which calculates the voltages for all n buses of the network.

LIN: A program to solve the linear set $\mathbf{Y} * \mathbf{u} = \mathbf{i}$ defined in Eq. (7.15) and in Chapter 3.

DEQS: Given angles $\boldsymbol{\delta}$ at t, it supplies $\boldsymbol{\delta}$ at $t + \Delta t$ by solving the differential equations.

PREP: Prepares the $\mathbf{Y}$ matrix for a given topology and impedances.

UPM: Updates machine currents and powers.

VPRIM: Computes all required derivatives.

The overall structure of the program is then as follows:

```
while {time span not completed}
    if {switching occurred} then
    begin
        LF; PREP
    end;
    UPM; VPRIM; DEQS; LIN;
    t := t + δt {δt is Δt}
end;
```

If the modified Euler's method is used, then UPM and DEQS are done twice, once to predict the voltages and again to correct them. The reader is also encouraged to look to more accurate methods: a fifth-order Runge–Kutta procedure with automatic adjustment of step size has been published in [ST74].

Programs for solution of differential equations are readily available in various mathematical libraries. It is more difficult to find programs tailored to solution of algebraic equations of a particular type. The algebraic equations were of two types: linear, as in Eq. (7.15), and LF and therefore nonlinear both initially and each time some switching occurs. As shown in Chapter 4, both can be solved by the fast Gauss–Seidel, the FGS routine if the right-hand side is $\cong p/u^2$ or constant. It is customary to use OOF, and the choice of FGS should be justified.

The solution of $\mathbf{A} * \mathbf{x} = \mathbf{b}$, where $\mathbf{b}$ either is constant or is updated in each iteration, is often done by *overrelaxation*. This means that instead of

$$x_i := b_i - \Sigma A_{ik} \cdot x_k; \quad k\Sigma = 1, \ldots, n \text{ but } k \neq i \tag{7.62}$$

this x_i is considered to be an approximation $\tilde{x}_i$ and the "new" x_i is calculated from

$$x_i := x_i^0 + \rho\cdot(\tilde{x}_i - x_i^0) \tag{7.63}$$

where x_i^0 is the "old" value of x_i and ρ is the *overrelaxation factor*.

It was found that $1.6 \leq \rho \leq 1.8$ leads to faster convergence. Note that for $\rho = 1$, Eq. (7.63) leads to Eq. (7.62).

An iteration of the method to be proposed consists of a "downward" overrelaxation sweep, in which the coordinates of the approximation vector $\mathbf{x}_i$ are updated through a Gauss–Seidel-like operation, followed by an "upward" sweep, which updates x_i in reverse order, with the order of equations reversed also. As such FGS or the symmetric successive overrelaxation method belongs to the family of *alternating iterative schemes*, i.e., schemes which consist of applying two different iterations α and β in an alternating fashion, $\alpha\beta\alpha\beta\alpha\beta\cdots$, until convergence is attained.

At first sight the number of arithmetic operations required for a composite step $\alpha\beta$ appears to be equal to the sum of the number of operations required by α and that required by β. Thus an FGS composite iteration for a full n-by-n matrix should require $\cong 2n^2$ operations, since the constituent Gauss–Seidel iterations require $\cong n^2$ operations. However, as shown in Chapter 2, substantial savings in running time can be achieved; actually, only $\cong n^2$ instead of $2n^2$ operations are required. Finally, [WK77/79] gives a generalization of the methods to the entire family of alternating iterative schemes and shows that FGS is optimal: no other method uses fewer operations.

We listed program GSA in Section 2.5 and program GSB in Section 4.3 and mentioned the FGS algorithm. Next we will develop FGS programs for two environments: off-line and on-line.

The main idea of FGS is to save during each sweep the results of certain intermediate calculations, which are then used in the following sweep; the savings in arithmetic stem from not having to recompute them. The intermediate results are saved in a vector $\mathbf{y}$. Essentially, the algorithm requires storage for the matrix $\mathbf{A}$, the right-hand side $\mathbf{b}$, the vector of unknowns $\mathbf{x}$, and the auxiliary vector $\mathbf{y}$. However, the implementation given here makes use only of $\mathbf{A}$, $\mathbf{x}$, and $\mathbf{y}$ (the value of $\mathbf{b}$ is transmitted to the subroutine in $\mathbf{y}$); the extra storage is provided by the diagonal elements of $\mathbf{A}$, whose contents after normalization are all equal to 1 and need not be stored.

The resulting program is "FISSOR" (Program 7.1). Next the reasons for choosing it instead of OOF for stability calculations are given.

A solution of linear equations by OOF requires $O(n^3)$ operations for factorization and $O(n^2)$ for each time $t = 0, \Delta t, \ldots, m\cdot\Delta t$. Thus altogether $\Omega_0 \cong O(n^3) + m\cdot O(n^2)$. The first part is required after each switching operation.

A double iteration of the algorithm as given here requires n^2 operations, so that for i iterations $\Omega_F \cong i \cdot O(n^2)$ are required. Dropping the "order of" O-notation shows that FGS will be faster at switching times and between switching times, respectively, if

$$i < n + m \quad \text{and} \quad i < m \tag{7.64}$$

The number of iterations i depends entirely on how close to the solution the initial assumption $\mathbf{x}^{(0)}$ is and how accurate the required solution is, i.e., when the iterations are stopped. In the particular case of stability analysis, both favor the FGS method for the following reasons.

- Each solution starts with $\mathbf{x}^{(0)}$ as the voltages computed for $t - \Delta t$, i.e., the results of the previous application of FGS. These voltages will not have changed much during the usually small integration time Δt. Had they remained constant, no iterations or a single iteration would have been sufficient. For small changes, i will be small and obey inequalities Eq. (7.64).
- Another reason has to do with accuracy. It was shown by singular values of power system matrices that OOF has a large roundoff error. Solution of FGS can be carried out for enough iterations to adapt the error to the chosen integration method and still obey Eq. (7.64).
- When switching occurs, matrix $\mathbf{A} = \mathbf{G} + j \cdot \mathbf{B}$ has to be recomputed and factored in OOF for $O(n^3)$. No factoring is required in FGS.
- The storage space required by OOF is increased by fill-in even if the best ordering is used. In FGS only space for $\mathbf{A}$ is required, and this matrix can be stored as in Table 3.5, since the operations are really only scalar products. Thus, storage space and operation time are saved because only nonzero elements are multiplied.

All these arguments are of the "handwaving" type. On the other hand, no close-form equation for i and m exists and the proofs have to rely on results of simulation runs. Such runs have been done and prove that FGS competes quite favorably with OOF for stability studies.

In real-time dispatching we will hardly solve stability problems. Still, an ASP solution for the FGS-algorithm is proposed for several reasons:

- It will show how to restructure the known algorithm in order to adapt it for the ASP.
- It will show how to simulate it on any sequential, ordinary computer.
- Most important, *it will show that even such "inherently sequential" algorithms as that of Gauss–Seidel can be useful on an ASP.*

```
procedure fissor(var a,y,n,m,om,manit,rmax);
(* Subroutine fissor ( Fast Iterative SSOR)
solves a set of linear equations
     a * x = b
by the symmetric successive overrelaxation
method in a way which requires only n**2
multiplications and additions for the
downward and upward sweeps (i.e., a 50%
reduction) without increase in the
storage required. The parameters are:
   a is an n_by_n matrix
   x is the solution n_vector
   b is the right_hand_side n_vector
   om is the overrelaxation factor used. If om=1,
   the "Fast Gauss-Seidel" or FGS method results.
   manit is the maximum number of iterations allowed.
   rmax is the maximal residual i.e. the algorithm stops
   whenever the number of iterations exceeds manit
   or max(abs(x[new]-x[old]))<rmax for all i=1,...,n.
vector y accumulates the negative sum of a[i,j]*x[j]
during a "downward" sweep and b minus this
sum during an "upward" sweep.
auxiliary variables are: i,j,k,m,n1,d,r,t and z.
   The upward and downward sweeps could have been
combined to make the program shorter. This
was not done, since it would both complicate
the program and destroy its simple structure. *)

var i,j,k,m,n1:integer; d,r,t,z:real;

(*Initialization during which:
we assume that a[i,i]<>0. Divide each row i by
a[i,i], insert b[i]/a[i,i] into the diagonal and
prepare vector y for the downward  sweep.
we define n1 so as not to compare i with n+1.   *)

n1:=n+1;
for i:=1 to n do
begin d:=a[i,i];
   for j:=y[i]/d; a[i,i]:=z; k:=i+1;
   if k=<n then
   (* We compute the normalized, initial y[i] through
      y[i] = b[i]-sum(a[i,j]*x[j])  *)
   for j:=k to n do z:=z-a[i,j]*x[j];
   y[i]:=z
end;



numit:=1;
repeat
   d:=0.0;

   (* In the next, downward sweep, y[i] will be the vector
      defined as y[i] = -sum(a[i,j]*x[j])
   Note that it will be accumulated by columns; this is the basis
   for efficient programming in this case. Accumulation of each
   y[i] is completed precisely one step ahead of its being used.*
```

Program 7.1

```
    for i:=1 to n do
    begin
       z:=0.0; k:=i-1; t:=x[i];
       if k<>0 then
       for j:=1 to k do z:=z-a[i,j]*x[j];
       d:=z+y[i]-t; x[i]:=t+om*d; y[i]:=z;

       (*Next we search for max(abs(d)) *)

       t:=abs(d); if t>r then r:=t
    end;

    (* Upward sweep similar to the downward sweep : *)

    for m:=1 to n do
    begin
       i:=n1-m; k:=i+1;

       (*Next, z is initialized to normalized b *)

       z:=a[i,i]; t:=x[i];
       d:=om*z+y[i]-t;
       x[i]:=t+d; y[i]:=z; t:=abs(d);
       if t>r then r:=t
    end;
    numit:=numit+1;

 until ((numit>manit) or (r<rmax));

 end.
```

Program 7.1 (cont.)

The set of linear equations to be solved is

$$x_1 + A_{12}x_2 + A_{13}x_3 + A_{14}x_4 + A_{15}x_5 + A_{16}x_6 = b_1$$

$$A_{21}x_1 + x_2 + A_{23}x_3 + A_{24}x_4 + A_{25}x_5 + A_{26}x_6 = b_2$$

$$A_{31}x_1 + A_{32}x_2 + x_3 + A_{34}x_4 + A_{35}x_5 + A_{36}x_6 = b_3$$

$$A_{41}x_1 + A_{42}x_2 + A_{43}x_3 + x_4 + A_{45}x_5 + A_{46}x_6 = b_4$$

$$A_{51}x_1 + A_{52}x_2 + A_{53}x_3 + A_{54}x_4 + x_5 + A_{56}x_6 = b_5$$

$$A_{61}x_1 + A_{62}x_2 + A_{63}x_3 + A_{64}x_4 + A_{65}x_5 + x_6 = b_6$$

In a computer we solve much larger sets, but to describe our topic, six equations will suffice.

In the Gauss–Seidel method we proceed for iteration i as follows: Compute $x_1^{(i)}$ from the first equation by assuming that $x_2^{(i-1)}, \ldots, x_6^{(i-1)}$ are known. Then compute $x_2^{(i)}$ from the second equation assuming $x_3^{(i-1)}, \ldots, x_6^{(i-1)}$ as known and using $x_1^{(i)}$ as computed earlier. For a general j compute

$$x_j = b_j - \Sigma A_{jk} \cdot x_k; \quad k\Sigma = 1, \ldots, n; \quad k \neq j \tag{7.65}$$

As defined, this process is considered to be strictly sequential, since the calculation of any $x_j^{(i)}$ has to wait for all $x_k^{(i)}$, $k < j$, to be computed first. Also, iteration $i + 1$ can start only after iteration i is completed. It is precisely because we want to show how such strictly sequential processes can be parallelized, that we have chosen the Gauss–Seidel algorithm. As a matter of fact, we will parallelize the fast Gauss–Seidel routine of Section 2.5.

For parallelization, we rewrite the main equation:

$$x_j = (b_j - \Sigma A_{jk} \cdot x_k) - \Sigma A_{jm} \cdot x_m = t_j - z_j \tag{7.66}$$
$$m\Sigma = 1, \ldots, j - 1; \quad k\Sigma = j + 1, \ldots, n$$

It is important to note that vector $\mathbf{t}^{(i-1)}$ or $x_k^{(i-1)}$ of iteration $i - 1$ is used, but $z_j^{(i)}$ and $x_k^{(i)}$ of iteration i are needed to compute $x_j^{(i)}$. Thus,

$$x_j^{(i)} = t_j^{(i-1)} - z_j^{(i)}; \quad j = 1, 2, \ldots, 6 = n \tag{7.67}$$

Also note that $z_1 = 0$, $t_6 = b_6$ for any iteration i.

Suppose we have two slaves ($p = 2$). Then we store matrix $\mathbf{A}$ and vectors $\mathbf{t}^{(i-1)}$ and $\mathbf{b}$ in slices as below and store the initial vector $\mathbf{x}^{(0)} = [x_1^{(0)}, x_2^{(0)}, \ldots, x_6^{(0)}]^T$ in each slice.

$$A_{12}, A_{13}, A_{14}, A_{15}, A_{16}, b_1, t_1^{(0)}$$
$$A_{21}, A_{23}, A_{24}, A_{25}, A_{26}, b_2, t_2^{(0)}$$
$$A_{31}, A_{32}, A_{34}, A_{35}, A_{36}, b_3, t_3^{(0)}$$

— — — — — — — — — — —

$$A_{41}, A_{42}, A_{43}, A_{45}, A_{46}, b_4, t_4^{(0)}$$
$$A_{51}, A_{52}, A_{53}, A_{54}, A_{56}, b_5, t_5^{(0)}$$
$$A_{61}, A_{62}, A_{63}, A_{64}, A_{65}, b_6, t_6^{(0)}$$

In what follows we first go through iteration 1, which computes $x_1^{(1)}, \ldots, x_6^{(1)}$. In particular, "broadcast" means that $x_j^{(i)}$ as computed is accessed by the master and broadcast to *all* remaining slaves (here to just one). "Final" indicates that the value of $z_j^{(i)}$ is complete, and "asymmetry" that the two slaves are not loaded equally. Parallel and sequential steps are denoted P_m and S_m, and SL_m indicates "in slave m do...."

SL_1: $x_1^{(1)} = t_1^{(0)} - z_1^{(0)} = t_1^{(0)} - 0 = t_1^{(0)}$ (broadcast) } S_1

$$\left.\begin{array}{l} SL_1\colon z_2^{(1)} = A_{21}x_1^{(1)} \text{ (final)};\ z_3^{(1)} = A_{31}x_1^{(1)} \\ SL_2\colon z_4^{(1)} = A_{41}x_1^{(1)};\ z_5^{(1)} = A_{51}x_1^{(1)};\ z_6^{(1)} = A_{61}x_1^{(1)} \end{array}\right\} P_1$$

$$SL_1\colon x_2^{(1)} = t_2^{(0)} - z_2^{(1)} \text{ (broadcast) } \} \ S_2$$

$$\left.\begin{array}{ll} SL_1\colon & z_3^{(1)} = z_3^{(1)} + A_{32}x_2 \text{ (final)} \\ & z_4^{(1)} = z_4^{(1)} + A_{42}\cdot x_2^{(1)}; \\ SL_2\colon & z_5^{(1)} = z_5^{(1)} + A_{52}\cdot x_2^{(1)}; \\ & z_6^{(1)} = z_6^{(1)} + A_{62}\cdot x_2^{(1)} \end{array}\right\} P_2$$

$$SL_1\colon x_3^{(1)} = t_3^{(0)} - z_3^{(1)} \text{ (broadcast) } \} \ S_3$$

$$\left.\begin{array}{ll} & z_4^{(1)} = z_4^{(1)} + A_{43}x_3^{(1)} \text{ (final)}; \\ SL_2\colon & z_5^{(1)} = z_5^{(1)} + A_{53}x_3^{(1)}; \\ & z_6^{(1)} = z_6^{(1)} + A_{63}x_3^{(1)} \text{ (asymmetry)} \end{array}\right\} P_3$$

$$SL_2\colon x_4^{(1)} = t_4^{(0)} - z_4^{(1)} \text{ (broadcast) } \} \ S_4$$

$$\left.\begin{array}{ll} SL_2\colon & z_5^{(1)} = z_5^{(1)} + A_{54}x_4^{(1)} \text{ (final)}; \\ & z_6^{(1)} = z_6^{(1)} + A_{64}x_4^{(1)} \end{array}\right\} P_4$$

$$SL_2\colon x_5^{(1)} = t_5^{(0)} - z_5^{(1)} \text{ (broadcast) } \} \ S_5$$

$$SL_2\colon z_6^{(1)} = z_6^{(1)} + A_{65}x_5^{(1)} \text{ (final) } \} \ P_5$$

$$SL_2\colon x_6^{(1)} = t_6^{(0)} - z_6^{(1)} \text{ (broadcast) } \} \ S_6$$

Add to the algorithm that each time an $x_j^{(1)}$ was calculated, $t_j^{(1)}$ was set to the corresponding b_j.

In step S_6 we computed $x_6^{(1)}$, and since it was broadcast, all $t_j^{(1)}$, $j = 5, 4, 3, 2, 1$, can be set to $t_j^{(1)} = t_j^{(1)} - A_{j,6}\cdot x_6^{(1)}$, the $x_5^{(2)}$ computed by $x_5^{(2)} = t_5^{(1)} - z_5^{(1)}$ (which still exists), and so on. As seen the upward step is completely symmetrical to the downward step.

Altogether — in both steps — we had to do all n^2 additions and multiplications: $\Omega = n^2$. This is half the number of operations required by the Gauss–Seidel method, so even in normal, sequential execution it is possible to improve on some work by Karl Friedrich Gauss.

In an ASP execution, the steps of the forward iteration are as in Fig. 7.15(a) where P', P'' are tasks done by processors 1 and 2 respectively.

The operations count depends on the asymmetry, and in this case is $\Omega = 25$. Additionally, we need 6τ to broadcast the 6 values $x_j^{(1)}$ over the bus and 12π for bit handshaking.

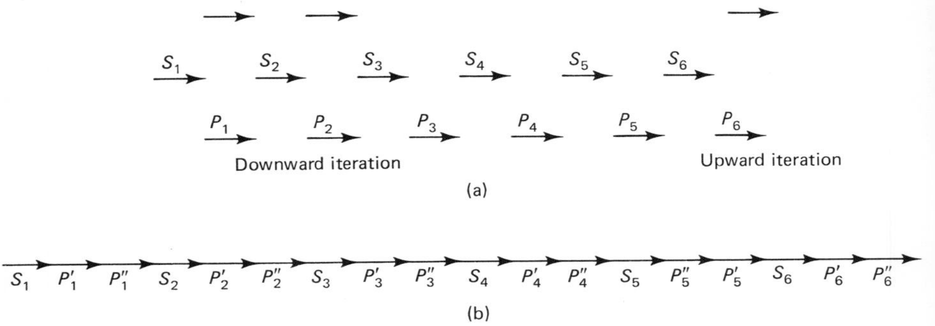

Figure 7.15 (a) General. (b) Simulation of the 6-equation set.

The inverse of the speedup here is

$$\rho = \frac{12(\alpha + \mu) + 12\pi + 6\tau}{6^2(\alpha + \mu)} = \frac{1}{2} + \frac{\tilde{\pi}}{3} + \frac{\tilde{\tau}}{6}$$

If it were not for the last two terms (i.e., for bit handshaking and transfer of words over the bus), the speedup would have been $\cong 2$. That is the ideal speedup for two slaves. We will nearly achieve it for $n >> 6$ (but not for much smaller n).

To calculate the speedup for a general case and especially for sparse systems, the running of the program must be simulated to get the asymmetry. The simulation can be done on any computer by sequentialization. Thus, if for Fig. 7.15(a) we draw the parallel steps so that time P_i'' follows P_i' of slave i, we get Fig. 7.15(b). Such programs will yield Ω for every S_k and the P_k' and P_k'' parts of any P_k. The master waits until both completed their tasks, so that (with ts = time of slave) we can simulate it through

if *ts*[2] > *ts*[1] **then** *p* [*k*] := *ts*[2]
else *p* [*k*] := *ts*[1]

The factors depending on bit handshaking (π) and transfer (τ) of words over the bus can *only* be ascertained through simulation. On the other hand, such simulations can be done not only on an ASP machine but on any other purely sequential, present-day computer.

7.6 NOTES

The material on the stability problem and on solving differential equations can be found in texts on power systems and numerical analysis, respectively.

A stability program is too large to be considered a one-person project. Instead, it is suggested that the reader use a library package for solving differential equations with the fissor routine (Program 7.1) for some simple cases.

A simulation program (pargas or Program 7.2) is also included and the reader may debug it and simulate running of FGS on an ASP system by replacing Program 7.1 by it. The results should demonstrate that the program shows a very good speedup indeed.

```
program pargas(input,output);
const p=2; n=6; h=3;
type     slrange=1..h;
var b,t,x,z:array[1..n] of real;
    f:array[1..p] of real;
    hig,low:array[1..p] of integer;
      a:array[1..n,1..n] of real;
      sl,slave,jj,i,ls,j:integer;
      y,e,g,eps,r:real;

procedure parset(ls:integer);
var i:integer;
begin e:=0;
   for i:=1 to h do z[i+ls-1]:=0
end;

procedure parinit(ls:integer);
var i,j,k:integer;
begin
   for i:=1 to h do
     begin j:=i+ls-1;
        z[j]:=0;t[j]:=-b[j];
        for k:=j+1 to n do t[j]:=t[j]+a[j,k]*x[k]
     end
end;

procedure parnew(i:integer);
begin y:=-(z[i]+t[i])/a[i,i];
   r:=y-x[i]; e:=e+r*r
end;

procedure parcom(i,lo,hi:integer);
var j:integer;
begin
   if i=lo then
      for j:=lo+1 to hi do z[j]:=z[j]+a[j,i]*x[i]
   else if i<lo then
      for j:=lo to hi do z[j]:=z[j]+a[j,i]*x[i]
   else if i=hi then
      for j:=lo to hi-1 do t[j]:=t[j]+a[j,i]*r
   else if i>hi then
      for j:=lo to hi do t[j]:=t[j]+a[j,i]*r
```

Program 7.2

```
    else begin
           for j:=lo to i-1 do t[j]:=t[j]+a[j,i]*r;
           for j:=i+1 to hi do z[j]:=z[j]+a[j,i]*x[j]
    end
end;

begin low[1]:=1; hig[1]:=h;
    for slave:=2 to p do low[slave]:=low[slave-1]+h;
    for slave:=2 to p do hig[slave]:=hig[slave-1]+h;
    for i:=1 to n do x[i]:=1.0;
    for slave:=1 to p do
    begin
       ls:=low[slave]; parinit(ls)
    end; j:=0;
    repeat j:=j+1;
       for slave:=1 to p do

          begin e:=0.0;
             for i:=low[slave] to hig[slave] do
             begin parnew(i); x[i]:=y;
             for sl:=1 to p do
                parcom(i,low[sl],hig[sl]);
             end; f[slave]:=e
          end;
          g:=0;
          for slave:=1 to p do g:=g+f[slave];
          if g>eps then
          for slave:=1 to p do
          begin
             ls:=low[slave]; parset(ls)
          end;  writeln(j,g)
      until j>15
  end.
```

Program 7.2 (cont.)

8 Contingency Analysis Problem

The *objectives* of this chapter are

1. To discuss the use of decoupling for contingency analysis.
2. To linearize the relations and show how contingency analysis can be done using the so-called distribution factors.
3. To describe a fast, parallel, optimally ordered factorization (POOF) algorithm.
4. To show how various contingencies are selected.

8.1 INTRODUCTION

An important aspect of the design and operation of a power system network is to maintain system security. Two examples of how security influences design will suffice: If a generator has to be disconnected because of failure in, say, its auxiliary equipment, then the remaining generators have to generate additional power. While designing the network, enough "spinning reserve" generation must be provided so that this power can be generated without an inadmissible frequency drop or need to shed some load. Second, the lines must be designed so that if a line is damaged (say, by a storm) and removed by relays, the power at its two buses is supplied by other lines satisfying the limits (of not too much current or too low a voltage). In particular, if protective relays remove other lines because of overload, a *cascading outage* may lead to a system *blackout*. The design and dispatch should make sure this does not happen.

Despite the fact that supervisory control and data-acquisition systems enable the operator to control circuit breakers, disconnect switches, and change transformer taps by remote control, the changes in a network are so fast that the operators cannot cope with them on time. To enable secure operation, contingency analysis programs (CAP) are provided. They model the existing, operating system and calculate whether for a possible outage (of a generator or line) the network can still be operated safely. Hence they allow the dispatchers to operate the network defensively so that no single contingency will cause overloads or too low or high voltages.

The effect of load changes, generation rescheduling, and outages (of lines or transformers) can be obtained by running load-flow studies. If these are run on-line, in real time, they have to be very fast indeed. The methods developed in Chapter 4 are not fast enough, but since accuracy is subordinated to speed for this case, certain simplifications of the algorithms can be made. The first is to simplify decoupled OOF and linearize it (Section 8.2); another is to prepare distribution factors based on linearization (Section 8.3).

In planning studies, a large number of possible (primary or secondary) contingencies are analyzed. This is very time consuming for the design stage and even more so for on-line applications. It seems much better to prepare and update continuously a list of selected contingencies and apply CAP programs only to the selected cases. Such contingency selection is discussed in Section 8.4.

It should be noted that a single change in a network can be accounted for by any of the updating methods discussed in Chapter 2. This was the main reason for introducing them, and the reader may view the application of these methods as a project. Changes can also easily be incorporated into the Gauss–Seidel or FGS programs — another project. In [Br75], the use of the Z-bus matrix is advocated for contingency evaluations. Finally, a possibility to speed up the solution is to use parallelization and ASP (Section 8.5).

Both in contingency analysis and even more so in stability problems we are confronted with the "curse of dimensionality," i.e., that the network is too large for the time available and the variety of programs to be solved on the computer. This is especially true for highly interconnected systems. The remedy is to simulate part of the (external) network by an equivalent generator or load (Chapter 7).

8.2 CONTINGENCY EVALUATION*

Decoupled OOF can be summarized by equations (4.39) and (4.40):

$$\frac{\mathbf{\Delta p}}{\mathbf{u}} = \tilde{\mathbf{B}} * \Delta\boldsymbol{\theta} \tag{8.1a}$$

$$\frac{\mathbf{\Delta q}}{\mathbf{u}} = \mathbf{B}^{\#} * \Delta\mathbf{u} \tag{8.1b}$$

where matrices $\tilde{\mathbf{B}}$ and $\mathbf{B}^{\#}$ are approximations of the Jacobian obtained from the partial derivatives of the exact network equations. (This was shown in Chapter 4.)

Because of the approximations made in arriving at Eq. (8.1), the quadratic convergence of the Newton–Raphson method is reduced. Nevertheless, since no approximation is made to the mismatch vectors, the solution is almost as accurate and two or three times faster than the Newton–Raphson method.

From Eq. (8.1) it can be seen that the AC characteristics of the power system are represented by two essentially DC equivalent network systems. The modifications of the two matrices **B** are as follows:*

Matrix $\tilde{\mathbf{B}}$ is the nodal admittance matrix of the power system where the swing bus is chosen as the reference node (voltage angle is zero). For a given iteration step, when a DC current source vector $\mathbf{\Delta p/u}$ is applied to the system, a DC voltage vector $\Delta\boldsymbol{\theta}$ results.

Similarly, $\mathbf{B}^{\#}$ can be viewed as the nodal admittance matrix of the system when the swing bus and all voltage-controlled buses are grounded and all voltage magnitudes are taken with respect to ground.

By this reasoning, the omission from $\tilde{\mathbf{B}}$ of grounded network elements such as shunt reactances and off-nominal in-phase transformer taps is justified. Neglecting the series resistance of the line in the calculation of the elements of $\tilde{\mathbf{B}}$ is experimentally feasible because the resistive component of a line is generally much smaller than the reactive component. The only elements still connected to the ground bus are the line-charging capacitances.

It was found that systems with many lines of charging capacitances greater than 0.5 pu tend to converge very slowly. They take over 20 iterations compared to an average of from 2 to 5 iterations for a normal power system to converge to 0.01 pu MW/MVAR mismatch. Removal of the line-charging capacitances in $\tilde{\mathbf{B}}$ improves the convergence speed of these power systems greatly. Since the swing bus is already chosen as voltage angle reference node, we conclude that the ground should be eliminated.

---

* Section 8.2 is based on L.D. Hong, "An Algorithm for Power-System Contingency Analysis," University of New South Wales, School of Electrical Engineering, Internal Report EE-Power-101-76, April 1976.

Chapter 4 reviewed a full, decoupled load-flow algorithm. Such an algorithm can be used for contingency analysis by repeated solution but can prove cumbersome and time consuming where a large number of contingencies are to be evaluated. We will describe a linearized model of the power-flow problem which provides a fast, efficient technique for the approximate analysis of contingencies following an initial load-flow solution. The model is linearized about the steady-state operating point found by a load flow program.

The algorithm for approximate outage studies follows [Ho76] and is based on two symmetric matrices which remain constant throughout the decoupled load-flow iterative process. Each matrix is factored during the load flow and can then be applied to study the effect of line outages.

8.2.1 Real Power Model

The real power injection at node k [Eq. (7.39)] was

$$p_k = u_k^2 \cdot g_{kk} + u_k \cdot \Sigma\, u_m \cdot [g_{km} \cos(\theta_{km}) + b_{km} \sin(\theta_{km})]$$

where $m\ \Sigma \neq k$. This equation can be rewritten as

$$p_k = u_k^2 \cdot g_{kk} + u_k \cdot \Sigma\, u_m \cdot [g_{km} \cdot (1 + \cos(\theta_{km}) - 1)]$$
$$+\, b_{km} \cdot [\sin(\theta_{km}) - \theta_{km}] + u_k \cdot \Sigma\, u_m \cdot b_{km} \cdot \theta_{km}$$

Dividing by u_k and rearranging its two sides yields

$$\Sigma\, u_m b_{km} \theta_{km} = \frac{p_k}{u_k} - u_k g_{kk} - \Sigma\, u_m g_{km}$$
$$-\, \Sigma\, u_m [g_{km}\{\cos(\theta_{km}) - 1\} + b_{km}\{\sin(\theta_{km}) - \theta_{km}\}]$$

Next, the following approximate substitutions are made: $\cos(\theta) - 1 \cong -\theta^2/2$, $\sin(\theta) - \theta \cong -\theta^3/6$. Hence

$$\Sigma\, u_m b_{km} \theta_{km} \tag{8.2}$$
$$= \frac{p_k}{u_k} - u_k g_{kk} - \Sigma\, u_m g_{km} + \Sigma\, u_m \left(\frac{g_{km}\theta_{km}^2}{2} + \frac{b_k \theta_{km}^3}{6} \right)$$

The left side of Eq. (8.2) can be rearranged as a system of n linear equations with n voltage phase angles as variables by making the substitution $\theta_{k,m} = \theta_k - \theta_m$, where θ_k and θ_m are the voltage phase angles at nodes k and m and n is the number of buses in the system except for the swing bus.

Another approximation is made at this stage to remove the influence of MVAR flow; the u_ms on the left-hand side of Eq. (8.2) are set equal to 1 pu.

The complete system of linearized equations for real power can therefore be written in matrix form as

$$\mathbf{A} * \boldsymbol{\theta} = \tilde{\mathbf{p}} + \mathbf{p}^{\#} \tag{8.3}$$

where the elements of the square n-by-n matrix $\mathbf{A}$ are $A_{k,k} = \Sigma\, b_{k,m}$ $(m\Sigma \neq k)$, $A_{k,m} = -b_{k,m}$, and where $\tilde{p}_k = p_k/u_k - u_k \cdot g_{k,k} - \Sigma\, u_m \cdot g_{k,m}$ and $p_k^{\#} = \Sigma\, u_m \cdot (g_{k,m} \cdot \theta_{k,m}^2/2 + b_{k,m} \cdot \theta_{k,m}^3/6)$, $m\Sigma \neq k$.

It can be seen that the off-diagonal elements of matrix $\mathbf{A}$ are the same as those of matrix $\tilde{\mathbf{B}}$. The diagonal elements of matrix $\tilde{\mathbf{B}}$ will be equal to those of matrix $\mathbf{A}$, if shunt-reactance, off-nominal in-phase transformer taps, and line-charging capacitance are all neglected. The resistive element of transmission line impedances can also be neglected in $\mathbf{A}$ without loss of accuracy.

8.2.2 Reactive Power Model

The reactive power injection at a bus k can be expressed as

$$q_k = -u_k^2 \cdot b_{k,k} + u_k \cdot \Sigma\, u_m [g_{k,m} \cdot \sin(\theta_{k,m}) - b_{k,m} \cdot \cos(\theta_{k,m})] \tag{8.4}$$

where $m\Sigma \neq k$ and $b_{k,k} = \Sigma\,(-b_{k,m}/t_{k,m} + by_{k,m}) + bc_k$, $m\Sigma \neq k$. Here $b_{k,m}$ is the transfer susceptance of branch km, i.e., the element $b_{k,m}$ of matrix $\mathbf{B}$. Thus, $b_{k,m} = x_{k,m}/[(x_{k,m}^2 + r_{k,m}^2) \cdot t_{k,m}]$ where $t_{k,m}$ is the off-nominal transformer tap ratio, with branch km being a transformer. When branch km is a line, $t_{k,m} = 1$.

The charging susceptance of the transmission line km is $by_{k,m}$, whereas bc_k is the susceptance of the shunt capacitor or reactor at node k.

Making the approximation for cosines and sines and dividing both sides of Eq. (8.4) by u_k yields

$$\frac{q_k}{u_k} = \Sigma\, u_m \cdot \left[g_{km}\left(\theta_{km} - \frac{\theta_{km}^3}{6}\right) + b_{km} \cdot \frac{\theta_{km}^2}{2} \right]$$

$$- \Sigma\, u_m b_{km} - u_k b_{kk}; \quad m\Sigma \neq k$$

This equation can be further rearranged with $m\Sigma \neq k$ and the second and third sums over generation and load nodes, respectively.

$$\frac{q_k}{u_k} = \Sigma\, u_m \cdot \left[g_{km}\left(\theta_{km} - \frac{\theta_{km}^3}{6}\right) + b_{km} \cdot \frac{\theta_{km}^2}{2} \right] + \Sigma\, b_{km} \cdot u_m$$

$$= -b_{kk} \cdot u_k - \Sigma\, b_{kj} \cdot u_j$$

Now the complete system of equations for reactive power can be written in matrix form as

$$\mathbf{C} * \mathbf{u} = \tilde{\mathbf{q}} \tag{8.5}$$

where the elements of the square matrix $\mathbf{C}$ of dimension n^c (the number of load buses) are $c_{kk} = \Sigma\,(b_{km}/t_{km} - by_{km}) - bc_k$, $c_{km} = -b_{km}$ (for load nodes only), and $\tilde{q}_k = q_k/u_k + \Sigma\, u_m \cdot b_{km} - \Sigma\, u_m \cdot [g_{km} \cdot (\theta_{km} - \theta_{km}^3/6) + b_{km} \cdot \theta_{km}^2/2]$.

The derivation of Eq. (8.5) has been arranged so that matrix $\mathbf{C}$ is the same as matrix $\mathbf{B}^{\#}$ of Eq. (8.1).

Since the same factorized matrices are used in the decoupled load flow and the linearized power flow, a choice of algorithms is available—a relatively slower but more accurate decoupled load flow incorporating the updating method at the end of each iteration, or a faster but less accurate linearized power flow well suited to approximate on-line assessment. Next, both methods are described.

In the decoupled load-flow algorithm all outages must, of course, be reflected in the calculation of $\Delta\mathbf{p}/\mathbf{u}$ and $\Delta\mathbf{q}/\mathbf{u}$. For branch outages two vectors $\tilde{\mathbf{a}}$ and $\mathbf{a}^{\#}$ must be calculated according to the relationships $\tilde{\mathbf{a}} = \tilde{\mathbf{B}} * \tilde{\mathbf{e}}$ and $\mathbf{a}^{\#} = \mathbf{B}^{\#} * \mathbf{e}^{\#}$, where $\tilde{\mathbf{e}}$ and $\mathbf{e}^{\#}$ are highly sparse column vectors, each containing one or two nonzero elements.

After each solution of Eq. (8.1a), $\Delta\boldsymbol{\theta}$ is corrected by an amount

$$-\tilde{c} \cdot \tilde{\mathbf{a}} * \tilde{\mathbf{e}}^{\mathrm{T}} * \Delta\boldsymbol{\theta} \tag{8.6a}$$

Similarly, after each solution of Eq. (8.1b) $\Delta\mathbf{u}$ is compensated by an amount

$$-c^{\#} \cdot \mathbf{a}^{\#} * (\mathbf{e}^{\#})^{\mathrm{T}} * \Delta\boldsymbol{\theta} \tag{8.6b}$$

Next is the derivation of scalars $\tilde{c}$ and $c^{\#}$ and vectors $\tilde{\mathbf{e}}$ and $\mathbf{e}^{\#}$.

Let either of Eqs. (8.1) be represented in the base-case as the equation $\mathbf{d} = \mathbf{B}_0 * \mathbf{x}_0$ for which the desired solution is $\mathbf{x}_0 = \mathbf{B}_0^{-1} * \mathbf{d}$.

We have seen that the outage of a branch can be reflected in $\mathbf{B}_0$ by modifying two elements in row k and two elements in row m. The new outage matrix is then

$$\mathbf{B}_1 = \mathbf{B}_0 + b * \mathbf{e} * \mathbf{e}^{\mathrm{T}}$$

where

b = line or nominal transformer series admittance

$\mathbf{e}$ = null column vector except for $e_k = 1/t$, $e_m = -1$

t = off-nominal turns ratio referred to the bus corresponding to row k, for a transformer, and $t = 1$ for a line

Depending on the types of connected buses, only one row, k or m, might be present in $\tilde{\mathbf{B}}$ or $\mathbf{B}^{\#}$, in which case either e_k or e_m is zero, as appropriate. If both of the connected buses are either a load or a swing bus, then $\tilde{\mathbf{B}}$ requires no modification.

It was shown in Chapter 2 that the use of the fundamental matrix leads to:

$$\mathbf{B}_1^{-1} = \mathbf{B}_0^{-1} - c \cdot \mathbf{a} * \mathbf{e}^{\mathrm{T}} * \mathbf{B}_0^{-1}$$

where $c = (-1/b + \mathbf{e}^{\mathrm{T}} * \mathbf{a})^{-1}$ and $\mathbf{a} = \mathbf{B}_0^{-1} * \mathbf{e}^{\mathrm{T}}$. The solution vector $\mathbf{x}_1$ to the outage problem is $\mathbf{x}_1 = \mathbf{B}_1^{-1} * \mathbf{d}$.

Insertion of $\mathbf{B}_1^{-1}$ yields $\mathbf{x}_1 = \mathbf{x}_0 - c \cdot \mathbf{a} * \mathbf{e}^{\mathrm{T}} * \mathbf{x}_0$. Hence, the solution to the base case problem is easily corrected, as in Eqs. (8.6). The foregoing procedure can be applied recursively for multiple simultaneous outages.

Next, we discuss the linearized power flow, where the solutions $\boldsymbol{\theta}$ and $\mathbf{u}$ of Eqs. (8.3) and (8.5) are compensated in a similar fashion to those indicated by Eq. (8.6).

The iterative scheme below was found by trial and error to provide a good compromise between speed and accuracy for line and generator outages [Ho76] when the initial approximation is the base-case load-flow solution (prior to the outage).

The main steps involved in the solution are as follows.

A. *Solution of load flow.*

A1. Input system data and initial estimates of $\boldsymbol{\theta}$ and $\mathbf{u}$.

A2. Form and triangulate matrices $\tilde{\mathbf{B}}$ and $\mathbf{B}^{\#}$, at the same time forming the nodal bus conductance and susceptance matrices.

A3. Iterate Eqs. (8.1) alternately until the system converges to base-case solutions $\boldsymbol{\theta}_0$ and $\mathbf{u}_0$. If it is divergent, stop.

A4. Store base-case solution.

A5. Calculate vector $\tilde{\mathbf{p}}$.

B. *Solution for line outage.*

B1. Form vector $\tilde{\mathbf{e}}$ corresponding to the outage of line km and solve $\tilde{\mathbf{a}} = \tilde{\mathbf{B}} * \tilde{\mathbf{e}}$ for vector $\tilde{\mathbf{a}}$.

B2. Use $\boldsymbol{\theta}_0$, $\tilde{\mathbf{e}}$, and $\tilde{\mathbf{a}}$ to compute $\Delta\boldsymbol{\theta}_0$ according to Eq. (8.6a) with $\Delta\boldsymbol{\theta}$ replaced by $\boldsymbol{\theta}_0$. The new solution for the line outage, $\boldsymbol{\theta}_1$, is $\boldsymbol{\theta}_1 = \boldsymbol{\theta}_0 + \Delta\boldsymbol{\theta}_0$.

B3. Check the maximum element of $\boldsymbol{\theta}_1$ for a trend toward divergence, i.e., if this maximum is too large, there is no solution.

B4. Compute $\tilde{\mathbf{q}}$ as a function of $\boldsymbol{\theta}_1$ and $\mathbf{u}_0$ taking into account the outage of line km.

B5. Calculate a new vector $\mathbf{u}_1$ using Eq. (8.5).

B6. Form $\mathbf{e}^{\#}$ corresponding to the outage of line km and solve $\mathbf{a}^{\#} = \mathbf{B}^{\#} * \mathbf{e}^{\#}$ for vector $\mathbf{a}^{\#}$.

B7. Calculate $\Delta\mathbf{u}_1$ by using Eq. (8.6b) with $\Delta\mathbf{u}$ replaced by $\mathbf{u}_1$. The updated solution $\mathbf{u}_2$ is given by $\mathbf{u}_2 = \mathbf{u}_1 + \Delta\mathbf{u}_1$.

B8. Check whether the real power flow in the line removed in the base case is greater than a certain percentage of the total real power generation of the system. If it is, go to step B10.

B9. Go through steps B4, B5, B6, and B7 once more to obtain the final value of vector $\mathbf{u}$. Then branch to step B11.

B10. Perform one decoupled load-flow cycle, reflecting the line outage in the calculation of the power-mismatch vectors and correct the updating vectors $\Delta\boldsymbol{\theta}$ or $\Delta\mathbf{u}$ at the end of each half iteration by an amount given by Eqs. (8.6).

B11. Output solution and reinitiate the base-case solution of the system.

C. *Solution for generator outage.*

C1. Check whether the swing bus can pick up the amount of real power generation lost. If not, go to step C6.

C2. Reflect the generator outage in vector $\tilde{\mathbf{p}}$.

C3. Compute $\mathbf{p}^{\#}$ and solve Eq. (8.3) for the new approximate solution of $\boldsymbol{\theta}_1$.

C4. Repeat step C3 and check the result for convergence. If it is divergent, there is no solution.

C5. Compute $\tilde{\mathbf{q}}$ as a function of $\boldsymbol{\theta}_1$ and $\mathbf{u}_0$ and solve Eq. (8.5) for the resulting approximate solution $\mathbf{u}_1$. Go to step C8.

C6. If the real generation loss cannot be distributed to all regulating generators of the system according to an assigned set of distribution factors, proceed to step C7. Otherwise redistribute the power loss in accordance with the generator distribution factors. Go to step C8.

C7. The real power loss is automatically distributed to all other regulating generators according to their capacities and governor action based on the steady-state frequency drop of the power system. A full decoupled load flow might be applied iteratively twice to take into account the new real losses of the system and to allow for any generator reaching its maximum real power output capacity.

C8. Output solution and reinitiate base-case solution of the power system.

The solution of the load flow (except step A5) can be replaced by an initialization using a base-case solution. A flat voltage start is, of course, acceptable in step A1. The solution of either line or generator outage can follow the initialization immediately.

It should be pointed out that $\tilde{\mathbf{p}}$ is never used for line-outage calculation. A further solution of $\boldsymbol{\theta}$ after step B3 by using Eq. (8.3) seems to reduce the accuracy of the angle solution.

The empirical criterion for testing at step B8 depends on the degree of accuracy required; 3% appears to be a reasonable figure. If a decoupled load-flow procedure is necessary (i.e., step B10 is used), the values of vectors $\boldsymbol{\theta}$ and $\mathbf{u}$ obtained by going from step B10 to step B7 are used as initial estimate for the load flow.

Steps B4 and B5 are not essential but seem to keep the overall reactive power mismatch at all load buses to a minimum value and ensure accurate voltage magnitudes.

Concerning the solution for generator outages, similar steps with minor alterations can be applied to the contingency of a sudden change in load.

Steps C6 and C7 provide an answer to the problem of redistribution of generation following a major generator outage. They are carried out by a subroutine which, in fact, can be applied in conjunction with any existing load flow. Naturally, increased speed is achieved when a decoupled load flow is used.

It is important to note that the updating method may be used for repeated CAP-programs with only slightly changed matrices. Even more important is to note that the algorithm can easily be programmed for ASP. As a matter of fact, the reader should only decide which of the steps in A, B and C can be executed in parallel and which must proceed sequentially.

8.3 DISTRIBUTION FACTORS

Distribution factors provide real power-flow changes due to network, generation, and load changes without resorting to load flow studies. This type of information can be used effectively to evaluate interchange transfer limits, effects of line outages, and evaluation of generation shifts. Since the use of distribution factors is declining, only a short review will be given. It is based on [Po84].

The primary assumption to be made when analyzing a system using distribution factors is linearity. That is, loads are treated as constant impedances or constant currents and generators as constant current sources. Also, as a secondary assumption, line-charging and shunt elements are neglected and transformers are assumed to be at nominal taps.

The system performance equations for the linear power system are of the form

$$\mathbf{i} = \mathbf{Y} * \mathbf{u} \tag{8.7}$$

where

$\mathbf{i}$ = vector of *known* bus currents
$\mathbf{Y}$ = short-circuit admittance matrix
$\mathbf{u}$ = vector of unknown bus voltages with respect to a reference bus

Multiplying each side of Eq. (8.7) by $\mathbf{Y}^{-1}$ yields $\mathbf{Y}^{-1} * \mathbf{i} = \mathbf{u}$ or

$$\mathbf{u} = \mathbf{Z} * \mathbf{i} \tag{8.8}$$

where $\mathbf{Z}$ is the short-circuit bus-impedance matrix. (Actually, complex numbers give little additional information, and in this section the reader may substitute the $\mathbf{X}$ for the $\mathbf{Z}$ matrix).

The unknown voltage vector $\mathbf{u}$ can now be determined by insertion.

The current from any bus p in the line between bus p and bus q is

$$i_{pq} = (u_p - u_q) \cdot y_{pq} \tag{8.9}$$

Here y_{pq} equals the line admittance.

From Eq. (8.8)

$$u_p = Z_{p1} \cdot i_1 + Z_{p2} \cdot i_2 + \cdots + Z_{pn} \cdot i_n$$

and

$$u_q = Z_{q1} \cdot i_1 + Z_{q2} \cdot i_2 + \cdots + Z_{qn} \cdot i_n$$

Substituting these voltages into Eq. (8.9) yields

$$i_{pq} = i_1 \cdot (Z_{p1} - Z_{q1}) \cdot y_{pq} + \cdots + i_n \cdot (Z_{pn} - Z_{qn}) \cdot y_{pq}$$

or

$$i_{pq} = i_1 \cdot d_{(pq)1} + i_2 \cdot d_{(pq)2} + \cdots + i_n \cdot d_{(pq)n} \tag{8.10}$$

where

$$d_{(pq)i} = (Z_{pi} - Z_{qi}) \cdot y_{pq}. \tag{8.11}$$

Here $d_{(pq)i}$ may be interpreted as a current-distribution factor, i.e., as the current which flows in the line between bus p and bus q when a unit current is injected at the ith bus.

We store matrix $\mathbf{Z}$ and line admittances y_{pq} in order to compute the distribution factors d.

8.3.1 Use for Generation Changes

To make use of distribution factors in power system analysis, it will be assumed that real power-flow changes are approximately equal to real current changes. This is a good assumption as long as system voltages are near $1 + j \cdot 0$.

For example, if the real power flow from bus p to bus q is known as p_{pq}, and generation is shifted from bus i to bus j by an amount Δp, the new flow $\tilde{p}_{pq}$ over line pq can be calculated using distribution factors and the superposition theorem.

$$\begin{aligned}\tilde{p}_{pq} &= p_{pq} + (Z_{pi} - Z_{qi}) \cdot y_{pq} \cdot \Delta p - (Z_{pj} - Z_{qj}) \cdot y_{pq} \cdot \Delta p \\ &= p_{pq} + \Delta p \cdot (d_{(pq)i} - d_{(pq)j})\end{aligned}$$

where $d_{(pq)i} - d_{(pq)j}$ is the generation shift distribution factor.

8.3.2 Use for Line Outages

Line outages can also be handled by using distribution factors. Consider Eq. (8.7) in expanded form:

$$\begin{bmatrix} i_1 \\ i_2 \\ \vdots \\ i_p \\ i_q \\ \vdots \\ i_n \end{bmatrix} = \begin{bmatrix} Y_{11} & Y_{12} & \cdots & Y_{1n} \\ Y_{21} & Y_{22} & \cdots & Y_{2n} \\ \vdots & \vdots & & \vdots \\ Y_{p1} & Y_{p2} & \cdots & Y_{pn} \\ Y_{q1} & Y_{q2} & \cdots & Y_{qn} \\ \vdots & \vdots & & \vdots \\ Y_{n1} & Y_{n2} & \cdots & Y_{nn} \end{bmatrix} * \begin{bmatrix} u_1 \\ u_2 \\ \vdots \\ u_p \\ u_q \\ \vdots \\ u_n \end{bmatrix}$$

Suppose a line is outaged between bus p and bus q. Then the system will have a new solution:

$$\mathbf{i}^{\#} = \mathbf{Y}^{\#} * \mathbf{u}^{\#} \tag{8.12}$$

The elements of the new matrix $\mathbf{Y}^{\#}$ are the same as the $\mathbf{Y}$ matrix except for the elements $Y^{\#}_{pp}$, $Y^{\#}_{qq}$, $Y^{\#}_{pq}$, and $Y^{\#}_{qp}$. In terms of the $\mathbf{Y}$ matrix, the new elements are

$$\begin{aligned} Y^{\#}_{pp} &= Y_{pp} - y_{pq}; & Y^{\#}_{qq} &= Y_{qq} - y_{pq} \\ Y^{\#}_{pq} &= Y_{pq} + y_{pq}; & Y^{\#}_{qp} &= Y_{qp} - y_{pq} \end{aligned}$$

Here y_{pq} is the admittance of the line being outaged.

The new $\mathbf{Y}^{\#}$ matrix can now be expressed in terms of the old $\mathbf{Y}$ matrix and a $\tilde{\mathbf{Y}}$ matrix, where

$$
\begin{array}{c} \\ 1 \\ \vdots \\ p \\ q \\ \vdots \\ n \end{array}
\begin{array}{c}
\begin{array}{cccccc} 1 & & p & q & & n \end{array} \\
\left[\begin{array}{cccccc}
0 & \cdots & 0 & 0 & \cdots & 0 \\
\vdots & & \vdots & \vdots & & \vdots \\
0 & \cdots & -y_{pq} & y_{pq} & \cdots & 0 \\
0 & \cdots & y_{pq} & -y_{pq} & \cdots & 0 \\
\vdots & & \vdots & \vdots & & \vdots \\
0 & & 0 & 0 & \cdots & 0
\end{array}\right]
\end{array}
= \tilde{\mathbf{Y}}
$$

Since $\tilde{\mathbf{Y}}$ can be formed by the vector product $\mathbf{a} * \mathbf{b}^T$ where $\mathbf{a}^T = [0, \ldots, 0, \ -y_{pq}, \ y_{pq}, \ 0, \ldots, 0]$ and $\mathbf{b}^T = [0, \ldots, 0, \ 1, \ -1, \ 0, \ldots, 0]$, with nonzeros in positions p and q, it follows that

$$\mathbf{Y}^{\#} = \mathbf{Y} + \mathbf{a} * \mathbf{b}^T$$

We could use here the updating method, but will use an electrical argument instead.

Substituting this equation into Eq. (8.12), we get $\mathbf{i}^{\#} = (\mathbf{Y} + \mathbf{a} * \mathbf{b}^T) * \mathbf{u}^{\#}$; $\mathbf{i}^{\#} - \mathbf{a} * \mathbf{b}^T * \mathbf{u}^{\#} = \mathbf{Y} * \mathbf{u}^{\#}$

Therefore, the effect of outaging a line from bus p to bus q is the same as adding a new current vector $\mathbf{a} * \mathbf{b}^T * \mathbf{u}^{\#}$ to the original current vector. This new current vector can be calculated by using the superposition principle as follows.

Setting the new current vector $\tilde{\mathbf{Y}} * \mathbf{u}^{\#}$ to 0 yields

$$\mathbf{i}^{\#} = \mathbf{Y} * \mathbf{u}^{\#}.$$

This is just the original solution to the network. Next the original current vector $\mathbf{i}$ is set equal to zero, and we have

$$-\tilde{\mathbf{Y}} * \mathbf{u}^{\#} = \mathbf{Y} * \tilde{\mathbf{u}}$$

Multiplying each side by $\mathbf{Z}$ yields

$$-\mathbf{Z} * \tilde{\mathbf{Y}} * \mathbf{u}^{\#} = \tilde{\mathbf{u}} \tag{8.13}$$

It is obvious that $\tilde{\mathbf{u}} + \mathbf{u} = \mathbf{u}^{\#}$ or $\tilde{\mathbf{u}} = \mathbf{u}^{\#} - \mathbf{u}$. Substituting $\tilde{\mathbf{u}}$ into Eq. (8.13), we have

$$-\mathbf{Z} * \tilde{\mathbf{Y}} * \mathbf{u}^{\#} = \mathbf{u}^{\#} - \mathbf{u}$$

Expanding it yields

$$Z_{pp} \cdot (u_p^{\#} - u_q^{\#}) \cdot y_{pq} - Z_{pq} \cdot (u_p^{\#} - u_q^{\#}) \cdot y_{pq} = u_p^{\#} - u_p \tag{8.14}$$

$$Z_{qp} \cdot (u_p^{\#} - u_q^{\#}) \cdot y_{pq} - Z_{pq} \cdot (u_p^{\#} - u_q^{\#}) \cdot y_{pq} = u_q^{\#} - u_q \tag{8.15}$$

We have two equations and two unknowns: $u_p^{\#}$ and $u_q^{\#}$. Now subtract the first equation from the second and rearrange:

$$(u_p - u_q) \tag{8.16}$$
$$= (u_p^{\#} - u_q^{\#}) + (-Z_{pp} + Z_{pq} + Z_{qp} - Z_{qq})\cdot(u_p^{\#} - u_q^{\#})\cdot y_{pq}$$

The new current vector is, in expanded form as in,

$$\begin{bmatrix} 0 \\ \cdot \\ \cdot \\ \cdot \\ 0 \\ (u_p^{\#} - u_q^{\#})\cdot y_{pq} \\ (u_q^{\#} - u_p^{\#})\cdot y_{pq} \\ 0 \\ \cdot \\ \cdot \\ \cdot \\ 0 \end{bmatrix} = \begin{bmatrix} 0 \\ \cdot \\ \cdot \\ \cdot \\ 0 \\ i_p^{\#} \\ i_q^{\#} \\ 0 \\ \cdot \\ \cdot \\ \cdot \\ 0 \end{bmatrix} \tag{8.17}$$

Therefore instead of solving Eqs. (8.14) and (8.15) for $u_p^{\#}$ and $u_q^{\#}$, we need only to solve equation (8.16) for $(u_p^{\#} - u_q^{\#})\cdot y_{pq}$. Multiplying each side of equation (8.16) and rearranging yield

$$i^{\#} = (u_p^{\#} - u_q^{\#})\cdot y_{pq}$$
$$= (u_p - u_q)\cdot\frac{y_{pq}}{1 - (Z_{pp} + Z_{qq} - Z_{pq} - Z_{qp})\cdot y_{pq}}$$

Here $(u_p - u_q)\cdot y_{pq}$ is the current that was flowing between bus p and bus q before that line was outaged. Therefore,

$$i_p^{\#} = \frac{i_{pq}}{1 - (Z_{pp} + Z_{qq} - Z_{qp} - Z_{pq})\cdot y_{pq}}$$

where

Z_{ij} = short-circuit bus impedances
y_{pq} = admittance of line to be outaged
i_{pq} = power flow over line to be outaged

This equation can be simplified by noting that

$$d_{(pq)p} = (Z_{pp} - Z_{qp})\cdot y_{pq}; \quad d_{(pq)q} = (Z_{pq} - Z_{qq})\cdot y_{pq} \tag{8.18}$$

$$i_p^{\#} = -i_q^{\#} = \frac{i_{pq}}{1 + d_{(pq)q} - d_{(pq)p}} \tag{8.19}$$

A line outage distribution factor can be defined. For example, if the power flow over the line between bus i and bus j is p_{ij}, then the new power flow, $p_{ij}^{\#}$, when the line between bus p and bus q is outaged is

$$p_{ij}^{\#} = p_{ij} + p_{pq} \cdot \frac{d_{(ij)p} - d_{(ij)q}}{1 + d_{(pq)q} - d_{(pq)p}} = p_{ij} + d \cdot p_{pq}$$

where d is an outage-distribution factor.

Double contingency can be handled by running a separate DC load flow for every case from scratch. This is, unfortunately, very costly in computation time.

Another possibility is to use a single outage study and linearize. Thus if ζ_{ij} is the current percentage in line i due to removal of line j and we write it for the case that two lines are outaged (lines 1 and 2), we get the set of linear equations

$$d_3^{\#} = d_3 + \zeta_{31} \cdot d_1^{\#} + \zeta_{32} \cdot d_2^{\#}$$

$$d_1^{\#} = d_1 + \zeta_{12} \cdot d_2^{\#}$$

$$d_2^{\#} = d_2 + \zeta_{21} \cdot d_1^{\#}$$

(Note that we can generalize these equations).

The solution of the preceding set of linear equations is

$$d_3^{\#} = \frac{d_1 \cdot (\zeta_{31} + \zeta_{32} \cdot \zeta_{21}) + d_2 \cdot (\zeta_{32} + \zeta_{31} \cdot \zeta_{12})}{(1 - \zeta_{21} \cdot \zeta_{12})} + d_3$$

Obviously this requires very little computation time but in most cases is rather inaccurate.

We could have used the previously developed method of updating matrix $\mathbf{Y}$ and write a double outage as

$$\mathbf{Y} = \mathbf{Y} + a \cdot \mathbf{v} * \mathbf{v}^{\mathrm{T}} + b \cdot \mathbf{w} * \mathbf{w}^{\mathrm{T}}$$

where $\mathbf{v}$ and $\mathbf{w}$ represent different outages. We could then solve both cases consecutively for the "price" of doubling the time. Another possibility is to try the following: Assume $a = b = -1$ and rewrite

$$\mathbf{Y} = \mathbf{Y} - \mathbf{v} * \mathbf{v}^{\mathrm{T}} - \mathbf{w} * \mathbf{w}^{\mathrm{T}} = \mathbf{L} * (\mathbf{D} - \mathbf{u} * \mathbf{u}^{\mathrm{T}}) * \mathbf{L}^{\mathrm{T}}$$

with

$$\mathbf{u} * \mathbf{u}^{\mathrm{T}} = \mathbf{v} * \mathbf{v}^{\mathrm{T}} + \mathbf{w} * \mathbf{w}^{\mathrm{T}}$$

Since $\mathbf{v}$ and $\mathbf{w}$ are known, it should be possible to calculate $\mathbf{u}$, in which case we would have the same problem as that solved in single contingency—the updating of the admittance matrix.

Multiple outages can thus be handled, but simultaneous equations must be used to obtain the new currents to be added to simulate the multiple contingency. If line pq and line ij are to be outaged simultaneously, the following equations are necessary:

$$\begin{aligned} p_{pk} &= p_p^{\#}\cdot(1 - d_{(pq)p} + d_{(pq)q}) + p_i^{\#}\cdot(d_{(pq)i} - d_{(pq)j}) \\ p_{ij} &= p_p^{\#}\cdot(d_{(ij)p} - d_{(ij)q}) + p_i^{\#}\cdot(1 - d_{(ij)i} + d_{(ij)j}) \end{aligned} \tag{8.20}$$

Here p_{pk} and p_{ij} are the initial power flows in line pk and line ij. Solving these equations for $p_p^{\#}$ and $p_i^{\#}$ will provide the required new power vector. In general, for n outages, n simultaneous equations will be needed with the same form as Eqs. (8.20).

In the derivation of distribution factors, transformers were assumed to be at nominal settings. The effect of off-nominal taps and of phase shifters could be included. Here, we will include shunt elements instead.

When shunt elements are neglected, a bus of the system is used as the reference bus. If shunt elements are to be included, ground must be used as the reference. In doing the latter, an extra row and column are added to the admittance matrix, which increases computer time and storage.

Shunt elements are included by converting the load, capacitor MVAR, reactor MVAR, and line charging to constant admittances by the following formula: $y_{n,0} = p_n/u_n^2 - j\cdot q_n/u_n^2$ where u_n = estimated bus voltage with respect to ground.

In general, especially in extra-high-voltage networks, little advantage is obtained by including the effect of shunt elements. Inclusion of shunt elements modifies the driving point admittances as follows: $Y_{n,n}^{\#} = Y_{n,n} + y_{n,0}$, where $Y_{n,n}^{\#}$ and $Y_{n,n}$ are the driving point admittance including and neglecting shunt elements, respectively.

In extra-high-voltage systems $Y_{n,n}$ can be in the order of magnitude of a 100 pu, whereas $y_{n,0}$ usually does not exceed 10 pu in magnitude.

As a *conclusion*, we offer the following:

Distribution factors provide a quick and efficient way of determining the effect of system changes. Once the initial calculation of the distribution factors is made, a simple calculation can give results of system changes. However, care must be taken in interpreting these results. For example, it was assumed that real power flow was equal to real current flow. This is only true if the bus voltages are near 1 pu. Another consideration is the fact that it was assumed that when a system change is made, the system voltages are not seriously affected. Of course, this is not always the case. Therefore, engineering judgment is a necessary ingredient when using distribution factors.

8.4 SELECTIVITY

The traditional approach to steady-state contingency analysis is to test sequentially all (primary) contingencies. This means to simulate outages of generators or lines and investigate their effects on bus voltages and line flows. It is possible to use the distribution factor method to prescreen contingencies and process only those which are serious. Unfortunately, distribution factors do not provide prediction of voltages, and to use decoupled OOF for all cases would be prohibitively costly (in terms of time) even if only single contingencies have to be analyzed.

On the other hand, "applying contingency testing to a *subset* of contingency cases selected on the basis of the planner's experience and intuition may be inadequate due to the possibility of omitting some critical cases."* The next-best policy seems to be in preparing a contingency list to be studied by a security analysis program based not only on operator experience but also on off-line simulation studies. However, in real time, the contingencies change continuously and would be different from those predicted off-line. Therefore, the selection of contingencies to be studied on-line should be based on the current operating conditions and not on a fixed list based upon off-line studies.

It may be advantageous to rank contingencies in approximate order of severity. Contingencies can then be simulated, starting with the most dangerous and running down the list to the less dangerous until a point is reached where contingencies no longer produce problems. There is thus no need to proceed further, since all remaining contingencies are less severe, and since the number of cases was reduced, the method is faster.

The method proposed in [EW78] is best described by Fig. 8.1. It shows that contingencies are ranked from worst to harmless and a decoupled load flow is run only on the case at the top of the list. Reference [EW78] discusses how contingencies are ranked by evaluating system constraint violations such as load bus voltages outside their limits and transmission line (or transformer) overloads.

"In light of these constraints, the system performance may be quantitatively evaluated in terms of indices reflecting the severity of out-of-limit voltage values or line overloads resulting from a particular contingency." For this, a "system performance index is defined as a penalty function to penalize severely any violation of bus voltage constraints or line flow constraints." [EW78]

Only the index quantifying the extent of line (power) overload will be used. It may be defined in terms of real powers as penalty

---

* G. C. Ejebe, B. F. Wollenberg, "Automatic Contingency Selection," *Trans. IEEE*, Vol. PAS-98, January/February 1979, pp. 97–109. © 1979 by IEEE. Used with permission.

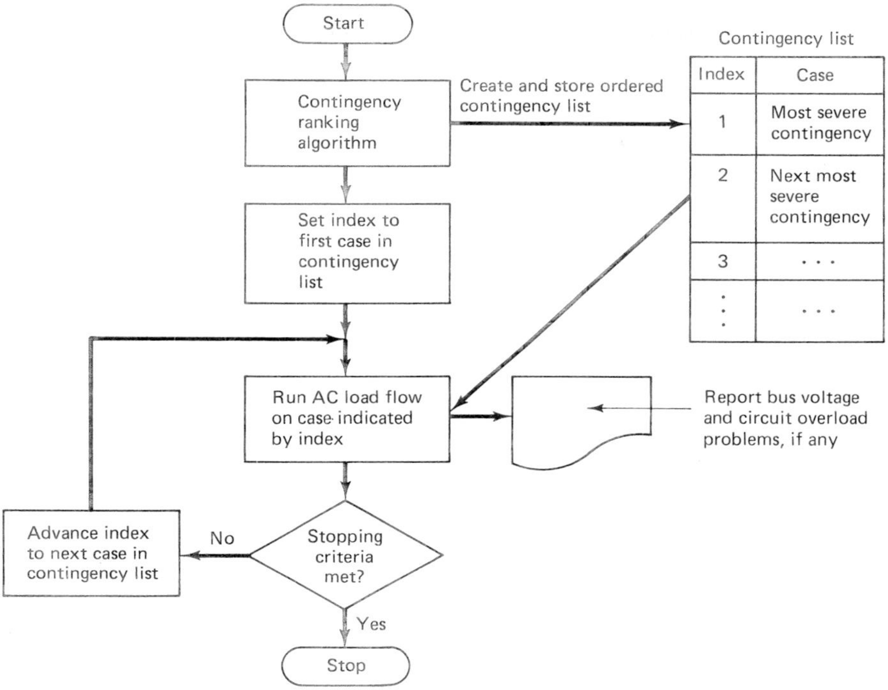

Figure 8.1 Flowchart.

$$\pi = \Sigma w_k \cdot \left(\frac{p_k}{p_k^{\mathrm{M}}} \right)^2 \tag{8.21}$$

where w_k is the weight of line k, p_k and p_k^{M} are the power flow (in MW) through line k (calculated by a DC load flow) and its maximal value.

The normalized flows of Eq. (8.21) are raised to an even power to avoid the use of absolute magnitudes. Index π has a small value, when all line flows are within their limits and a high value when there are line overloads. Thus, it provides a good measure of the severity of line overloads for a given state of the power system. According to [EW78]:

"Since the purpose of a contingency selection process is to identify quickly (without performing a complete load flow or predictive analysis for each outage) those critical outages that need to be studied more rigorously, the absolute value of the index for each outage is not significant, and in fact, is not available. What is needed is the relative change of the performance index with respect to these outages. In a manner analogous to the AC case, these sensitivities are generated from the results of two DC load-flow solutions—one for the original (base-case) power system and the other for the adjoint power system."

"The ordered list of contingency cases is based upon the relative ranking of the sensitivities of the performance index to the outages. The sensitivities are the first derivatives of the performance index with respect to a change in admittance for a line outage or with respect to a change in net power output for a generator outage. As such, the sensitivities only give the incremental change in performance index to an incremental change in line admittance or generator output. The full effect of a contingency is then approximated by multiplying the derivative by the full line admittance for a line outage and by the full net power being delivered for the generator to be outaged. If this is done, two problems result."

"One of the problems which arises in the use of this performance index is the phenomenon of masking, wherein a contingency which leaves a number of lines heavily loaded but not overloaded is ranked equally with a contingency which produces a single overloaded line. This effect can only be mitigated by increasing the power in π. Unfortunately, thus far an efficient technique for evaluating the change in π has been found only for quadratic functions."

The other problem which was encountered in contingency ranking resulted from the use of the gradient method to evaluate changes in the performance index for each line outage. In [EW78] Tellegen's theorem was used to calculate the first derivative of π with respect to the line susceptance of each line. Then, the total change in π was approximated by multiplying each such derivative by the total susceptance of the line: $\Delta\pi = \Delta b_k \cdot (\partial\pi/\partial b_k)$ where $\Delta b_k = -b_k$ for an outage of line k (b_k is susceptance).

The obvious problem with this technique is that π is a nonlinear function and a prediction of the change in π using a linear projection based on the first derivative will be in error. Plots of π versus b_k in Fig. 8.2 show this error to be large.

The problem can be solved. The calculation of the penalty factor π as given in [MW81]* (with certain changes) is as follows:

The DC load

$$p_k = b_k \cdot \theta_k \tag{8.22}$$

can be substituted into the sum in Eq. (8.21). This yields

---

* T. A. Mikolinnas, B. F. Wollenberg, "An Advanced Contingency Selection Algorithm," *Trans. IEEE*, vol. PAS-100, No. 2, February 1981, pp. 608–17. © 1981 by IEEE. Used with permission.

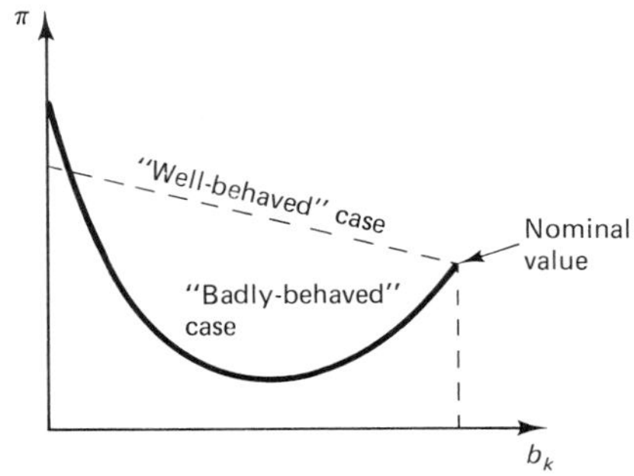

Figure 8.2 Two cases.

$$\pi = w_i \cdot \left(b_1 \cdot \frac{\theta_1}{p_1^{\mathrm{M}}} \right)^2 + \cdots + w_k \cdot \left(b_k \cdot \frac{\theta_k}{p_k^{\mathrm{M}}} \right)^2 + \cdots + w_L \cdot \left(b_L \cdot \frac{\theta_L}{p_L^{\mathrm{M}}} \right)^2 \tag{8.23}$$

The maximum power in line i, i.e., p_i^{M}, is assumed to be proportional to b_i:

$$p_i^{\mathrm{M}} = e_i \cdot b_i \tag{8.24}$$

Insertion for all i will remove the maximum powers:

$$\pi_\theta = w_i \cdot \left(\frac{\theta_1}{e_1} \right)^2 + \cdots + w_k \cdot \left(\frac{\theta_k}{e_k} \right)^2 + \cdots + w_L \cdot \left(\frac{\theta_L}{e_L} \right)^2 \tag{8.25}$$

Consider π and π_θ as functions of the single variable, b_k, the susceptance of the outaged circuit. The values of π and π_θ are of interest at only two values of b_k: the initial value (circuit in service), and $b_k = 0$ (circuit out of service).

The way e_i is defined in Eq. (8.24), shows that the two functions are equal at the initial value of b_k.

"It is also clear that at $b_k = 0$, the two functions are not equal. They are, however, very simply related. Notice that as the value of b_k changes from its initial value, the only pair of corresponding terms in the two summations which are not equal are the terms associated with circuit k. In the limit, as b_k goes to zero, these two terms become"

$$\tilde{\pi} = \lim \left[w_k \cdot \left(\frac{p_k}{p_k^{\mathrm{M}}} \right)^2 \right] = 0$$

$$\tilde{\pi}_\theta = \lim \left[w_k \cdot \left(\frac{\theta_k}{e_k} \right)^2 \right] = w_k \cdot \left(\frac{\theta_k^{\mathrm{F}}}{e_k} \right)^2$$

where the limit is for $b_k \rightarrow 0$ and superscript F denotes a final value.

The difference is due to the fact that while p_k goes to zero as b_k goes to zero, the circuit angle θ, as measured by the difference between the "from" and "to" bus angles, does not.

An example of how these functions might appear is shown in Fig. (8.3). At $b_k = 0$ they are related by

$$\pi^{\mathrm{F}} = \pi_\theta^{\mathrm{F}} - w_k \cdot \left(\frac{\theta_k^{\mathrm{F}}}{e_k} \right)^2 \tag{8.26}$$

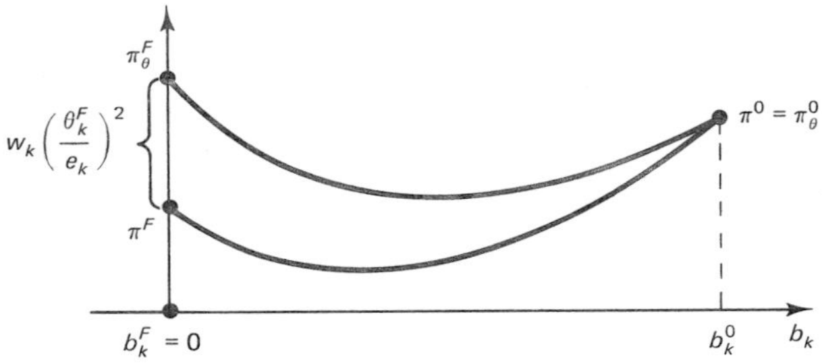

Figure 8.3 The functions.

The final angle θ_k^{F} will be calculated next on the basis of Section 2.6. According to Fig. 2.10, if line k (between nodes p and q) is dropped, then the susceptance matrix $\mathbf{B}$ is changed into $\tilde{\mathbf{B}}$ as follows:

$$\tilde{\mathbf{B}} := \mathbf{B} - b_k \cdot \mathbf{c}_k * \mathbf{c}_k^{\mathrm{T}} \tag{8.27}$$

where $\mathbf{c}_k^{\mathrm{T}} = [0, \ldots, 1, 0, \ldots, 0, -1, 0, \ldots, 0]$ with 1 in location p and -1 in location q. The product $\mathbf{c}_k * \mathbf{c}_k^{\mathrm{T}}$ yields a matrix of all zeros except for elements

$$E_{p,p} = E_{q,q} = 1; \quad E_{p,q} = E_{q,p} = -1$$

Premultiplying this matrix by the scalar susceptance b_k will change 1s into b_k and -1s into $-b_k$. Since the mutual susceptance $B_{p,q} = -b_k$ and the self-susceptance had included b_k in its summation, Eq. (8.27) reflects correctly the change. As for Eq. (2.59), matrix $\tilde{\mathbf{B}}$ is factored:

$$\tilde{\mathbf{B}} = \mathbf{B} * [\mathbf{I} - \mathbf{B}^{-1} * (b_k \cdot \mathbf{c}_k * \mathbf{c}_k^T)];$$

Here b_k is a scalar and can be written as premultiplying $\mathbf{B}^{-1} \equiv \mathbf{X}$. A vector $\mathbf{z}$ is defined through

$$\mathbf{z}_k \equiv (\mathbf{X} * \mathbf{c}_k) \tag{8.28}$$

and $\tilde{\mathbf{B}} = \mathbf{B} * (\mathbf{I} - b_k \cdot \mathbf{z}_k * \mathbf{c}_k^T)$. The inverse of $\tilde{\mathbf{B}}$ is

$$\tilde{\mathbf{X}} = (\mathbf{I} - b_k \cdot \mathbf{z}_k * \mathbf{c}_k^T)^{-1} * \mathbf{B}^{-1}$$

The first is a fundamental matrix and its inverse is

$$\mathbf{F} = \mathbf{I} - d \cdot \mathbf{z}_k * \mathbf{c}_k^T \text{ where } d = \frac{-b_k}{1 - b_k \cdot \mathbf{c}_k^T * \mathbf{z}_k}$$

Again, we give the derivation of $\mathbf{c}_k^T * \mathbf{z}_k \cong \mathbf{c}_k^T * (\mathbf{X} * \mathbf{c}_k)$:

$$\mathbf{X} * \mathbf{c}_k = \begin{bmatrix} X_{1p} - X_{1q} \\ \cdots \\ X_{pp} - X_{pq} \\ \cdots \\ X_{qp} - X_{qq} \\ \cdots \\ X_{np} - X_{nq} \end{bmatrix}$$

$$[\ldots\ 1\ \ldots\ -1\ \ldots] * \begin{bmatrix} X_{1p} - X_{1q} \\ \cdots \\ X_{pp} - X_{pq} \\ \cdots \\ X_{qp} - X_{qq} \\ \cdots \\ X_{np} - X_{nq} \end{bmatrix} = X_{p,p} + X_{q,q} - 2 \cdot X_{p,q} = x$$

The updated $\tilde{\mathbf{X}}$ matrix is therefore

$$\tilde{\mathbf{X}} = \mathbf{X} + \frac{b_k}{1 - b_k \cdot x} \cdot \mathbf{X} * \mathbf{c}_k * \mathbf{c}_k^T * \mathbf{X} = \mathbf{X} + \Delta\mathbf{X} \tag{8.29}$$

with the second part being the change in $\mathbf{X}$, namely, $\Delta\mathbf{X}$.

The angle across line k (from node p to node q) is θ_k. If by θ_N we denote the bus angle vector $\mathbf{X} * \mathbf{p}_N$, then

$$\theta_k = \mathbf{c}_k^T * \boldsymbol{\theta}_N = \mathbf{c}_k^T * \mathbf{X} * \mathbf{p}_N$$

Here, $\mathbf{p}_N$ is the bus (real power) injection vector so it is not affected by removal of the line. The change is therefore

$$\Delta\theta_k = \mathbf{c}_k^{\mathrm{T}} * \Delta\mathbf{X} * \mathbf{p}_N$$

Inserting $\Delta\mathbf{X}$ from Eq. (8.29) yields

$$\Delta\theta_k = \mathbf{c}_k^{\mathrm{T}} * \left[\frac{b_k}{1 - b_k \cdot x}\right] \cdot \mathbf{X} * \mathbf{c}_k * \mathbf{c}_k^{\mathrm{T}} * \mathbf{X} * \mathbf{p}_N$$

$$\Delta\theta_k = \left[\frac{b_k}{1 - b_k \cdot x}\right] \cdot (\mathbf{c}_k^{\mathrm{T}} * \mathbf{X} * \mathbf{c}_k) \cdot \theta_k .$$

Inserting x as defined earlier shows that $\Delta\theta_k = [b_k/(1 - b_k \cdot x)] \cdot x \cdot \theta_k$ and the final angle is

$$\theta_k^{\mathrm{F}} = \frac{\theta_k}{1 - b_k \cdot x} \tag{8.30}$$

This is next substituted into Eq. (8.26), to produce

$$\pi^{\mathrm{F}} = \pi_\theta^{\mathrm{F}} - \frac{w_k \cdot (p_k / p_k^{\mathrm{M}})^2}{(1 - b_k \cdot x)^2} \tag{8.31}$$

Next, we develop an expression for the final value of

$$\pi_\theta = [\theta_1 \theta_2 \cdots \theta_L] * \begin{bmatrix} w_1/e_1^2 & & 0 \\ & \ddots & \\ 0 & & w_L/e_L^2 \end{bmatrix} * \begin{bmatrix} \theta_1 \\ \theta_2 \\ \cdot \\ \cdot \\ \cdot \\ \theta_L \end{bmatrix} = \boldsymbol{\theta}_L^{\mathrm{T}} * \mathbf{D} * \boldsymbol{\theta}_L \tag{8.32}$$

where the definition of the diagonal matrix $\mathbf{D}$ is obvious. With $\mathbf{A}$ being the incidence matrix, substitution of $\boldsymbol{\theta}_L = \mathbf{A}^{\mathrm{T}} * \boldsymbol{\theta}_N$ and $\boldsymbol{\theta}_N = \mathbf{X} * \mathbf{p}_N$ yields $\pi_\theta = \mathbf{p}_N^{\mathrm{T}} * \mathbf{X} * \mathbf{A} * \mathbf{D} * \mathbf{A}^{\mathrm{T}} * \mathbf{X} * \mathbf{p}_N$. Letting

$$\mathbf{W} \equiv \mathbf{A} * \mathbf{D} * \mathbf{A}^{\mathrm{T}} \tag{8.33}$$

and recognizing that $\mathbf{p}_N$ and $\mathbf{W}$ are constants yields the final value of π_θ when line k is dropped as

$$\pi^{\mathrm{F}} = \mathbf{p}^{\mathrm{T}} * \mathbf{X}^{\mathrm{F}} * \mathbf{W} * \mathbf{X}^{\mathrm{F}} * \mathbf{p} = \mathbf{p}^{\mathrm{T}} * (\mathbf{X} + \Delta\mathbf{X}) * \mathbf{W} * (\mathbf{X} + \Delta\mathbf{X}) * \mathbf{p}_N$$

Insert $\Delta\mathbf{X}$ from Eq. (8.29) and use the fact that $\Delta\mathbf{X}$ is obviously symmetric. This will yield with ξ defined as $b_k/(1 - b_k \cdot x)$:

$$\pi_\theta = 2 \cdot \xi \cdot \mathbf{p}_N^{\mathrm{T}} * \mathbf{X} * \mathbf{c}_k * \mathbf{c}_k^{\mathrm{T}} * \mathbf{X} * \mathbf{W} * \mathbf{X} * \mathbf{p}_N$$

$$+ \xi^2 \cdot \mathbf{p}_N^{\mathrm{T}} * \mathbf{X} * \mathbf{c}_k * \mathbf{c}_k^{\mathrm{T}} * \mathbf{X} * \mathbf{W} * \mathbf{X} * \mathbf{c}_k * \mathbf{c}_k^{\mathrm{T}} * \mathbf{X} * \mathbf{p}_N$$

This will be simplified by substituting

$$\boldsymbol{\theta} = \mathbf{X} * \mathbf{p}; \quad \tilde{p} = \mathbf{W} * \boldsymbol{\theta} \tag{8.34}$$

$$\tilde{\boldsymbol{\theta}} = \mathbf{X} * \tilde{\mathbf{p}}; \quad \mathbf{T} = \mathbf{X} * \mathbf{W} * \mathbf{X}; \quad \tau = \mathbf{c}^{\mathrm{T}} * (\mathbf{T} * \mathbf{c}_k)$$

where τ_k is a scalar. Thus π_θ is simplified to

$$\pi_\theta = 2 \cdot \xi \cdot \boldsymbol{\theta}_n^{\mathrm{T}} * \mathbf{c} * \mathbf{c}^{\mathrm{T}} * \tilde{\boldsymbol{\theta}} + \tau_k \cdot \xi^2 \cdot \boldsymbol{\theta}^{\mathrm{T}} * \mathbf{c} * \mathbf{c}^{\mathrm{T}} * \boldsymbol{\theta}$$

$$\pi_\theta = \left(\frac{2b_k}{1 - b_k \cdot x}\right) \cdot \theta_k * \tilde{\boldsymbol{\theta}} + \left[\frac{\tau_k \cdot b^2}{(1 - b_k \cdot x)^2}\right] \cdot \theta_k^2 \tag{8.35}$$

This is next substituted into Eq. (8.31) to yield

$$\Delta\pi = \frac{\tau_k * p^2}{(1 - b_k \cdot x)^2} + \frac{2 \cdot \tilde{\theta}_k \cdot p_k}{1 - b_k \cdot x} - \frac{w_k \cdot (p_k / p_k^{\mathrm{M}})^2}{(1 - b_k \cdot x)^2}$$

The quantities b_k, b_k^{M}, and $\mathbf{W}$ are constants and need no reevaluation. The base-case powers, p_k, are obtained from a single DC load-flow solution.

For the $\tilde{\theta}_k$s of all circuits, a single additional DC load-flow has to be run. They are evaluated by forming the vector $\tilde{p}_n = \mathbf{W} * \boldsymbol{\theta}_n$ where $\boldsymbol{\theta}_n$ is the bus angle vector, and $\mathbf{W}$ is a constant (n-by-n) matrix. It depends on the w_ks, p_k^{M}, and the b_ks.

Next, $\tilde{\theta}_n = \mathbf{X} * \mathbf{p}_n$ is solved. Then for circuit k, connecting buses i and j, we have $\theta_k^{\#} = \tilde{\theta}_i - \tilde{\theta}_j$.

The xs can be found by evaluating the system matrix $\mathbf{X}$ as in Section 3.1. This requires the factors of the $\mathbf{B}$ matrix, and the additional work involved is of the same order of magnitude as the original factorization.

"The remaining quantities required are the τ_ks. The derivation above shows how these quantities arise, and that an exact evaluation of them would require an amount of work equivalent to one forward-backward solution for each circuit. This is prohibitive, since it equals the amount of work in solving a DC load flow for each contingency."

The τ factor for line l, connecting buses i and j, is

$$\tau_l = T_{i,j} + T_{j,j} - 2T_{i,j} \tag{8.36}$$

where $\mathbf{T} \equiv \mathbf{X} * \mathbf{W} * \mathbf{X}$. Therefore, evaluation of τ_l, $l = 1, 2, \ldots, L$ requires those elements of $\mathbf{T}$ where nonzeros appear in the matrix $\mathbf{B}$ of the system.

Recall that the system $\mathbf{W}$ matrix is defined by Eq. (8.33) and could be constructed as follows:

$$\mathbf{W} = \Sigma\ \mathbf{c}_l * \mathbf{c}_l^{\mathrm{T}} \cdot \frac{w_l}{e_l^2}; \quad l\Sigma = 1, \ldots, L$$

Therefore $\mathbf{T}$ is

$$\mathbf{T} = \Sigma\ (\mathbf{X} * \mathbf{c}_m * \mathbf{c}_m^{\mathrm{T}} * \mathbf{X}) \cdot \frac{w_m}{e_m^2}; \quad m\Sigma = 1, \ldots, L \tag{8.37}$$

Since $\mathbf{X} = \mathbf{B}^{-1}$, we have $\mathbf{X} * \mathbf{B} = \mathbf{I}$, and differentiating it yields $(\partial\mathbf{X}/\partial b_k) * \mathbf{B} + \mathbf{X} * (\partial\mathbf{B}/\partial b_k) = 0$ or $(\partial\mathbf{X}/\partial b_k) = -\mathbf{X} * (\partial\mathbf{B}/\partial b_k) * \mathbf{X}$. Since the $\mathbf{B}$ matrix can be produced as the product

$$\mathbf{B} = \mathbf{A} * \mathbf{B}_d * \mathbf{A}^{\mathrm{T}}$$

where $\mathbf{A}$ as previously defined is the incidence matrix and $\mathbf{B}_d$ is a diagonal matrix such that its ith element is b_i, we have $\partial\mathbf{B}/\partial b_k = \mathbf{c}_k * \mathbf{c}_k^{\mathrm{T}}$ and $\partial\mathbf{X}/\partial b_k = -\mathbf{X} * \mathbf{c}_k * \mathbf{c}_k^{\mathrm{T}} * \mathbf{X}$.

This is exactly the negative of the parenthesized expression in Eq. (8.37), so that

$$\mathbf{T} = -\Sigma \left(\frac{\partial\mathbf{X}}{\partial b_k}\right) \cdot \frac{w_k}{e_k^2}; \quad k\ \Sigma = 1, \ldots, L$$

Multiplying and dividing by some scalar number r gives

$$\mathbf{T} = -r \cdot \left[\Sigma \left(\frac{\partial\mathbf{X}}{\partial b_k}\right) \cdot \frac{w_k/e_k^2}{r}\right] \tag{8.38}$$

"The terms in brackets in [Eq. (8.38)] are linear terms in a Taylor series expansion of $\Delta\mathbf{X}$, where the susceptance of circuit l changes by $\Delta B_l = w_l/re_l^2$, $l = 1, 2, \ldots, L$. By increasing the size r, the ΔB_ls can be decreased to the point where the linear terms in the series are dominant. At that point the summation in brackets can be approximated by ΔX:

$$T \cong -r \cdot \Delta X \tag{8.39}$$

Therefore, the τ factors can be approximated as follows:

1. Evaluate x_l, $l = 1, 2, \ldots, L$, from the sparse **X** matrix.
2. Add $\Delta b_l = w_l / re_l^2$ to b_l, $l = 1, 2, \ldots, L$.
3. Evaluate $\tilde{X}_l$, $l = 1, 2, \ldots, L$, from the new system sparse **X** matrix.
4. Then $\tau_l = -r(\tilde{X}_l - X_l)$, $l = 1, 2, \ldots, L$."

We have now all the items needed for contingency analysis.

8.5 PARALLEL, OPTIMALLY ORDERED FACTORIZATION

If the contingency analysis is to be done in real time for the control personnel, at least for the base case, then a fast, parallel solution of

$$\mathbf{A} * \mathbf{x} = \mathbf{b} \tag{8.40}$$

is required.

Moreover, most of the calculations in this book have been based on solving $\mathbf{A} * \mathbf{x} = \mathbf{b}$. If on-line processing is to be used, an efficient solution must be provided (in my opinion for the alternating sequential parallel processing system).

We will first show the difficulties in solving Eq. (8.40) on ASP if **A** is sparse and then describe an algorithm specifically designed for such cases. It was called POOF, for parallel, optimally ordered factorization in [Wa82] and [CW77].*

Elimination instead of factorization of Eq. (8.40) will be used to show that in fact we need a new method. In elimination algorithms, row i operates on row k by replacing

$$\tilde{a}_{km} := a_{km} - a_{im} * \frac{a_{ki}}{a_{ii}}; \quad m = 1, 2, \ldots, n \tag{8.41}$$

to eliminate a_{ki}. This is called a basic Gaussian operation or BG (i, k). Row i here is the pivot; row k will henceforth be called simply row.

It is assumed that each slave memory holds the entire n-by-n matrix **A** as well as vector **b**. (Normally, these memories are supposed to hold a slice of **A** each, but since **A** is now very sparse, the present assumption seems valid.) Each slave is assigned a subset of rows of **A** as its slice.

The algorithm is as follows:

(a) The master chooses a pivot (according to some optimal strategy) and broadcasts it over the bus to all slaves.

---

* V. Conrad, Y. Wallach, "Parallel, Optimally Ordered Factorization," PICA-Conference 1977, pp. 302–6. © 1977 by IEEE. Used with permission.

(b) Each slave performs basic elimination on all its rows with pivot i, i.e., BG (i, k) for all k of its slice.

(c) Elements which will constitute row i and column k of **L** and **U** are now available. If the slaves have insufficient storage, those elements will have to be transferred over the bus to the core memory.

All three steps have to be repeated $n - 1$ times. Steps (a) and (c) are sequential; step (b) is parallel.

As indicated, the ratio achieved when eliminating full matrices is nearly $\rho = 1/p$. However, power system networks have very sparse Jacobian matrices, over 90% of the elements being zero. For such matrices the preceding algorithm shows the following disadvantages:

1. Step (a) is executed $n - 1$ times, and each time:

   - The master initiates its sequential step only after all p slaves have completed their assignments, so that some of them are compelled to wait. The synchronization time is an unwanted overhead.
   - The master needs a time interval π to set up the system for transferring the pivot, and as π is independent of the amount of information transferred, the bus is used inefficiently.

2. In step (b) each slave works only on those of its rows k for which $a_{ki} \neq 0$. For a sparse matrix, there is little work for each slave in each substep P, and the parallelization principle is violated.
3. Where data transfer over the bus is involved, the objection in (1) applies to step (c) as well.

These disadvantages are removed by the algorithm below.

8.5.1 Theoretical Preliminaries

Let *zet* stand for a zero term (element) of matrix **A**. The following considerations will be based on the fact that a Jacobian exhibits a symmetrical pattern of *zets*; it will be called a z-symmetric matrix.

The basic idea of the algorithm is that for z-symmetric matrices, BG (i, j) and BG (j, k) are commutative operations provided $a_{ij} = 0$. This property actually enhances parallelism for sparse matrices by enabling a large number of pivots to be applied independently. We now pursue this line in a more rigorous manner using Fig. 8.4 as example:

Theorem 1: In a z-symmetric matrix, BG (i, k) and BG (j, k) commute if $a_{i,j} = 0$.

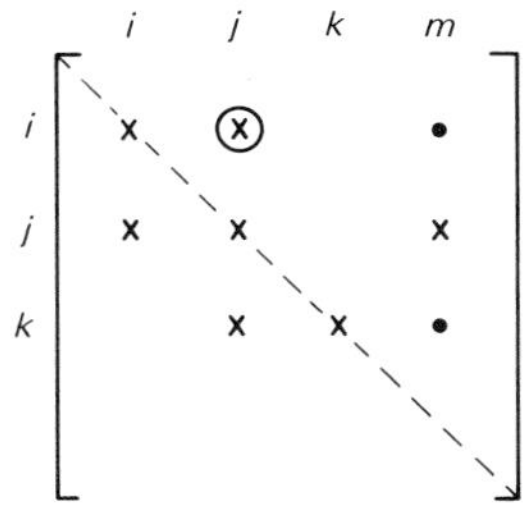

Figure 8.4 An example matrix.

Proof: Let i,j be two pivots and k a "row" (to be operated on). If first BG (i, k) is applied and then BG (j, k), the result for any element $a_{k,m}$ in row k is

$$\tilde{a}_{k,m} := a_{k,m} - \frac{a_{i,m} \cdot a_{k,i}}{a_{i,i}} \quad \text{[after } BG\ (i, k)\text{]} \tag{8.42}$$

$$a^{\#}_{k,m} := \tilde{a}_{k,m} - \frac{a_{j,m} \cdot a_{k,j}}{a_{j,j}} \quad \text{[after } BG\ (j, k)\text{]} \tag{8.43}$$

The assumption was that $a_{i,j} = 0$, so that if in Eq. (8.43) m is made j, we have $\tilde{a}_{k,m} := a_{k,j} = \tilde{a}_{k,j}$, and as seen, the $a_{k,j}$ elements do not change.

Substituting this and Eq. (8.42) into Eq. (8.43) yields

$$a^{\#}_{k,m} := a_{k,m} - \frac{a_{i,m} \cdot a_{k,i}}{a_{i,i}} - \frac{a_{j,m} \cdot a_{k,j}}{a_{j,j}}$$

Subscripts i,j in Eq. (8.42) are interchangeable, and the operations may be also be performed in the reverse order. Q.E.D.

Theorem 1 indicates the condition for a number of pivots to act interchangeably and independently on the same row. Obviously, elimination of rows j and k by pivot i are also independent operations.

Theorem 2: If after BG (k, m), $m > 1$, both row and column i are discarded, the symmetric pattern of *zet*s is retained.

Proof: Suppose (Fig. 8.4) that $a_{k,i} = 0$, but $a_{j,i} \neq 0$ and $a_{l,i} \neq 0$. Since $a_{k,i} = 0$, the zero elements in row and column k are not affected: element $a_{l,j}$ changes but so does $a_{j,l}$ and z-symmetry is preserved.

Corollary: If a matrix **A** is z-symmetric and $a_{i,j} = 0$, then all operations using pivots i and j may be performed independently and simultaneously, and the matrix which remains after elimination of rows and columns i and j is also z-symmetric. This clearly applies to any *set* $\{i, j\}$.

8.5.2 The Algorithm

It is obvious that parallelism is enhanced by employing the maximal subset of nodes as pivots. There should also be no links between the pivot nodes. Unfortunately, this leads to an optimization problem for which no efficient solution is known.

A practical alternative is to make do with a suboptimal instead of an optimal policy. This is also in line with the practice of power systems which depend on heuristically developed algorithms.

The following procedure for finding a large set of independent nodes is recommended:

1. The node with the least number of links is given index 1. (If there are several, one is chosen arbitrarily.)
2. Assume nodes $1, \ldots, k$ have been chosen. Next, choose as node $k + 1$ the node which has the least number of links and is not connected to any of the first k nodes.
3. When rule 2 can no longer by applied (at, say, $k = m$), number the remaining nodes $m, \ldots, n$ arbitrarily.

The POOF algorithm based on the preceding renumbering scheme is best illustrated by a concrete example. (It is difficult to achieve meaningful sparsity for matrices of size less than 100-by-100. Accordingly, the network in Fig. 8.5(a) is intended only for description of the algorithm.)

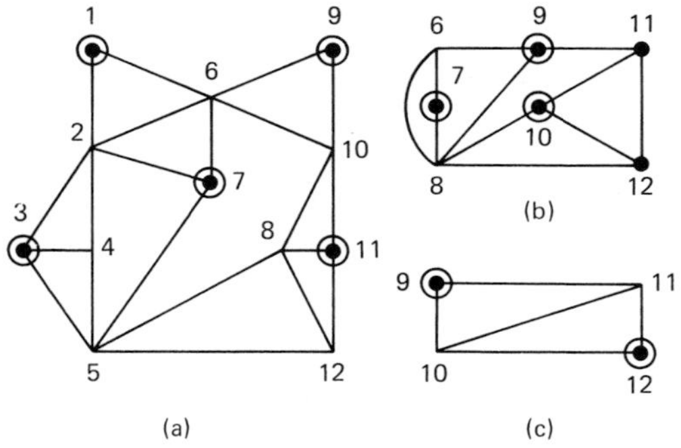

Figure 8.5 (a) Original network. (b), (c) Steps 2 and 3.

The initial renumbering step by step [Fig. 8.5(a)] is as follows:

1. Node 1 is chosen as the first node.
2. Nodes 2 and 6 are crossed out, 9 is chosen as pivot, 10 is crossed out, 3 is chosen as pivot, 4 and 5 are crossed out, 7 and 11 are chosen as pivots. (Pivots are circled in Fig. 8.5.)
3. The renumbered network and the resulting adjacency matrix are shown in Table 8.1(a) and (d). It can be seen in Table 8.1(d) that the rows and columns corresponding to the chosen 5 pivots form a diagonal block.

TABLE 8.1 POOF algorithm applied to network of Fig. 8.5. (a) First step. (b) Second step. (c) Third step.

Old	New	Old	New	Old	New
1	1	6	9	9	9
2	6	7	6	10	11
3	3	8	10	11	12
4	7	9	7	12	10
5	8	10	8		
6	9	11	11		
7	4	12	12		
8	10				
9	2				
10	11				
11	5				
12	12				

	1	2	3	4	5	6	7	8	9	10	11	12
1	x					x			x			
2		x							x		x	
3			x			x	x	x				
4				x		x		x	x			
5					x					x	x	x
6	x		x	x		x	x		x			
7			x			x	x	x				
8			x	x			x	x		x		x
9	x	x		x		x		x	x			
10					x			x		x	x	x
11		x			x				x	x	x	
12					x			x		x		x

(d)

6	x			x	x		
7		x		x	x	x	
8			x		x	x	x
9	x	x		x	x		
10	x	x	x	x	x		x
11		x	x			x	x
12			x		x	x	x

(e)

9	x		x	x
10		x	x	x
11	x	x	x	x
12	x	x	x	x

(f)

According to the corollary, all 5 pivots may next be used simultaneously. For example, if two slaves work in parallel, the first could use pivots 1 and 2 at the same time as the second uses 3, 4, and 5. The network which corresponds to noneliminated nodes is shown in Fig. 8.5(b) and the renumbered network with the adjacency matrix in Table 8.1(b) and (e). Figure 8.5(c) and Tables 8.1(c) and (f) show the next step, in which elimination of the two remaining nodes, 11 and 12, completes POOF.

The POOF algorithm results in elimination, but it was shown in Chapter 2 that such algorithms can easily be changed into factorization.

8.5.3 Discussion of Results

The POOF algorithm can be realized on ASP in the following way:

(a) The master decides on the basis of the remaining adjacency table which nodes are pivots and assigns rows to be operated on to each slave. This information (in form of indices) is broadcast to the slaves.

(b) Each slave calculates BG (i, k) for all its rows k using all pivots i in this (parallel) substep.

(c) Each slave sends its modified rows (blockwise) to the master, which in turn rebroadcasts them.

(d) If elimination is not complete, revert to (a).

Substeps (a) and (c) are sequential and reduce the speedup; they may be improved and the speedup increased if the following is done:

TABLE 8.2 Fill-in ϕ% for $k = 2.4$.

PS	60	80	100	120	140	160	180	200
1	5.60	4.20	3.30	2.85	2.42	2.12	1.85	1.67
2	12.00	8.81	7.17	6.39	5.18	4.64	3.81	3.53
3	25.00	19.70	16.50	14.60	11.80	10.00	8.23	8.14
4	55.80	42.40	37.40	33.70	28.70	25.50	19.80	19.10
5	84.10	77.50	68.70	53.00	60.00	52.90	44.70	42.00
6	100.00	98.30	93.00	91.70	88.80	80.00	78.10	73.70
7		100.00	100.00	99.00	96.70	97.00	97.90	94.60
8				100.00	90.20	100.00	100.00	99.00

TABLE 8.3 Percentage $\Omega\%$ of operations for $k = 2.4$.

PS	60	80	100	120	140	160	100	200
1	41.0	38.9	34.7	31.0	29.3	28.0	26.4	25.0
2	61.7	57.9	54.9	47.4	45.6	43.6	41.1	41.1
3	77.2	71.9	63.0	59.0	58.0	53.7	51.1	51.4
4	87.9	82.5	78.4	69.3	69.3	64.4	60.2	60.4
5	95.1	91.5	87.1	79.2	78.5	73.2	70.6	69.5
6	97.9	95.5	92.9	87.4	86.4	81.4	80.5	78.7
7	99.3	97.0	96.0	92.0	88.9	86.9	85.8	84.5
8	99.9	99.2	98.0	95.1	95.0	92.4	91.0	90.5

TABLE 8.4 Fill-in $\phi\%$ for $k = 3$.

PS	60	80	100	120	140	160	180	200
1	6.58	4.91	3.03	3.20	2.78	2.46	2.18	1.06
2	15.7	12.1	9.73	7.97	6.88	6.20	5.49	5.03
3	35.6	29.1	24.3	20.6	17.1	15.4	13.0	12.5
4	68.7	59.3	51.0	43.2	40.2	38.1	32.7	28.9
5	94.9	85.7	80.3	69.6	66.6	66.2	60.8	53.3
6	99.7	98.6	96.2	89.6	89.9	88.4	85.2	79.9
7	100.	100.	99.9	97.3	87.0	96.0	97.0	94.8
8	0	0	100.	99.6	99.6	99.3	99.7	99.7
9	0	0	0	0	0	99.8	100.	99.9

TABLE 8.5 Percentage $\Omega\%$ of operations for $k = 3$.

PS	60	80	100	120	140	160	180	200
1	21.7	16.9	12.1	11.6	9.89	8.03	6.86	6.25
2	38.2	30.7	23.0	21.6	18.2	14.5	12.5	11.2
3	54.4	44.0	35.5	31.1	27.5	22.2	19.0	16.7
4	68.4	50.7	48.0	41.6	37.4	31.6	27.1	23.3
5	80.4	71.3	59.9	52.9	48.9	42.6	36.2	31.7
6	87.1	79.7	71.4	62.5	58.4	51.3	47.3	41.1
7	91.7	85.0	77.8	71.2	68.7	61.1	56.0	50.0
8	95.0	89.3	82.7	77.0	76.0	67.6	62.6	56.1
9	97.3	92.7	87.0	81.6	80.3	72.9	67.3	61.8

($\tilde{a}$) The work of the master — choosing the pivots and assigning rows so as to achieve a uniform load for the slaves — does not depend on the numerical values but only on the adjacency table. The master is therefore able to determine the indices for the next step while the slaves are at substep (b).

In fact, the indices for the entire process can be chosen before elimination starts. Such preconditioning is advantageous if elimination is to be performed a number of times on the same network (as is the case in optimization and contingency programs).

($\tilde{c}$) Rows to be operated on may be preassigned for the entire program duration. In that case, only pivot rows have to be sent in step (c′) with considerable saving in transfer time. Such rigid preassignment may, however, result in a nonuniform work load.

As POOF (or any other factorization) proceeds, the remaining matrix becomes less sparse because of fill-in. When the fraction of nonzero elements exceeds a certain limit, it may be preferable to switch to one of the parallel methods suggested in [Wa82] for dense matrices.

This critical percentage was determined in an extensive series of numerical experiments, in each of which a random network with a given number of nodes n and a given average node degree (the number of links issuing from a node) was generated. The method of generation did not generate any nodes connected to the rest of the network by a single link.

The results for 128 of these networks are listed in Tables 8.2 to 8.5, with 8.2 and 8.4 showing the fill-in ϕ, 8.3 and 8.5 the percentage of operations $\Omega\%$ as functions of the number of nodes N and of POOF steps PS. (The POOF-step is defined as the set of operations comprising choice of the pivots and their subsequent parallel elimination.) Each entry is an average of 8 cases.

Assuming that the critical percentage for switching from POOF to other algorithms is $\phi = 50\%$, Tables 8.2 and 8.3 show that this occurs after 4, 5, or 6 POOF-steps. At these point $\Omega\%$ is 73.2% to 91.5%, proving *that POOF completes the bulk of its numerical work in a very small number of POOF steps.* To emphasize this point, Table 8.6 shows how many nodes would have remained uneliminated at this point. Note how small is the percentage of uneliminated nodes despite the fact that only a few PS were done altogether.

TABLE 8.6

N	$2.4 = k$	$= 3$
60	5	9
80	6	10
100	9	10
120	11	12
140	12	21
160	15	23
180	13	30
200	15	32

In conclusion, POOF was shown to be very suited for parallel factorization.

As an illustration of *applicability of POOF in programs* run *on single computers*, the same 128 matrices were processed by "policy 2" of Chapter 4. Results are summarized in Table 8.7, from which it is seen that the ratios of fill-in and numbers of operations for the two methods are nearly equal. On the other hand, the network is repeatedly renumbered in POOF, but left in its original form by the OOF algorithm of Chapter 4. The conclusion is that POOF should be used for parallel execution, OOF of Chapter 4 for execution on a single computer.

TABLE 8.7

	Policy 2		POOF	
N	Ω	ϕ	Ω'	ϕ'
60	.94	.03	0.98	1.02
80	.95	.03	1.04	1.03
100	.95	.03	1.06	1.03
120	.96	.02	0.98	1.01
140	.98	.03	0.96	1.00
160	.96	.03	1.13	1.05
180	.97	.02	1.00	1.05
200	102.	.03	1.13	1.06

References

[Ad64] B. Adkins, *The General Theory of Electrical Machines*, Chapman and Hall, 1964.

[AIEE42] *American Institute of Electrical Engineers*, "American Standard Definition of Electrical Terms," 35.20.200 and 35.20 203, 1942.

[APA77] F. C. Aschmoneit, N. M. Peterson, E. C. Adrian, "State Estimation with Equality Constraints," *IEEE PICA-Conference*, 1977.

[ARB77] F. L. Alvarado, D. K. Reitan, M. Bahari-Kashani, "Sparsity in Diakoptics Algorithms," *Trans. IEEE*, Vol. PAS-96, No. 5, pp. 1450–59, September-October 1977.

[BAR78] G. C. Bull, M. D. Anderson, E. F. Richards, "An Analysis of the Fast Decoupled Load Flow Applied in an Economic Dispatch Routine," Paper A78-065-5, *Winter-Power Meeting of the IEEE*, January-February 1978.

[Bea81] Å. Bjorck et al., *Large Scale Matrix Problems*, North Holland, 1981.

[BMR76] J. P. Bickford, N. Mullineux, J. R. Reed, "Computation of Power System Transients," *IEE-Monograph*, Series 18, Peter Peregrinus Ltd., 1976.

[Br75] H. E. Brown, *Solution of Large Networks by Matrix Methods*, John Wiley & Sons Inc., 1975.

[BS76] G. Bell, S. Strecker, "Computer Structures," *Third Annual Symposium on Computer Architecture*, IEEE Computer Society, 1976, pp. 1–14.

[BSCN69] H. E. Brown, R. B. Shipley, D. Coleman, R. E. Nied, "A Study of Stability Equivalents," *Trans. IEEE*, Vol. PAS-88. No. 3, pp. 200–7, March 1969.

[BSM75] R. T. Byerly, D. E. Sherman, D. K. McLain, "Normal Modes and Mode Shapes Applied to Dynamic Stability Analysis," *Trans. IEEE*, Vol. PAS-94, 1975.

[CD78] G. Contaxis, A. S. Debs, "Identification of External System Equivalents for Steady-State Security Assessment," *Trans. IEEE*, Vol. PAS-97. No. 2, pp. 409 – 14, March/April 1978.

[CL75] L. O. Chua, P. M. Lin, *Numerical Solution of Networks*, Prentice-Hall, 1975.

[CW77] V. Conrad, Y. Wallach, "Parallel, Optimally-Ordered Factorization," IEEE *PICA-Conference*, 1977, pp. 302 – 6.

[DB74] G. Dahlquist, Å. Bjorck, *Numerical Methods*, Prentice-Hall, 1974.

[Dea76] J. W. Daniel et al., "Reorthogonalization and Stable Algorithms for Updating the Gram-Schmidt QR-Factorization," *Math. Comp.*, Vol. 30, pp. 772 – 95, 1976.

[DoD83] *Department of Defense*, *ADA Reference Manual*, Springer-Verlag, 1983.

[DT78] H. W. Dommel, W. F. Tinney, "Optimal Power Flow Solutions," *Trans. IEEE*, Vol. PAS-87, No. 10, October 1968, pp. 1866 – 76.

[E171] O. I. Elgerd, *Electric Energy System Theory: An Introduction*, McGraw-Hill, 1971.

[EP77] EPRI, "Development of Dynamic Equivalents for Transient Stability Studies," EL-456, Project 763, Final Report, May 1977.

[EPRI77] EPRI, "Exploring Applications of Digital Parallel Processing to Power System Problems," Seminar Proceedings, October 4 – 7, 1977.

[EW78] G. C. Ejebe, B. F. Wollenberg, "Automatic Contingency Selection," *Trans. IEEE*, Vol PAS-98, pp. 97 – 109, January/February 1979.

[FKK71] A. E. Fitzgerald, C. Kingsley, A. Kusko, *Electric Machinery*, McGraw-Hill, 1971.

[FM67] G. E. Forsythe, C. B. Moler, *Computer Solution of Linear Algebraic Systems*, Prentice-Hall, 1967.

[Fo65] L. Fox, *An Introduction to Numerical Linear Algebra*, Oxford University Press, 1965.

[FS67] L. L. Freris, A. M. Sasson, "Investigation on the Load-Flow Problem," *Proc. IEE*, Vol. 115, No. 10, pp. 1450 – 60, October 1968.

[Ge73] W. M. Gentleman, "Least-Squares Computations by Given's Transformations without Square Roots," *J. Inst. Math. Appl.*, Vol. 12, pp. 329 – 36, 1973.

[Gea74] P. E. Gill, G. H. Golub, W. Murray, M. A. Saunders, "Methods for Modifying Matrix Factorizations," *Math. Comput.*, Vol. 28, No. 126, April 1974, pp. 505 – 35.

[GH81] A. George, M. T. Heath, "Solution of Sparse Linear Least Squares Problems using Givens Rotations," in [Bea81] pp. 69 – 83.

[Gi84] M. Gilles, Private Communication, 1984.

[GL81] A. George, J. W. Liu, *Computer Solution of Large Sparse Positive-Definite Systems*, Prentice-Hall, 1981.

[Gr79] C. A. Gross, *Power System Analysis*, John Wiley & Sons, 1979.

[Gr81] P. Grogono, *Programming in Pascal*, Addison-Wesley, 1981.

[Ha72] E. Handschin, *Real-Time Control of Electric Power Systems*, Elsevier Publishing Company, 1972.

[Ha79] E. Handschin, Private Communication, 1979.

[Ha80] H. H. Happ, *Piecewise Methods and Applications to Power Systems*, John Wiley & Sons, 1980.

[He64] P. Henrici, *Elements of Numerical Analysis*, John Wiley & Sons, 1964.

[Ho53] A. S. Householder, *Principles of Numerical Analysis*, McGraw-Hill, 1953.

[Ho76] L. D. Hong, "An Algorithm for Power-System Contingency Analysis," University of New South Wales, School of Electrical Engineering, Internal Report, EE-Power-101-76, April 1976.

[HW82] E. C. Housos, O. Wing, "Parallel Optimization with Applications to Power Systems," *Trans. IEEE*, Vol. PAS-101, No. 1, January 1982, pp. 244 – 48.

[HW84] E. C. Housos, O. Wing, "Pseudo-Conjugate Directions for the Solution of the Nonlinear Unconstrained Optimization Problem on a Parallel Computer," *Journal of Optimization Theory & Applications*, Vol. 42, No. 2, February 1984, pp. 169 – 80.

[IEEE80] IEEE Systems Dynamics Performance Subcommittee, "Proposed Terms and Definitions for Power-System Stability."

[IEEE81] Report on "Electric Power System Textbooks," *Trans. IEEE*, Vol. PAS-100, 1981, pp. 4255 – 61.

[JW78] H. Jalali-Kushki, M. D. Wvong, "Fast Decoupled Line-Loss Load-Flow Algorithm," Paper A78-290-9, *IEEE Winter Power Meeting*, January 1978.

[Ki56] E. W. Kimbark, *Power System Stability*, John Wiley & Sons, 1956.

[Ki58] L. K. Kirchmayer, *Economic Operation of Power Systems*, John Wiley & Sons, 1958.

[KK79] R. Kober, Ch. Kuznia, "SMS: A Multiprocessor Architecture for High Speed Numerical Calculations," *Euromicro-Journal*, Vol. 5, No. 1, 1979, pp. 48 – 54.

[Kn72] U. G. Knight, *Power System Engineering and Mathematics*, Pergamon, 1972.

[LH73] C. L. Lawson, R. J. Hanson, *Solving Least-Squares Problems*, Prentice-Hall, 1973.

[Mo78] W. Morven-Gentleman, "Some Complexity Results for Matrix Computations," *Journal of the ACM*, Vol. 25, pp. 112–15, 1978.

[MW81] T. A. Mikolinnas, B. F. Wollenberg, "An Advanced Contingency Selection Algorithm," *Trans. IEEE*, Vol. PAS-100, No. 2, February 1981, pp. 608–17.

[Ne71] J. R. Neuenswander, *Modern Power Systems*, International Textbooks, 1971.

[No69] B. Noble, *Applied Linear Algebra*, Prentice-Hall, 1969.

[OR70] J. M. Ortega, W. C. Rheinboldt, *Iterative Solution of Nonlinear Equations in Several Variables*, Academic Press, 1970.

[Or83] E. I. Organick, *A Programmer's View of the Intel 432 System*, McGraw-Hill, 1983.

[Po74] M. J. D. Powell, "Unconstrained Minimization Algorithms without Computation of Derivatives," *Bolletino U.M.I.*, Vol. 4, No. 9, 1974.

[Po84] N. Podwoisky, Private Communication, 1984.

[Re71] J. K. Reid (ed), *Large Sparse Sets of Linear Equations*, Academic Press, 1971, pp. 231–54.

[RW81] L. Richter, Y. Wallach, "Remarks on a Real-Time Master-Slaves Operating System," *Microprogramming and Microprocessing*, Vol. 7, 1981, pp. 304–11.

[SA74] B. Stott, O. Alsac, "Fast Decoupled Load-Flow," *Trans. IEEE*, Vol. PAS-93, May/June 1974, pp. 859–69.

[SBN82] D. P. Sieworek, H. S. Bell, A. Newell, *Computer Structures: Principles and Examples*, McGraw-Hill, 1982.

[SE68] G. W. Stagg, A. H. El-Abiad, *Computer Methods in Power System Analysis*, McGraw-Hill, 1968.

[SGH79] R. R. Shoults, W. Mack Grady, S. Helmick, "An Efficient Method for Computing Loss Coefficients based upon the Method of Least Squares," *Trans. IEEE*, Vol. PAS-98, November/December 1979, pp. 2144–52.

[SM74] A. M. Sasson, H. M. Merril, "Some Applications of Optimization Techniques to Power-System Problems," *Proc. IEEE*, Vol. 62, No. 7, 1974, pp. 959–72.

[SQ81] A. Simoes-Costa, V. H. Quintana, "A Robust Numerical Technique for Power System State Estimation," *Trans. IEEE*, Vol. PAS-100, 1981, pp. 691–98.

[SRS73] H. R. Schwarz, H. Rutishauser, E. Stiefel, *Numerical Analysis of Symmetric Matrices*, Prentice-Hall, 1973.

[St62] W. D. Stevenson, *Elements of Power System Analysis*, McGraw-Hill, 1962.

[St74] A. H. Stroud, *Numerical Quadrature and Solution of Differential Equations*, Springer-Verlag, 1974.

[SWP82] G. M. Schneider, S. W. Weingart, D. M. Perlman, *An Introduction to Programming and Problem Solving with Pascal*, John Wiley & Sons, 1982.

[Te82] J. Tenenbaum, Ph.D. Thesis, Wayne State University, Detroit, 1982.

[TFC73] K. Takahashi, J. Fagan, M. Chen, "Formation of a Sparse Bus-Impedance Matrix," *IEEE PICA-Conference*, 1973, pp. 63–69.

[TH67] W. F. Tinney, C. E. Hart, "Power-Flow Solution by Newton's Method," *Trans. IEEE*, Vol. PAS-86, November 1967, pp. 1449–56.

[TW67] W. F. Tinney, J. W. Walker, "Direct Solution of Sparse Network Equations by Optimally Ordered Factorization," *Proc. IEEE*, Vol. 55, November 1967, pp. 1801–5.

[TW78] S. Tolub, Y. Wallach, "Sorting on a MIMD-type Parallel Processing System," *Euromicro-Journal*, No. 4, 1978, pp. 155–61.

[VD73] L. S. VanSlyck, J. F. Dopazo, "Conventional Load-Flow not Suited for Real-Time Power-System Monitoring," *IEEE PICA-Conference*, June 1973, pp. 369–75.

[VR83] Th. Van Cutsem, M. Ribbens-Pavella, "Critical Survey of Hierarchical Methods," *Trans. IEEE*, Vol. PAS-102, No. 10, October 1983, pp. 3415–24.

[Wa68] Y. Wallach, "Gradient Methods for Load-Flow Problems," *Trans IEEE*, Vol. PAS-87, No. 5, May 1968, pp. 1314–18.

[Wa82] Y. Wallach, *Alternating Sequential-Parallel Processing*, Springer-Verlag, 1982.

[Wa83] Y. Wallach, "Orthogonalization for Power-System Computations," *Archiv fur Elektrotechnik*, Vol. 67, 1983, pp. 57–64.

[Wa84] Y. Wallach, "On Some Power-System Simulation Studies," *Transactions of the Society for Computer Simulations*, Vol. 1. No. 2, December 1984, pp. 133–53.

[WC76] Y. Wallach, V. Conrad, "Parallel Solutions of Load-Flow Problems," *Archiv fur Elektrotechnik*, Vol. 57, 1976, pp. 345–54, and Vol. 61, 1978, pp. 1–6.

[WC77] Y. Wallach, V. Conrad, "Iterative Solution of Linear Equations on a Parallel Processing System," *Trans. IEEE*, Vol. C-26, 1977, pp. 838–47.

[WE33] C. F. Wagner, R. D. Evans, *Symmetrical Components*, McGraw-Hill, 1933.

[We64] Westinghouse Electric Company, *Electric Transmission and Distribution Reference Book*, Pittsburgh, Pa., 1964.

[WE67] Y. Wallach, R. Even, "Application of Newton's Method to Load-Flow Calculations," *Proc. IEE*, Vol. 114, 1967, pp. 372–74.

[WH56] J. B. Ward, H. W. Hale, "Digital Computer Solution of Power-Flow Problems," *Trans. AIEE*, Vol. 75, Pt. III, June 1956, pp. 398–404.

[WH82] Y. Wallach, E. Handschin, "State Estimation by Orthogonalization and Splitting," *Electrical Power & Energy Systems*, Vol. 4, No. 3, July 1982, pp. 177-84.

[WHB81] Y. Wallach, E. Handschin, C. Bongers, "An Efficient Parallel-Processing Method for Power-System State-Estimation," *Trans. IEEE*, Vol. PAS-100, November 1981, pp. 4402–6.

[Wi63] J. A. Wilkinson, *Rounding Errors in Algebraic Processes*, Prentice-Hall, 1963.

[Wi73] N. Wirth, *Systematic Programming — An Introduction*, Prentice-Hall, 1973.

[WK77/79] Y. Wallach, V. Konrad, "A Faster SSOR Algorithm," *Num. Math*, Vol. 27, 1977, pp. 371–72, and Vol. 32, 1979, pp. 105–8.

[WS74] B. F. Wollenberg, W. O. Stadlin, "A Real-Time Optimizer for Security Dispatch," *Trans. IEEE*, Vol. PAS-93, No. 5, Sept/Oct 1974, pp. 1640–49.

[Wu75] F. Wu, "Diakoptic Network Analysis," *IEEE PICA-Conference*, June 1975, pp. 364–71.

[WW84] A. J. Wood, B. F. Wollenberg, *Power Generation, Operation & Control*, John Wiley & Sons, 1984.

[YG72] D. M. Young, R. T. Gregory, *A Survey of Numerical Mathematics*, Addison-Wesley, 1972.

Index

K

L

M

N

O

T

U

V